FIFTH EDITION

Research Methods and Statistics

A Critical Thinking Approach

Sherri L. Jackson

Jacksonville University

Cengage

Australia • Brazil • Canada • India • Mexico • Singapore • United Kingdom • United States

Cengage

Research Methods and Statistics: A Critical Thinking Approach,
5th Edition

Sherri L. Jackson

For product information and technology assistance, contact us at
asia.infoindia@cengage.com

For permission to use material from this text or product, submit all requests online at
www.cengage.com/permissions

ISBN-13: 978-93-6053-692-3
ISBN-10: 93-6053-692-X

Cengage Learning India Pvt. Ltd.
T-303, 3rd Floor
DAV Complex, Plot 3
Mayur Vihar Phase 1
Delhi 110091

Cengage is a leading provider of customized learning solutions with employees residing in nearly 40 different countries and sales in more than 125 countries around the world. Find your local representative at: **www.cengage.com.**

Cengage is committed to creating inclusive and diverse products, including perspectives that represent the diversity of people across all backgrounds, identities, opinions, and experiences.

If you have any feedback related to this, please contact us at **support.cengage.com.**

To learn more about Cengage products, platforms and services, visit **www.cengage.co.in.**

Disclaimer:
This book contains link to resources which are a part of the imported edition. The same may not be available with the Indian edition. The buyer needs to purchase a copy of the imported edition to have full access to those resources. In no event the publisher shall be liable for any limitation or performance due to unavailability of these resources.

Printed by:
Saurabh Printers Pvt Ltd
67A-68 Ecotech Ext-I Greater Noida
Tel-0120-2341180

Printed in India
Print Number: 02 Print Year: 2026

To all my furry muses past and present,
Bennie, Henry, and Percy

About the Author

Sherri L. Jackson is professor of psychology at Jacksonville University, where she has taught since 1988. At JU, she has won Excellence in Scholarship (2003), University Service (2004), and Teaching (2009) awards, the university-wide Professor of the Year Award in 2004, the Woman of the Year Award in 2005, and the Institutional Excellence Award in 2007. She received her B.A. from North Adams State College and her M.S. and Ph.D. in cognitive/experimental psychology from the University of Florida. Her research interests include human reasoning and the teaching of psychology. She has published numerous articles in both areas. She is also the author of *Statistics Plain and Simple*, 3rd edition (Belmont, CA: Cengage, 2014), *Research Methods: A Modular Approach*, 3rd edition (Belmont, CA: Cengage, 2015), and *A Concise Guide to Statistical Analyses Using Excel, SPSS, and the TI-84 Calculator* (Belmont, CA: Cengage, 2013). She currently serves as Chair of the Division of Social Sciences.

Brief Contents

Contents

Preface

When I first began teaching research methods 26 years ago, I did not include statistics in my class because my students took a separate statistics course as a prerequisite. However, as time passed, I began to integrate more and more statistical content so that students could understand more fully how methods and statistics relate to one another. Eventually I reached the point where I decided to adopt a textbook that integrated statistics and research methods. However, I was somewhat surprised to find that there were only a few integrated texts. In addition, these texts covered statistics in much greater detail than I needed or wanted. Thus, I wrote the present text to meet the market need for a brief, introductory-level, integrated text. My other writing goals were to be *concise yet comprehensive,* to use an *organization* that progresses for the most part from nonexperimental methods to experimental methods, to incorporate *critical thinking* throughout the text, and to use a simple, easy-to-understand *writing style.*

Concise yet Comprehensive

The present text is concise (it can be covered in a one-semester course if necessary, and if paired with supplements, can easily fit a two-semester course) yet still integrates statistics with methods. To accomplish these twin goals, I chose to cover only those statistics most used by psychologists rather than to include all the statistics that might be covered in a regular statistics class. The result is a text that, in effect, integrates a statistical supplement within a methods text. The advantage of using this text rather than a statistical supplement with a methods text is that the statistics are integrated throughout the text. In other words, I have described the statistics that would be used with a particular research method in the same chapter or in a chapter immediately following the pertinent methods chapter.

I realize that some instructors may like the integrated approach but not want to cover inferential statistics in as much detail as I do. I have therefore structured the coverage of each inferential statistical test so that the calculations may be omitted if so desired. I have divided the section on each statistical test into four clear subsections. The first describes the statistical test and what it does for a researcher. The second subsection provides the formulas for the test and an example of how to apply the formulas. In the third subsection, I demonstrate how to interpret the results from the test; and in the final subsection, I list the assumptions that underlie the test. Instructors who simply want their students to understand the test, how to interpret it, and the assumptions behind it can omit (not assign) the subsection on statistical calculations without any problems of continuity. Thus, the text is appropriate both in methods classes for which statistics is not a prerequisite and in those classes for which statistics is a prerequisite. In the latter case, the calculation subsections may be omitted, or they may be used as a statistical review and as a means of demonstrating how statistics are used by psychologists.

Organization

The text begins with chapters on science and getting started in research (Chapters 1 and 2). Measurement issues and descriptive methods and statistics are then covered, followed by correlational methods and statistics (Chapters 3 to 6). Probabliity, hypothesis testing, and inferential statistics are introduced in Chapters 7 and 8, followed by experimental design and the appropriate inferential statistics for analyzing such designs (Chapters 9 to 12 and 14). The remaining two chapters present quasi-experimental and single-case designs (Chapter 13) and APA guidelines on writing (Chapter 15).

Critical Thinking

Evaluation of any research design involves critical thinking, so this particular goal is not a novel one in research methods texts. However, I have made a special effort to incorporate a critical thinking mind-set into the text in the hopes of fostering this in students. I attempt to teach students to adopt a skeptical approach to research analysis through instructive examples and an explicit pedagogical aid incorporated within the text. At the end of each major section in each chapter, I have inserted a *Critical Thinking Check.* This feature varies in length and format but generally involves a series of application questions concerning the section information. The questions are designed to foster analytical/critical thinking skills in addition to reviewing the section information.

Writing Style

I present the information in a simple, direct, easy-to-understand fashion. Because research methods is one of the more difficult courses for students, I also try to write in an engaging, conversational style, much as if the reader were a student seated in front of me in my classroom. I hope, through this writing style, to help students better understand some of the more troublesome concepts without losing their interest.

Pedagogical Aids

The text incorporates several pedagogical aids at the chapter level. Each chapter begins with a *chapter outline,* which is followed by *learning objectives.* Key terms are defined in a *running glossary* in the margins within each chapter. *In Review* summary matrices, at the end of major sections in each chapter, provide a review of the major concepts of the section in a tabular format. These summaries are immediately followed by the *Critical Thinking Checks* described previously. Thus, students can use the In Review summary after reading a chapter section and then engage in the Critical Thinking Check on that information. *Chapter Exercises* are provided at the end of each chapter so that students can further review and apply the knowledge in that chapter. Answers to the odd-numbered chapter exercises are provided in Appendix C. *Answers to the Critical Thinking Checks* appear at the end of each chapter. As in the previous edition, the Study Guide has been incorporated into the text in this edition so there is no additional cost to the student. The built-in Study Guide appears at the end of each chapter and includes a *chapter summary, fill-in questions, multiple-choice questions,* and *extra problems* for chapters with statistics.

New to This Edition

The fifth edition contains 15 chapters, as did the previous edition. However, several of the chapters have been reorganized and new information has been added. Chapters 9 and 10 have been reorganized so an experimental design and the parametric statistic appropriate for that design are covered in the same chapter. Thus, Chapter 9 introduces simple between-subjects designs and the parametric statistic appropriate to analyze the data from this design. Chapter 10 does the same for correlated-groups designs. The new Chapter 14 covers nonparametric statistics, including new coverage of two advanced nonparametric statistics: the Kruskal-Wallis test and the Friedman test. Chapter 15 covers APA manuscript guidelines according to the 6th edition of the publication manual, and the APA sample paper has been moved to an appendix.

In addition, more recent research examples have been added throughout the text, and full coverage of how to use Excel, SPSS, and the TI-84 calculator to perform statistical analyses has been added to the end of each chapter in which statistics are covered (Chapters 5, 6, 8, 9, 10, 11, 12, and 14) in the Statistical Software Resource section at the end of these chapters.

For the Instructor

An *Instructor's Manual/Test Bank* accompanies the text. The *Instructor's Manual* contains lecture outlines, PowerPoint slides of most of the tables and figures from the text, resources to aid in the development of classroom exercises/demonstrations, and answers to all chapter exercises. A test bank includes multiple-choice, short-answer, and essay questions.

For the Student

In addition to the pedagogical aids built into the text, Web resources include glossaries and flashcards.

Acknowledgments

I must acknowledge many people for their help with this project. I thank the students in my research methods classes on which the text was pretested. Their comments were most valuable. I also thank my husband for his careful proofreading and insightful comments, and Percy for the encouragement of her ever-present wagging tail. In addition, I would like to thank those who reviewed the text in the first through fifth editions. They include Patrick Ament, Central Missouri State University; Michele Breault, Truman State University; Stephen Levine, Georgian Court College; Patrick McKnight, University of Arizona; William Moyer, Millersville University; Michael Politano, The Citadel; Jeff Smith, Northern Kentucky University; Bart Van Voorhis, University of Wisconsin, LaCrosse; Zoe Warwick, University of Maryland, Baltimore County; and Carolyn Weisz, University of Puget Sound; Scott Bailey, Texas Lutheran University; James Ballard, California State University, Northridge; Stephen Blessing, University of Tampa; Amy Bohmann, Texas Lutheran University; Anne Cook, University of Utah; Julie Evey, University of Southern Indiana; Rob Mowrer, Angelo State University; Sandra Nicks, Christian Brothers University; Clare Porac, Pennsylvania State University, Erie, The Behrend College; and Diane Winn, Colby College. In this third edition, I was fortunate again to have reviewers who took their task seriously and provided very constructive suggestions for strengthening and improving the text. I am grateful for the suggestions and comments provided by Martin Bink, Western Kentucky University; David Falcone, La Salle University; Tiara Falcone, The College of New Jersey; Cary S. Feria, Morehead State University; Greg Galardi, Peru State College; Natalie Gasson, Curtin University; Brian Johnson, University of Tennessee at Martin; Maya Khanna, Creighton University; David Kreiner, University of Central Missouri; Martha Mann, University of Texas at Arlington; Benjamin Miller, Salem State College; Erin Murdoch, University of Central Florida; Mary Nebus, Georgian Court University; Michael Politano, The Citadel; and Linda Rueckert, Northeastern Illinois University.

Special thanks to all the team at Cengage, specifically Timothy Matray, Editor, for his support and guidance, Amelia Blevins, Associate Content Developer, Ruth Sakata Corley, Senior Content Project Manager, and Vernon Boes, Senior Art Director. Thanks also to Sumathy Kumaran, Project Manager at Lumina Datamatics.

Sherri L. Jackson

CHAPTER 1

Thinking Like a Scientist

Learning Objectives

- Identify and describe the areas of psychological research.
- Identify and differentiate between the various sources of knowledge.
- Describe the three criteria of the scientific (critical thinking) approach.
- Explain the difference between basic and applied research.
- Explain the goals of science.
- Identify and compare descriptive methods.
- Identify and compare predictive (relational) methods.
- Describe the explanatory method. Your description should include independent variable, dependent variable, control group, and experimental group.
- Explain how we "do" science and how proof and disproof relate to doing science.

Welcome to what is most likely your first research methods class. If you are like most psychology students, you are probably wondering what in the world this class is about—and, more important, why you have to take it. Most psychologists and the American Psychological Association (APA) consider the research methods class especially important in the undergraduate curriculum. In fact, along with the introductory psychology class, the research methods class is one of the courses required by most psychology departments (Messer, Griggs, & Jackson, 1999). Why is this class considered so important, and what exactly is it all about?

Before answering these questions, I will ask you to complete a couple of exercises related to your knowledge of psychology. I usually begin my research methods class by asking my students to do these exercises. I assume that you have had at least one other psychology class prior to this one. Thus, these exercises should not be too difficult.

Exercise 1: Try to name five psychologists. Make sure that your list does not include any "pop" psychologists such as Dr. Ruth or Dr. Laura. These individuals are considered by most psychologists to be "pop" psychologists because, although they are certified to do some sort of counseling, neither actually completed a degree in psychology. Dr. Ruth has an Ed.D. in the interdisciplinary study of the family, and Dr. Laura has a Ph.D. in physiology and a postdoctoral certification in marriage, family, and child counseling.

Okay, whom did you name first? If you are like most people, you named Sigmund Freud. In fact, if we were to stop 100 people on the street and ask the same question of them, we would probably find that, other than "pop" psychologists, Freud would be the most commonly named psychologist (Stanovich, 2007). What do you know about Freud? Do you believe that he is representative of all that psychology encompasses? Most people on the street believe so. In fact, most of them believe that psychologists "do" what they see "pop" psychologists doing and what they believe Freud did. That is, they believe that most psychologists listen to people's problems and try to help them solve those problems. If this represents your schema for psychology, this class should help you to see the discipline in a very different light.

Exercise 2 (taken from Bolt, 1998): Make two columns on a piece of paper, one labeled "Scientist" and one labeled "Psychologist." Now, write five descriptive terms for each. You may include terms or phrases that describe what you believe the "typical" scientist or psychologist looks like, dresses like, or acts like, as well as what personality characteristics you believe these individuals have. After you have finished this task, evaluate your descriptions. Do they differ? Again, if you are like most students, even psychology majors, you have probably written very different terms to describe each of these categories.

First, consider your descriptions of a scientist. Most students see the scientist as a middle-aged man, usually wearing a white lab coat with a pocket protector on it. The terms for the scientist's personality usually describe someone who is analytical, committed, and introverted with poor people/social skills. Are any of these similar to your descriptions?

Now let's turn to your descriptions of a typical psychologist. Once again, a majority of students tend to picture a man, although some picture a woman. They definitely do not see the psychologist in a white lab coat but instead in some sort of professional attire. The terms for personality characteristics tend to describe someone who is warm, caring, empathic, and concerned about others. Does this sound similar to what you have written?

What is the point behind these exercises? First, they illustrate that most people have misconceptions about what psychologists do and about what psychology is. In other words, most people believe that the majority of psychologists do what Freud did—try to help others with their problems. They also tend to see psychology as a discipline devoted to the mental health profession. As you will soon see, psychology includes many other areas of specialization, some of which may actually involve wearing a white lab coat and working with technical equipment.

I asked you to describe a scientist versus a psychologist because I hoped that you would begin to realize that a psychologist *is* a scientist. Wait a minute, you may be saying. I decided to major in psychology because I don't like science. What you have failed to recognize is that what makes something a science is not *what* is studied but *how* it is studied. This is what you will be learning about in this course—how to use the scientific method to conduct research in psychology. This is also why you may have had to take statistics as a prerequisite or corequisite to this class and why statistics are covered in this text—because doing research requires an understanding of how to use statistics. In this text, you will learn about both research methods and the statistics most useful for these methods.

Areas of Psychological Research

As we noted, psychology is not just about mental health. Psychology is a very diverse discipline that encompasses many areas of study. To illustrate this, examine Table 1.1, which lists the divisions of the American Psychological Association (APA). You will notice that the areas of study within psychology range from those that are closer to the so-called "hard" sciences (chemistry, physics, biology) to those that are closer to the so-called "soft" social sciences (sociology, anthropology, political science). The APA has 54 divisions, each representing an area of research or practice. To understand what psychology is, it is important that you have an appreciation of its diversity. In the following sections, we will briefly discuss some of the more popular research areas within the discipline of psychology.

TABLE 1.1 Divisions of the American Psychological Association

Divisions
1. Society for General Psychology
2. Society for the Teaching of Psychology
3. Experimental Psychology
5. Evaluation, Measurement, and Statistics
6. Behavioral Neuroscience and Comparative Psychology
7. Developmental Psychology
8. Society for Personality and Social Psychology
9. Society for Psychological Study of Social Issues
10. Society for the Psychology of Aesthetics, Creativity, and the Arts
12. Society for Clinical Psychology
13. Society for Consulting Psychology
14. Society for Industrial and Organizational Psychology
15. Educational Psychology
16. School Psychology
17. Society for Counseling Psychology
18. Psychologists in Public Service
19. Society for Military Psychology
20. Adult Development and Aging
21. Applied Experimental and Engineering Psychology
22. Rehabilitation Psychology
23. Society for Consumer Psychology

(continued)

TABLE 1.1 Divisions of the American Psychological Association (*continued*)

24. Society for Theoretical and Philosophical Psychology
25. Behavior Analysis
26. Society for the History of Psychology
27. Society for Community Research and Action: Division of Community Psychology
28. Psychopharmacology and Substance Abuse
29. Psychotherapy
30. Society for Psychological Hypnosis
31. State, Provincial, and Territorial Psychological Association Affairs
32. Society for Humanistic Psychology
33. Intellectual and Developmental Disabilities
34. Society for Environmental, Population, and Conservation Psychology
35. Society for the Psychology of Women
36. Psychology of Religion and Spirituality
37. Society for Child and Family Policy and Practice
38. Health Psychology
39. Psychoanalysis
40. Clinical Neuropsychology
41. American Psychology-Law Society
42. Psychologists in Independent Practice
43. Society for Family Psychology
44. Society for the Psychological Study of Lesbian, Gay, Bisexual, and Transgender Issues
45. Society for the Psychological Study of Ethnic and Minority Issues
46. Media Psychology
47. Exercise and Sport Psychology
48. Society for the Study of Peace, Conflict, and Violence: Peace Psychology Division
49. Society of Group Psychology and Group Psychotherapy
50. Society of Addiction Psychology
51. Society for the Psychological Study of Men and Masculinity
52. International Psychology
53. Society of Clinical Child and Adolescent Psychology
54. Society of Pediatric Psychology
55. American Society for the Advancement of Pharmacotherapy
56. Trauma Psychology

NOTE: There is no Division 4 or 11.

Psychobiology

One of the most popular research areas in psychology today is psychobiology. As the name implies, this research area combines biology and psychology. Researchers in this area typically study brain organization or the chemicals within the brain (neurotransmitters). Using the appropriate research methods, psychobiologists have discovered links between illnesses such as schizophrenia and Parkinson's disease and various neurotransmitters in the brain—leading, in turn, to research on possible drug therapies for these illnesses.

Cognition

Researchers who study cognition are interested in how humans process, store, and retrieve information; solve problems; use reasoning and logic; make decisions; and use language. Understanding and employing the appropriate research methods have enabled scientists in these areas to develop models of how memory works, ways to improve memory, methods to improve problem solving and intelligence, and theories of language acquisition. Whereas psychobiology researchers study the brain, cognitive scientists study the mind.

Human Development

Psychologists in this area conduct research on the physical, social, and cognitive development of humans. This might involve research from the prenatal development period throughout the life span to research on the elderly (gerontology). Research on human development has led, for example, to better understanding of prenatal development and hence better prenatal care, knowledge of cognitive development and cognitive limitations in children, and greater awareness of the effects of peer pressure on adolescents.

Social Psychology

Social psychologists are interested in how we view and affect one another. Research in this area combines the disciplines of psychology and sociology, in that social psychologists are typically interested in how being part of a group affects the individual. Some of the best-known studies in psychology represent work by social psychologists. For example, Milgram's (1963, 1974) classic experiments on obedience to authority and Zimbardo's (1972) classic prison simulation are social psychology studies.

Psychotherapy

Psychologists also conduct research that attempts to evaluate psychotherapies. Research on psychotherapies is designed to assess whether a therapy is effective in helping individuals. Might patients have improved without the therapy, or did they improve simply because they thought the therapy was supposed to help? Given the widespread use of various therapies, it is important to have an estimate of their effectiveness.

Sources of Knowledge

There are many ways to gain knowledge, and some are better than others. As scientists, psychologists must be aware of each of these methods. Let's look at several ways of acquiring knowledge, beginning with sources that may not be as reliable or accurate as scientists might desire. We will then consider sources that offer greater reliability and will ultimately discuss using science as a means of gaining knowledge.

Superstition and Intuition

knowledge via superstition Knowledge that is based on subjective feelings, interpreting random events as nonrandom events, or believing in magical events.

Gaining **knowledge via superstition** means acquiring knowledge that is based on subjective feelings, interpreting random events as nonrandom events, or believing in magical events. For example, you may have heard someone say "Bad things happen in threes." Where does this idea come from? As far as I know, no study has ever documented that bad events occur in threes, yet people frequently say this and act as if they believe it. Some people believe that breaking a mirror brings 7 years of bad luck or that the number 13 is unlucky. Once again, these are examples of superstitious beliefs that are not based on observation or hypothesis testing. As such, they represent a means of gaining knowledge that is neither reliable nor valid.

knowledge via intuition Knowledge gained without being consciously aware of its source.

When we gain **knowledge via intuition**, it means that we have knowledge of something without being consciously aware of where the knowledge came from. You have probably heard people say things like "I don't know, it's just a gut feeling" or "I don't know, it just came to me, and I know it's true." These statements represent examples of intuition. However, sometimes we intuit something based not on a "gut feeling" but on events we have observed. The problem is that the events may be misinterpreted and not representative of all events in that category. For example, many people believe that more babies are born during a full moon or that couples who have adopted a baby are more likely to conceive after the adoption. These are examples of *illusory correlation*—the perception of a relationship that does not exist. More babies are not born when the moon is full nor are couples more likely to conceive after adopting (Gilovich, 1991). Instead, we are more likely to notice and pay attention to those couples who conceive after adopting and not notice those who did not conceive after adopting.

Authority

knowledge via authority Knowledge gained from those viewed as authority figures.

When we accept what a respected or famous person tells us, we are gaining **knowledge via authority**. You may have gained much of your own knowledge through authority figures. As you were growing up, your parents provided you with information that, for the most part, you did not question, especially when you were very young. You believed that they knew what they were talking about, and thus you accepted the answers they gave you. You have probably also gained knowledge from teachers whom you viewed as authority figures, at times blindly accepting what they said as truth. Most people tend to accept information imparted by those they view as authority figures. Historically, authority figures have been a primary means of information. For example, in some time periods and cultures, the church and its leaders were responsible for providing much of the knowledge that individuals gained throughout the course of their lives.

Even today, many individuals gain much of their knowledge from authority figures. This may not be a problem if the perceived authority figure truly is an authority on the subject. However, problems may arise in situations where the perceived authority figure really is not knowledgeable about the material he or she is imparting. A good example is the information given in "infomercials." Celebrities are often used to deliver the message or a testimonial concerning a product. For example, Cindy Crawford may tell us about a makeup product, or Jessica Simpson may provide a testimonial regarding a an acne product. Do Cindy Crawford or Jessica Simpson have degrees in dermatology? These individuals may be experts on modeling or singing, but they are not authorities on the products they are advertising. Yet many individuals readily accept what they say.

In conclusion, accepting the word of an authority figure may be a reliable and valid means of gaining knowledge, but only if the individual is truly an authority on the subject. Thus, we need to question "authoritative" sources of knowledge and develop an attitude of skepticism so that we do not blindly accept whatever is presented to us.

Tenacity

knowledge via tenacity Knowledge gained from repeated ideas that are stubbornly clung to despite evidence to the contrary.

Gaining **knowledge via tenacity** involves hearing a piece of information so often that you begin to believe it is true, and then, despite evidence to the contrary, you cling stubbornly to the belief. This method is often used in political campaigns, where a particular slogan is repeated so often that we begin to believe it. Advertisers also use the method of tenacity by repeating their slogan for a certain product over and over until people begin to associate the slogan with the product and believe that the product meets its claims. For example, the makers of Visine advertised for over 40 years that "It gets the red out," and, although Visine eventually changed the slogan, most of us have heard the original so many times that we probably now believe it. The problem with gaining knowledge through tenacity is that we do not know whether the claims are true. As far as we know, the accuracy of such knowledge may not have been evaluated in any valid way.

Rationalism

knowledge via rationalism Knowledge gained through logical reasoning.

Gaining **knowledge via rationalism** involves logical reasoning. With this approach, ideas are precisely stated and logical rules are applied to arrive at a logically sound conclusion. Rational ideas are often presented in the form of a syllogism. For example:

All humans are mortal;
I am a human;
Therefore, I am mortal.

This conclusion is logically derived from the major and minor premises in the syllogism. Consider, however, the following syllogism:

Attractive people are good;
Nellie is attractive;
Therefore, Nellie is good.

This syllogism should identify for you the problem with gaining knowledge by logic. Although the syllogism is logically sound, the content of both premises is not necessarily true. If the content of the premises were true, then the conclusion would be true in addition to being logically sound. However, if the content of either of the premises is false (as is the premise "Attractive people are good"), then the conclusion is logically valid but empirically false and therefore of no use to a scientist. Logic deals with only the form of the syllogism and not its content. Obviously, researchers are interested in both form and content.

Empiricism

Knowledge via empiricism Knowledge gained through objective observations of organisms and events in the real world.

Knowledge via empiricism involves gaining knowledge through objective observation and the experiences of your senses. An individual who says "I believe nothing until I see it with my own eyes" is an empiricist. The empiricist gains knowledge by seeing, hearing, tasting, smelling, and touching. This method dates back to the age of Aristotle. Aristotle was an empiricist who made observations about the world in order to know it better. Plato, in contrast, preferred to theorize about the true nature of the world without gathering any data.

Empiricism alone is not enough, however. Empiricism represents a collection of facts. If, as scientists, we relied solely on empiricism, we would have nothing more than a long list of observations or facts. For these facts to be useful, we need to organize them, think about them, draw meaning from them, and use them to make predictions. In other words, we need to use rationalism together with empiricism to make sure that we are being logical about the observations that we make. As you will see, this is what science does.

knowledge via science Knowledge gained through a combination of empirical methods and logical reasoning.

Science

hypothesis A prediction regarding the outcome of a study involving the potential relationship between at least two variables.

Gaining **knowledge via science**, then, involves a merger of rationalism and empiricism. Scientists collect data (make empirical observations) and test hypotheses with these data (assess them using rationalism). A **hypothesis** is a prediction regarding the outcome of a study. This prediction concerns the

variable An event or behavior that has at least two values.

potential relationship between at least two variables (a **variable** is an event or behavior that has at least two values). Hypotheses are stated in such a way that they are testable. By merging rationalism and empiricism, we have the advantage of using a logical argument based on observation. We may find that our hypothesis is not supported, and thus we have to reevaluate our position. On the other hand, our observations may support the hypothesis being tested.

theory An organized system of assumptions and principles that attempts to explain certain phenomena and how they are related.

In science, the goal of testing hypotheses is to arrive at or test a **theory**—an organized system of assumptions and principles that attempts to explain certain phenomena and how they are related. Theories help us to organize and explain the data gathered in research studies. In other words, theories allow us to develop a framework regarding the facts in a certain area. For example, Darwin's theory organizes and explains facts related to evolution. To develop his theory, Darwin tested many hypotheses. In addition to helping us organize and explain facts, theories help in producing new knowledge by steering researchers toward specific observations of the world.

Students are sometimes confused about the difference between a hypothesis and a theory. A *hypothesis* is a prediction regarding the outcome of a single study. Many hypotheses may be tested and several research studies conducted before a comprehensive theory on a topic is put forth. Once a *theory* is developed, it may aid in generating future hypotheses. In other words, researchers may have additional questions regarding the theory that help them to generate new hypotheses to test. If the results from these additional studies further support the theory, we are likely to have greater confidence in the theory. However, further research can also expose weaknesses in a theory that may lead to future revisions of the theory.

Sources of Knowledge — IN REVIEW

SOURCE	DESCRIPTION	ADVANTAGES/DISADVANTAGES
Superstition	Gaining knowledge through subjective feelings, interpreting random events as nonrandom events, or believing in magical events	Not empirical or logical
Intuition	Gaining knowledge without being consciously aware of where the knowledge came from	Not empirical or logical
Authority	Gaining knowledge from those viewed as authority figures	Not empirical or logical; authority figure may not be an expert in the area
Tenacity	Gaining knowledge by clinging stubbornly to repeated ideas, despite evidence to the contrary	Not empirical or logical
Rationalism	Gaining knowledge through logical reasoning	Logical but not empirical
Empiricism	Gaining knowledge through observations of organisms and events in the real world	Empirical but not necessarily logical or systematic
Science	Gaining knowledge through empirical methods and logical reasoning	The only acceptable way for researchers/scientists to gain knowledge

CRITICAL THINKING CHECK 1.1

Identify the source of knowledge in each of the following examples:

1. A celebrity is endorsing a new diet program, noting that she lost weight on the program and so will you.
2. Based on several observations that Pam has made, she feels sure that cell phone use does not adversely affect driving ability.
3. A friend tells you that she is not sure why but, because she has a feeling of dread, she thinks that you should not take the plane trip you were planning for next week.

The Scientific (Critical Thinking) Approach and Psychology

Now that we have briefly described what science is, let's discuss how this applies to the discipline of psychology. As mentioned earlier, many students believe that they are attracted to psychology because they think it is *not* a science. The error in their thinking is that they believe that subject matter alone defines what is and what is not science. Instead, what defines science is the manner in which something is studied. Science is a way of thinking about and observing events to achieve a deeper understanding of these events. Psychologists apply the scientific method to their study of human beings and other animals.

skeptic A person who questions the validity, authenticity, or truth of something purporting to be factual.

The scientific method involves invoking an attitude of skepticism. A **skeptic** is a person who questions the validity, authenticity, or truth of something purporting to be factual. In our society, being described as a skeptic is not typically thought of as a compliment. However, for a scientist, it is a compliment. It means that you do not blindly accept any new idea that comes along. Instead, the skeptic needs data to support an idea and insists on proper testing procedures when the data were collected. Being a skeptic and using the scientific method involve applying three important criteria that help define science: systematic empiricism, publicly verifiable knowledge, and empirically solvable problems (Stanovich, 2007).

Systematic Empiricism

systematic empiricism Making observations in a systematic manner to test hypotheses and develop or refute a theory.

As you have seen, empiricism is the practice of relying on observation to draw conclusions. Most people today probably agree that the best way to learn about something is to observe it. This reliance on empiricism was not always a common practice. Before the 17th century, most people relied more on intuition, religious doctrine provided by authorities, and reason than they did on empiricism. Notice, however, that empiricism alone is not enough; it must be **systematic empiricism**. In other words, simply observing a series of events does not lead to scientific knowledge. The observations must be made in a systematic manner to test a hypothesis and develop or refute a theory (in other words, empiricism and rationalism). For example, if a researcher is interested in the relationship between vitamin C and the incidence of colds, she will not simply ask people haphazardly whether they take vitamin C and how many colds they have had. This approach involves empiricism but not systematic empiricism. Instead, the researcher might design a study to assess the effects of vitamin C on colds. Her study will probably involve using a representative group of individuals, with each individual then randomly assigned to either take or not take vitamin C supplements. She will then observe whether the groups differ in the number of colds they report. We will go into more detail on designing such a study later in this chapter. By using systematic empiricism, researchers can draw more reliable and valid conclusions than they can from observation alone.

Publicly Verifiable Knowledge

publicly verifiable knowledge Presenting research to the public so that it can be observed, replicated, criticized, and tested.

Scientific research should be **publicly verifiable knowledge**. This means that the research is presented to the public in such a way that it can be observed, replicated, criticized, and tested for veracity by others. Most commonly, this involves submitting the research to a scientific journal for possible publication. Most journals are peer-reviewed—other scientists critique the research to decide whether it meets the standards for publication. If a study is published, other researchers can read about the findings, attempt to replicate them, and through this process demonstrate that the results are reliable. You should be suspicious of any claims made without the support of public verification. For example, many people have claimed that they were abducted by aliens. These claims do not meet the criteria of publicly verifiable knowledge; they are simply the claims of individuals with no evidence to support them. Other people claim that they have lived past lives. Once again, there is no evidence to support such claims. These types of claims are unverifiable—there is no way that they are open to public verification.

Empirically Solvable Problems

empirically solvable problems Questions that are potentially answerable by means of currently available research techniques.

Science always investigates **empirically solvable problems**—questions that are potentially answerable by means of currently available research techniques. If a theory cannot be tested using empirical techniques, then scientists are not interested in it. For example, the question "Is there life after death?" is not an empirical question and thus cannot be tested scientifically. However, the question "Does an intervention program minimize rearrests in juvenile delinquents?" can be empirically studied and thus is within the realm of science.

principle of falsifiability The idea that a scientific theory must be stated in such a way that it is possible to refute or disconfirm it.

When empirically solvable problems are studied, they are always open to the **principle of falsifiability**—the idea that a scientific theory must be stated in such a way that it is possible to refute or disconfirm it. In other words, the theory must predict not only what will happen but also what will not happen. A theory is not scientific if it is irrefutable. This may sound counterintuitive, and you may be thinking that if a theory is irrefutable, it must be really good. However, in science, this is not so. Read on to see why.

pseudoscience Claims that appear to be scientific but that actually violate the criteria of science.

Pseudoscience (claims that appear to be scientific but that actually violate the criteria of science) is usually irrefutable and is also often confused with science. For example, those who believe in extrasensory perception (ESP, a pseudoscience) often argue with the fact that no publicly verifiable example of ESP has ever been documented through systematic empiricism. The reason they offer is that the conditions necessary for ESP to occur are violated under controlled laboratory conditions. This means that they have an answer for every situation. If ESP were ever demonstrated under empirical conditions, then they would say their belief is supported. However, when ESP repeatedly fails to be demonstrated in controlled laboratory conditions, they say their belief is not falsified because the conditions were not "right" for ESP to be demonstrated. Thus, because those who believe in ESP have set up a situation in which they claim falsifying data are not valid, the theory of ESP violates the principle of falsifiability.

You may be thinking that the explanation provided by the proponents of ESP makes some sense to you. Let me give you an analogous example from Stanovich (2007). Stanovich jokingly claims that he has found the underlying brain mechanism that controls behavior and that you will soon be able to read about it in the *National Enquirer*. According to him, two tiny green men reside in the left hemisphere of our brains. These little green men have the power to control the processes taking place in many areas of the brain. Why have we not heard about these little green men before? Well, that's easy to explain. According to Stanovich, the little green men have the ability to detect any intrusion into the brain, and when they do, they become invisible.

You may feel that your intelligence has been insulted with this foolish explanation of brain functioning. However, you should see the analogy between this explanation and the one offered by proponents of ESP, despite any evidence to support it and much evidence to refute it.

The Scientific Approach — **IN REVIEW**

CRITERIA	DESCRIPTION	WHY NECESSARY
Systematic empiricism	Making observations in a systematic manner	Aids in refuting or developing a theory in order to test hypotheses
Publicly verifiable knowledge	Presenting research to the public so that it can be observed, replicated, criticized, and tested	Aids in determining the veracity of a theory
Empirically solvable problems	Stating questions in such a way that they are answerable by means of currently available research techniques	Aids in determining whether a theory can potentially be tested using empirical techniques and whether it is falsifiable

CRITICAL THINKING CHECK 1.2

1. Explain how a theory such as Freud's, which attributes much of personality and psychological disorders to unconscious drives, violates the principle of falsifiability.
2. Identify a currently popular pseudoscience, and explain how it might violate each of the criteria identified previously.

Basic and Applied Research

basic research The study of psychological issues to seek knowledge for its own sake.

Some psychologists conduct research because they enjoy seeking knowledge and answering questions. This is referred to as **basic research**—the study of psychological issues to seek knowledge for its own sake. Most basic research is conducted in university or laboratory settings. The intent of basic research is not immediate application but the gaining of knowledge. However, many treatments and procedures that have been developed to help humans and animals began with researchers asking basic research questions that later led to applications. Examples of basic research in psychology include identifying differences in capacity and duration in short-term memory and long-term memory, identifying whether cognitive maps can be mentally rotated, determining how various schedules of reinforcement affect learning, and determining how lesioning a certain area in the brains of rats affects their behavior. In October of 2013, after winning the Nobel Prize for physics for their work in helping explain how matter formed after the Big Bang, based on the Higgs boson, or "God particle," Peter Higgs and Francois Englert both commented on the importance of basic research. Higgs was quoted as saying he hoped that the prize would help people recognize "the value of blue-sky research." Englert said the award pointed to the importance of scientific freedom and the need for scientists to be allowed to do fundamental (basic) research that doesn't have immediate practical applications.

applied research The study of psychological issues that have practical significance and potential solutions.

A second type of research is **applied research**, which involves the study of psychological issues that have practical significance and potential solutions. Scientists who conduct applied research are interested in finding an answer to a question because the answer can be immediately applied to some situation. Much applied research is conducted by private businesses and the government. Examples of applied research include identifying how stress affects the immune system, determining the accuracy of eyewitness testimony, determining the relationship between watching violent TV and aggression in children, and determining whether cell phone use while driving negatively affects driving performance. Some people think that most research should be directly relevant to a social problem or issue. In other words, some people favor *only* applied research. The problem with this approach is that much of what started out as basic research eventually led to some sort of application. If researchers stopped asking questions simply because they wanted to know the answer (stopped engaging in basic research), then many great ideas and eventual applications would undoubtedly be lost.

Goals of Science

Scientific research has three basic goals: (1) to describe behavior, (2) to predict behavior, and (3) to explain behavior. All of these goals lead to a better understanding of behavior and mental processes.

Description

description Carefully observing behavior in order to describe it.

Description begins with careful observation. Psychologists might describe patterns of behavior, thought, or emotions in humans. They might also describe the behavior(s) of animals. For example, researchers might observe and describe the type of play behavior exhibited by children or the mating behavior of chimpanzees. Description allows us to learn about behavior and when it occurs. Let's say, for example, that you were interested in the channel-changing behavior of men and women. Careful observation and description would be needed to determine whether or not there were any gender differences in channel changing. Description allows us to observe that two events are systematically related to one another. Without description as a first step, predictions cannot be made.

Prediction

prediction Identifying the factors that indicate when an event or events will occur.

Prediction allows us to identify the factors that indicate when an event or events will occur. In other words, knowing the level of one variable allows us to predict the approximate level of the other variable. We know that if one variable is present at a certain level, then it is likely that the other variable will be present at a certain level. For example, if we observed that men change channels with greater frequency than women, we could then make predictions about how often men and women might change channels when given the chance.

Explanation

explanation Identifying the causes that determine when and why a behavior occurs.

Finally, **explanation** allows us to identify the causes that determine when and why a behavior occurs. To explain a behavior, we need to demonstrate that we can manipulate the factors needed to produce or eliminate the behavior. For example, in our channel-changing example, if gender predicts channel changing, what might cause it? It could be genetic or environmental. Maybe men have less tolerance for commercials and thus change channels at a greater rate. Maybe women are more interested in the content of commercials and are thus less likely to change channels. Maybe the attention span of women is longer. Maybe something associated with having a Y chromosome increases channel changing, or something associated with having two X chromosomes leads to less channel changing. Obviously there are a wide variety of possible explanations. As scientists, we test these possibilities to identify the best explanation of why a behavior occurs. When we try to identify the best explanation for a behavior, we must systematically eliminate any alternative explanations. To eliminate alternative explanations, we must impose control over the research situation. We will discuss the concepts of control and alternative explanations shortly.

An Introduction to Research Methods in Science

The goals of science map very closely onto the research methods scientists use. In other words, there are methods that are descriptive in nature, predictive in nature, and explanatory in nature. We will briefly introduce these methods here; the remainder of the text covers these methods in far greater detail. Descriptive methods are covered in Chapter 4, and descriptive statistics are discussed in Chapter 5; predictive methods and statistics are covered in Chapters 6 and 13; and explanatory methods are covered in Chapters 9 through 12. Thus, what follows will briefly introduce you to some of the concepts that we will be discussing in greater detail throughout the remainder of this text.

Descriptive Methods

observational method Making observations of human or animal behavior.

naturalistic observation Observing the behavior of humans or animals in their natural habitat.

laboratory observation Observing the behavior of humans or animals in a more contrived and controlled situation, usually the laboratory.

Psychologists use three types of descriptive methods. First is the **observational method**—simply observing human or animal behavior. Psychologists approach observation in two ways. **Naturalistic observation** involves observing how humans or animals behave in their natural habitat. Observing the mating behavior of chimpanzees in their natural setting is an example of this approach. **Laboratory observation** involves observing behavior in a more contrived and controlled situation, usually the laboratory. Bringing children to a laboratory playroom to observe play behavior is an example of this approach. Observation involves description at its most basic level. One advantage of the observational method, as well as other descriptive methods, is the flexibility to change what you are studying. A disadvantage of descriptive methods is that the researcher has little control. As we use more powerful methods, we gain control but lose flexibility.

case study method An in-depth study of one or more individuals.

A second descriptive method is the **case study method**. A case study is an in-depth study of one or more individuals. Freud used case studies to develop his theory of personality development. Similarly, Jean Piaget used case studies to develop his theory of cognitive development in children. This method is descriptive in nature because it involves simply describing the individual(s) being studied.

survey method Questioning individuals on a topic or topics and then describing their responses.

sample The group of people who participate in a study.

population All of the people about whom a study is meant to generalize.

random sample A sample achieved through random selection in which each member of the population is equally likely to be chosen.

The third method that relies on description is the **survey method**—questioning individuals on a topic or topics and then describing their responses. Surveys can be administered by mail, over the phone, on the Internet, or in a personal interview. One advantage of the survey method over the other descriptive methods is that it allows researchers to study larger groups of individuals more easily. This method has disadvantages, however. One concern is whether the group of people who participate in the study (the **sample**) is representative of all of the people about whom the study is meant to generalize (the **population**). This concern can usually be overcome through random sampling. A **random sample** is achieved when, through random selection, each member of the population is equally likely to be chosen as part of the sample. Another concern has to do with the wording of questions. Are they easy to understand? Are they written in such a manner that they bias the respondents' answers? Such concerns relate to the validity of the data collected.

Predictive (Relational) Methods

correlational method A method that assesses the degree of relationship between two variables.

Two methods allow researchers not only to describe behaviors but also to predict from one variable to another. The first, the **correlational method**, assesses the degree of relationship between two measured variables. If two variables are correlated with each other, then we can predict from one variable to the other with a certain degree of accuracy. For example, height and weight are correlated. The relationship is such that an increase in one variable (height) is generally accompanied by an increase in the other variable (weight). Knowing this, we can predict an individual's approximate weight, with a certain degree of accuracy, based on knowing the person's height.

One problem with correlational research is that it is often misinterpreted. Frequently, people assume that because two variables are correlated, there must be some sort of causal relationship between the variables. This is not so. *Correlation does not imply causation.* Please remember that a correlation simply means that the two variables are related in some way. For example, being a certain height does not cause you also to be a certain weight. It would be nice if it did because then we would not have to worry about being either underweight or overweight. What if I told you that watching violent television and displaying aggressive behavior were correlated? Psychologists have established that such a relationship exists (Bushman & Anderson, 2007; Gunter, 2008; Murray, 2008). What could you conclude based on this correlation? Many people might conclude that watching violent television causes one to act more aggressively. Based on the evidence given (a correlational study), however, we cannot draw this conclusion. All we can conclude is that those who watch more violent television programs also tend to act more aggressively. It is possible that violent television causes aggression, but we cannot draw this conclusion based only on correlational data. It is also possible that those who are aggressive by nature are attracted to more violent television programs, or that some other "third" variable is causing both aggressive behavior and violent television watching. The point is that observing a correlation between two variables means only that they are related to each other.

positive relationship A relationship between two variables in which an increase in one variable is accompanied by an increase in the other variable.

negative relationship A relationship between two variables in which an increase in one variable is accompanied by a decrease in the other variable.

quasi-experimental method Research that compares naturally occurring groups of individuals; the variable of interest cannot be manipulated.

subject (participant) variable A characteristic inherent in the subjects that cannot be changed.

The correlation between height and weight, or violent television and aggressive behavior, is a **positive relationship**: As one variable (height) increases, we observe an increase in the second variable (weight). Some correlations indicate a **negative relationship**, meaning that as one variable increases, the other variable systematically decreases. Can you think of an example of a negative relationship between two variables? Consider this: As mountain elevation increases, temperature decreases. Negative correlations also allow us to predict from one variable to another. If I know the mountain elevation, it will help me predict the approximate temperature.

Besides the correlational method, a second method that allows us to describe and predict is the quasi-experimental method. The **quasi-experimental method** allows us to compare naturally occurring groups of individuals. For example, we could examine whether alcohol consumption by students in a fraternity or sorority differs from that of students not in such organizations. You will see in a moment that this method differs from the experimental method, described later, in that the groups studied occur naturally. In other words, we do not control whether or not people join a Greek organization. They have chosen their groups on their own, and we are simply looking for differences (in this case, in the amount of alcohol typically consumed) between these naturally occurring groups. This is often referred to as a **subject** or **participant variable**—a characteristic inherent in the subjects that cannot be changed. Because we are using groups that occur naturally, any differences that we find may be due to the variable of being or not being a Greek member, or they may be due to other factors that we were unable to control in this study. For example, maybe those who like to drink more are also more likely to join a Greek organization. Once again, if we find a difference between these groups in amount of alcohol consumed, we can use this finding to predict what type of student (Greek or non-Greek) is likely to drink more. However, we cannot conclude that belonging to a Greek organization *causes* one to drink more because the subjects came to us after choosing to belong to these organizations. In other words, what is missing when we use predictive methods such as the correlational and quasi-experimental methods is control.

When using predictive methods, we do not systematically manipulate the variables of interest; we only measure them. This means that, although we may observe a relationship between variables (such as that described between drinking and Greek membership), we cannot conclude that it is a causal relationship because there could be other *alternative explanations* for

alternative explanation The idea that it is possible that some other, uncontrolled, extraneous variable may be responsible for the observed relationship.

this relationship. An **alternative explanation** is the idea that it is possible that some other, uncontrolled, extraneous variable may be responsible for the observed relationship. For example, maybe those who choose to join Greek organizations come from higher-income families and have more money to spend on such things as alcohol. Or maybe those who choose to join Greek organizations are more interested in socialization and drinking alcohol before they even join the organization. Thus, because these methods leave the possibility for alternative explanations, we cannot use them to establish cause-and-effect relationships.

Explanatory Method

experimental method A research method that allows a researcher to establish a cause-and-effect relationship through manipulation of a variable and control of the situation.

When using the experimental method, researchers pay a great deal of attention to eliminating alternative explanations by using the proper controls. Because of this, the **experimental method** allows researchers not only to describe and predict but also to determine whether a cause-and-effect relationship exists between the variables of interest. In other words, this method enables researchers to know when and why a behavior occurs. Many preconditions must be met for a study to be experimental in nature; we will discuss many of these in detail in later chapters. Here, we will simply consider the basics—the minimum requirements needed for an experiment.

independent variable The variable in a study that is manipulated by the researcher.

dependent variable The variable in a study that is measured by the researcher.

The basic premise of experimentation is that the researcher controls as much as possible to determine whether a cause-and-effect relationship exists between the variables being studied. Let's say, for example, that a researcher is interested in whether cell phone use while driving affects driving performance. The idea behind experimentation is that the researcher manipulates at least one variable (known as the **independent variable**) and measures at least one variable (known as the **dependent variable**). In our study, what should the researcher manipulate? If you identified the use of cell phones while driving, then you are correct. If cell phone use while driving is the independent variable, then driving performance is the dependent variable. For comparative purposes, the independent variable has to have at least two groups or conditions. We typically refer to these two groups or conditions as the control group and the experimental group. The **control group** is the group that serves as the baseline or "standard" condition. In our cell phone use while driving study, the control group does not use a cell phone while driving. The **experimental group** is the group that receives the treatment—in this case, those who use cell phones while driving. Thus, in an experiment, one thing that we control is the level of the independent variable that subjects receive.

control group The group of subjects that does not receive any level of the independent variable and serves as the baseline in a study.

experimental group The group of subjects that receives some level of the independent variable.

What else should we control to help eliminate alternative explanations? Well, we need to control the type of subjects in each of the treatment conditions. We should begin by drawing a random sample of subjects from the population. After we have our sample of subjects, we have to decide who will serve in the control group versus the experimental group. To gain as much control as possible and eliminate as many alternative explanations as possible, we should use **random assignment**—assigning subjects to conditions in such a way that every participant has an equal probability of being

random assignment Assigning subjects to conditions in such a way that every participant has an equal probability of being placed in any condition.

placed in any condition. Random assignment helps us to gain control and eliminate alternative explanations by minimizing or eliminating differences between the groups. In other words, we want the two groups of participants to be as alike as possible. The only difference we want between the groups is that of the independent variable we are manipulating—either using or not using cell phones while driving. After subjects are assigned to conditions, we measure driving performance (the dependent variable) for subjects in each condition using a driving simulator. Studies such as this one have already been completed by researchers. What researchers have found is that cell phone use while driving has a negative effect on driving performance (Beede & Kass, 2006; Dula, Martin, Fox, & Leonard, 2011).

Let's review some of the controls we have used in the present study. We have controlled who is in the study (we want a sample representative of the population about whom we are trying to generalize), who participates in each group (we should randomly assign subjects to the two conditions), and the treatment each group receives as part of the study (some take the driving test while using cell phones whereas others take the driving test while not using cell phones). Can you identify other variables that we might need to consider controlling in the present study? How about past driving record, how long subjects have driven, age, and their proficiency with cell phones? There are undoubtedly other variables we would need to control if we were to complete this study. We will discuss control in greater detail in later chapters, but the basic idea is that when using the experimental method, we try to **control** as much as possible by manipulating the independent variable and controlling any other extraneous variables that could affect the results of the study. Randomly assigning participants also helps to control for participant differences between the groups. What does all of this control gain us? If, after completing this study with the proper controls, we found that those in the experimental group (those who drove while using a cell phone) did in fact have lower driving performance scores than those in the control group, we would have evidence supporting a cause-and-effect relationship between these variables. In other words, we could conclude that driving while using a cell phone negatively impacts driving performance.

control Manipulating the independent variable in an experiment and controlling any other extraneous variables that could affect the results of a study.

An Introduction to Research Methods — IN REVIEW

GOAL MET	RESEARCH METHODS	ADVANTAGES/DISADVANTAGES
Description	Observational method Case study method Survey method	Allows description of behavior(s) Does not support reliable predictions Does not support cause-and-effect explanations
Prediction	Correlational method Quasi-experimental method	Allows description of behavior(s) Supports reliable predictions from one variable to another Does not support cause-and-effect explanations
Explanation	Experimental method	Allows description of behavior(s) Supports reliable predictions from one variable to another Supports cause-and-effect explanations

CRITICAL THINKING CHECK 1.3

1. In a recent study, researchers found a negative correlation between income level and incidence of psychological disorders. Jim thinks this means that being poor leads to psychological disorders. Is he correct in his conclusion? Why or why not?
2. In a study designed to assess the effects of smoking on life satisfaction, subjects were assigned to groups based on whether or not they reported smoking. All subjects then completed a life satisfaction inventory.
   a. What is the independent variable?
   b. What is the dependent variable?
   c. Is the independent variable a subject variable or a true manipulated variable?
3. What type of method would you recommend researchers use to answer the following questions?
   a. What percentage of cars run red lights?
   b. Do student athletes spend as much time studying as student nonathletes?
   c. Is there a relationship between type of punishment used by parents and aggressiveness in children?
   d. Do athletes who are randomly assigned to use imaging techniques perform better than those who are not randomly assigned to use such techniques?
4. Your mother claims that she has found a wonderful new treatment for her arthritis. She read "somewhere" that rubbing vinegar into the affected area for 10 minutes twice a day would help. She tried this and is convinced that her arthritis has been lessened. She now thinks that the medical community should recommend this treatment. What alternative explanation(s) might you offer to your mother for why she feels better? How would you explain to her that her evidence is not sufficient for the medical/scientific community?

Doing Science

Although the experimental method can establish a cause-and-effect relationship, most researchers would not wholeheartedly accept a conclusion from only one study. Why is that? Any one of a number of problems can occur in a study. For example, there may be control problems. Researchers may believe they have controlled everything but miss something, and the uncontrolled factor may affect the results. In other words, a researcher may believe that the manipulated independent variable caused the results when, in reality, it was something else.

Another reason for caution in interpreting experimental results is that a study may be limited by the technical equipment available at the time. For example, in the early part of the 19th century, many scientists believed that studying the bumps on a person's head allowed them to know something about the internal mind of the individual being studied. This movement, known as phrenology, was popularized through the writings of physician Joseph Gall (1758–1828). Based on what you have learned in this chapter, you can most likely see that phrenology is a pseudoscience. However, at the time it was popular, phrenology appeared very "scientific" and "technical." Obviously, with hindsight and with the technological advances that we have today, the idea of phrenology seems somewhat laughable to us now.

Finally, we cannot completely rely on the findings of one study because a single study cannot tell us everything about a theory. The idea of science is that it is not static; the theories generated through science change. For example, we often hear about new findings in the medical field, such as "Eggs are so high in cholesterol that you should eat no more than two a week." Then, a couple of years later, we might read "Eggs are not as bad for you as originally thought. New research shows that it is acceptable to eat them every day," followed a few years later by even more recent research indicating that "two eggs a day are as bad for you as smoking cigarettes every day" (Spence, Jenkins, & Davignon, 2012). People may complain when confronted with such contradictory findings: "Those doctors, they don't know what they're talking about. You can't believe any of them. First they say one thing, and then they say completely the opposite. It's best to just ignore all of them." The point is that when testing a theory scientifically, we may obtain contradictory results. These contradictions may lead to new, very valuable information that subsequently leads to a theoretical change. Theories evolve and change over time based on the consensus of the research. Just because a particular idea or theory is supported by data from one study does not mean that the research on that topic ends and that we just accept the theory as it currently stands and never do any more research on that topic.

Proof and Disproof

When scientists test theories, they do not try to prove them true. Theories can be supported based on the data collected, but obtaining support for something does not mean it is true in all instances. Proof of a theory is logically impossible. As an example, consider the following problem, adapted from Griggs and Cox (1982). This is known as the Drinking Age Problem (the reason for the name will become readily apparent).

> Imagine that you are a police officer responsible for making sure that the drinking age rule is being followed. The four cards below represent information about four people sitting at a table. One side of a card indicates what the person is drinking, and the other side of the card indicates the person's age. The rule is: "If a person is drinking alcohol, then the person is 21 or over." In order to test whether the rule is true or false, which card or cards below would you turn over? Turn over only the card or cards that you need to check to be sure.

Drinking a beer	16 years old	Drinking a Coke	22 years old

Does turning over the beer card and finding that the person is 21 years of age or older prove that the rule is always true? No, the fact that one person is following the rule does not mean that it is always true. How, then, do we test a hypothesis? We test a hypothesis by attempting to falsify or disconfirm it. If it cannot be falsified, then we say we have support for it. Which cards would you choose in an attempt to falsify the rule in the Drinking Age Problem? If you identified the beer card as being able to falsify the rule, then you were correct. If we turn over the beer card and find that the individual is under 21 years of age, then the rule is false. Is there another card that could also falsify the rule? Yes, the 16 years of age card can. How? If we turn that card over and find that the individual is drinking alcohol, then the rule is false. These are the only two cards that can potentially falsify the rule. Thus, they are the only two cards that need to be turned over.

Even though disproof or disconfirmation is logically sound in terms of testing hypotheses, falsifying a hypothesis does not always mean that the hypothesis is false. Why? There may be design problems in the study, as described earlier. Thus, even when a theory is falsified, we need to be cautious in our interpretation. The point to be taken is that we do not want to completely discount a theory based on a single study.

The Research Process

The actual process of conducting research involves several steps, the first of which is to identify a problem. Accomplishing this step is discussed more fully in Chapter 2. The other steps include reviewing the literature (Chapter 2), generating hypotheses (Chapter 7), designing and conducting the study (Chapters 4 and 8 through 13), analyzing the data and interpreting the results (Chapters 5 through 6, 8, 10 through 12, and 14), and communicating the results (Chapter 15).

Summary

We began the chapter by stressing the importance of research in psychology. We identified different areas within the discipline of psychology in which research is conducted such as psychobiology, cognition, human development, social psychology, and psychotherapy. We discussed various sources of knowledge, including intuition, superstition, authority, tenacity, rationalism, empiricism, and science. We stressed the importance of using the scientific method to gain knowledge in psychology. The scientific method is a combination of empiricism and rationalism; it must meet the criteria of systematic empiricism, public verification, and empirically solvable problems.

We outlined the three goals of science (description, prediction, and explanation) and related them to the research methods used by psychologists. Descriptive methods include observation, case study, and survey methods. Predictive methods include correlational and quasi-experimental methods. The experimental method allows for explanation of cause-and-effect relationships. Finally, we introduced some practicalities of doing research, discussed proof and disproof in science, and noted that testing a hypothesis involves attempting to falsify it.

KEY TERMS

knowledge via superstition
knowledge via intuition
knowledge via authority
knowledge via tenacity
knowledge via rationalism
knowledge via empiricism
knowledge via science
hypothesis
variable
theory
skeptic
systematic empiricism
publicly verifiable knowledge
empirically solvable problems
principle of falsifiability
pseudoscience
basic research
applied research
description
prediction
explanation
observational method
naturalistic observation
laboratory observation
case study method
survey method
sample
population
random sample
correlational method
positive relationship
negative relationship
quasi-experimental method
subject (participant) variable
alternative explanation
experimental method
independent variable
dependent variable
control group
experimental group
random assignment
control

CHAPTER EXERCISES

(Answers to odd-numbered exercises appear in Appendix C.)

1. Identify a piece of information that you have gained through each of the sources of knowledge discussed in this chapter (superstition and intuition, authority, tenacity, rationalism, empiricism, and science).
2. Provide an argument for the idea that basic research is as important as applied research.
3. Why is it a compliment for a scientist to be called a skeptic?
4. An infomercial asserts "A study proves that Fat-B-Gone works, and it will work for you also." What is wrong with this statement?
5. Many psychology students believe that they do not need to know about research methods because they plan to pursue careers in clinical/counseling psychology. What argument can you provide against this view?
6. In a study of the effects of types of study on exam performance, subjects are randomly assigned to one of two conditions. In one condition, subjects study in a traditional manner—alone using notes they took during class lectures. In a second condition, subjects study in interactive groups with notes from class lectures. The amount of time spent studying is held constant. All students then take the same exam on the material.
   a. What is the independent variable in this study?
   b. What is the dependent variable in this study?
   c. Identify the control and experimental groups in this study.
   d. Is the independent variable manipulated, or is it a subject variable?
7. Researchers interested in the effects of caffeine on anxiety have randomly assigned participants to one of two conditions in a study—the no-caffeine condition or the caffeine condition. After drinking two cups of either regular or decaffeinated coffee, participants will take an anxiety inventory.
   a. What is the independent variable in this study?
   b. What is the dependent variable in this study?
   c. Identify the control and experimental groups in this study.
   d. Is the independent variable manipulated, or is it a subject variable?
8. Gerontologists interested in the effects of aging on reaction time have two groups of subjects take a test in which they must indicate as quickly as possible whether a probe word was a member of a previous set of words. One group of subjects is between the ages of 25 and 45, and the other group is between the ages of 65 and 85. The time it takes to make the response is measured.
   a. What is the independent variable in this study?
   b. What is the dependent variable in this study?
   c. Identify the control and experimental groups in this study.
   d. Is the independent variable manipulated, or is it a subject variable?

CRITICAL THINKING CHECK ANSWERS

1.1

1. Knowledge via authority
2. Knowledge via empiricism
3. Knowledge via superstition or intuition

1.2

1. A theory such as Freud's violates the principle of falsifiability because it is not possible to falsify or test the theory. Freud attributes much of personality to unconscious drives, and there is no way to test whether this is so—or, for that matter, whether there is such a thing as an unconscious drive. The theory is irrefutable not just because it deals with unconscious drives but also because it is too vague and flexible—it can explain any outcome.
2. Belief in paranormal events is a currently popular pseudoscience (based on the popularity of various cable shows on ESP, psychics, and ghost-hunters). Belief in paranormal events

violates all three criteria that define science. First, the ideas have not been supported by systematic empiricism. Most "authorities" in this area do not test hypotheses but rather offer demonstrations of their abilities. Second, there has been little or no public verification of these claims. There is little reliable and valid research on this topic and what there is does not support the claims. Instead, most evidence tends to be testimonials. Third, many of the claims are stated in such a way that they are not solvable problems. In other words, they do not open themselves to the principle of falsifiability ("My powers do not work in a controlled laboratory setting" or "My powers do not work when skeptics are present").

1.3

1. Jim is incorrect because he is inferring causation based on correlational evidence. He is assuming that because the two variables are correlated, one must be causing changes in the other. In addition, he is assuming the direction of the inferred causal relationship—that a lower income level causes psychological disorders, not that having a psychological disorder leads to a lower income level. The correlation simply indicates that these two variables are related in an inverse manner. That is, those with psychological disorders also tend to have lower income levels.
2. a. The independent variable is smoking.
   b. The dependent variable is life satisfaction.
   c. The independent variable is a subject variable.
3. a. Naturalistic observation
   b. Quasi-experimental method
   c. Correlational method
   d. Experimental method
4. An alternative explanation might be that simply rubbing the affected area makes it feel better, regardless of whether she is rubbing in vinegar. Her evidence is not sufficient for the medical/scientific community because it was not gathered using the scientific method. Instead, it is simply a testimonial from one person.

WEB RESOURCES

The book-specific website at CengageBrain.com offers students a variety of study tools and useful resources such as glossaries and flashcards.

Chapter 1 ▪ Study Guide

CHAPTER 1 SUMMARY AND REVIEW: THINKING LIKE A SCIENTIST

We began the section by stressing the importance of research in psychology. We identified different areas within the discipline of psychology in which research is conducted, such as psychobiology, cognition, human development, social psychology, and psychotherapy. We discussed various sources of knowledge, including intuition, superstition, authority, tenacity, rationalism, empiricism, and science. We stressed the importance of using the scientific method to gain knowledge in psychology. The scientific method is a combination of empiricism and rationalism; it must meet the criteria of systematic empiricism, public verification, and empirically solvable problems.

We outlined the three goals of science (description, prediction, and explanation) and related them to the research methods used by psychologists. Descriptive methods include observation, case study, and survey methods. Predictive methods include correlational and quasi-experimental methods. The experimental method allows for explanation of cause-and-effect relationships. Finally, we introduced some practicalities of doing research, discussed proof and disproof in science, and noted that testing a hypothesis involves attempting to falsify it.

CHAPTER 1 REVIEW EXERCISES

(Answers to exercises appear in Appendix C.)

FILL-IN SELF-TEST

Answer the following questions. If you have trouble answering any of the questions, restudy the relevant material before going on to the multiple-choice self-test.

1. To gain knowledge without being consciously aware of where the knowledge was gained exemplifies gaining knowledge via ________.
2. To gain knowledge from repeated ideas and to cling stubbornly to them despite evidence to the contrary exemplifies gaining knowledge via ________.
3. A ________ is a prediction regarding the outcome of a study that often involves a prediction regarding the relationship between two variables in a study.
4. A person who questions the validity, authenticity, or truth of something purporting to be factual is a ________.
5. ________ are questions that are potentially answerable by means of currently available research techniques.
6. ________ involves making claims that appear to be scientific but that actually violate the criteria of science.
7. The three goals of science are ________, ________, and ________.
8. ________ research involves the study of psychological issues that have practical significance and potential solutions.
9. A ________ is an in-depth study of one or more individuals.
10. All of the people about whom a study is meant to generalize are the ________.
11. The ________ method is a method in which the degree of relationship between at least two variables is assessed.
12. A characteristic inherent in the subjects that cannot be changed is known as a ________ variable.
13. The variable in a study that is manipulated is the ________ variable.
14. The ________ group is the group of subjects that serves as the baseline in a study. They do not receive any level of the independent variable.

MULTIPLE-CHOICE SELF-TEST

Select the single best answer for each of the following questions. If you have trouble answering any of the questions, restudy the relevant material.

1. A belief that is based on subjective feelings is gaining knowledge via ________ and stubbornly clinging to knowledge gained from repeated ideas is gaining knowledge via ________.
   a. authority; superstition
   b. superstition; intuition
   c. tenacity; intuition
   d. superstition; tenacity
2. Tom did really well on his psychology exam last week, and he believes that it is because he used his lucky pen. He has now decided that he must use this pen for every exam that he writes because he believes that it will make him lucky. This belief is based on:
   a. superstition
   b. rationalism
   c. authority
   d. science

3. A prediction regarding the outcome of a study is a(an) ________ and an organized system of assumptions and principles that attempts to explain certain phenomena and how they are related is a(an) ________.
   a. theory; hypothesis
   b. hypothesis; theory
   c. independent variable; dependent variable
   d. dependent variable; independent variable
4. ________ involves making claims that appear to be scientific but that actually violate the criteria of science.
   a. The principle of falsifiability
   b. Systemic empiricism
   c. Being a skeptic
   d. Pseudoscience
5. The study of psychological issues to seek knowledge for its own sake is ________ research, and the study of psychological issues that have practical significance and potential solutions is ________ research.
   a. basic; applied
   b. applied; basic
   c. naturalistic; laboratory
   d. laboratory; naturalistic
6. Ray was interested in the mating behavior of squirrels so he went into the field to observe them. Ray is using the ________ method of research.
   a. case study
   b. laboratory observational
   c. naturalistic observational
   d. correlational
7. Negative correlation is to ________ and positive correlation is to ________.
   a. increasing or decreasing together; moving in opposite directions
   b. moving in opposite directions; increasing or decreasing together
   c. independent variable; dependent variable
   d. dependent variable; independent variable
8. Which of the following is a subject (participant) variable?
   a. amount of time given to study a list of words
   b. fraternity membership
   c. the number of words in a memory test
   d. all of the above
9. If a researcher assigns subjects to groups based on, for example, their earned GPA, the researcher would be employing:
   a. a manipulated independent variable.
   b. random assignment.
   c. a subject variable.
   d. a manipulated dependent variable.
10. In an experimental study of the effects of time spent studying on grades, time spent studying would be the:
    a. control group.
    b. independent variable.
    c. experimental group.
    d. dependent variable.
11. Baseline is to treatment as ________ is to ________.
    a. independent variable; dependent variable
    b. dependent variable; independent variable
    c. experimental group; control group
    d. control group; experimental group
12. In a study of the effects of alcohol on driving performance, driving performance would be the:
    a. control group.
    b. independent variable.
    c. experimental group.
    d. dependent variable.

CHAPTER

2 Getting Started: Ideas, Resources, and Ethics

Learning Objectives

- Use resources in the library to locate information.
- Understand the major sections of a journal article.
- Briefly describe APA ethical standards in research with human subjects.
- Explain what an IRB is.
- Explain when deception is acceptable in research.
- Identify what it means to be a subject at risk versus a subject at minimal risk.
- Explain why debriefing is important.
- Briefly describe the ethical standards in research with animals.

In Chapter 1, we discussed the nature of science and how to think critically like a scientist. In addition, we offered a brief introduction to the various research methods used by psychologists. In this chapter, we will discuss some issues related to getting started on a research project, beginning with library research and moving on to conducting research ethically. We will discuss how to use some of the resources available through most libraries, and we will cover the guidelines set forth by the APA (American Psychological Association) for the ethical treatment of both humans and animals used in research. APA has very specific ethical guidelines for the treatment of humans used in research. These guidelines are set forth in the APA's *Ethical Principles of Psychologists and Code of Conduct* (2002). In discussing these guidelines, we will pay particular attention to several issues: how to obtain approval for a research project, the meaning of informed consent, how to minimize risk to subjects, when it may be acceptable to use deception in a research study, debriefing your subjects, and special considerations when using children as subjects. We will also review the APA guidelines for using animals in research.

Selecting a Problem

Getting started on a research project begins with selecting a problem. Some students find selecting a problem the most daunting task of the whole research process, whereas other students have so many ideas for research projects that they don't know where to begin. If you fall into the first category and are not sure what topic you might want to research, you can get an idea for a research project from a few different places.

If you are one of the people who have trouble generating research ideas, it's best to start with what others have already done. One place to start is with past research on a topic rather than just jumping in with a completely new idea of your own. For example, if you are interested in treatments for depression, you should begin by researching some of the treatments currently available. While reading about these treatments, you may find that one or more of the journal articles you read raise questions that have yet to be addressed. Thus, looking at the research already completed in an area gives you a firm foundation from which to begin your own research and may help suggest a hypothesis that your research project might address.

A second place from which to generate ideas is past theories on a topic. A good place to find a cursory review of theories on a particular topic is in your psychology textbooks. For example, when students are having trouble coming up with an idea for a research project, I have them identify which psychology class they have found most interesting. I then have them look at the textbook from that class and identify which chapter they found most interesting. The students can then narrow it down to which topic within the chapter was most interesting, and the topical coverage within the chapter will usually provide details on several theories.

A third source of ideas for a research project is observation. We are all capable of observing behavior and, based on these observations, questions may arise. For example, you may have observed that some students at your institution cheat on exams or papers, whereas most students would never consider doing such a thing. Or you may have observed that certain individuals overindulge in alcohol, whereas others know their limits. Or maybe you believe, based on observation, that the type of music listened to affects a person's mood. Any of these observations may lead to a future research project.

Last, ideas for research projects are often generated from practical problems encountered in daily life. This should sound familiar to you from Chapter 1 because research designed to find answers to practical problems is applied research. Thus, many students easily develop research ideas because they base them on practical problems that they or someone they know have encountered. For example, here are two ideas generated by my students based on practical problems they encountered: Do alcohol awareness programs lead to more responsible alcohol consumption by college students? Does art therapy improve the mood and general well-being of those recovering from surgery?

Reviewing the Literature

After you decide on a topic of interest, the next step is to conduct a literature review. A literature review involves searching the published studies on a topic to ensure that you have a grasp of all the research that has been conducted in that area that might be relevant to your intended study. This may sound like an overwhelming task, but several resources are available that help simplify this process. Notice that I did not say the process is simple—only that these resources help to simplify it. A thorough literature review takes time, but the resources discussed here will help you make the best use of that time.

Library Research

Usually, the best place to begin your research is at the library. Several resources available through most libraries are invaluable when conducting a literature review. One important resource, often overlooked by students, is the library staff. Reference librarians have been trained to find information—this is their job. Thus, if you provide them with sufficient information, they should be able to provide you with numerous resources. Do not expect them to do this on the spot, however. Plan ahead, and give the librarian sufficient time to help you.

Journals

Most published research in psychology appears in the form of journal articles (see Table 2.1 for a list of major journals in psychology). Notice that the titles listed in Table 2.1 are journals, not magazines such as *Psychology Today*. The difference is that each paper published in these journals is first submitted to the editor of the journal, who sends the paper out for review by other scientists (specialists) in that area. This process is called *peer review*, and, based on the reviews, the editor then decides whether to accept the paper for publication. Because of the limited space available in each journal, most papers that are submitted are ultimately rejected for publication. Thus, the research published in journals represents a fraction of the research conducted in an area, and, because of the review process, it should be the best research in that area.

TABLE 2.1 Some Journals Whose Articles Are Summarized in the *Psychological Abstracts*

Applied Psychology

Applied Cognitive Psychology
Consulting Psychology Journal: Practice and Research
Educational and Psychological Measurement
Educational Psychologist
Educational Psychology Review
Environment and Behavior
Health Psychology
Journal of Applied Behavior Analysis
Journal of Applied Developmental Psychology
Journal of Applied Psychology
Journal of Educational Psychology
Journal of Environmental Psychology
Journal of Experimental Psychology: Applied
Journal of Occupational Health Psychology
Journal of Sport Psychology
Law and Human Behavior
Psychology, Public Policy, and Law
School Psychology Quarterly

Biological Psychology

Behavioral and Brain Sciences
Behavioral Neuroscience
Biological Psychology
Brain and Language
Experimental and Clinical Psychopharmacology
Journal of Comparative Psychology
Neuropsychology
Physiological Psychology

Clinical/Counseling Psychology

Clinician's Research Digest
The Counseling Psychologist
Journal of Abnormal Child Psychology
Journal of Abnormal Psychology
Journal of Clinical Child & Adolescent Psychology
Journal of Clinical Psychology
Journal of Consulting and Clinical Psychology
Journal of Contemporary Psychotherapy
Journal of Counseling Psychology
Journal of Psychotherapy Integration
Professional Psychology: Research and Practice
Psychoanalytic Psychology
Psychological Services
Psychotherapy: Theory, Research, Practice, Training
Training and Education in Professional Psychology

Developmental Psychology

Child Development
Developmental Psychobiology
Developmental Review
Infant Behavior and Development
Journal of Experimental Child Psychology
Psychology and Aging

Experimental Psychology

Cognition
Cognition and Emotion
Cognitive Psychology
Cognitive Science
Journal of Experimental Psychology: Animal Behavior Processes
Journal of Experimental Psychology: Applied
Journal of Experimental Psychology: General
Journal of Experimental Psychology: Human Perception and Performance
Journal of Experimental Psychology: Learning, Memory, and Cognition
Journal of Memory and Language
Journal of the Experimental Analysis of Behavior
Learning and Motivation
Memory and Cognition
Perception
Quarterly Journal of Experimental Psychology

Family Therapy

American Journal of Family Therapy
Families, Systems, & Health
Journal of Family Psychology

General Psychology

American Psychologist
Journal of Contemporary Psychology
History of Psychology
Psychological Bulletin
Psychological Methods
Psychological Review
Psychological Science
Review of General Psychology

(continued)

TABLE 2.1 Some Journals Whose Articles Are Summarized in the *Psychological Abstracts* (continued)

Personality and Social Psychology	*Journal of Social and Personal Relationships*	*Behavior Modification*
Basic and Applied Social Psychology	*Journal of Social Issues*	*Behavior Therapy*
Journal of Applied Social Psychology	*Personality and Social Psychology Bulletin*	*International Journal of Stress Management*
Journal of Experimental Social Psychology	*Personality and Social Psychology Review*	*Journal of Anxiety Disorders*
Journal of Personality	***Treatment***	*Journal of Behavioral Medicine*
Journal of Personality and Social Psychology	*Addictive Behaviors*	*Psychology of Addictive Behaviors*
Journal of Personality Assessment		*Rehabilitation Psychology*

As you can see in Table 2.1, a great many journals publish psychology papers. Obviously, keeping up with all the research published in these journals is impossible. In fact, it would be very difficult to read all of the studies that are published in a given area. As a researcher, then, how can you identify those papers most relevant to your topic? Browsing through the psychology journals in your library to find articles of interest to you would take forever. Fortunately, this browsing is not necessary.

Psychological Abstracts

Besides reference librarians, your other best friend in the library is *Psychological (Psych) Abstracts*. Psych Abstracts is a reference resource published by the APA that contains abstracts, or brief summaries, of articles in psychology and related disciplines. *Psych Abstracts* is updated monthly and can be found in the reference section of your library. To use *Psych Abstracts*, begin with the index at the back of each monthly issue, and look up the topic in which you are interested. Next to the topic, you will find several numbers referencing abstracts in that issue. You can then refer to each of these abstracts to find where the full article is published, who wrote it, when it was published, the pages on which it appears, and a brief summary of the article.

PsycINFO

Most libraries have *Psych Abstracts* in electronic form. If your library has such a resource, you will probably find it easier to use than the hard copy of *Psych Abstracts* described previously. PsycINFO is an electronic database that provides abstracts and citations to the scholarly literature in the behavioral sciences and mental health. The database, which is updated monthly, includes material of relevance to psychologists and professionals in related fields such as psychiatry, business, education, social sciences, neuroscience, law, and medicine.

To use this resource, you simply enter your topic of interest into the "Search" box, and the database provides a listing of abstracts relevant to that topic. When you use this resource, you don't want your topic to be either too broad or too narrow. In addition, you should try several phrases when searching a particular topic. Students often type in their topic and find nothing because the keyword they used may not be the word used by researchers in the field. To help you choose appropriate keywords, use the APA's *Thesaurus of Psychological Index Terms* (2007). This resource is based on the vocabulary used in psychology and will direct you to the terms to use to locate articles on that topic. Ask your reference librarian for help in finding and using this resource. You will probably find, when using PsycINFO, that you need to complete several searches on a topic using different words and phrases. For example, if you selected the topic depression and entered this word into the Search box, you would find a very large number of articles because PsycINFO looks for the key word in the article and in the abstract itself. In addition, you can limit your search by using some of the Boolean operators such as AND, OR, and NOT and also by using some of the limiters available through the Field Selection boxes to let PsycINFO know where you want to search for the word depression (e.g., in the text, the title, the abstract)

For example, I conducted a search using the key word "depression" in the title of papers and limited it to articles published in 2012. The search returned abstracts for 2,901 articles—obviously too many to review. I then limited my search further by using the Boolean operator AND by typing "depression" in the first Search box along with using the Boolean operator AND in the second Search box and typing "college students." I once again limited the search to articles published in 2012. This second search returned abstracts for 17 articles—a much more manageable number. I could further refine the search by using the Boolean operators NOT and OR. For example, some of the 17 journal articles returned in the second search were about scales used to measure depression. If I were not really interested in this aspect of depression, I could further limit my search by utilizing the third Search box, selecting the Boolean operator NOT, and then typing the following into the Search box: "measures OR scales." When the search was conducted this way, it narrowed the number of journal articles published in 2012 to 11. Thus, with a little practice, PsycINFO should prove an invaluable resource to you in searching the literature.

Social Science Citation Index and *Science Citation Index*

Other resources that are valuable when conducting a literature review are the *Social Science Citation Index* (SSCI) and the *Science Citation Index* (SCI). Whereas *Psych Abstracts* helps you to work backward in time (find articles published on a certain topic within a given year), the SSCI can help you to work from a given article (a "key article") and see what has been published on that topic since the key article was published. The SSCI includes the disciplines from the social and behavioral sciences, whereas the SCI includes disciplines such as biology, chemistry, and medicine. Both resources are used in a similar way. Imagine that you found a very interesting paper on the effects of music on mood that was published in 2007. Because this paper was published several years ago, you need to know what has been published since then on this topic. The SSCI and the SCI enable you to search for subsequent articles that have cited the key article, and they also allow you to search for articles published by the author(s) of the key article. If a subsequent article cites your key article, the chances are good that it's on the same topic and will therefore be of interest to you. Moreover, if the author(s) of the key article have since published additional papers, those would also likely be of interest to you. Thus, the SSCI and the SCI allow you to fill in the gap between 2007 and the present. In this way, you can compile an up-to-date reference list and become familiar with most of the material published on a topic. When using the SSCI or the SCI, you may also find that one of the "new" articles you discover is another key article on your topic, and you can then look for subsequent articles that cite or were written by the author(s) of the new key article. The SSCI and the SCI are often available online through your library's home page.

Other Resources

Another resource often overlooked by students is the set of references provided at the end of a journal article. If you have found a key article of interest to you, begin with the papers cited in the key article. The reference list provides information on where these cited papers were published, enabling you to obtain any of the cited articles that appear to be of interest.

In addition to the resources already described, several other resources and databases may be helpful to you:

- *PsycARTICLES* is an online database that provides full-text articles from many psychology journals and is available through many academic libraries.
- ProQuest is an online database that searches both scholarly journals and popular media sources. Full-text articles are often available. ProQuest is available through most academic libraries.
- *Sociological Abstracts* are similar to *Psych Abstracts*, except they summarize journal articles on sociological topics.
- The Educational Resources Information Center (ERIC) is a clearinghouse for research on educational psychology, testing, counseling, child development, evaluation research, and related areas. ERIC is available online through most academic libraries.
- *Dissertation Abstracts International*, published monthly, includes abstracts of doctoral dissertations from hundreds of universities in the United States and Canada.

In addition to these resources, interlibrary loan (ILL) is a service provided by most libraries that allows you to borrow resources from other libraries if your library does not hold them. If, for example, you need a book that your library does not have or an article from a journal to which your library does not subscribe, you can use interlibrary loan to obtain it. Your library will borrow the resources needed from the closest library that holds them. See your reference librarian to use this service.

Finally, the Web may also be used as a resource. Many of the resources already described, such as PsycINFO, the SSCI, and ERIC, are available online through your library's home page. Be wary, however, of information you retrieve from the Web through some source other than a library. Bear in mind that anyone can post anything on the Web. Just because it looks scientific and appears to be written in the same form as a scientific journal article does not necessarily mean that it is. Thus, it would not be appropriate to simply Google a topic to find resources. However, an alternative to simply Googling something is to use Google Scholar (http://scholar.google.com/), which is a more reliable source for scholarly publications. Keep in mind that your best option is typically to use the resources available through your library's home page. As with the resources available on the shelves of the library, these resources have been chosen by the librarians. This means that editors and other specialists have most likely reviewed them before they were published—unlike information on the Web, which is frequently placed there by the author without any review by others.

Library Research — IN REVIEW

TOOL	WHAT IT IS
Psych Abstracts	A reference resource published by the APA that contains abstracts or brief summaries of articles in psychology and related disciplines
PsycINFO	The online version of *Psych Abstracts*, updated monthly
Social Science Citation Index (SSCI)	A resource that allows you to search for subsequent articles from the social and behavioral sciences that have cited a key article
Science Citation Index (SCI)	A resource that allows you to search for subsequent articles from disciplines such as biology, chemistry, or medicine that have cited a key article
Interlibrary loan (ILL)	A service provided by most libraries that allows you to borrow resources from other libraries if your library does not hold them
Sociological Abstracts	A reference that contains abstracts or brief summaries of articles in sociology and related disciplines
PsycARTICLES	An online database that contains full-text articles from many psychology journals
ProQuest	An online database that searches both scholarly journals and popular media sources, often including full-text articles
ERIC	A clearinghouse for research on educational psychology, testing, counseling, child development, evaluation research, and related areas
Dissertation Abstracts	Abstracts of doctoral dissertations from hundreds of universities in the United States and Canada, published monthly

Reading a Journal Article: What to Expect

Your search for information in the library will undoubtedly provide you with many journal articles. Research articles have a very specific format that includes five main sections: Abstract, Introduction, Method, Results, and Discussion. Following is a brief description of what to expect from each of these sections.

Abstract

The Abstract is a brief description of the entire paper that typically discusses each section of the paper (Introduction, Method, Results, and Discussion). It should be between 150 and 250 words. The Abstract describes the problem under investigation and the purpose of the study; the subjects and general methodology; the findings, including statistical significance levels; and the conclusions and implications or applications of the study.

Introduction

The Introduction has three basic components: an introduction to the problem under study; a review of relevant previous research, which cites works that are pertinent to the issue but not works of marginal or peripheral significance; and the purpose and rationale for the study.

Method

The Method section describes exactly how the study was conducted, in sufficient detail that a person who reads the Method section could replicate the study. The Method section is generally divided into Subjects (or Participants), Materials (or Apparatus), and Procedure subsections. The Subjects subsection includes a description of the subjects and how they were obtained. The Materials subsection usually describes any testing materials that were used, such as a particular test or inventory or a type of problem that participants were asked to solve. An Apparatus subsection describes any specific equipment that was used. The Procedure subsection summarizes each step in the execution of the research, including the groups used in the study, instructions given to the subjects, the experimental manipulation, and specific control features in the design.

Results

The Results section summarizes the data collected and the type of statistic(s) used to analyze the data. In addition, the results of the statistical tests used are reported with respect to the variables measured and/or manipulated. This section should include a description of the results only, not an explanation of the results. In addition, the results are often depicted in tables and graphs or figures.

Discussion

The results are evaluated and interpreted in the Discussion section. Typically, this section begins with a restatement of the predictions of the study and tells whether or not the predictions were supported. It also typically includes a discussion of the relationship between the results and past research and theories. Last, criticisms of the study (such as possible confounds) and implications for future research are presented.

Ethical Standards in Research with Human Subjects

When conducting research with human (or nonhuman) subjects, the researcher is ultimately responsible for the welfare of the subjects. Thus, the researcher is responsible for protecting the participants from harm. What harm, you may be wondering, could a participant suffer in a simple research study? Let's consider some of the research studies that helped to initiate the implementation of ethical guidelines for using human subjects in research.

The ethical guidelines we use today have their basis in the Nuremberg Code. This code lists 10 principles, developed in 1948, for the Nazi war crimes trials following World War II. The Nazis killed and abused millions of Jewish people, many of whom died in the name of "research." For example, Nazi doctors used many Jewish people for inhumane medical research projects that involved determining the effects on humans of viruses, poisons, toxins, and drugs.

The Nazis were not the only researchers who conducted ethically questionable research. For example, researchers who conducted the Tuskegee syphilis study, which began in 1932 and continued until 1972, examined the course of the disease in untreated individuals. The subjects were approximately 400 black men living in and around Tuskegee, Alabama. The individuals, most of whom were poor and illiterate, were offered free meals, physical examinations, and money for their eventual burial for participating in the study (Jones, 1981). They were told that they were being treated for the disease by the U.S. Public Health Service (USPHS). In reality, they were never treated, nor were they ever told the real purpose of the study—to observe the progression of syphilis in an untreated population. Some of the subjects realized that something was amiss and consulted other doctors in the area. Those who did so were eliminated from the study. In addition, the USPHS told doctors in the surrounding area not to treat any of the subjects should they request treatment—even though an effective treatment for syphilis, penicillin, was discovered by the 1940s. The Tuskegee study continued until 1972, providing little new knowledge about syphilis but costing about 400 lives.

Obviously, the Nuremberg Code, established in 1948, had little effect on the researchers who conducted the Tuskegee study. In any case, the Nuremberg Code applied only to medical research. In 1953, therefore, the members of the APA decided to develop their own ethical guidelines for research with human subjects.

In 1963, Stanley Milgram's paper detailing some of his research on obedience to authority brought ethical considerations to the forefront once again. In Milgram's study, each participant was assigned the role of "teacher" and given the responsibility of teaching a series of words to another individual, called the "learner." What the teachers did not realize was that the learner was really an accomplice of the experimenter. The teachers were told that the study was designed to investigate the effects of punishment on learning. Thus, they were instructed to deliver an electric shock each time the learner made a mistake. The shocks were not of a constant voltage level but increased in voltage for each mistake made. Because the learner (who was located in a separate room from the teacher) was working for the experimenter, he purposely made mistakes. Milgram was interested in whether the teachers would continue to deliver stronger and stronger electric shocks given that (1) the learner appeared to be in moderate to extreme discomfort, depending on the level of shock administered, and (2) the experimenter repeatedly ordered the teachers to continue administering the electric shocks. In reality, the learner was not receiving electric shocks; however, the teachers believed that he was. Milgram found that nearly two-thirds of the teachers obeyed the experimenter and continued to deliver the supposed electric shocks up to the maximum level available.

"IT'S FROM THE PROTOZOA RIGHTS COMMITTEE. THEY WANT TO KNOW WHAT YOU'RE USING THEIR CLIENTS FOR."

Although the results of this experiment were valuable to society, the study was ethically questionable. Was it really an ethical use of human subjects to place them in a situation where they were put under extreme psychological stress and where they may have learned things about themselves that they would have preferred not to know? This type of study is generally not allowed today because the APA has continually revised and strengthened its ethical guidelines since 1953. The latest revision occurred in 2002, with some amendments in 2010. You can find the most recent information at http://www.apa.org/ethics. The general principles outlined in 2002 are provided in Table 2.2. Some of the ethical standards outlined by APA in 2002 appear in Table 2.3. In addition to the APA guidelines, federal guidelines (Federal Protection Regulations), developed in 1982, are enforced by institutional review boards at most institutions.

Institutional Review Boards

Institutional Review Board (IRB) A committee charged with evaluating research projects in which human subjects are used.

An **Institutional Review Board (IRB)** is typically made up of several faculty members, usually from diverse backgrounds, and members of the community who are charged with evaluating research projects in which human subjects are used. IRBs oversee all federally funded research involving human subjects. Most academic institutions have either an IRB (if they receive federal funding) or some other committee responsible for evaluating research projects that use human subjects. The evaluation process involves completing an application form in which the researcher details the method to be used in the study, the risks or benefits related to participating in the study, and the means of maintaining subjects' confidentiality. In addition, the researcher should provide an informed consent form (discussed next). The purpose of the IRB is not necessarily to evaluate the scientific merit of the research study but rather to evaluate the treatment of subjects to ensure that the study meets established ethical guidelines.

Informed Consent

informed consent form A form given to individuals before they participate in a study to inform them of the general nature of the study and to obtain their consent to participate.

In studies where subjects are at risk, an informed consent form is needed. (We will discuss exactly what "at risk" means later in the chapter.) The **informed consent form** is given to individuals before they participate in a research study to inform them of the general nature of the study and to obtain their consent to participate in the study. The informed consent form typically describes the nature and purpose of the study. However, to avoid compromising the outcome of the study, the researcher obviously cannot inform subjects about the expected results. Thus, informed consent forms often offer only broad, general statements about the nature and purpose of a study. In cases where deception is used in the study, the informed consent form, for obvious reasons, tells subjects nothing about the true nature and purpose of the study. (We will address the ethical ramifications of using deception later in the chapter.) The subjects are also informed about what they will be asked to do as part of the study and that the researchers will make every effort to maintain confidentiality with respect to their performance in the study. Subjects are told that they have the right to refuse to participate in the study and the right to change their mind about participation at any point during the study. Subjects sign the form, indicating that they have given their informed consent to participate in the study. Typically, the form is also signed by a witness. Researchers should keep informed consent forms on file for 2 to 3 years after completion of a study and should also give

TABLE 2.2 General Principles of the APA Code of Ethics

This section consists of General Principles. General Principles, as opposed to Ethical Standards, are aspirational in nature. Their intent is to guide and inspire psychologists toward the very highest ethical ideals of the profession. General Principles, in contrast to Ethical Standards, do not represent obligations and should not form the basis for imposing sanctions. Relying upon General Principles for either of these reasons distorts both their meaning and purpose.

Principle A: Beneficence and Nonmaleficence

Psychologists strive to benefit those with whom they work and take care to do no harm. In their professional actions, psychologists seek to safeguard the welfare and rights of those with whom they interact professionally and other affected persons, and the welfare of animal subjects of research. When conflicts occur among psychologists' obligations or concerns, they attempt to resolve these conflicts in a responsible fashion that avoids or minimizes harm. Because psychologists' scientific and professional judgments and actions may affect the lives of others, they are alert to and guard against personal, financial, social, organizational, or political factors that might lead to misuse of their influence. Psychologists strive to be aware of the possible effect of their own physical and mental health on their ability to help those with whom they work.

Principle B: Fidelity and Responsibility

Psychologists establish relationships of trust with those with whom they work. They are aware of their professional and scientific responsibilities to society and to the specific communities in which they work. Psychologists uphold professional standards of conduct, clarify their professional roles and obligations, accept appropriate responsibility for their behavior, and seek to manage conflicts of interest that could lead to exploitation or harm. Psychologists consult with, refer to, or cooperate with other professionals and institutions to the extent needed to serve the best interests of those with whom they work. They are concerned about the ethical compliance of their colleagues' scientific and professional conduct. Psychologists strive to contribute a portion of their professional time for little or no compensation or personal advantage.

Principle C: Integrity

Psychologists seek to promote accuracy, honesty, and truthfulness in the science, teaching, and practice of psychology. In these activities, psychologists do not steal, cheat, or engage in fraud, subterfuge, or intentional misrepresentation of fact. Psychologists strive to keep their promises and to avoid unwise or unclear commitments. In situations in which deception may be ethically justifiable to maximize benefits and minimize harm, psychologists have a serious obligation to consider the need for, the possible consequences of, and their responsibility to correct any resulting mistrust or other harmful effects that arise from the use of such techniques.

Principle D: Justice

Psychologists recognize that fairness and justice entitle all persons to access and benefit from the contributions of psychology and to equal quality in the processes, procedures, and services being conducted by psychologists. Psychologists exercise reasonable judgment and take precautions to ensure that their potential biases, the boundaries of their competence, and the limitations of their expertise do not lead to or condone unjust practices.

Principle E: Respect for People's Rights and Dignity

Psychologists respect the dignity and worth of all people and the rights of individuals to privacy, confidentiality, and self-determination. Psychologists are aware that special safeguards may be necessary to protect the rights and welfare of persons or communities whose vulnerabilities impair autonomous decision making. Psychologists are aware of and respect cultural, individual, and role differences, including those based on age, gender, gender identity, race, ethnicity, culture, national origin, religion, sexual orientation, disability, language, and socioeconomic status, and consider these factors when working with members of such groups. Psychologists try to eliminate the effect on their work of biases based on those factors, and they do not knowingly participate in or condone activities of others based upon such prejudices.

SOURCE: American Psychological Association. (2010a). Ethical principles of psychologists and code of conduct (2002, amended June 1, 2010). Retrieved from http://www.apa.org/ethics/code/index.aspx

TABLE 2.3 Selected Standards from the APA's Ethical Principles of Psychologists and Code of Conduct

3.04 Avoiding Harm

Psychologists take reasonable steps to avoid harming their clients/patients, students, supervisees, research participants, organizational clients, and others with whom they work, and to minimize harm where it is foreseeable and unavoidable.

4. Privacy and Confidentiality

4.01 Maintaining Confidentiality

Psychologists have a primary obligation and take reasonable precautions to protect confidential information obtained through or stored in any medium, recognizing that the extent and limits of confidentiality may be regulated by law or established by institutional rules or professional or scientific relationship. (See also Standard 2.05, Delegation of Work to Others.)

4.02 Discussing the Limits of Confidentiality

(a) Psychologists discuss with persons (including, to the extent feasible, persons who are legally incapable of giving informed consent and their legal representatives) and organizations with whom they establish a scientific or professional relationship (1) the relevant limits of confidentiality and (2) the foreseeable uses of the information generated through their psychological activities. (See also Standard 3.10, Informed Consent.)

(b) Unless it is not feasible or is contraindicated, the discussion of confidentiality occurs at the outset of the relationship and thereafter as new circumstances may warrant.

(c) Psychologists who offer services, products, or information via electronic transmission inform clients/patients of the risks to privacy and limits of confidentiality.

4.03 Recording

Before recording the voices or images of individuals to whom they provide services, psychologists obtain permission from all such persons or their legal representatives. (See also Standards 8.03, Informed Consent for Recording Voices and Images in Research; 8.05, Dispensing with Informed Consent for Research; and 8.07, Deception in Research.)

4.04 Minimizing Intrusions on Privacy

(a) Psychologists include in written and oral reports and consultations, only information germane to the purpose for which the communication is made.

(b) Psychologists discuss confidential information obtained in their work only for appropriate scientific or professional purposes and only with persons clearly concerned with such matters.

4.05 Disclosures

(a) Psychologists may disclose confidential information with the appropriate consent of the organizational client, the individual client/patient, or another legally authorized person on behalf of the client/patient unless prohibited by law.

(b) Psychologists disclose confidential information without the consent of the individual only as mandated by law, or where permitted by law for a valid purpose such as to (1) provide needed professional services; (2) obtain appropriate professional consultations; (3) protect the client/patient, psychologist, or others from harm; or (4) obtain payment for services from a client/patient, in which instance disclosure is limited to the minimum that is necessary to achieve the purpose. (See also Standard 6.04e, Fees and Financial Arrangements.)

4.06 Consultations

When consulting with colleagues, (1) psychologists do not disclose confidential information that reasonably could lead to the identification of a client/patient, research participant, or other person or organization with whom they have a confidential relationship unless they have obtained the prior consent of the person or organization or the disclosure cannot be avoided, and (2) they disclose information only to the extent necessary to achieve the purposes of the consultation. (See also Standard 4.01, Maintaining Confidentiality.)

(continued)

TABLE 2.3 Selected Standards from the APA's Ethical Principles of Psychologists and Code of Conduct (*continued*)

4.07 Use of Confidential Information for Didactic or Other Purposes

Psychologists do not disclose in their writings, lectures, or other public media, confidential, personally identifiable information concerning their clients/patients, students, research participants, organizational clients, or other recipients of their services that they obtained during the course of their work, unless (1) they take reasonable steps to disguise the person or organization, (2) the person or organization has consented in writing, or (3) there is legal authorization for doing so.

8. Research and Publication

8.01 Institutional Approval

When institutional approval is required, psychologists provide accurate information about their research proposals and obtain approval prior to conducting the research. They conduct the research in accordance with the approved research protocol.

8.02 Informed Consent to Research

(a) When obtaining informed consent as required in Standard 3.10, Informed Consent, psychologists inform participants about (1) the purpose of the research, expected duration, and procedures; (2) their right to decline to participate and to withdraw from the research once participation has begun; (3) the foreseeable consequences of declining or withdrawing; (4) reasonably foreseeable factors that may be expected to influence their willingness to participate such as potential risks, discomfort, or adverse effects; (5) any prospective research benefits; (6) limits of confidentiality; (7) incentives for participation; and (8) whom to contact for questions about the research and research participants' rights. They provide opportunity for the prospective participants to ask questions and receive answers. (See also Standards 8.03, Informed Consent for Recording Voices and Images in Research; 8.05, Dispensing with Informed Consent for Research; and 8.07, Deception in Research.)

(b) Psychologists conducting intervention research involving the use of experimental treatments clarify to participants at the outset of the research (1) the experimental nature of the treatment; (2) the services that will or will not be available to the control group(s) if appropriate; (3) the means by which assignment to treatment and control groups will be made; (4) available treatment alternatives if an individual does not wish to participate in the research or wishes to withdraw once a study has begun; and (5) compensation for or monetary costs of participating including, if appropriate, whether reimbursement from the participant or a third-party payor will be sought. (See also Standard 8.02a, Informed Consent to Research.)

8.03 Informed Consent for Recording Voices and Images in Research

Psychologists obtain informed consent from research participants prior to recording their voices or images for data collection unless (1) the research consists solely of naturalistic observations in public places, and it is not anticipated that the recording will be used in a manner that could cause personal identification or harm; or (2) the research design includes deception, and consent for the use of the recording is obtained during debriefing. (See also Standard 8.07, Deception in Research.)

8.04 Client/Patient, Student, and Subordinate Research Participants

(a) When psychologists conduct research with clients/patients, students, or subordinates as participants, psychologists take steps to protect the prospective participants from adverse consequences of declining or withdrawing from participation.

(b) When research participation is a course requirement or an opportunity for extra credit, the prospective participant is given the choice of equitable alternative activities.

(*continued*)

TABLE 2.3 Selected Standards from the APA's Ethical Principles of Psychologists and Code of Conduct (*continued*)

8.05 Dispensing with Informed Consent for Research

Psychologists may dispense with informed consent only (1) where research would not reasonably be assumed to create distress or harm and involves (a) the study of normal educational practices, curricula, or classroom management methods conducted in educational settings; (b) only anonymous questionnaires, naturalistic observations, or archival research for which disclosure of responses would not place participants at risk of criminal or civil liability or damage their financial standing, employability, or reputation, and confidentiality is protected; or (c) the study of factors related to job or organization effectiveness conducted in organizational settings for which there is no risk to participants' employability, and confidentiality is protected; or (2) where otherwise permitted by law or federal or institutional regulations.

8.06 Offering Inducements for Research Participation

(a) Psychologists make reasonable efforts to avoid offering excessive or inappropriate financial or other inducements for research participation when such inducements are likely to coerce participation.

(b) When offering professional services as an inducement for research participation, psychologists clarify the nature of the services, as well as the risks, obligations, and limitations. (See also Standard 6.05, Barter with Clients/Patients.)

8.07 Deception in Research

(a) Psychologists do not conduct a study involving deception unless they have determined that the use of deceptive techniques is justified by the study's significant prospective scientific, educational, or applied value and that effective nondeceptive alternative procedures are not feasible.

(b) Psychologists do not deceive prospective participants about research that is reasonably expected to cause physical pain or severe emotional distress.

(c) Psychologists explain any deception that is an integral feature of the design and conduct of an experiment to participants as early as is feasible, preferably at the conclusion of their participation but no later than at the conclusion of the data collection, and permit participants to withdraw their data. (See also Standard 8.08, Debriefing.)

8.08 Debriefing

(a) Psychologists provide a prompt opportunity for participants to obtain appropriate information about the nature, results, and conclusions of the research, and they take reasonable steps to correct any misconceptions that participants may have of which the psychologists are aware.

(b) If scientific or humane values justify delaying or withholding this information, psychologists take reasonable measures to reduce the risk of harm.

(c) When psychologists become aware that research procedures have harmed a participant, they take reasonable steps to minimize the harm.

8.09 Humane Care and Use of Animals in Research

(a) Psychologists acquire, care for, use, and dispose of animals in compliance with current federal, state, and local laws and regulations, and with professional standards.

(b) Psychologists trained in research methods and experienced in the care of laboratory animals supervise all procedures involving animals and are responsible for ensuring appropriate consideration of their comfort, health, and humane treatment.

(c) Psychologists ensure that all individuals under their supervision who are using animals have received instruction in research methods and in the care, maintenance, and handling of the species being used, to the extent appropriate to their role. (See also Standard 2.05, Delegation of Work to Others.)

(d) Psychologists make reasonable efforts to minimize the discomfort, infection, illness, and pain of animal subjects.

(*continued*)

TABLE 2.3 Selected Standards from the APA's Ethical Principles of Psychologists and Code of Conduct (*continued*)

(e) Psychologists use a procedure subjecting animals to pain, stress, or privation only when an alternative procedure is unavailable and the goal is justified by its prospective scientific, educational, or applied value.

(f) Psychologists perform surgical procedures under appropriate anesthesia and follow techniques to avoid infection and minimize pain during and after surgery.

(g) When it is appropriate that an animal's life be terminated, psychologists proceed rapidly, with an effort to minimize pain and in accordance with accepted procedures.

SOURCE: American Psychological Association. (2010a). Ethical principles of psychologists and code of conduct (2002, amended June 1, 2010). Retrieved from http://www.apa.org/ethics/code/index.aspx

a copy of the form to each subject. If subjects in a study are under 18 years of age, then informed consent must be given by a parent or legal guardian. A sample informed consent form appears in Figure 2.1.

Risk

Typically, subjects in a study are classified as being either "at risk" or "at minimal risk." Those at minimal risk are placed under no more physical or emotional risk than would be encountered in daily life or in routine physical or psychological examinations or tests (U.S. Department of Health and Human Services, 1981). In what types of studies might a subject be classified as being at minimal risk? Studies in which subjects are asked to fill out paper-and-pencil tests, such as personality inventories or depression inventories, are classified as minimal risk. Other examples of studies in which subjects are classified as at minimal risk include most research on memory processes, problem-solving abilities, and reasoning. If the subjects in a study are classified as at minimal risk, then an informed consent is not always mandatory. However, it is probably best to obtain informed consent anyway.

In contrast, the subjects in the Tuskegee study and in Milgram's (1963) obedience study would definitely be classified as at risk. Studies in which the subjects are at risk for physical or emotional harm fit the definition of subjects being at risk. When proposing a study in which subjects are classified as at risk, the researcher and the members of the IRB must determine whether the benefits of the knowledge to be gained from the study outweigh the risk to subjects. Clearly, Milgram believed that this was the case; members of IRBs today might not agree.

Subjects are also often considered at risk if their privacy is compromised. Subjects expect that researchers will protect their privacy and keep their participation in, and results from, the study confidential. In most research studies, there should be no need to tie data to individuals. Thus, in such cases, privacy and confidentiality are not issues, because the subjects have anonymity. However, in those situations in which it is necessary to tie data to an individual (for example, when data will be collected from the same subjects

FIGURE 2.1 A sample informed consent form

Informed Consent Form

You, ______________________, are being asked to participate in a research project titled ______________. This project is being conducted under the supervision of ______________ and was approved by ______________ University/College's IRB (or Committee on the Use of Human Subjects) on ______________.

The investigators hope to learn ______________________ from this project.

While participating in this study, you will be asked to ______________ for ______________ period of time.

The nature of this study has been explained by ______________. The anticipated benefits of your participation are ______________. The known risks of your participation in this study are ______________.

The researchers will make every effort to safeguard the confidentiality of the information that you provide. Any information obtained from this study that can be identified with you will remain confidential and will not be given to anyone without your permission.

If at any time you would like additional information about this project, you can contact ______________ at ______________.

You have the right to refuse to participate in this study. If you do agree to participate, you have the right to change your mind at any time and stop your participation. The grades and services you receive from ______________ University/College will not be negatively affected by your refusal to participate or by your withdrawal from this project. Your signature below indicates that you have given your informed consent to participate in the above-described project. Your signature also indicates that:

- ⇨ You have been given the opportunity to ask any and all questions about the described project and your participation and all of your questions have been answered to your satisfaction.
- ⇨ You have been permitted to read this document and you have been given a signed copy of it.
- ⇨ You are at least 18 years old.
- ⇨ You are legally able to provide consent.
- ⇨ To the best of your knowledge and belief, you have no physical or mental illness or weakness that would be adversely affected by your participation in the described project.

______________________ ______________

Signature of Participant Date

______________________ ______________

Signature of Witness Date

over many sessions), every precaution should be made to safeguard the data and keep them separate from the identities of the participants. In other words, a coding system should be used that allows the researcher to identify the individual, but the information identifying them should be kept separate from the actual data so that if the data were seen by anyone, they could not be linked to any particular individual. In studies in which researchers need to be able to identify the subjects, an informed consent form should be used because anonymity and confidentiality are at risk.

Deception

deception Lying to the subjects concerning the true nature of a study because knowing the true nature of the study might affect their performance.

Besides the risk of emotional harm, you may be wondering about another aspect of Milgram's (1963) study. Milgram deceived his subjects by telling them that the experiment was about the effects of punishment on learning, not about obedience to authority. **Deception** in research involves lying to subjects about the true nature of a study because knowing the true nature of the study might affect their performance. Clearly, in some research studies, it isn't possible to fully inform subjects of the nature of the study because this knowledge might affect their responses. How, then, do researchers obtain informed consent when deception is necessary? They give subjects a general description of the study—not a detailed description of the hypothesis being tested. Remember that subjects are also informed that they do not have to participate, that a refusal to participate will incur no penalties, and that they can stop participating in the study at any time. Given these precautions, deception can be used, when necessary, without violating ethical standards. After the study is completed, however, researchers should debrief (discussed next) the subjects, informing them of the deception and the true intent of the study.

Debriefing

debriefing Providing information about the true purpose of a study as soon after the completion of data collection as possible.

One final ethical consideration concerns the debriefing of subjects. **Debriefing** means providing information about the true purpose of the study as soon after the completion of data collection as possible. In the Milgram study, for example, debriefing entailed informing subjects of the true nature of the study (obedience to authority) as soon after completion of the study as possible. Based on immediate debriefings and one-year follow-up interviews, Milgram (1977) found that only about 1% of the subjects wished they had not participated in the study and that most were very glad they had participated. Debriefing is necessary in all research studies, not just those that involve deception. Through debriefing, subjects learn more about the benefits of the research to them and to society in general, and the researcher has the opportunity to alleviate any discomfort the subjects may be experiencing. During debriefing, the researcher should try to bring subjects back to the same state of mind they were in before they participated in the study.

Ethical Standards in Research with Children

Special considerations arise in research studies that use children as subjects. For example, how does informed consent work with children, and how do researchers properly debrief a child? Informed consent must be obtained from the parents or legal guardians for all persons under the age of 18. However, with children who are old enough to understand language, the researcher should also try to inform them of the nature of the study, explain what they will be asked to do during the study, and tell them that they do not have to participate and can request to end their participation at any time. The question remains, however, whether children really understand this information and whether they would feel comfortable exercising these rights. Thus, when doing research with children, the researcher must be especially careful to use good judgment when deciding whether to continue collecting data from an individual or whether to use a particular child in the research project.

Ethical Standards in Research with Animals

Using animals in research has become a controversial issue. Some people believe that no research should be conducted on animals; others believe that research with animals is advantageous but that measures should be taken to ensure humane treatment. Taking the latter position, the APA has developed *Guidelines for Ethical Conduct in the Care and Use of Animals* (1996). These guidelines can be found at http://www.apa.org/science/leadership/care/guidelines.aspx.

There is little argument that animal research has led to many advances for both humans and animals, especially in medical research. For example, research with animals has led to the development of human blood transfusions, advances in painkillers, antibiotics, behavioral medications, and drug treatments, as well as knowledge of the brain, nervous system, and psychopathology. However, animal rights activists believe that the cost of these advances is often too high.

The APA guidelines address several issues with respect to animal welfare. For example, the researcher must provide a justification for the study, be sure that the personnel interacting with the animals are familiar with the guidelines and are well trained, ensure that the care and housing of the animals meet federal regulations, and acquire the animals lawfully. The researcher must also ensure that all experimental procedures are humane, that treatments involving pain are used only when necessary, that alternative procedures that minimize discomfort are used when available, that surgical procedures use anesthesia and techniques to avoid pain and infection, and that all animals are treated in accordance with local, state, and federal laws. As an additional measure to make sure that animals are treated humanely, the U.S. Department of Agriculture is responsible for regulating and inspecting animal facilities. Finally, the Animal Welfare Act of 1985 requires that institutions establish Animal Care and Use Committees. These committees function in a manner similar to IRBs, reviewing all research proposals using animals to determine whether the animals are being treated in an ethical manner.

CRITICAL THINKING CHECK 2.1

1. In what type of research might an investigator argue that deception is necessary? How can informed consent be provided in such a situation?
2. What is the purpose of an IRB?
3. When is it necessary and not necessary to obtain informed consent?

Summary

In the preceding sections, we discussed many elements relevant to getting started on a research project. We began with how to select a problem and conduct a literature search. This included discussion of several library resources, including *Psych Abstracts*, PsycINFO, the *Social Science Citation Index*, and the *Science Citation Index*. In the second half of the chapter, we discussed the APA's ethical principles. In reviewing ethical guidelines for using humans for research purposes, we discussed the importance of IRBs and obtaining informed consent, which is a necessity when subjects are at risk. We also considered the use of deception in research, along with the nature and intent of debriefing subjects. Finally, we discussed special considerations when using children as research subjects, and we presented the APA guidelines on the use of animals in research.

KEY TERMS

Institutional Review Board (IRB)
informed consent form
deception
debriefing

CHAPTER EXERCISES

(Answers to odd-numbered exercises appear in Appendix C.)

1. Select a topic of interest to you in psychology, and use *Psych Abstracts* or PsycINFO to search for articles on this topic. Try to find at least five journal articles relevant to your topic.
2. What should be accomplished by debriefing subjects?
3. Describe what is meant by "at risk" and "at minimal risk."
4. In addition to treating animals in a humane manner during a study, what other guidelines does APA provide concerning using animals for research purposes?
5. What special ethical considerations must be taken into account when conducting research with children?

CRITICAL THINKING CHECK ANSWERS

2.1

1. The researcher could argue that deception is necessary in situations where, if the subjects knew the true nature or hypothesis of the study, their behavior or responses might be altered. Informed consent is provided by giving subjects a general description of the study and also by informing them that they do not have to participate and can withdraw from the study at any time.
2. IRBs are charged with evaluating research projects in which humans participate to ensure the ethical treatment of subjects.
3. In any study in which a subject is classified as "at risk," informed consent is necessary. Although informed consent is not necessary when subjects are classified as "at minimal risk," it is usually wise to obtain informed consent anyway.

WEB RESOURCES

The book-specific website at CengageBrain.com offers students a variety of study tools and useful resources such as glossaries and flashcards.

Chapter 2 ▪ Study Guide

CHAPTER 2 SUMMARY AND REVIEW: GETTING STARTED: IDEAS, RESOURCES, AND ETHICS

This chapter presented many elements crucial to getting started on a research project. It began with how to select a problem and conduct a literature search. The chapter discussed several resources, including the *Psychological Abstracts* and the *Social Science Citation Index*. A brief description of how to read a journal article followed.

After reading the second half of the chapter, you should have an understanding of APA's ethical principles. In reviewing ethical guidelines for using humans for research purposes, the importance of IRBs and obtaining informed consent, which is a necessity when subjects are at risk, were discussed. We also considered the use of deception in research, along with the nature and intent of debriefing subjects. Finally, we presented special considerations when using children as research subjects and the APA guidelines on the use of animals in research.

CHAPTER 2 REVIEW EXERCISES

(Answers to exercises appear in Appendix C.)

FILL-IN SELF-TEST

Answer the following questions. If you have trouble answering any of the questions, restudy the relevant material before going on to the multiple-choice self-test.

1. ________ is the electronic version of the *Psychological Abstracts*.
2. The ________ can help you to work from a given article to see what has been published on that topic since the article was published.
3. The form given to individuals before they participate in a study in order to inform them of the general nature of the study and to obtain their consent to participate is called a(n) ________.
4. Lying to the subjects concerning the true nature of the study because knowing the true nature of the study would affect how they might perform in the study involves using ________.
5. A(n) ________ is the committee charged with evaluating research projects in which human subjects are used.

MULTIPLE-CHOICE SELF-TEST

Select the single best answer for each of the following questions. If you have trouble answering any of the questions, restudy the relevant material.

1. The Milgram obedience to authority study is to ________ and the Tuskegee syphilis study is to ________.
   a. the use of deception; subject selection problems
   b. failure to use debriefing; the use of deception
   c. the use of deception; failure to obtain informed consent
   d. failure to obtain informed consent; the use of deception
2. Debriefing involves:
   a. explaining the purpose of a study to subjects after the completion of data collection.
   b. having the subjects read and sign an informed consent before the study begins.
   c. lying to the participants about the true nature of the study.
   d. none of the above.
3. An IRB reviews research proposals to ensure:
   a. that ethical standards are met.
   b. that the proposal is methodologically sound.
   c. that enough subjects are being used.
   d. that there will be no legal ramifications from the study.
4. ________ is to research involving no more risk than that encountered in daily life and ________ is to being placed under some emotional or physical risk.
   a. Moderate risk; minimal risk
   b. Risk; minimal risk
   c. Minimal risk; risk
   d. Minimal risk; moderate risk

CHAPTER 3

Defining, Measuring, and Manipulating Variables

Learning Objectives

- Explain and give examples of an operational definition.
- Explain the four properties of measurement and how they are related to the four scales of measurement.
- Identify and describe the four types of measures.
- Explain what reliability is and how it is measured.
- Identify and explain the four types of reliability discussed in the text.
- Explain what validity is and how it is measured.
- Identify and explain the four types of validity discussed in the text.

In Chapter 2, we discussed library research, how to read journal articles, and ethics. In this chapter, we will discuss the definition, measurement, and manipulation of variables. As noted in Chapter 1, we typically refer to measured variables as dependent variables and manipulated variables as independent variables. Hence, some of the ideas addressed in this chapter are how we define independent and dependent variables, how we measure variables, the types of measures available to us, and finally, the reliability and validity of the measures.

Defining Variables

An important step when beginning a research project is to define the variables in your study. Some variables are fairly easy to define, manipulate, and measure. For example, if a researcher were studying the effects of exercise on blood pressure, she could manipulate the amount of exercise by varying the length of time that individuals exercised or by varying the intensity of the exercise (as by monitoring target heart rates). She could also measure blood pressure periodically during the course of the study; a machine already exists that will take this measurement in a consistent and accurate manner. Does this mean that the measurement will always be accurate? No. We'll discuss this issue later in the chapter when we address measurement error.

Now let's suppose that a researcher wants to study a variable that is not as concrete or easily measured as blood pressure. For example, many people study abstract concepts such as aggression, attraction, depression, hunger, or anxiety. How would we either manipulate or measure any of these variables? My definition of what it means to be hungry may be quite different from yours. If I decided to measure hunger by simply asking subjects in an experiment if they were hungry, the measure would not be accurate because each individual may define hunger in a different way. We need an **operational definition** of hunger—a definition of the variable in terms of the operations the researcher uses to measure or manipulate it. Because this is a

operational definition A definition of a variable in terms of the operations (activities) a researcher uses to measure or manipulate it.

somewhat circular definition, let's reword it in a way that makes more sense. An operational definition specifies the activities of the researcher in measuring and/or manipulating a variable (Kerlinger, 1986). In other words, we might define hunger in terms of specific activities, such as not having eaten for 12 hours. Thus, one operational definition of hunger could be that simple: Hunger occurs when 12 hours have passed with no food intake. Notice how much more concrete this definition is than simply saying hunger is that "gnawing feeling" that you get in your stomach. Specifying hunger in terms of the number of hours without food is an operational definition, whereas defining hunger as that "gnawing feeling" is not an operational definition.

Researchers must operationally define all variables—those measured (dependent variables) and those manipulated (independent variables). One reason for doing so is to ensure that the variables are measured consistently or manipulated in the same way during the course of the study. Another reason is to help us communicate our ideas to others. For example, what if a researcher said that she measured anxiety in her study. You would need to know how she operationally defined anxiety because it can be defined in many different ways. Thus, it can be measured in many different ways. Anxiety could be defined as the number of nervous actions displayed in a 1-hour time period, a person's score on a galvanic skin response (GSR) machine, a person's heart rate, or a person's score on the Taylor Manifest Anxiety Scale. Some measures are better than others—*better* meaning more reliable and valid, concepts we will discuss later in this chapter. After you understand how a researcher has operationally defined a variable, you can replicate the study if you desire. You can begin to have a better understanding of the study and whether or not it may have problems. You can also better design your own study based on how the variables were operationally defined in other research studies.

Properties of Measurement

identity A property of measurement in which objects that are different receive different scores.

magnitude A property of measurement in which the ordering of numbers reflects the ordering of the variable.

equal unit size A property of measurement in which a difference of 1 is the same amount throughout the entire scale.

In addition to operationally defining independent and dependent variables, we must consider the level of measurement of the dependent variable. The four levels of measurement are each based on the characteristics or properties of the data. These properties include identity, magnitude, equal unit size, and absolute zero. When a measure has the property of **identity**, objects that are different receive different scores. For example, if subjects in a study had different political affiliations, they would receive different scores. Measurements have the property of **magnitude** (also called *ordinality*) when the ordering of the numbers reflects the ordering of the variable. In other words, numbers are assigned in order so that some numbers represent more or less of the variable being measured than others.

Measurements have an **equal unit size** when a difference of 1 is the same amount throughout the entire scale. For example, the difference between people who are 64 inches tall and 65 inches tall is the same as the difference between people who are 72 inches tall and 73 inches tall. The difference in each situation (1 inch) is identical. Notice how this differs from the property of magnitude. If we simply lined up and ranked a group of individuals based on their height, the scale would have the properties of identity and magnitude but not equal unit size. This is true because we would not actually measure people's height in inches but simply order them according to how tall they appear, from shortest (the person receiving a score of 1) to tallest (the person receiving the highest score). Thus, our scale would not meet the criterion of equal unit size. In other words, the difference in height between the two people receiving scores of 1 and 2 might not be the same as the difference in height between the two people receiving scores of 3 and 4.

absolute zero A property of measurement in which assigning a score of zero indicates an absence of the variable being measured.

Last, measures have an **absolute zero** when assigning a score of zero indicates an absence of the variable being measured. For example, time spent studying has the property of absolute zero because a score of zero on this measure means an individual spent no time studying. However, a score of zero is not always equal to the property of absolute zero. As an example, think about the Fahrenheit temperature scale. That measurement scale has a score of zero (the thermometer can read 0 degrees); however, does that score indicate an absence of temperature? No, it indicates a very cold temperature. Hence, it does not have the property of absolute zero.

Scales (Levels) of Measurement

As noted previously, the level or scale of measurement depends on the properties of the data. Each of the four scales of measurement (nominal, ordinal, interval, and ratio) has one or more of the properties described in the previous section. We'll discuss the scales in order, from the one with the fewest properties to the one with the most properties—that is, from least to most sophisticated. As you'll see in later chapters, it's important to establish the scale of measurement of your data to determine the appropriate statistical test to use when analyzing the data.

Nominal Scale

nominal scale A scale in which objects or individuals are assigned to categories that have no numerical properties.

A **nominal scale** is one in which objects or individuals are assigned to categories that have no numerical properties. Nominal scales have the characteristic of identity but lack the other properties. Variables measured on a nominal scale are often referred to as *categorical variables* because the measuring scale involves dividing the data into categories. However, the categories carry no numerical weight. Some examples of categorical variables, or data measured on a nominal scale, are ethnicity, gender, and political affiliation. We can assign numerical values to the levels of a nominal variable. For example, for ethnicity, we could label Asian Americans as 1, African Americans as 2, Latin Americans as 3, and so on. However, these scores do not carry any numerical weight; they are simply names for the categories.

In other words, the scores are used for identity but not for magnitude, equal unit size, or absolute value. We cannot order the data and claim that 1s are more than or less than 2s. We cannot analyze these data mathematically. It would not be appropriate, for example, to report that the mean ethnicity was 2.56. We cannot say that there is a true zero where someone would have no ethnicity. As you'll see in later chapters, however, you can use certain statistics to analyze nominal data.

Ordinal Scale

ordinal scale A scale in which objects or individuals are categorized, and the categories form a rank order along a continuum.

In an **ordinal scale**, objects or individuals are categorized, and the categories form a rank order along a continuum. Data measured on an ordinal scale have the properties of identity and magnitude but lack equal unit size and absolute zero. Ordinal data are often referred to as *ranked data* because the data are ordered from highest to lowest or biggest to smallest. For example, reporting how students did on an exam based simply on their rank (highest score, second highest, and so on) is an ordinal scale. This variable carries identity and magnitude because each individual receives a rank (a number) that carries identity and that rank also conveys information about order or magnitude (how many students performed better or worse in the class). However, the ranking score does not have equal unit size (the difference in performance on the exam between the students ranked 1 and 2 is not necessarily the same as the difference between the students ranked 2 and 3) or an absolute zero.

Interval Scale

interval scale A scale in which the units of measurement (intervals) between the numbers on the scale are all equal in size.

In an **interval scale**, the units of measurement (intervals) between the numbers on the scale are all equal in size. When you use an interval scale, the criteria of identity, magnitude, and equal unit size are met. For example, the Fahrenheit temperature scale is an interval scale of measurement. A given temperature carries identity (days with different temperatures receive different scores on the scale), magnitude (cooler days receive lower scores and hotter days receive higher scores), and equal unit size (the difference between 50 and 51 degrees is the same as that between 90 and 91 degrees). However, the Fahrenheit scale does not have an absolute zero. Because of this, you cannot form ratios based on this scale (for example, 100 degrees is not twice as hot as 50 degrees).

Ratio Scale

ratio scale A scale in which, in addition to order and equal units of measurement, an absolute zero indicates an absence of the variable being measured.

In a **ratio scale**, in addition to order and equal units of measurement, an absolute zero indicates an absence of the variable being measured. Ratio data have all four properties of measurement—identity, magnitude, equal unit size, and absolute zero. Examples of ratio scales of measurement include weight, time, and height. Each of these scales has identity (individuals who weigh different amounts receive different scores), magnitude (those who weigh less receive lower scores than those who weigh more), and equal unit size (one pound is the same weight anywhere along the scale and for any person using the scale). Ratio scales also have an absolute zero, which means that a score of zero reflects an absence of that variable. This also means that ratios can be formed. For example, a weight of 100 pounds is twice as much as a weight of 50 pounds. Because interval and ratio data are very similar, many psychologists simply refer to the category as *interval-ratio data* and typically do not distinguish between these two types of data. You should be familiar with the difference between interval and ratio data but aware that because they are so similar, they are often referred to as one type of data—interval-ratio.

Features of Scales of Measurement — IN REVIEW

	SCALES OF MEASUREMENT			
	NOMINAL	**ORDINAL**	**INTERVAL**	**RATIO**
Examples	Ethnicity Religion Sex	Class rank Letter grade	Temperature (Fahrenheit and Celsius) Many psychological tests	Weight Height Time
Properties	Identity	Identity Magnitude	Identity Magnitude Equal unit size	Identity Magnitude Equal unit size Absolute zero
Mathematical Operations	Determine whether = or ≠	Determine whether = or ≠ Determine whether < or >	Determine whether = or ≠ Determine whether < or > Add Subtract	Determine whether = or ≠ Determine whether < or > Add Subtract Multiply Divide

CRITICAL THINKING CHECK 3.1

1. Provide several operational definitions of *anxiety*. Include nonverbal measures and physiological measures. How would your operational definitions differ from a dictionary definition?
2. Identify the scale of measurement for each of the following variables:
   a. ZIP code
   b. Grade of egg (large, medium, small)
   c. Reaction time
   d. Score on the SAT
   e. Class rank
   f. Number on a football jersey
   g. Miles per gallon

Discrete and Continuous Variables

discrete variables Variables that usually consist of whole number units or categories and are made up of chunks or units that are detached and distinct from one another.

Another means of classifying variables is in terms of whether they are discrete or continuous in nature. **Discrete variables** usually consist of whole number units or categories. They are made up of chunks or units that are detached and distinct from one another. A change in value occurs a whole unit at a time, and decimals do not make sense with discrete scales. Most nominal and ordinal data are discrete. For example, gender, political party, and ethnicity are discrete scales. Some interval or ratio data can be discrete. For example, the number of children someone has is reported as a whole number (discrete data), yet it is also ratio data (you can have a true zero and form ratios).

continuous variables Variables that usually fall along a continuum and allow for fractional amounts.

Continuous variables usually fall along a continuum and allow for fractional amounts. The term *continuous* means that it "continues" between the whole number units. Examples of continuous variables are age (22.7 years), height (64.5 inches), and weight (113.25 pounds). Most interval and ratio data are continuous in nature. Discrete and continuous data will become more important in later chapters when we discuss research design and data presentation.

Types of Measures

When psychology researchers collect data, the types of measures used can be classified into four basic categories: self-report measures, tests, behavioral measures, and physical measures. We will discuss each category, noting the advantages and possible disadvantages of each.

Self-Report Measures

self-report measures Usually questionnaires or interviews that measure how people report that they act, think, or feel.

Self-report measures are typically administered as questionnaires or interviews to measure how people report that they act, think, or feel. Thus, self-report measures aid in collecting data on behavioral, cognitive, and affective events (Leary, 2001).

Behavioral self-report measures typically ask people to report how often they do something. This could be how often they eat a certain food, eat out at a restaurant, go to the gym, or have sex. The problem with this and the other self-report measures is that we are relying on the individuals to report on their own behaviors. When collecting data in this manner, we must be concerned with the veracity of the reports and also with the accuracy of the individual's memory. Researchers much prefer to collect data using a behavioral measure, but direct observation of some events is not always possible or ethical.

Cognitive self-report measures ask individuals to report what they think about something. You have probably participated in a cognitive self-report measure of some sort. For example, you may have been stopped on campus and asked what you think about parking, food services, or residence halls. Once again, we are relying on the individual to make an accurate and truthful report.

Affective self-report measures ask individuals to report how they feel about something. You may have participated in an affective self-report measure if you ever answered questions concerning emotional reactions such as happiness, depression, anxiety, or stress. Many psychological tests are affective self-report measures. These tests also fit into the category of measurement tests described in the following section.

Tests

test A measurement instrument used to assess individual differences in various content areas.

A **test** is a measurement instrument used to assess individual differences in various content areas. Psychologists frequently use two types of tests: personality tests and ability tests. Many personality tests are also affective self-report measures; they are designed to measure aspects of an individual's personality and feelings about certain things. Ability tests, however, are not self-report measures and generally fall into two different categories: aptitude tests and achievement tests. *Aptitude tests* measure an individual's potential to do something, whereas *achievement tests* measure an individual's competence in an area. In general, intelligence tests are aptitude tests, whereas school exams are achievement tests.

Most tests used by psychologists have been subjected to extensive testing and are therefore considered objective, non-biased means of collecting data. Keep in mind, however, that any measuring instrument always has the potential for problems. The problems may range from the psychological and physical state of the subject on a given day to the scoring and interpretation of the test.

Behavioral Measures

behavioral measures Measures taken by carefully observing and recording behavior.

Psychologists take **behavioral measures** by carefully observing and recording behavior. Behavioral measures are often referred to as *observational measures* because they involve observing anything that a participant does. Because we will discuss observational research studies in more detail in the next chapter, our discussion of behavioral measures will be brief here. Behavioral measures can be used to measure anything that a person or animal does—a pigeon pecking a disk, the way men and women carry their books, or how many cars actually stop at a stop sign. The observations can be direct (while the participant is engaging in the behavior) or indirect (via audiotape or videotape).

When taking behavioral measures, a researcher usually uses some sort of coding system. A coding system is a means of converting the observations to numerical data. A very basic coding system involves simply counting the number of times that subjects do something. For example, how many times does the pigeon peck the lighted disk, or how many cars stop at the stop sign? A more sophisticated coding system involves assigning behaviors to particular categories. For example, a researcher might watch children playing and classify their behavior into several categories of play (solitary, parallel, and cooperative). In the example of cars stopping at a stop sign, simply counting the number of stops might not be adequate. What is a stop? The researcher might operationally define a stop as the car stops moving for at least 3 seconds. Other categories might include a complete stop of less than 3 seconds, a rolling stop, and no stop. The researcher would then have a more complex coding system consisting of various categories.

You might also think about the problems of collecting data at a stop sign. If someone is standing there with a clipboard taking measures, how might this affect the behavior of drivers approaching the stop sign? Are we going to get a realistic estimate of how many cars actually stop at the sign? Probably not. For this reason, measures are sometimes taken in an unobtrusive manner. Observers may hide what they are doing, or hide themselves, or use a more indirect means of collecting the data (videotape). Using an unobtrusive means of collecting data reduces **reactivity**—subjects reacting in an unnatural way to being observed. This issue will be discussed more fully in Chapter 4.

reactivity A possible reaction by subjects in which they act unnaturally because they know they are being observed.

Notice some of the possible problems with behavioral measures. First, they all rely on humans observing events. How do we know that they observed the events accurately? Second, the observers must then code the events into some numerical format. There is tremendous potential for error in this situation. Last, if the observers are visible, subjects may not be acting naturally because they know they are being observed.

Physical Measures

physical measures Measures of bodily activity (such as pulse or blood pressure) that may be taken with a piece of equipment.

Most **physical measures**, or measures of bodily activity, are not directly observable. Physical measures are usually taken with a piece of equipment. For example, weight is measured with a scale, blood pressure with a blood pressure cuff, and temperature with a thermometer. Sometimes the equipment used to take physical measures is more sophisticated. For example, psychologists frequently use the GSR to measure emotional arousal, electromyography (EMG) recordings to measure muscle contractions, and electroencephalogram (EEG) recordings to measure electrical activity in the brain.

Notice that physical measures are much more objective than the previously described behavioral measures. A physical measure is not simply an observation (which may be subjective) of how a person or animal is acting. Instead, it is a measure of some physical activity that takes place in the brain or body. This is not to say that physical measures are problem-free. Keep in mind that humans are still responsible for running the equipment that takes the measures and, ultimately, for interpreting the data provided by the measuring instrument. Thus, even when using physical measures, a researcher needs to be concerned with the accuracy of the data.

Features of Types of Measures — **IN REVIEW**

	TYPES OF MEASURES			
	SELF-REPORT	**TESTS**	**BEHAVIORAL**	**PHYSICAL**
Description	Questionnaires or interviews that measure how people report that they act, think, or feel	A measurement instrument used to assess individual differences	Careful observations and recordings of behavior	Measures of bodily activity
Examples	Behavioral self-report Cognitive self-report Affective self-report	Ability tests Personality tests	Counting behaviors Classifying behaviors	Weight EEG GSR Blood pressure
Considerations	Are subjects being truthful?	Are subjects being truthful?	Is there reactivity?	Is the individual taking the measure skilled at using the equipment?
	How accurate are subjects' memories?	How reliable and valid are the tests?	How objective are the observers?	How reliable and valid is the measuring instrument?

CRITICAL THINKING CHECK 3.2

1. Which types of measures are considered more subjective in nature? Which are more objective?
2. Why might there be measurement errors even when using an objective measure such as a blood pressure cuff? How would you recommend trying to control for or minimize this type of measurement error?

Reliability

reliability An indication of the consistency or stability of a measuring instrument.

One means of determining whether the measure you are using is effective is to assess its reliability. **Reliability** refers to the consistency or stability of a measuring instrument. In other words, we want a measure to measure exactly the same way each time it is used. This means that individuals should receive a similar score each time they use the measuring instrument. For example, a bathroom scale needs to be reliable. It needs to measure the same way each time an individual uses it; otherwise, it is a useless measuring instrument.

Error in Measurement

Consider some of the problems with the four types of measures discussed previously. Some problems, known as *method error,* stem from the experimenter and the testing situation. Does the individual taking the measures know how to use the measuring instrument properly? Is the measuring equipment working correctly? Other problems, known as *trait error*, stem from the subjects. Were the subjects being truthful? Did they feel well on the day of the test? Both types of problems can lead to measurement error.

In effect, a measurement is a combination of the true score and an error score. The formula that follows represents the *observed score* for an individual on a measure; that is, the score recorded for a participant on the measuring instrument used. The observed score is the sum of the true score and the measurement error. The true score is what the actual score on the measuring instrument would be if there were no error. The measurement error is any error (method or trait) that might be present (Leary, 2001; Salkind, 1997).

$$\text{Observed score} = \text{True score} + \text{Measurement error}$$

The observed score would be more reliable (more consistent) if we could minimize error and thus have a more accurate measure of the true score. True scores should not vary much over time, but error scores can vary tremendously from testing session to testing session. To minimize error in measurement, you should make sure that all of the problems discussed for the four types of measures are minimized. This includes problems in recording or scoring data (method error) and problems in understanding instructions, motivation, fatigue, and the testing environment (trait error). The conceptual formula for reliability is

$$\text{Reliability} = \frac{\text{True score}}{\text{True Score} + \text{Error score}}$$

Based on this conceptual formula, a reduction in error would lead to an increase in reliability. Notice that if there were no error, reliability would be equal to 1.00; hence, 1.00 is the highest possible reliability score. You should also see that as error increases, reliability drops below 1.00. The greater the error, the lower the reliability of a measure.

How to Measure Reliability: Correlation Coefficients

Reliability is measured using correlation coefficients. We will briefly discuss correlation coefficients here; a more comprehensive discussion, along with the appropriate formulas, appears in Chapter 6.

correlation coefficient A measure of the degree of relationship between two sets of scores. It can vary between −1.00 and +1.00.

A **correlation coefficient** measures the degree of relationship between two sets of scores and can vary between −1.00 and +1.00. The stronger the relationship between the variables, the closer the coefficient will be to either −1.00 or +1.00. The weaker the relationship between the variables, the closer the coefficient will be to 0. For example, if we measured individuals on two variables and found that the top-scoring individual on variable 1 was also the top-scoring person on variable 2, the second-highest-scoring person on variable 1 was also the second-highest on variable 2, and so on down to the lowest-scoring person; there would be a perfect positive correlation (+1.00) between variables 1 and 2. If we observed a perfect negative correlation (−1.00), then the person with the highest score on variable 1 would have the lowest score on variable 2; the person with the second-highest score on variable 1 would have the second-lowest score on variable 2, and so on. In reality, variables are almost never perfectly correlated. Thus, most correlation coefficients are less than 1.

A correlation of 0 between two variables indicates the absence of any relationship, as might occur by chance. For example, if we were to draw a person's score on variable 1 out of a hat, do the same for the person's score on variable 2, and continue in this manner for each person in the group, we would expect no relationship between individuals' scores on the two variables. It would be impossible to predict a person's performance on variable 2 based on that person's score on variable 1 because there would be no relationship (a correlation of 0) between the variables.

The sign preceding the correlation coefficient indicates whether the observed relationship is positive or negative. The terms *positive* and *negative* do not refer to good and bad relationships or strong or weak relationships but rather to how the variables are related. A **positive correlation** indicates a direct relationship between variables: In other words, when we see high scores on one variable, we tend to see high scores on the other variable; when we see low or moderate scores on one variable, we see similar scores on the second variable. Variables that are positively correlated include height with weight and high school GPA with college GPA. A **negative correlation** between two variables indicates an inverse or negative relationship: High scores on one variable go with low scores on the other variable, and vice versa. Examples of negative relationships are sometimes more difficult to generate and to think about. In adults, however, many variables are negatively correlated with age: As age increases, variables such as sight, hearing ability, strength, and energy level begin to decrease.

positive correlation A direct relationship between two variables in which an increase in one is related to an increase in the other, and a decrease in one is related to a decrease in the other.

negative correlation An inverse relationship between two variables in which an increase in one variable is related to a decrease in the other and vice versa.

Correlation coefficients can be weak, moderate, or strong. Table 3.1 gives some guidelines for these categories. To establish the reliability (or consistency) of a measure, we expect a strong correlation coefficient—usually in the .80s or .90s—between the two variables or scores being measured (Anastasi & Urbina, 1997). We also expect that the coefficient will be positive. Why? A positive coefficient indicates that those who scored high on the measuring instrument at one time also scored high at another time, those

TABLE 3.1 Values for Weak, Moderate, and Strong Correlation Coefficients

CORRELATION COEFFICIENT	STRENGTH OF RELATIONSHIP
±.70–1.00	Strong
±.30–.69	Moderate
±.00–.29	None (.00) to weak

who scored low at one point scored low again, and those with intermediate scores the first time scored similarly the second time. If the coefficient measuring reliability were negative, this would indicate an inverse relationship between the scores taken at two different times. A measure would hardly be consistent if a person scored very high at one time and very low at another time. Thus, to establish that a measure is reliable, we need a positive correlation coefficient of around .80 or higher.

Types of Reliability

Now that we have a basic understanding of reliability and how it is measured, let's talk about four specific types of reliability: test/retest reliability, alternate-forms reliability, split-half reliability, and interrater reliability. Each type provides a measure of consistency, but the various types of reliability are used in different situations.

test/retest reliability A reliability coefficient determined by assessing the degree of relationship between scores on the same test administered on two different occasions.

Test/Retest Reliability. One of the most often used and obvious ways of establishing reliability is to repeat the same test on a second occasion—**test/retest reliability**. The obtained correlation coefficient is between the two scores of each individual on the same test administered on two different occasions. If the test is reliable, we expect the two scores for each individual to be similar, and thus the resulting correlation coefficient will be high (close to +1.00). This measure of reliability assesses the stability of a test over time. Naturally, some error will be present in each measurement (for example, an individual may not feel well at one testing or may have problems during the testing session such as a broken pencil). Thus, it is unusual for the correlation coefficient to be +1.00, but we expect it to be +.80 or higher. A problem related to test/retest measures is that on many tests, there will be *practice effects*—some people will get better at the second testing, which lowers the observed correlation. A second problem may occur if the interval between test times is short: Individuals may remember how they answered previously, both correctly and incorrectly. In this case, we may be testing their memories and not the reliability of the testing instrument, and we may observe a spuriously high correlation.

alternate-forms reliability A reliability coefficient determined by assessing the degree of relationship between scores on two equivalent tests.

Alternate-Forms Reliability. One means of controlling for test/retest problems is to use **alternate-forms reliability**—using alternate forms of the testing instrument and correlating the performance of individuals on the two different forms. In this case, the tests taken at times 1 and 2 are different but equivalent or parallel (hence, the terms *equivalent-forms reliability* and *parallel-forms reliability* are also used). As with test/retest reliability, alternate-forms reliability establishes the stability of the test over time and also the equivalency of the items from one test to another. One problem with alternate-forms reliability is making sure that the tests are truly parallel. To help ensure equivalency, the tests should have the same number of items, the items should be of the same difficulty level, and instructions, time limits, examples, and format should all be equal—often difficult if not impossible to accomplish. Second, if the tests are truly equivalent, there is the potential for practice effects, although not to the same extent as when exactly the same test is administered twice.

Split-Half Reliability. A third means of establishing reliability is by splitting the items on the test into equivalent halves and correlating scores on one half of the items with scores on the other half. This **split-half reliability** gives a measure of the equivalence of the content of the test but not of its stability over time as test/retest and alternate-forms reliability do. The biggest problem with split-half reliability is determining how to divide the items so that the two halves are, in fact, equivalent. For example, it would not be advisable to correlate scores on multiple-choice questions with scores on short-answer or essay questions. What is typically recommended is to correlate scores on even-numbered items with scores on odd-numbered items. Thus, if the items at the beginning of the test are easier or harder than those at the end of the test, the half scores are still equivalent.

split-half reliability A reliability coefficient determined by correlating scores on one half of a measure with scores on the other half of the measure.

Interrater Reliability. Finally, to measure the reliability of observers rather than tests, you can use interrater reliability. **Interrater reliability** is a measure of consistency that assesses the agreement of observations made by two or more raters or judges. Let's say that you are observing play behavior in children. Rather than simply making observations on your own, it's advisable to have several independent observers collect data. The observers all watch the children playing but they independently count the number and types of play behaviors they observe. After the data are collected, interrater reliability needs to be established by examining the percentage of agreement between the raters. If the raters' data are reliable, then the percentage of agreement should be high. If the raters are not paying close attention to what they are doing or if the measuring scale devised for the various play behaviors is unclear, the percentage of agreement among observers will not be high. Although interrater reliability is measured using a correlation coefficient, the following formula offers a quick means of estimating interrater reliability:

interrater reliability A reliability coefficient that assesses the agreement of observations made by two or more raters or judges.

$$\text{Interrater reliability} = \frac{\text{Number of agreements}}{\text{Number of possible agreements}} \times 100$$

Thus, if your observers agree 45 times out of a possible 50, the interrater reliability is 90 %—fairly high. However, if they agree only 20 times out of 50, then the interrater reliability is low (40 %). Such a low level of agreement indicates a problem with the measuring instrument or with the individuals using the instrument and should be of great concern to a researcher.

Features of Types of Reliability — **IN REVIEW**

	TYPES OF RELIABILITY			
	TEST/RETEST	**ALTERNATE-FORMS**	**SPLIT-HALF**	**INTERRATER**
What It Measures	Stability over time	Stability over time and equivalency of items	Equivalency of items	Agreement between raters
How It Is Accomplished	Administer the same test to the same people at two different times	Administer alternate but equivalent forms of the test to the same people at two different times	Correlate performance for a group of people on two equivalent halves of the same test	Have at least two people count or rate behaviors, and determine the percentage of agreement between them

CRITICAL THINKING CHECK 3.3

1. Why does alternate-forms reliability provide a measure of both equivalency of items and stability over time?
2. Two people observe whether or not vehicles stop at a stop sign. They make 250 observations and disagree 38 times. What is the interrater reliability? Is this good, or should it be of concern to the researchers?

Validity

validity A measure of the truthfulness of a measuring instrument. It indicates whether the instrument measures what it claims to measure.

In addition to being reliable, measures must also be valid. **Validity** refers to whether a measure is truthful or genuine. In other words, a measure that is valid measures what it claims to measure. Several types of validity may be examined; we will discuss four types here. As with reliability, validity is measured by the use of correlation coefficients. For example, if researchers developed a new test to measure depression, they might establish the validity of the test by correlating scores on the new test with scores on an already established measure of depression, and as with reliability, we would expect the correlation to be positive. Unlike reliability coefficients, however, there is no established criterion for the strength of the validity coefficient. Coefficients as low as .20 or .30 may establish the validity of a measure (Anastasi & Urbina, 1997). For validity coefficients, the important thing is that they are *statistically significant* at the .05 or .01 level. We'll explain this term in a later chapter, but in brief, it means that the results are most likely not due to chance.

Content Validity

content validity The extent to which a measuring instrument covers all dimensions of a construct.

A systematic examination of the test content to determine whether it covers a representative sample of the domain of behaviors to be measured assesses **content validity**. In other words, a test with content validity has items that satisfactorily assess all dimensions of the construct. For example, a depression scale may lack content validity if it only assesses the behavioral dimension of depression and does not assess the affective dimension. To determine whether a test has content validity, you should consult experts in the area being tested. For example, when designing the GRE subject exam for psychology, professors of psychology are asked to examine the questions to establish that they represent relevant information from the entire discipline of psychology as we know it today.

Face validity The extent to which a measuring instrument appears valid on its surface.

Sometimes face validity is confused with content validity. **Face validity** simply addresses whether or not a test looks valid on its surface. Does it appear to be an adequate measure of the conceptual variable? This is not really validity in the technical sense, because it refers not to what the test actually measures but to what it appears to measure. Face validity relates to whether or not the test looks valid to those who selected it and those who take it. For example, does the test selected by the school board to measure student achievement "appear" to be an actual measure of achievement? Face validity has more to do with rapport and public relations than with actual validity (Anastasi & Urbina, 1997).

Criterion Validity

criterion validity The extent to which a measuring instrument accurately predicts behavior or ability in a given area.

The extent to which a measuring instrument accurately predicts behavior or ability in a given area establishes **criterion validity**. Two types of criterion validity may be used, depending on whether the test is used to estimate present performance (*concurrent validity*) or to predict future performance (*predictive validity*). The SAT and GRE are examples of tests that have predictive validity because performance on the tests correlates with later performance in college and graduate school, respectively. The tests can be used with some degree of accuracy to "predict" future behavior. A test used to determine whether or not someone qualifies as a pilot is a measure of concurrent validity. We are estimating the person's ability at the present time, not attempting to predict future outcomes. Thus, concurrent validation is used for diagnosis of existing status rather than prediction of future outcomes.

Construct Validity

construct validity The degree to which a measuring instrument accurately measures a theoretical construct or trait that it is designed to measure.

Construct validity is considered by many to be the most important type of validity. The **construct validity** of a test assesses the extent to which a measuring instrument accurately measures a theoretical construct or trait that it is designed to measure. Some examples of theoretical constructs or traits are verbal fluency, neuroticism, depression, anxiety, intelligence, and scholastic aptitude. One means of establishing construct validity is by correlating performance on the test with performance on a test for which construct validity has already been determined. For example, performance on a newly developed intelligence test might be correlated with performance on an existing intelligence test for which construct validity has been previously established. Another means of establishing construct validity is to show that the scores on the new test differ across people with different levels of the trait being measured. For example, if you are measuring depression, you can compare scores on the test for those known to be suffering from depression with scores for those not suffering from depression. The new measure has construct validity if it measures the construct of depression accurately.

The Relationship Between Reliability and Validity

Obviously, a measure should be both reliable and valid. It is possible, however, to have a test or measure that meets one of these criteria and not the other. Think for a moment about how this might occur. Can a test be reliable without being valid? Can a test be valid without being reliable? To answer these questions, imagine that you are measuring intelligence in a group of individuals with a "new" intelligence test. The test is based on a rather ridiculous theory of intelligence, which states that the larger your brain, the more intelligent you are. The theory also assumes that the larger your brain, the larger your head is. Thus, you are going to measure intelligence by measuring head circumference. You gather a sample of individuals, and measure the circumference of each person's head. Is this a reliable measure? Many people immediately say no because head circumference seems like such a laughable way to measure intelligence. But remember, reliability is a measure of consistency, not truthfulness. Is this test going to consistently measure the same thing? Yes, it is consistently measuring head circumference, which is not likely to change over time. Thus, your score at one time will be the same or very close to the same as your score at a later time. The test is therefore very reliable. Is it a valid measure of intelligence? No, the test in no way measures the construct of intelligence. Thus, we have established that a test can be reliable without being valid. However, because the test lacks validity, it is not a good measure. Can the reverse be true? In other words, can we have a valid test (a test that truly measures what it claims to measure) that is not reliable? If a test truly measured intelligence, individuals would score about the same each time they took it because intelligence does not vary much over time. Thus, if the test is valid, it must be reliable. Therefore, a test can be reliable and not valid, but if it is valid, it is by default reliable.

Features of Types of Validity **IN REVIEW**

	TYPES OF VALIDITY			
	CONTENT	CRITERION/ CONCURRENT	CRITERION/ PREDICTIVE	CONSTRUCT
What It Measures	Whether the test covers a representative sample of the domain of behaviors to be measured	The ability of the test to estimate present performance	The ability of the test to predict future performance	The extent to which the test measures a theoretical construct or trait
How It Is Accomplished	Ask experts to assess the test to establish that the items are representative of the trait being measured	Correlate performance on the test with a concurrent behavior	Correlate performance on the test with a behavior in the future	Correlate performance on the test with performance on an established test or with people who have different levels of the trait the test claims to measure

CRITICAL THINKING CHECK 3.4

1. You have just developed a new comprehensive test for introductory psychology that covers all aspects of the course. What type(s) of validity would you recommend establishing for this measure?
2. Why is face validity not considered a true measure of validity?
3. How is it possible for a test to be reliable but not valid?
4. If on your next psychology exam, you find that all of the questions are about American history rather than psychology, would you be more concerned about the reliability or validity of the test?

Summary

In the preceding sections, we discussed many elements important to measuring and manipulating variables. We learned the importance of operationally defining both the independent and dependent variables in a study in terms of the activities involved in measuring or manipulating each variable. It is also important to determine the scale or level of measurement of a variable based on the properties (identity, magnitude, equal unit size, and absolute zero) of the particular variable. Once established, the level of measurement (nominal, ordinal, interval, or ratio) helps determine the appropriate statistics to be used with the data. Data can also be classified as discrete (whole number units) or continuous (allowing for fractional amounts).

We next described several types of measures, including self-report (reporting on how you act, think, or feel), test (ability or personality), behavioral (observing and recording behavior), and physical (measurements of bodily activity) measures. Finally, we examined various types of reliability (consistency) and validity (truthfulness) in measures. Here we discussed error in measurement, correlation coefficients used to assess reliability and validity, and the relationship between reliability and validity.

KEY TERMS

operational definition
identity
magnitude
equal unit size
absolute zero
nominal scale
ordinal scale
interval scale
ratio scale
discrete variables
continuous variables
self-report measures
tests
behavioral measures
reactivity
physical measures
reliability
correlation coefficient
positive correlation
negative correlation
test/retest reliability
alternate-forms reliability
split-half reliability
interrater reliability
validity
content validity
face validity
criterion validity
construct validity

CHAPTER EXERCISES

(Answers to odd-numbered exercises appear in Appendix C.)

1. Which of the following is the best operational definition of depression?
   a. Depression is defined as that low feeling you get sometimes.
   b. Depression is defined as what happens when a relationship ends.
   c. Depression is defined as your score on a 50-item depression inventory.
   d. Depression is defined as the number of boxes of tissues that you cry your way through.
2. Identify the type of measure used in each of the following situations:
   a. As you leave a restaurant, you are asked to answer a few questions regarding what you thought about the service you received.
   b. When you join a weight-loss group, they ask that you keep a food journal noting everything that you eat each day.
   c. As part of a research study, you are asked to complete a 30-item anxiety inventory.
   d. When you visit your career services office, they give you a test that indicates professions to which you are best suited.
   e. While eating in the dining hall one day, you notice that food services has people tallying the number of patrons selecting each entrée.
   f. As part of a research study, your professor takes pulse and blood pressure measurements on students before and after completing a class exam.
3. Which of the following correlation coefficients represents the highest (best) reliability score?
   a. +.10
   b. −.95
   c. +.83
   d. .00
4. When you arrive for your psychology exam, you are flabbergasted to find that all of the questions are on calculus and not psychology. The next day in class, students complain so much that the professor agrees to give you all a makeup exam the following day. When you arrive in class the next day, you find that although the questions are different, they are once again on calculus. In this example, there should be high reliability of what type? What type(s) of validity is the test lacking? Explain your answers.

5. The librarians are interested in how the computers in the library are being used. They have three observers watch the terminals to see if students do research on the Internet, use e-mail, browse the Internet, play games, use social media sites, or do schoolwork (write papers, type homework, and so on). The three observers disagree 32 out of 75 times. What is the interrater reliability? How would you recommend that the librarians use the data?

CRITICAL THINKING CHECK ANSWERS

3.1

1. Nonverbal measures:
   - Number of twitches per minute
   - Number of fingernails chewed to the quick

   Physiological measures:
   - Blood pressure
   - Heart rate
   - Respiration rate
   - Galvanic skin response (GSR)

   These definitions are quantifiable and based on measurable events. They are not conceptual, as a dictionary definition would be.
2.
   a. Nominal
   b. Ordinal
   c. Ratio
   d. Interval
   e. Ordinal
   f. Nominal
   g. Ratio

3.2

1. Self-report measures and behavioral measures are more subjective; tests and physical measures are more objective.
2. The machine may not be operating correctly or the person using the machine may not be doing so correctly. Recommendations: proper training of individuals taking the measures; checks on equipment; multiple measuring instruments; multiple measures.

3.3

1. Because different questions on the same topic are used, alternative-forms reliability tells us whether the questions measure the same concepts (equivalency). Whether individuals perform similarly on equivalent tests at different times indicates the stability of a test.
2. If they disagreed 38 times out of 250 times, then they agreed 212 times out of 250 times. Thus, $212/250 = .85 \times 100 = 85\%$, which is very high interrater agreement.

3.4

1. Content and construct validity should be established for the new test.
2. Face validity has to do with only whether or not a test looks valid, not whether it truly is valid.
3. A test can consistently measure something other than what it claims to measure.
4. You should be more concerned about the validity of the test—it does not measure what it claims to measure.

WEB RESOURCES

The book-specific website at CengageBrain.com offers students a variety of study tools and useful resources such as glossaries and flashcards.

Chapter 3 ▪ Study Guide

CHAPTER 3 SUMMARY AND REVIEW: DEFINING, MEASURING, AND MANIPULATING VARIABLES

This chapter presented many elements crucial to getting started on a research project. It began with discussing the importance of operationally defining both the independent and dependent variables in a study. This involves defining them in terms of the activities of the researcher in measuring and/or manipulating each variable. It is also important to determine the scale or level of measurement of a variable by looking at the properties of measurement (identity, magnitude, equal unit size, and true zero) of the variable. Once established, the level of measurement (nominal, ordinal, interval, or ratio) helps determine the appropriate statistics for use with the data. Data can also be classified as discrete (whole number units) or continuous (allowing for fractional amounts).

The chapter also described several types of measures, including self-report (reporting on how you act, think, or feel), test (ability or personality), behavioral (observing and recording behavior), and physical (measurements of bodily activity) measures. Finally, various types of reliability (consistency) and validity (truthfulness) in measures were discussed, including error in measurement, using correlation coefficients to assess reliability and validity, and the relationship between reliability and validity.

CHAPTER 3 REVIEW EXERCISES

(Answers to exercises appear in Appendix C.)

FILL-IN SELF-TEST

Answer the following questions. If you have trouble answering any of the questions, restudy the relevant material before going on to the multiple-choice self-test.

1. A definition of a variable in terms of the activities a researcher used to measure or manipulate it is an ________.
2. ________ is a property of measurement in which the ordering of numbers reflects the ordering of the variable.
3. A(n) ________ scale is a scale in which objects or individuals are broken into categories that have no numerical properties.
4. A(n) ________ scale is a scale in which the units of measurement between the numbers on the scale are all equal in size.
5. Questionnaires or interviews that measure how people report that they act, think, or feel are ________.
6. ________ occurs when subjects act unnaturally because they know they are being observed.
7. When reliability is assessed by determining the degree of relationship between scores on the same test, administered on two different occasions, ________ is being used.
8. ________ produces a reliability coefficient that assesses the agreement of observations made by two or more raters or judges.
9. ________ assesses the extent to which a measuring instrument has items that cover all dimensions of the construct.
10. The degree to which a measuring instrument accurately measures a theoretic construct or trait that it is designed to measure is assessed by ________.

MULTIPLE-CHOICE SELF-TEST

Select the single best answer for each of the following questions. If you have trouble answering any of the questions, restudy the relevant material.

1. Gender is to the ______ property of measurement and time is to the ______ property of measurement.
   a. magnitude; identity
   b. equal unit size; magnitude
   c. absolute zero; equal unit size
   d. identity; absolute zero
2. Arranging a group of individuals from heaviest to lightest represents the ______ property of measurement.
   a. identity
   b. magnitude
   c. equal unit size
   d. absolute zero
3. The letter grade on a test is to the ______ scale of measurement and height is to the ______ scale of measurement.
   a. ordinal; ratio
   b. ordinal; nominal
   c. nominal; interval
   d. interval; ratio
4. Weight is to the ______ scale of measurement and political affiliation is to the ______ scale of measurement.
   a. ratio; ordinal
   b. ratio; nominal
   c. interval; nominal
   d. ordinal; ratio
5. Measuring in whole units is to ______ and measuring in whole units and/or fractional amounts is to ______.
   a. discrete variable; continuous variable
   b. continuous variable; discrete variable
   c. nominal scale; ordinal scale
   d. both a and c
6. ______ measure an individual's potential to do something, and ______ measure an individual's competence in a given area.
   a. Tests; self-report measures
   b. Aptitude tests; achievement tests
   c. Achievement tests; aptitude tests
   d. Self-report measures; behavioral measures
7. Sue decided to have subjects in her study of the relationship between amount of time spent studying and grades keep a journal of how much time they spent studying each day. The type of measurement that Sue is employing is known as a(n):
   a. behavioral self-report measure.
   b. cognitive self-report measure.
   c. affective self-report measure.
   d. aptitude test.
8. Which of the following correlation coefficients represents the variables with the weakest degree of relationship?
   a. −.99
   b. −.49
   c. +.83
   d. +.01
9. Which of the following is true?
   a. Test-retest reliability is determined by assessing the degree of relationship between scores on one half of a test with scores on the other half of the test.
   b. Split-half reliability is determined by assessing the degree of relationship between scores on the same test, administered on two different occasions.
   c. Alternate-forms reliability is determined by assessing the degree of relationship between scores on two different, equivalent tests.
   d. None of the above.
10. If observers disagree 20 times out of 80, then the interrater reliability is:
    a. 40%.
    b. 75%.
    c. 25%.
    d. not able to be determined.
11. Which of the following is not a type of validity?
    a. criterion validity
    b. content validity
    c. face validity
    d. alternate-forms validity
12. Which of the following is true?
    a. Construct validity is the extent to which a measuring instrument covers a representative sample of the domain of behaviors to be measured.
    b. Criterion validity is the extent to which a measuring instrument accurately predicts behavior or ability in a given area.
    c. Content validity is the degree to which a measuring instrument accurately measures a theoretic construct or trait that it is designed to measure.
    d. Face validity is a measure of the truthfulness of a measuring instrument.

CHAPTER 4

Descriptive Methods

Learning Objectives

- Explain the difference between naturalistic and laboratory observation.
- Explain the difference between participant and nonparticipant observation.
- Explain the difference between disguised and nondisguised observation.
- Describe how to use a checklist versus a narrative record.
- Describe an action checklist versus a static checklist.
- Describe the case study method.
- Describe the archival method.
- Describe the interview method.
- Describe the field study method.
- Describe what action research is.
- Differentiate open-ended, closed-ended, and partially open-ended questions.
- Explain the differences among loaded questions, leading questions, and double-barreled questions.
- Identify the three methods of surveying.
- Identify advantages and disadvantages of the three survey methods.
- Differentiate probability and nonprobabililty sampling.
- Differentiate random sampling, stratified random sampling, and cluster sampling.

In the preceding chapters, we discussed certain aspects of getting started with a research project. We will now turn to a discussion of actual research methods—the nuts and bolts of conducting a research project—starting with various types of nonexperimental designs. In this chapter, we'll discuss descriptive methods. These methods, as the name implies, allow you to describe a situation; however, they do not allow you to make accurate predictions or to establish a cause-and-effect relationship between variables. We'll examine three different types of descriptive methods—observational methods, qualitative methods, and surveys—providing an overview and examples of each method. In addition, we will note any special considerations that apply when using each of these methods.

Observational Methods

As noted in Chapter 1, the observational method in its most basic form is as simple as it sounds—making observations of human or animal behavior. This method is not used as widely in psychology as in other disciplines such as sociology, ethology, and anthropology, because most psychologists want to be able to do more than describe. However, this method is of great value in some situations. When we begin research in an area, it may be appropriate to start with an observational study before doing anything more complicated. In addition, certain behaviors that cannot be studied in experimental situations lend themselves nicely to observational research. We will discuss two types of observational studies—naturalistic, or field observation, and laboratory, or systematic observation—along with the advantages and disadvantages of each type.

Naturalistic Observation

Naturalistic observation (sometimes referred to as *field observation*) involves watching people or animals in their natural habitats. The greatest advantage of this type of observation is the potential for observing natural or true behaviors. The idea is that animals or people in their natural habitat, rather than an artificial laboratory setting, should display more realistic, natural behaviors. For this reason, naturalistic observation has greater ecological validity than most other research methods. **Ecological validity** refers to the extent to which research can be generalized to real-life situations (Aronson & Carlsmith, 1968). Both Jane Goodall and Dian Fossey engaged in naturalistic observation in their work with chimpanzees and gorillas, respectively. However, as you'll see, they used the naturalistic method slightly differently.

ecological validity The extent to which research can be generalized to real-life situations.

"SHE'S BEEN WATCHING US FOR YEARS. WHEN THE HELL IS SHE GOING TO WRITE HER BOOK?"

Options When Using Observation

undisguised observation Studies in which the subjects are aware that the researcher is observing their behavior.

nonparticipant observation Studies in which the researcher does not participate in the situation in which the research subjects are involved.

participant observation Studies in which the researcher actively participates in the situation in which the research subjects are involved.

Both Goodall and Fossey used **undisguised observation**—they made no attempt to disguise themselves while making observations. Goodall's initial approach was to observe the chimpanzees from a distance. Thus, she attempted to engage in **nonparticipant observation**—a study in which the researcher does not take part (participate) in the situation in which the research subjects are involved. Fossey, on the other hand, attempted to infiltrate the group of gorillas that she was studying. She tried to act as they did in the hopes of being accepted as a member of the group so that she could observe as an insider. In **participant observation**, then, the researcher actively participates in the situation in which the research subjects are involved.

Take a moment to think about the issues involved when using either of these methods. In nonparticipant observation, there is the issue of reactivity—subjects reacting in an unnatural way to someone obviously watching them. Thus, Goodall's sitting back and watching the chimpanzees may have caused them to "react" to her presence, and she therefore may not have observed naturalistic or true behaviors from the chimpanzees. Fossey, on the other hand, claimed that the gorillas accepted her as a member of their group, thereby minimizing or eliminating reactivity. This claim is open to question, however, because no matter how much like a gorilla she acted, she was still human.

disguised observation Studies in which the subjects are unaware that the researcher is observing their behavior.

Imagine how much more effective both participant and nonparticipant observation might be if researchers used **disguised observation**—concealing the fact that they were observing and recording participants' behaviors. Disguised observation allows the researcher to make observations in a more unobtrusive manner. As a nonparticipant, a researcher can make observations by hiding or by videotaping participants. Reactivity is not an issue because subjects are unaware that anyone is observing their behavior. Hiding or videotaping, however, may raise ethical problems if the subjects are humans. This is one reason that all research, both human and animal, must be approved by an Institutional Review Board (IRB) or the Animal Care and Use Committee, as described in Chapter 2, prior to beginning a study.

Disguised observation may also be used when someone is acting as a participant in the study. Rosenhan (1973) demonstrated this in his classic study on the validity of psychiatric diagnoses. Rosenhan had 8 sane individuals seek admittance to 12 different mental hospitals. Each was asked to go to a hospital and complain of the same symptoms—hearing voices that said "empty," "hollow," and "thud." Once admitted to the mental ward, the individuals no longer reported hearing voices. If admitted, each individual was to make recordings of patient-staff interactions. Rosenhan was interested in how long it would take a "sane" person to be released from the mental hospital. He found that the length of stay varied from 7 to 52 days, although the hospital staff never detected that the individuals were "sane" and part of a disguised participant study.

expectancy effects The influence of the researcher's expectations on the outcome of the study.

As we have seen, one of the primary concerns of naturalistic studies is reactivity. Another concern for researchers who use this method is expectancy effects. **Expectancy effects** are the effect of the researcher's expectations on the outcome of the study. For example, the researcher may pay more attention to behaviors that they expect or that support their hypotheses, while possibly ignoring behaviors that might not support their hypotheses. Because the only data in an observational study are the observations made by the researcher, expectancy effects can be a serious problem, leading to biased results.

Besides these potential problems, naturalistic observation can be costly—especially in studies like those conducted by Goodall and Fossey where travel to another continent is required—and are usually time-consuming. One reason is that often researchers are open to studying many different behaviors when conducting this type of study; anything of interest may be observed and recorded. This flexibility often means that the research can go on indefinitely, and there is little control over what happens in the study.

Laboratory Observation

An observational method that is usually less costly and time-consuming and affords more control is laboratory or *systematic observation.* In contrast to naturalistic observation, systematic or laboratory observation involves observing behavior in a more contrived setting, usually a laboratory, and focusing on a small number of carefully defined behaviors. The subjects are more likely to know that they are participating in a research study in which they will be observed. However, as with naturalistic observation, the researcher can be either a participant or a nonparticipant and either disguised or undisguised. For example, in the classic "strange situation" study by Ainsworth and Bell (1970), mothers brought their children to a laboratory playroom. The mothers and children were then observed through a two-way mirror in various situations, such as when the child explored the room, was left alone in the room, was left with a stranger, and was reunited with the mother. This study used nonparticipant observation. In addition, it was conducted in an undisguised manner for the mothers (who were aware they were being observed) and disguised for the children (who were unaware they were being observed).

Laboratory observation may also be conducted with the researcher as a participant in the situation. For example, a developmental psychologist could observe play behavior in children as an undisguised participant by playing with the children. In other studies involving laboratory observation, the subject is disguised. Research on helping behavior (altruism) often uses this method. For example, researchers might stage what appears to be an emergency while subjects are supposedly waiting for an experiment to begin. The researcher participates in a disguised manner in the "emergency situation" and observes how the "real" subjects act in this situation. Do they offer help right away, and does offering help depend on the number of people present?

In laboratory observation, as with naturalistic observation, we are concerned with reactivity and expectancy effects. In fact, reactivity may be a greater concern because most people will "react" simply to being in a laboratory. As noted, one way of attempting to control reactivity is by using a disguised type of design.

An advantage of systematic or laboratory settings is that they are contrived (not natural) and thus offer the researcher more control. The situation has been manufactured to some extent to observe a specific behavior or set of behaviors. Because the situation is contrived, the likelihood that the subjects will actually engage in the behavior of interest is far greater than it would be in a natural setting. Most researchers view this control as advantageous because it reduces the length of time needed for the study. Notice, however, that as control increases, flexibility decreases. You are not free to observe whatever behavior you find of interest on any given day, as you would be with a naturalistic study. Researchers have to decide what is of greatest importance to them and then choose either the naturalistic or laboratory method.

Data Collection

Another decision to be faced when conducting observational research is how to collect the data. In Chapter 3, we discussed several types of measures: self-report measures, tests, behavioral measures, and physical measures. Because observational research involves observing and recording behavior, data are most often collected through the use of behavioral measures. As noted in Chapter 3, behavioral measures can be taken in a direct (at the time the behavior occurs) or in an indirect manner (via audio- or videotape). In addition, researchers using the observational technique can collect data using narrative records or checklists.

narrative records Full narrative descriptions of a subject's behavior.

Narrative Records. **Narrative records** are full narrative descriptions of a subject's behavior. These records may be created in a direct manner—writing notes by hand—or an indirect manner—audio- or videotaping the subjects and then taking notes at a later time. The purpose of narrative records is to capture, in a complete manner, everything the participant said or did during a specified period of time.

One of the best examples of the use of narrative records is the work of Jean Piaget. Piaget studied cognitive development in children and kept extensive narrative records concerning everything a child did during the specified time period. His records were a running account of exactly what the child said and did.

Although narrative records provide a complete account of what took place with each participant in a study, they are a very subjective means of collecting data. In addition, narrative records cannot be analyzed quantitatively. To be analyzed, the data must be coded in some way, reducing the huge volume of narrative information to a more manageable quantitative form, such as the number of problems solved correctly by children in different age ranges. The data should be coded by more than one person to establish interrater reliability. You may recall from Chapter 3 that interrater reliability is a measure of reliability that assesses the agreement of observations made by two or more raters or judges.

checklist A tally sheet on which the researcher records attributes of the subjects and whether particular behaviors were observed.

Checklists. A more structured and objective method of collecting data involves using a **checklist**—a tally sheet on which the researcher records attributes of the subjects and whether particular behaviors were observed. Checklists enable researchers to focus on a limited number of specific behaviors.

static item A type of item used on a checklist on which attributes that will not change are recorded.

Researchers use two basic types of items on checklists. A **static item** is a means of collecting data on characteristics that will not change while the observations are being made. These static features may include how many people are present; the gender, race, and age of the participant; or what the weather is like (if relevant). Many different characteristics may be noted using static items, depending on the nature of the study. For example, observations of hospital patients might include information on general health, whereas observations of driving behavior might include the make and type of vehicle driven.

action item A type of item used on a checklist to note the presence or absence of behaviors.

The second type of item used on a checklist, an **action item**, is used to record whether specific behaviors were present or absent during the observational time period. Action items could be used to record the type of stop made at a stop sign (complete, rolling, or none) or the type of play behavior observed in children (solitary, cooperative, or parallel). Typically, action items provide a means of tallying the frequency of different categories of behavior.

As discussed in Chapter 3, it is important that researchers who use checklists understand the operational definition of each characteristic being measured to increase the reliability and validity of the measures. As you may recall, an operational definition of a variable is a definition of the variable in terms of the operations (activities) a researcher uses to measure or manipulate it. Thus, to use a checklist accurately, the person collecting the data must clearly understand what constitutes each category of behavior being observed.

The advantage of checklists over narrative records is that the data are already quantified and do not have to be reduced in any way. The disadvantage is that the behaviors and characteristics to be observed are determined when the checklist is devised. Thus, an interesting behavior that would have been included in a narrative record may be missed or not recorded because it is not part of the checklist.

Features of Types of Observational Studies — **IN REVIEW**

	TYPES OF OBSERVATIONAL STUDIES	
	NATURALISTIC	**LABORATORY**
Description	Observing people or animals in their natural habitats	Observing people or animals in a contrived setting, usually a laboratory
Options	Participant versus nonparticipant Disguised versus nondisguised	Participant versus nonparticipant Disguised versus nondisguised
Means of Data Collection	Narrative records Checklists	Narrative records Checklists
Concerns	Reactivity Expectancy effects Time Money Lack of control	Reactivity Expectancy effects Lack of flexibility

CRITICAL THINKING CHECK 4.1

1. Explain the differences in flexibility and control between naturalistic and laboratory observational research.
2. If reactivity were your greatest concern in an observational study, which method would you recommend using?
3. Why is data reduction of greater concern when using narrative records as opposed to checklists?

Qualitative Methods

qualitative research A type of social research based on field observations that is analyzed without statistics.

Qualitative research focuses on phenomena that occur in natural settings, and the data are analyzed without the use of statistics. Qualitative research usually takes place in the field or wherever the subjects normally conduct their activities. When using qualitative methods, however, researchers are typically not interested in simplifying, objectifying, or quantifying what they observe. Instead, when conducting qualitative studies, researchers are more interested in interpreting and making sense of what they have observed. Researchers using this approach may not necessarily believe that there is a single "truth" to be discovered but rather that there are multiple positions or opinions and that each have some degree of merit.

Qualitative research entails observation and/or unstructured interviewing in natural settings. The data are collected in a spontaneous and open-ended fashion. Consequently, these methods have far less structure and control than do quantitative methods. Researchers who prefer quantitative methods often regard this tendency toward flexibility and lack of control as a threat to the reliability and validity of a study. Those who espouse qualitative methods, however, see these characteristics as strengths. They believe that the subjects eventually adjust to the researcher's presence (thus reducing reactivity) and that once they adjust, the researcher is able to acquire perceptions from different points of view. Please keep in mind that most of the methodologies used by qualitative researchers are also used by quantitative researchers. The difference is in the intent of the study. The quantitative researcher typically starts with a hypothesis for testing, observes and collects data, statistically analyzes the data, and draws conclusions. Qualitative researchers are far less structured and go more with the flow of the research setting and the subjects. They may change what they are observing based on changes that occur in the field setting. Qualitative researchers typically make passive observations with no intent of manipulating a causal variable. Qualitative research has been more commonly used by other social researchers, such as sociologists and anthropologists, but it is growing in applicability and popularity among psychologists.

Case Study Method

One of the oldest qualitative research methods is the *case study method,* an in-depth study of one or more individuals, groups, social settings, or events in the hope of revealing things that are true of all of us. For instance, Freud's theory of personality development was based on a small number of case studies. Piaget, whose research was used as an example of observational methods, began studying cognitive development by completing case studies on his own three children. This inquiry piqued his interest in cognitive development to such an extent that he then began to use observational methods to study hundreds of other children. As another example, much of the research on split-brain patients and hemispheric specialization was conducted using case studies of the few individuals whose corpus callosum had been severed.

One advantage of case study research is that it often suggests hypotheses for future studies, as in Piaget's case. It also provides a method to study rare phenomena, such as rare brain disorders or diseases, as in the case of split-brain patients. Case studies may also offer tentative support for a psychological theory.

Case study research also has problems. The individual, group, setting, or event being observed may be atypical, and, consequently, any generalizations made to the general population would be erroneous. For example, Freud formulated a theory of personality development that he believed applied to everyone based on case studies of a few atypical individuals. Another potential problem is expectancy effects: Researchers may be biased in their interpretations of their observations or data collection, paying more attention to data that support their theory and ignoring data that present problems for it. Because of these limitations, case study research should be used with caution, and the data should be interpreted for what they are—observations on one or a few possibly unrepresentative individuals, groups, settings, or events.

Archival Method

archival method A descriptive research method that involves describing data that existed before the time of the study.

A second qualitative method is the **archival method**, which involves describing data that existed before the time of the study. In other words, the data were not generated as part of the study. One of the biggest advantages of archival research is that the problem of reactivity is minimized because the data have already been collected and the researcher does not have to interact with the subjects in any way. As an example, Linda Gordon (1988) used welfare records to try to understand family violence. She used case records from social work agencies to investigate how social conceptions of family violence changed over time. You can see, based on this example, that another advantage of archival research is that it is usually less time-consuming than most other research methods because the data already exist. Thus researchers are not confronted with the problems of getting participants for their study and taking the time to observe them because these tasks have already been done for them.

There are many sources for archival data. The best-known is the U.S. Census Bureau. However, any organization that collects data is an archival source: the National Opinion Research Center, the Educational Testing Service, and local, state, and federal public records can all be sources of archival data. In addition to organizations that collect data, archival research may be conducted based on the content of newspapers or magazines, data in a library, police incident reports, hospital admittance records, computer databases, or private records.

Some data sources might be considered better than others. For instance, reviewing letters to the editor at a local newspaper to gauge public sentiment on a topic might lead to biases in the data. In other words, there is a selection bias in who decided to write to the editor, and some opinions or viewpoints may be overlooked simply because the individuals who hold those viewpoints decided not to write to the editor. Moreover, in all archival research studies, researchers are basing their conclusions on data collected by another person or organization. This secondhand collection means that the researchers can never be sure whether the data are reliable or valid. In addition, they cannot be sure that what is currently in the archive represents everything that was originally collected. Some of the data may have been purged at some time, and researchers will not know this. Nor will they know why any data were purged or why some data were purged and some left. Thus as a research method archival research typically provides a lot of flexibility in terms of what is studied but no control in terms of who was studied or how they were studied.

Interviews and Focus Group Interviews

interview A method that typically involves asking questions in a face-to-face manner, and it may be conducted anywhere.

Interviews can be thought of as the verbal equivalent of a pencil and paper survey. During an interview the researcher is having a conversation with the respondent and the conversation has a purpose. An **interview** typically involves asking questions in a face-to-face manner, and it may be conducted anywhere—at the individual's home, on the street, or in a shopping mall. There are three different types of interviews: the standardized interview, the semistandardized interview, and the unstandardized interview (Berg, 2009; Esterberg, 2002). The *standardized interview* is somewhat formal in structure, and the questions are typically asked in a specific order. There is little deviation on the wording of the questions. That is, questions are asked just as they are written, and there is no question clarification provided to respondents nor are general questions about the interview answered or additional questions added on the spur of the moment.

The *semistandardized interview* has some structure to it, but the wording of the questions is flexible, the level of the language may be modified, and the interviewer may choose to answer questions and provide further explanation if requested. Respondents have a greater ability to express their opinions in their own words when using this type of interview structure. Lastly, there is more flexibility in terms of the interviewer adding or deleting questions.

The *unstandardized interview* is completely unstructured in that there is no set order to the questions nor a set wording to the questions. The questions are more spontaneous and free flowing. This flexibility obviously means that the level of the language can be modified and that the interviewer may provide question clarification, answer questions the respondent may have, and add or delete questions.

When conducting an interview, no matter the type of interview, the researcher needs to think about the order of the questions. It is generally recommended that one begins with questions that the respondent should find easy and nonthreatenting before moving on to the more important questions. Sensitive questions should come later in the interview when the respondent is more at ease with the situation. At some point there should be validation of the more sensitive questions, that is, questions that restate important or sensitive questions. These validation questions should be worded differently than the previous questions on the same topic. If your interview involves several topics, you should arrange the questions on each topic in the manner described above. In addition, when interviewing on more than one topic, there should be some sort of transition between the questions on each topic such as 'The next series of questions will ask you about..."

One advantage of interviews is that they allow the researcher to record not only verbal responses but also any facial or bodily expressions or movements, such as grins, grimaces, or shrugs. These nonverbal responses may give the researcher greater insight into the respondent's true opinions and beliefs.

focus group interview A method that involves interviewing six to ten individuals at the same time.

A variation on interviewing individuals is the **focus group interview**. Focus group interviews involve interviewing six to ten individuals at the same time. Focus groups usually meet once for 1 to 2 hours. The questions asked of the subjects are open-ended and addressed to the whole group. This procedure allows subjects to answer in any way they choose and to respond to each other. One concern with focus group interviews is that one or two of the participants may dominate the conversation. Consequently, it is important that the individual conducting the focus group is skilled at dealing with such problems.

Focus group interviews are a flexible methodology that permit the gathering of a large amount of information from many people in a fairly short amount of time. Because of their flexibility, focus group interviews allow the moderator to explore other topics that might arise based on the discussion of the group.

Field Studies

field studies A method that involves observing everyday activities as they happen in a natural setting.

Earlier in the chapter, we discussed a methodology that is very similar to field studies: naturalistic observation. **Field studies** involve observing everyday activities as they happen in a natural setting. In addition, the observer is directly involved with those that are being observed. In this sense, field studies are similar to participant observation. The main difference is that when field studies are used, data are always collected in a narrative form and left in that form because the research is qualitative. The hope of the researcher conducting a field study is to acquire the perspective and point of view of an insider while also keeping an objective analytic perspective. The data produced are in the form of extensive written notes that provide detailed descriptions. Observers should take note of the ongoing social processes, but they should not interfere with these processes or attempt to impose their perspectives. This balancing act requires quite a bit of skill because the researcher is a participant in the situation but cannot influence those being observed. In other words, we want those being observed to act as they would if the researcher were not there, and we want the outcomes to be the same as they would have been if the researcher were not there. This method is unlike participant observation in which those being observed may not realize they are being observed. With field studies, subjects realize they are being observed, meaning there is the issue of reactivity that we discussed earlier in the chapter. The goal of field studies is a holistic understanding of a culture, subculture, or group.

Action Research

action research A method in which research is conducted by a group of people to identify a problem, attempt to resolve it, and then assess how successful their efforts were.

The final type of qualitative research we will discuss is **action research**, research conducted by a group of people to identify a problem, attempt to resolve it, and then assess how successful their efforts were. This research is highly applied in that it is typically conducted by those who have a problem in order to solve the problem. That is, action research follows the old adage: "If you want something done right, do it yourself." So rather than hire someone to analyze a social program in order to assess its effectiveness, those who work in the program would identify a problem to be evaluated, explore the problem, and then define an agenda for action.

Action research has a wide range of applications, for example, in schools, hospitals, social agencies, the justice system, and community contexts. The methodology uses a collaborative approach that as an end result gives people a course of action to fix a problem. It utilizes a participatory democratic style.

There are three basic phases to action research. The first process is *looking*, when the researchers gather information, identify a problem, and identify who the stakeholders are. The second process is *thinking*, which involves thinking about the problem, gathering the information to answer the questions posed, and analyzing and interpreting the data. Areas of success should be identified along with possible deficiencies. The final process is *action*—thus the name action research. After looking and thinking, action needs to be taken to improve the lives of the participants (i.e., the stakeholders). This last process also involves sharing the results not only with the stakeholders but with the larger community.

Unlike other methodologies, action research is typically not published in academic journals but instead might be presented in a newspaper article, on television, or in a magazine. These venues mean that the language and content of action research is easier to understand and typically does not include difficult-to-understand statistical techniques; that is, it is written at a level that a lay person can understand.

As a means of illustrating action research, consider the following example of a possible action research study designed to address complaints of noise in a residence hall on a college campus (Sommer & Sommer, 2002). A committee of students in the residence hall makes up the key people undertaking the study, with some of the students coming from the preference-for-quiet-while-studying side of the issue and some coming from the preference-for-music-while-studying side of the issue. The students decide to conduct a door-to-door survey to learn how much the residents are bothered by noise. A survey instrument that utilizes a series of open-ended questions is developed, and given that the questions used for the interview are open-ended, the research is qualitative in nature. However, you should appreciate that the question type could be changed to rating scale questions or that the answers to the open-ended questions could be coded into numerical data, making this action research study quantitative in nature. Thus, as stated earlier, most of the qualitative methods described in this section could also be used as quantitative methods. The data from the interview would be reviewed and discussed by the committee in order to assess the general consensus of the members of the residence hall. Based on these qualitative results, an action plan should be developed and implemented in the residence hall that addresses the problem. The committee should then revisit the issue a month or two later to assess the effectiveness of the action plan, closing the loop in the action research process.

Qualitative Data Analysis

Let's begin our discussion of qualitative data analysis by identifying the similarities between it and quantitative data analysis. Both types of data analysis involve the researcher making some type of inference based on the data. In addition, both types of data analysis involve the researcher carefully examining the data that have been collected in order to reach a conclusion. Finally, researchers who use both types of analyses make their findings public so that they can be scrutinized and reviewed by others.

The main difference between qualitative and quantitative data analyses is that statistics and mathematical formulas are not used with qualitative analyses. Most of the data collected are nominal in scale and are collected via extensive note taking. Consequently, the data are verbal in nature rather than numerical and consist of very detailed notes on what was observed via the particular methodology used. Unlike quantitative analyses in which data analysis cannot take place until after all data have been collected, with qualitative analyses the results of an early review of the data might guide what data are collected later in the study. Qualitative analyses usually involve reading through the notes taken and trying to conceptualize from the data. During this stage the researcher is looking for patterns in the data. Accordingly, researchers might code the data by organizing it into conceptual categories. They then would attempt to create themes or concepts. Computers or word processors can be used to help with the data analysis by searching through the notes to identify certain words or phrases that might help to develop themes and concepts.

Features of Types of Qualitative Studies — **IN REVIEW**

TYPE OF STUDY	DESCRIPTION
Case Study	An in-depth study of one or more individuals, groups, social settings, or events in the hope of revealing things that are true of all of us
Archival Study	A method that involves describing data that existed before the time of the study
Interview	A method that involves asking questions in a face-to-face manner; it may be conducted anywhere
Focus Group Interview	A method that involves interviewing six to ten individuals at the same time
Field Studies	A method that involves observing everyday activities as they happen in a natural setting
Action Research	Research conducted by a group of people to identify a problem, attempt to resolve it, and then assess how successful their efforts were

Survey Methods

Another means of collecting data for descriptive purposes is to use a survey. We will discuss several elements to consider when using surveys, including constructing the survey, administering the survey, and choosing sampling techniques.

Survey Construction

We begin our coverage of the survey method by discussing survey construction. For the data collected to be both reliable and valid, the researcher must carefully plan the survey instrument. The type of questions used and the order in which they appear may vary depending on how the survey is ultimately administered (for example, a mail survey versus a telephone survey).

Writing the Questions. The first task in designing a survey is to write the survey questions. Questions should be written in clear, simple language to minimize any possible confusion. Take a moment to think about surveys or exam questions you may have encountered where, because of poor wording, you misunderstood what was being asked of you. For example, consider the following questions:

- How long have you lived in Harborside?
- How many years have you lived in Harborside?

In both instances, the researcher is interested in determining the number of years the individual has resided in the area. Notice, however, that the first question does not actually ask this. An individual might answer "Since I was 8 years old" (meaningless unless the survey also asks for current age) or "I moved to Harborside right after I got married." In either case, the participant's interpretation of the question is different from the researcher's intent. It is important, therefore, to spend time thinking about the simplest wording that will elicit the specific information of interest to the researcher.

Another consideration when writing survey questions is whether to use open-ended, closed-ended, partially open-ended, or rating-scale questions. Table 4.1 provides examples of these types of questions. **Open-ended questions** ask subjects to formulate their own responses. On written surveys, researchers can control the length of the response to some extent by the amount of room they leave for the respondent to answer the question. A single line encourages a short answer, whereas several lines indicate that a longer response is expected. **Closed-ended questions** ask the respondent to choose from a limited number of alternatives. Subjects may be asked to choose the one answer that best represents their beliefs or to check as many answers as apply to them. When writing closed-ended questions, researchers must make sure that the alternatives provided include all possible answers. For example, suppose a question asks how many hours of television the respondent watched the previous day and provides the following alternatives: 0–1 hour, 2–3 hours, 4–5 hours, or 6 or more hours. What if an individual watched 1.5 hours? Should this respondent select the first or second alternative? Each participant would have to decide which alternative to choose. This, in turn, would compromise the data collected. In other words, the data would be less reliable and valid. **Partially open-ended questions** are similar to closed-ended questions, but one alternative is "Other" with a

open-ended questions Questions for which subjects formulate their own responses.

closed-ended questions Questions for which subjects choose from a limited number of alternatives.

partially open-ended questions Closed-ended questions with an open-ended "Other" option.

TABLE 4.1 Examples of Types of Survey Questions

Open-ended

Has your college experience been satisfying thus far?____________________

____

Closed-ended

Has your college experience been satisfying thus far?

Yes __________ No __________

Partially open-ended

With regard to your college experience, which of the following factors do you find satisfying?

Academics __________
Relationships __________
Residence halls __________
Residence life __________
Social life __________
Food service __________
Other ____________________

____

Likert Rating Scale

I am very satisfied with my college experience.

1	2	3	4	5
Strongly Disagree	Disagree	Neutral	Agree	Strongly Agree

blank space next to it. If none of the alternatives provided is appropriate, the respondent can mark "Other" and then write a short explanation.

rating scale A numerical scale on which survey respondents indicate the direction and strength of their response.

likert rating scale A type of numerical rating scale developed by Renis Likert in 1932.

Finally, researchers may use some sort of **rating scale** that asks participants to choose a number that represents the direction and strength of their response. One advantage of using a rating scale is that it's easy to convert the data to an ordinal or interval scale of measurement and proceed with statistical analysis. One popular version is the Likert rating scale, named after the researcher who developed the scale in 1932. A **Likert rating scale** presents a statement rather than a question, and respondents are asked to rate their level of agreement with the statement. The example in Table 4.1 uses a Likert scale with five alternatives. If you want to provide respondents with a neutral alternative, you should use a scale with an odd number of alternatives. If, however, you want to force respondents to lean in one direction or another, you should use an even number of alternatives. Also note that each of the five numerical alternatives has a descriptive word associated with it. Using a descriptor for each numerical alternative is usually best, rather than just anchoring words at the beginning and end of the scale (in other words, just the words Strongly Agree and Strongly Disagree at the beginning and end of the scale), because when all numerical alternatives are labeled, we can be assured that all respondents are using the scale consistently.

Each type of question has advantages and disadvantages. Open-ended questions allow for a greater variety of responses from participants but are difficult to analyze statistically because the data must be coded or reduced in some manner. Closed-ended questions are easy to analyze statistically, but they seriously limit the responses that participants can give. Many researchers prefer to use a Likert-type scale because it's very easy to analyze statistically. Most psychologists view this scale as interval in nature, although there is some debate, as others see it as an ordinal scale. As you'll see in later chapters, a wide variety of statistical tests can be used with interval data.

loaded question A question that includes nonneutral or emotionally laden terms.

leading question A question that sways the respondent to answer in a desired manner.

double-barreled question A question that asks more than one thing.

When researchers write survey items, it's very important that the wording not mislead the respondent. Several types of questions can mislead participants. A **loaded question** is one that includes nonneutral or emotionally laden terms. Consider this example: "Do you believe radical extremists should be allowed to burn the American flag?" The phrase *radical extremists* loads the question emotionally, conveying the opinion of the person who wrote the question. A **leading question** is one that sways the respondent to answer in a desired manner. For example: "Most people agree that conserving energy is important. Do you agree?" The phrase *Most people agree* encourages the respondent to agree also. Finally, a **double-barreled question** asks more than one thing in a single item. Double-barreled questions often include the word *and* or *or*. For example, the following question is double-barreled: "Do you find using a cell phone to be convenient and time saving?" This question should be divided into two separate items, one addressing the convenience of cell phones and one addressing whether they save time.

response bias The tendency to consistently give the same answer to almost all of the items on a survey.

Finally, when writing a survey, the researcher should also be concerned with participants who employ a particular response set or **response bias**—the tendency to consistently give the same answer to almost all of the items on a survey. This is often referred to as "yea-saying" or "nay-saying." In other words, respondents might agree (or disagree) with one or two of the questions, but to make answering the survey easier on themselves, they simply respond yes (or no) to almost all of the questions. One way to minimize participants adopting such a response bias is to word the questions so that a positive (or negative) response to every question would be unlikely. For example, an instrument designed to assess depression might phrase some of the questions so that agreement means the respondent is depressed ("I frequently feel sad"), and other questions might have the meaning reversed so that disagreement indicates depression ("I am happy almost all of the time"). Although some individuals might legitimately agree to both of these items, when a respondent consistently agrees (or disagrees) with questions phrased in standard and reversed formats, "yea-saying" or "nay-saying" is a reasonable concern.

Arranging the Questions. Another consideration is how to arrange questions on the survey. Writers of surveys sometimes assume that the questions should be randomized, but this is not the best arrangement to use. Dillman (1978) provides some tips for arranging questions on surveys. First, present related questions in subsets. This arrangement ensures that the general concept being investigated is made obvious to the respondents. It also helps the respondents to focus on one issue at a time. However, this suggestion should not be followed if you do not want the general concept being investigated to be obvious to the respondents. Second, place questions that deal with sensitive topics (such as drug use or sexual experiences) at the end of the subset of questions to which they apply. Respondents will be more likely to answer questions of a sensitive nature if they have already committed themselves to filling out the survey by answering questions of a less sensitive nature. Last, to prevent participants from losing interest in the survey, place **demographic questions**—questions that ask for basic information such as age, gender, ethnicity, or income—at the end of the survey. Although this information is important for the researcher, many respondents view it as boring, so avoid beginning your survey with these items.

demographic questions Questions that ask for basic information, such as age, gender, ethnicity, or income.

Administering the Survey

In this section we examine three methods of surveying: mail surveys, telephone surveys, and personal interviews, along with the advantages and disadvantages of each.

mail survey A written survey that is self-administered.

Mail Surveys. **Mail surveys** are written surveys that are self-administered. They can be sent through the traditional mail system or by e-mail. It is especially important that a mail survey be clearly written and self-explanatory because no one is available to answer questions regarding the survey once it has been mailed out.

sampling bias A tendency for one group to be overrepresented in a sample.

Mail surveys have several advantages. Traditional mail surveys were generally considered to have less **sampling bias**, a tendency for one group to be overrepresented in a sample, than phone surveys or personal interviews. This trait was considered to be the case because almost everyone has a mailing address and thus can receive a survey, but not everyone has a phone or is available to spend time on a personal interview. However, one mechanism researchers used to employ to obtain mailing addresses was via phone books. This practice now presents a problem with respect to mail surveys because 25% of the U.S. population has unlisted phone numbers and thus will not be included in phone books. In addition, many phone books no longer provide full mailing addresses. One way, however, to counter this problem is by using the U.S. Postal Service DSF (delivery sequence file), an electronic file containing all delivery point addresses serviced by the U.S. Postal Service. It is estimated that the DSF provides up to 95% coverage rates (Dillman, Smyth, & Christian, 2009).

interviewer bias The tendency for the person asking the questions to bias the participants' answers.

Mail surveys do eliminate the problem of **interviewer bias**, that is, the tendency for the person asking the questions (usually the researcher) to bias or influence the participants' answers. An interviewer might bias participants' answers by nodding and smiling more when they answer as expected or frowning when they give unexpected answers.

Mail surveys also have the advantage of allowing the researcher to collect data on more sensitive information. Participants who might be unwilling to discuss personal information with someone over the phone or face-to-face might be more willing to answer such questions on a written survey. A mail survey is also usually less expensive than a phone survey or personal interview in which the researcher has to pay workers to phone or canvas neighborhoods. Additionally, the answers provided on a mail survey are sometimes more complete because participants can take as much time as they need to think about the questions and to formulate their responses without feeling the pressure of someone waiting for an answer.

Mail surveys also have potential problems. One is that no one is available to answer questions. So if an item is unclear to the respondent, it may be left blank or misinterpreted, thereby biasing the results. Another problem with mail surveys is a generally low return rate. Typically a single mailing produces a response rate of 25 to 30%, much lower than is usually achieved with phone surveys or personal interviews. However, follow-up mailings may produce a response rate as high as 50% (Bourque & Fielder, 2003; Erdos, 1983). A good response rate is important in order to maintain a representative sample. If only a small portion of the original sample returns the survey, the final sample may be biased. Online response rates tend to be as problematic as the response rates for traditional mail surveys, typically in the 10 to 20% range (Bourque & Fielder, 2003).

Shere Hite's (1987) work, based on surveys completed by 4,500 women, is a classic example of the problem of a biased survey sample. In her book *Women and Love* Hite claimed, based on her survey, that 70% of women married 5 or more years were having affairs, 84% of them were dissatisfied with their intimate relationships with men, and 95% felt emotionally harassed by the men they loved. These results were widely covered by news programs and magazines and were even used as a cover story in *Time* (Wallis, 1987). Although Hite's book became a best seller, largely because of the news coverage that her results received, researchers questioned her findings. It was discovered that the survey respondents came from one of two sources. Some surveys were mailed to women who were members of various women's organizations such as professional groups, political groups, and women's rights organizations. Other women were solicited through talk-show interviews given by Hite in which she publicized an address women could write to in order to request a copy of the survey. Both of these methods of gathering participants for a study should set off warning bells for you. In the first situation, women who are members of women's organizations are hardly representative of the average woman in the United States. The second situation represents a case of self-selection. Those who are interested in their relationships and who are possibly having problems in their relationships might be more likely to write for a copy of the survey and participate in it.

After beginning with a biased sample, Hite had a return rate of only 4.5%. That is, the 4,500 women who filled out the survey represented only 4.5% of those who received surveys. Hite sent out 100,000 surveys and received only 4,500 back. This percentage represents a very poor and unacceptable return rate. How does a low return rate further bias the results? Who is likely to take the time to return a long (127-question) survey with questions of a personal nature, often pertaining to problems in relationships with male partners? Most likely it would be women with strong opinions on the topic, possibly women who were having problems in their relationships and wanted to tell someone about them. Thus Hite's results were based on a specialized group of women, yet she attempted to generalize her results to all American women. The Hite survey has become a classic example of how a biased sample can lead to erroneous conclusions.

telephone survey A survey in which the questions are read to participants over the telephone.

Telephone Surveys. **Telephone surveys** involve telephoning participants and reading questions to them. Years ago surveying via telephone was problematic because only wealthier individuals had telephones. We eventually reached a point where 95% of the population had a landline telephone, and at that time, this method typically provided a representative sample. In fact, researchers did not even have to worry about those with unlisted numbers (typically individuals who are better off financially) because of a technique known as random-digit dialing (RDD) in which random numbers are dialed—RDD obviously included unlisted numbers.

However, with technological advances came problems for surveying via telephone. First, increased telemarketing led many people to use answering machines, caller ID, or call blocking as a way to screen and/or avoid unwanted calls. Moreover, people became more willing to say "no" to unwanted callers. Individual homes also began to have more than one phone line, which is problematic when attempting to generate a representative sample of respondents. In addition, many homes also had fax lines installed, which obviously would not be answered when RDD was used to call them. Finally, with the increase in use of cellular telephones, many people have begun to cancel their landline telephones in favor of cellular telephones. In 2003 almost 50% of U.S. citizens used cellular telephones and 3% substituted cellular telephones for landlines. However, by 2007 16% of U.S. citizens had substituted cellular telephones for landlines, and by 2011 31% of the United States had done so (Blumberg & Luke, 2011). This practice effectively means that a significant percentage of the U.S. population would be missed by RDD sampling. Consequently we have a situation in which the opposite of what was true 30 years ago is true now—mail surveys can now achieve a more representative sample than the typical telephone survey (Dillman, Smyth, & Christian, 2009).

Nevertheless, telephone surveys can help to alleviate one of the problems with mail surveys because respondents can ask that the questions be clarified. Moreover, the researchers can ask follow-up questions if needed in order to provide more reliable data.

On the other hand, telephone surveys do have other disadvantages than mail surveys. First, they are more time-consuming than a mail survey because the researchers must read each of the questions and record the responses. Second, they can be costly. The researchers must call the individuals themselves or pay others to do the calling. If the calls are long distance, then the cost is even greater. Third is the problem of interviewer bias. Finally, participants are more likely to give socially desirable responses over the phone than on a mail survey. A **socially desirable response** is a response that is given because participants believe it is deemed appropriate by society rather than because it truly reflects their own views or behaviors. For example, respondents may say that they attend church at least twice a month or read to their children several times a week because they believe these actions are what society expects of them, not because they actually perform them.

socially desirable response A response that is given because a respondent believes it is deemed appropriate by society.

Personal Interviews. A **personal interview** in which the questions are asked face-to-face may be conducted anywhere—at the individual's home, on the street, or in a shopping mall. We discussed this interview method earlier in the chapter as a type of qualitative method, and thus you are familiar with the general concepts behind this methodology. We discuss it again here as a quantitative method.

personal interview A survey in which the questions are asked face-to-face.

One advantage of personal interviews is that they allow the researcher to record not only verbal responses but also any facial or bodily expressions or movements such as grins, grimaces, or shrugs. These nonverbal responses may give the researcher greater insight into the respondent's true opinions and beliefs. A second advantage to personal interviews is that participants usually devote more time to answering the questions than they do in telephone surveys. As with telephone surveys, respondents can ask for question clarification.

Potential problems with personal interviews include many of those discussed in connection with telephone surveys: interviewer bias, socially desirable responses, and even greater time and expense than with telephone surveys. In addition, the lack of anonymity in a personal interview may affect the responses. Participants may not feel comfortable answering truthfully when someone is standing right there listening to them and writing down their responses. Finally, although personal interviews once generated response rates that were fairly high (typically around 80%, Dillman, 1978; Erdos, 1983), they no longer do so. This decreased response rate is due to several reasons. One obstacle is that more people live in gated communities or locked apartment buildings to which interviewers cannot gain access. A second barrier is that people are very hesitant to open their door to a stranger for any reason (Dillman, Smyth, & Christian, 2009). Thus we have reached a point where using the personal interview as a type of quantitative survey technique is somewhat rare.

In summary the three traditional survey methods offer different advantages and disadvantages, and because of changes in society and technological advances, researchers have found it necessary to rethink traditional views on what might be the best way to conduct a survey. In fact, the recommended approach now is multimodal, with the preferred modes being mail, e-mail/web-based, and telephone. This method is referred to as the total design method by Dillman, Smyth, and Christian (2009) and involves using multiple modes and multiple follow-up procedures. Using this method, respondents might be contacted via mail to let them know they can go online to complete a survey. They might be sent a postcard as a first reminder, an e-mail as a second reminder, and a telephone call as a third. If they do not answer the survey online after all of these reminders, they might be called and given the opportunity to respond to the survey via telephone; oftentimes the telephone survey might be automated rather than given by a live person. Using this multimodal approach with varying follow-up procedures will often lead to response rates between 75 to 85% (Dillman, Smyth, & Christian, 2009; Greene, Speizer, & Wiitala, 2007). This multimodal approach also means that survey methodologists must now be competent in multiple modes of surveying rather than specializing in only one mode.

Sampling Techniques

Another concern for researchers using the survey method is who will participate in the survey. For the results to be meaningful, the individuals who take the survey should be representative of the population under investigation. As discussed in Chapter 1, the population consists of all of the people about whom a study is meant to generalize, whereas the sample represents the subset of people from the population who actually participate in the study. In almost all cases, it isn't feasible to survey the entire population. Instead, we select a subgroup or sample from the population and give the survey to them. To draw any reliable and valid conclusions concerning the population, it is imperative that the sample be "like" the population—a **representative sample**. When the sample is representative of the population, we can be fairly confident that the results we find based on the sample also hold for the population. In other words, we can generalize from the sample to the population. There are two ways to sample individuals from a population: probability sampling and nonprobability sampling.

representative sample A sample that is like the population.

Probability Sampling. When researchers use **probability sampling**, each member of the population has a known probability of being selected to be part of the sample. We will discuss three types of probability sampling: random sampling, stratified random sampling, and cluster sampling.

probability sampling A sampling technique in which each member of the population has a known probability of being selected to be part of the sample.

random selection A method of generating a random sample in which each member of the population is equally likely to be chosen as part of the sample.

A random sample is achieved through **random selection**, in which each member of the population is equally likely to be chosen as part of the sample. Let's say we start with a population of 300 students enrolled in introductory psychology classes at a university. Assuming we want to select a random sample of 30 students, how should we go about it? We do not want to get all of the students by simply going to a 30-person section of introductory psychology because depending on the instructor and the time of day of the class, there could be biases in who registered for this section. For example, if it's an early morning class, it could represent students who like to get up early or those who registered for classes so late that nothing else was available. Thus, these students would not be representative of all students in introductory psychology.

Generating a random sample can be accomplished by using a table of random numbers, such as that provided in Appendix A (Table A.1). When using a random numbers table, the researcher chooses a starting place arbitrarily. After the starting point is determined, the researcher looks at the number—say, a 6—counts down six people in the population, and chooses the sixth person to be in the sample. The researcher continues in this manner by looking at the next number in the table, counting down through the population, and including the appropriately numbered person in the sample. For our sample, we would continue this process until we had selected a sample of 30 people. A random sample can be generated in other ways, for example, by computer or by pulling names randomly out of a hat. The point is that in random sampling, each member of the population is equally likely to be chosen as part of the sample.

Sometimes a population is made up of members of different groups or categories. For example, both men and women make up the 300 students enrolled in introductory psychology but maybe not in equal proportions. To draw conclusions about the population of introductory psychology students based on our sample, our sample must be representative of the strata within the population. For example, if the population consists of 70% women and 30% men, then we need to ensure that the sample is similar on this dimension.

stratified random sample A sampling technique designed to ensure that subgroups or strata are fairly represented.

One means of attaining such a sample is stratified random sampling. A **stratified random sample** allows you to take into account the different subgroups of people in the population and helps guarantee that the sample accurately represents the population on specific characteristics. We begin by dividing the population into subsamples or strata. In our example, the strata would be based on gender—men and women. We would then randomly select 70% of our sample from the female stratum and 30% of our sample from the male stratum. In this manner, we ensure that the characteristic of gender in the sample is representative of the population.

cluster sampling A sampling technique in which clusters of participants that represent the population are used.

Often the population is too large for random sampling of any sort. In these cases, it is common to use cluster sampling. As the name implies, **cluster sampling** involves using participants who are already part of a group or "cluster." For example, if you were interested in surveying students at a large university where it might not be possible to use true random sampling, you might sample from classes that are required of all students at the university, such as English composition. If the classes are required of all students, they should contain a good mix of students, and if you use several classes, the sample should represent the population.

nonprobability sampling A sampling technique in which the individual members of the population do not have an equal or known likelihood of being selected to be a member of the sample.

Nonprobability Sampling. **Nonprobability sampling** is used when the individual members of the population do not have an equal or known likelihood of being selected to be a member of the sample. Nonprobability sampling is typically used because it tends to be less expensive, and it's easier to generate samples using this technique. We'll discuss two types of nonprobability sampling: convenience sampling and quota sampling.

convenience sampling A sampling technique in which participants are obtained wherever they can be found and typically wherever is convenient for the researcher.

Convenience sampling involves getting participants wherever you can find them and typically wherever is convenient. This is sometimes referred to as *haphazard sampling*. For example, if you wanted a sample of 100 college students, you could stand outside of the library and ask people who pass by to participate, or you could ask students in some of your classes to participate. This might sound somewhat similar to cluster sampling; however, there is a difference. With cluster sampling, we try to identify clusters that are representative of the population. This is not the case with convenience sampling. We simply take whomever is convenient as a participant in the study.

A second type of nonprobability sampling is quota sampling. Quota sampling is to nonprobability sampling what stratified random sampling is

quota sampling A sampling technique that involves ensuring that the sample is like the population on certain characteristics but uses convenience sampling to obtain the participants.

to probability sampling. In other words, **quota sampling** involves ensuring that the sample is like the population on certain characteristics. However, even though we try to ensure similarity with the population on certain characteristics, we do not sample from the population randomly—we simply take participants wherever we find them, through whatever means is convenient. Thus, this method is slightly better than convenience sampling, but there is still not much effort devoted to creating a sample that is truly representative of the population nor one in which all members of the population have a known chance of being selected for the sample.

Survey Methods — IN REVIEW

Types of Survey Method	Mail survey	A written survey that is self-administered
	Telephone survey	A survey conducted by telephone in which the questions are read to the respondents
	Personal interview	A face-to-face interview of the respondent
Question Types	Open-ended questions	Questions for which respondents formulate their own responses
	Closed-ended questions	Questions on which respondents must choose from a limited number of alternatives
	Partially open-ended questions	Closed-ended questions with an open-ended "Other" option
	Rating scales (Likert scale)	Questions on which respondents must provide a rating on a numerical scale
Sampling Techniques	Random sampling	A sampling technique in which each member of the population is equally likely to be chosen as part of the sample
	Stratified random sampling	A sampling technique intended to guarantee that the sample represents specific subgroups or strata
	Cluster sampling	A sampling technique in which clusters of participants that represent the population are identified and included in the sample
	Convenience sampling	A sampling technique that involves getting participants wherever you can find them and typically wherever is convenient
	Quota sampling	A sampling technique that involves getting participants wherever you can find them and typically wherever is convenient; however, you ensure that the sample is like the population on certain characteristics
Concerns	Sampling bias	
	Interviewer bias	
	Socially desirable responses	
	Return rate	
	Expense	

CRITICAL THINKING CHECK 4.2

1. With which survey method(s) is interviewer bias of greatest concern?
2. Shere Hite had 4,500 surveys returned to her. This is a large sample (something desirable), so what was the problem with using all of the surveys returned?
3. How is stratified random sampling different from random sampling?
4. What are the problems with the following survey questions?
   a. Do you agree that school systems should be given more money for computers and recreational activities?
   b. Do you favor eliminating the wasteful excesses in the city budget?
   c. Most people feel that teachers are underpaid. Do you agree?

Summary

In this chapter, we discussed various ways of conducting a descriptive study. The three methods presented were the observational method (naturalistic versus laboratory), qualitative methods (case study, archival, interviews, field studies, or action research), and the survey method (mail, telephone, or personal interview). Several advantages and disadvantages of each method were discussed. For observational methods the important issues are reactivity, experimenter expectancies, time, cost, control, and flexibility. The case study method is limited because it describes only one or a few people and is very subjective in nature, but it is often a good means of beginning a research project. The archival method is limited by the fact that the data already exist and were collected by someone other than the researcher. The interview method may be limited by the quality of the interviewer, whereas field research is limited by the ability of the researcher to blend in and not affect the behaviors of those being observed. Action research is a very applied type of research that can be limited because the very people who are conducting the research are also the participants in the research. The various survey methods may have problems of biased samples, poor return rates, interviewer biases, socially desirable responses, and expense. Various methods of sampling participants were discussed, along with how best to write a survey and arrange the questions on the survey.

Keep in mind that all of the methods presented here are descriptive in nature. They allow researchers to describe what has been observed in a group of people or animals, but they do not allow you to make accurate predictions or determine cause-and-effect relationships. In the next chapter, we'll discuss descriptive statistics—statistics that can be used to summarize the data collected in a study. In later chapters, we'll address methods that allow you to do more than simply describe; we'll investigate methods that allow you to make predictions and assess causality.

KEY TERMS

ecological validity
undisguised observation
nonparticipant observation
participant observation
disguised observation
expectancy effects
narrative records
checklist
static item
action item
qualitative research
archival method
interview
focus group interview
field studies
action research
open-ended questions
closed-ended questions
partially open-ended questions
rating scale
Likert rating scale
loaded question
leading question
double-barreled question
response bias
demographic questions
mail survey
sampling bias
interviewer bias
telephone survey
socially desirable response
personal interview
representative sample
probability sampling
random selection
stratified random sampling
cluster sampling
nonprobability sampling
convenience sampling
quota sampling

CHAPTER EXERCISES

(Answers to odd-numbered exercises appear in Appendix C.)

1. Imagine that you want to study cell phone use by drivers. You decide to conduct an observational study of drivers by making observations at three locations—a busy intersection, an entrance/exit to a shopping mall parking lot, and a residential intersection. You are interested in the number of people who use cell phones while driving. How would you recommend conducting this study? How would you recommend collecting the data? What concerns do you need to take into consideration?
2. Explain the difference between participant and nonparticipant observation and disguised and undisguised observation.
3. How does using a narrative record differ from using a checklist?
4. Explain how qualitative research differs from quantitative research.
5. Explain the archival method.
6. Explain the difference between an interview and a focus group interview.
7. Why is action research considered an applied form of research?
8. A student at your school wants to survey students regarding their credit card use. She decides to conduct the survey at the student center during lunch hour by interviewing every fifth person leaving the student center. What type of survey would you recommend she use? What type of sampling technique is being used? Can you identify a better way of sampling the student body?
9. Imagine that the following questions represent some of those from the survey described in Exercise 8. Can you identify any problems with these questions?
   a. Do you believe that capitalist bankers should charge such high interest rates on credit card balances?
   b. How much did you charge on your credit cards last month? $0–$400; $500–$900; $1,000–$1,400; $1,500–$1,900; $2,000 or more.
   c. Most Americans believe that a credit card is a necessity—do you agree?

CRITICAL THINKING CHECK ANSWERS

4.1

1. Naturalistic observation has more flexibility because researchers are free to observe any behavior they may find interesting. Laboratory observation has less flexibility because the behaviors to be observed are usually determined before the study begins. It is thus difficult to change what is being observed after the study has begun. Because naturalistic observation affords greater flexibility, it also has less control; the researcher does not control what happens during the study. Laboratory observation, having less flexibility, also has more control; the researcher determines more of the research situation.
2. If reactivity were your greatest concern, you might try using disguised observation. In addition, you might opt for a more naturalistic setting.
3. Data reduction is of greater concern when using narrative records because the narrative records must be interpreted and reduced to a quantitative form, using multiple individuals to establish interrater reliability. Checklists do not involve interpretation or data reduction because the individual collecting the data simply records whether a behavior is present or how often a behavior occurs.

4.2

1. Interviewer bias is of greatest concern with personal interviews because the interviewer is physically with the respondent. It is also of some concern with telephone interviews. However, because the telephone interviewer is not actually with the respondent, it isn't as great a concern as it is with personal interviews.
2. The problem with using all 4,500 returned surveys was that Hite sent out 100,000 surveys. Thus, 4,500 represented a very small return rate (4.5%). If the 100,000 individuals who were sent surveys were a representative sample, it is doubtful that the 4,500 who returned them were representative of the population.
3. Stratified random sampling involves randomly selecting individuals from strata or groups. Using stratified random sampling ensures that subgroups, or strata, are fairly represented. This does not always happen when simple random sampling is used.
4. a. This is a double-barreled question. It should be divided into two questions, one pertaining to money for computers and one pertaining to money for recreational activities.
   b. This is a loaded question. The phrase *wasteful excesses* loads the question emotionally.
   c. This is a leading question. Using the phrase *Most people feel* sways the respondent.

WEB RESOURCES

The book-specific website at CengageBrain .com offers students a variety of study tools and useful resources such as glossaries and flashcards.

Chapter 4 ■ Study Guide

CHAPTER 4 SUMMARY AND REVIEW: DESCRIPTIVE METHODS

In this chapter we discussed various ways of conducting a descriptive study. The methods presented were the observational method (naturalistic versus laboratory), various qualitative methods (i.e., the case study method, the archival method, the interview method, and the field study method), and the survey method (mail, telephone, or personal interview). Several advantages and disadvantages of each method were discussed. For observational methods, important issues include reactivity, experimenter expectancies, time, cost, control, and flexibility. The case study method is limited because it describes only one or a few people and is very subjective in nature, but it is often a good means of beginning a research project. The archival method is limited by the fact that the data already exist and were collected by someone other than the researcher. The interview method and the field study method can be limited by the quality of the interviewer/observer. The various survey methods may have problems of biased samples, poor return rates, interviewer biases, socially desirable responses, and expense. We discussed various methods of sampling participants for surveys along with how best to write a survey and arrange the questions on the survey.

Keep in mind that all of the methods presented here are descriptive in nature. They allow researchers to describe what has been observed in a group of people or otheranimals, but they do not allow us to make accurate predictions or to determine cause-and-effect relationships. In later sections we address methods that allow us to do more than simply describe; we will discuss methods that allow us to make predictions and assess causality.

CHAPTER 4 REVIEW EXERCISES

(Answers to exercises appear in Appendix C.)

FILL-IN SELF-TEST

Answer the following questions. If you have trouble answering any of the questions, restudy the relevant material before going on to the multiple-choice self-test.

1. Observational studies in which the researcher does not participate in the situation in which the research participants are involved utilize ________ observation.
2. The extent to which an experimental situation can be generalized to natural settings and behaviors is known as ________.
3. Observational studies in which the participants are unaware that the researcher is observing their behavior utilize ________ observation.
4. ________ are full narrative descriptions of a participant's behavior.
5. A ________ item is a type of item used on a tally sheet on which attributes that will not change are recorded.
6. ________ involves a tendency for one group to be overrepresented in a study.
7. When participants give a response that they believe is deemed appropriate by society, they are giving a ________.
8. Using ________ involves generating a random sample in which each member of the population is equally likely to be chosen as part of the sample.
9. ________ is a sampling technique designed to ensure that subgroups are fairly represented.
10. Questions for which participants choose from a limited number of alternatives are known as ________.
11. A numerical scale on which survey respondents indicate the direction and strength of their responses is a ________.
12. A question that sways a respondent to answer in a desired manner is a ________.

MULTIPLE-CHOICE SELF-TEST

Select the single best answer for each of the following questions. If you have trouble answering any of the questions, restudy the relevant material.

1. ______ observation has greater ______ validity than ______ observation.
   a. Laboratory; construct; naturalistic
   b. Laboratory; ecological; naturalistic
   c. Naturalistic; ecological; laboratory
   d. Naturalistic; content; laboratory
2. Which of the following is true?
   a. Naturalistic observation involves observing humans or animals behaving in their natural setting.
   b. Naturalistic observation decreases the ecological validity of a study.
   c. Laboratory observation increases the ecological validity of a study.
   d. All of the above.
3. ______ is (are) a greater concern when using ______ observation because the observations are made in a (an) ______ manner.
   a. Reactivity; undisguised; obtrusive
   b. Expectancy effects; disguised; unobtrusive
   c. Reactivity; disguised; unobtrusive
   d. Expectancy effects; disguised; obtrusive
4. Naturalistic observation is to ______ and laboratory observation is to ______.
   a. more control; more flexibility
   b. more control; less control
   c. more flexibility; more control
   d. more flexibility; less control
5. Checklists are to ______ and narrative records are to ______.
   a. more subjective; less subjective
   b. less subjective; more subjective
   c. less objective; more objective
   d. both b and c
6. A tally sheet on which attributes that will not change are recorded utilizes ______ items.
   a. static
   b. action
   c. narrative
   d. nonnarrative
7. Personal interview surveys have the concern of ______ but have the advantage of ______.
   a. low return rate; eliminating interviewer bias
   b. interviewer bias; question clarification
   c. sampling bias; eliminating interviewer bias
   d. both b and c
8. Rich is conducting a survey of student opinion of the dining hall at his university. Rich decided to conduct his survey by using every tenth name on the registrar's alphabetical list of all students at his school. The type of sampling technique that Rich is using is:
   a. representative cluster sampling.
   b. cluster sampling.
   c. stratified random sampling.
   d. random sampling.
9. Imagine that you wanted to assess student opinion of the dining hall by surveying a subgroup of 100 students at your school. In this situation, the subgroup of students represents the ______, and all of the students at your school represent the ______.
   a. sample; random sample
   b. population; sample
   c. sample; population
   d. cluster sample; sample
10. A question including nonneutral or emotionally laden terms is a ______ question.
    a. loaded
    b. leading
    c. double-barreled
    d. open-ended
11. An open-ended question is to a ______ question as a closed-ended question is to a ______ question.
    a. multiple choice; short answer
    b. short answer; multiple choice
    c. short answer; essay
    d. multiple choice; essay
12. Consider the following survey question: "*Most Americans consider a computer to be a necessity. Do you agree?*" This is an example of a ______ question.
    a. leading
    b. loaded
    c. rating scale
    d. double-barreled

CHAPTER

5 Data Organization and Descriptive Statistics

Learning Objectives

- Organize data in either a frequency distribution or a class interval frequency distribution.
- Graph data in either a bar graph, a histogram, or a frequency polygon.
- Know how to differentiate measures of central tendency.
- Know how to calculate the mean, median, and mode.
- Know how to differentiate measures of variation.
- Know how to calculate the range, average deviation, and standard deviation.
- Explain the difference between a normal distribution and a skewed distribution.
- Explain the difference between a positively skewed distribution and a negatively skewed distribution.
- Know how to differentiate the types of kurtosis.
- Describe what a *z*-score is, and know how to calculate it.
- Understand how to use the area under the normal curve to determine proportions and percentile ranks.

In this chapter, we'll begin to discuss what to do with the observations made in the course of a study—namely, how to describe the data set through the use of descriptive statistics. First, we'll consider ways of organizing the data by taking the large number of observations made during a study and presenting them in a manner that is easier to read and understand. Then we'll discuss some simple descriptive statistics. These statistics allow us to do some "number crunching" to condense a large number of observations into a summary statistic or set of statistics. The concepts and statistics described in this chapter can be used to draw conclusions from data collected through descriptive, predictive, or explanatory methods. They do not come close to covering all that can be done with data gathered from a study. They do, however, provide a place to start.

TABLE 5.1 Exam Scores for 30 Students

56	74
69	70
78	90
80	74
47	59
85	86
82	92
74	60
95	63
65	45
54	94
60	93
87	82
76	77
75	78

Organizing Data

Two methods of organizing data are frequency distributions and graphs.

Frequency Distributions

To illustrate the processes of organizing and describing data, let's use the data set presented in Table 5.1. These data represent the scores of 30 students on an introductory psychology exam. One reason for organizing data and using statistics is to draw meaningful conclusions. The list of exam scores in Table 5.1 is simply that—a list in no particular order. As shown here, the data are not especially meaningful. One of the first steps in organizing these data might be to rearrange them from highest to lowest or from lowest to highest.

frequency distribution A table in which all of the scores are listed along with the frequency with which each occurs.

After the scores are ordered (see Table 5.2), you can condense the data into a **frequency distribution**—a table in which all of the scores are listed along with the frequency with which each occurs. You can also show the relative frequency, which is the proportion of the total observations included in each score. When a relative frequency is multiplied by 100, it is read as a percentage. For example, a relative frequency of .033 would mean that 3.3% of the sample received that score. A frequency distribution and a relative frequency distribution of the exam data are presented in Table 5.3.

TABLE 5.2 Exam Scores Ordered from Lowest to Highest

45	76
47	77
54	78
56	78
59	80
60	82
60	82
63	85
65	86
69	87
70	90
74	92
74	93
74	94
75	95

TABLE 5.3 Frequency and Relative Frequency Distributions of Exam Data

SCORE	*f* (FREQUENCY)	*rf* (RELATIVE FREQUENCY)
45	1	.033
47	1	.033
54	1	.033
56	1	.033
59	1	.033
60	2	.067
63	1	.033
65	1	.033
69	1	.033
70	1	.033
74	3	.100
75	1	.033
76	1	.033
77	1	.033
78	2	.067
80	1	.033
82	2	.067
85	1	.033
86	1	.033
87	1	.033
90	1	.033
92	1	.033
93	1	.033
94	1	.033
95	1	.033
	$N = 30$	1.00

The frequency distribution is a way of presenting data that makes the pattern of the data easier to see. You can make the data set even easier to read (especially desirable with large data sets) by grouping the scores and creating a class interval frequency distribution. In a **class interval frequency distribution**, individual scores are combined into categories, or intervals, and then listed along with the frequency of scores in each interval. In the exam score example, the scores range from 45 to 95—a 50-point range. A rule of thumb when creating class intervals is to have between 10 and 20 categories (Hinkle, Wiersma, & Jurs, 1988). A quick method of calculating what the width of the interval should be is to subtract the lowest score from the highest score and then divide the result by the number of intervals you want (Schweigert, 1994). If we want 10 intervals in our example, we proceed as follows:

class interval frequency distribution A table in which the scores are grouped into intervals and listed along with the frequency of scores in each interval.

$$\frac{95 - 45}{10} = \frac{50}{10} = 5$$

Table 5.4 is the frequency distribution using class intervals with a width of 5. Notice how much more compact the data appear when presented in a class interval frequency distribution. Although such distributions have the advantage of reducing the number of categories, they have the disadvantage of not providing as much information as a regular frequency distribution. For example, although we can see from the class interval frequency distribution that five people scored between 75 and 79, we do not know their exact scores within the interval.

TABLE 5.4 A Class Interval Distribution of the Exam Data

CLASS INTERVAL	*f*	*rf*
45–49	2	.067
50–54	1	.033
55–59	2	.067
60–64	3	.100
65–69	2	.067
70–74	4	.133
75–79	5	.166
80–84	3	.100
85–89	3	.100
90–94	4	.133
95–99	1	.033
	$N = 30$	1.00

Graphs

Frequency distributions provide valuable information, but sometimes a picture is of greater value. Several types of pictorial representations can be used to represent data. The choice depends on the type of data collected and what the researcher hopes to emphasize or illustrate. The most common graphs used by psychologists are bar graphs, histograms, and frequency polygons (line graphs). Graphs typically have two coordinate axes: the x-axis (the horizontal axis) and the y-axis (the vertical axis). Most commonly, the y-axis is shorter than the x-axis, typically 60 to 75% of the length of the x-axis.

qualitative variable A categorical variable for which each value represents a discrete category.

bar graph A graphical representation of a frequency distribution in which vertical bars are centered above each category along the x-axis and are separated from each other by a space, indicating that the levels of the variable represent distinct, unrelated categories.

quantitative variable A variable for which the scores represent a change in quantity.

histogram A graphical representation of a frequency distribution in which vertical bars centered above scores on the x-axis touch each other to indicate that the scores on the variable represent related, increasing values.

Bar Graphs and Histograms. Bar graphs and histograms are frequently confused. If the data collected are on a nominal scale or if the variable is a **qualitative variable** (a categorical variable for which each value represents a discrete category), then a bar graph is most appropriate. A **bar graph** is a graphical representation of a frequency distribution in which vertical bars are centered above each category along the x-axis and are separated from each other by a space, indicating that the levels of the variable represent distinct, unrelated categories. If the variable is a **quantitative variable** (the scores represent a change in quantity) or if the data collected are ordinal, interval, or ratio in scale, then a histogram can be used.

A **histogram** is also a graphical representation of a frequency distribution in which vertical bars are centered above scores on the x-axis; however, in a histogram, the bars touch each other to indicate that the scores on the variable represent related, increasing values. In both bar graph and histogram, the height of each bar indicates the frequency for that level of the variable on the x-axis. The spaces between the bars on the bar graph indicate not only the qualitative differences among the categories but also that the order of the values of the variable on the x-axis is arbitrary. In other words, the categories on the x-axis in a bar graph can be placed in any order. The fact that the bars are contiguous in a histogram indicates not only the increasing quantity of the variable but also that the values of the variable have a definite order that cannot be changed.

A bar graph is illustrated in Figure 5.1. For a hypothetical distribution, the frequencies of individuals who affiliate with various political parties are indicated. Notice that the different political parties are listed on the x-axis, whereas frequency is recorded on the y-axis. Although the political parties are presented in a certain order, this order could be rearranged because the variable is qualitative.

Figure 5.2 illustrates a histogram. In this figure, the frequencies of intelligence test scores from a hypothetical distribution are indicated. A histogram is appropriate because the IQ score variable is quantitative. The values of the variable have a specific order that cannot be rearranged.

frequency polygon A line graph of the frequencies of individual scores.

Frequency Polygons (Line Graphs). You can also depict the data in a histogram as a **frequency polygon**—a line graph of the frequencies of individual scores or

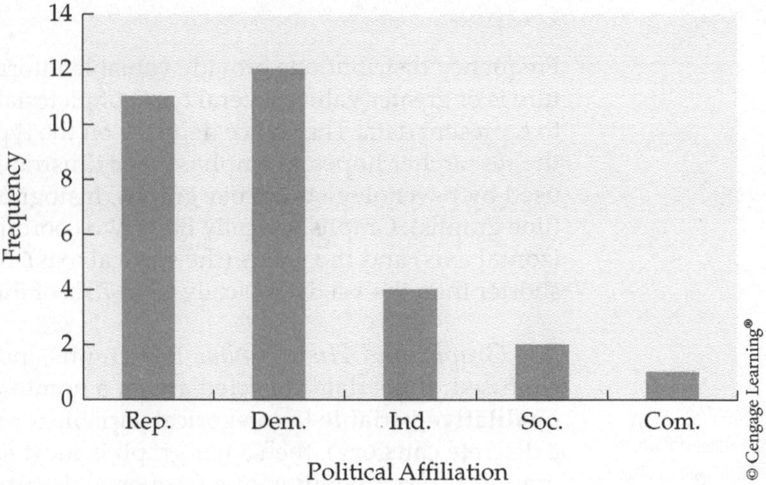

FIGURE 5.1 Bar graph representing political affiliation for a distribution of 30 individuals

intervals. Again, scores (or intervals) are shown on the *x*-axis and frequencies on the *y*-axis. After all the frequencies are plotted, the data points are connected. You can see the frequency polygon for the intelligence score data in Figure 5.3. Frequency polygons are appropriate when the variable is quantitative, or the data are ordinal, interval, or ratio. In this respect, frequency polygons are similar to histograms. Frequency polygons are especially useful for continuous data (such as age, weight, or time), in which it is theoretically possible for values to fall anywhere along the continuum. For example, an individual may weigh 120.5 pounds or be 35.5 years old. Histograms are more appropriate when the data are discrete (measured in whole units)—for example, number of college classes taken or number of siblings.

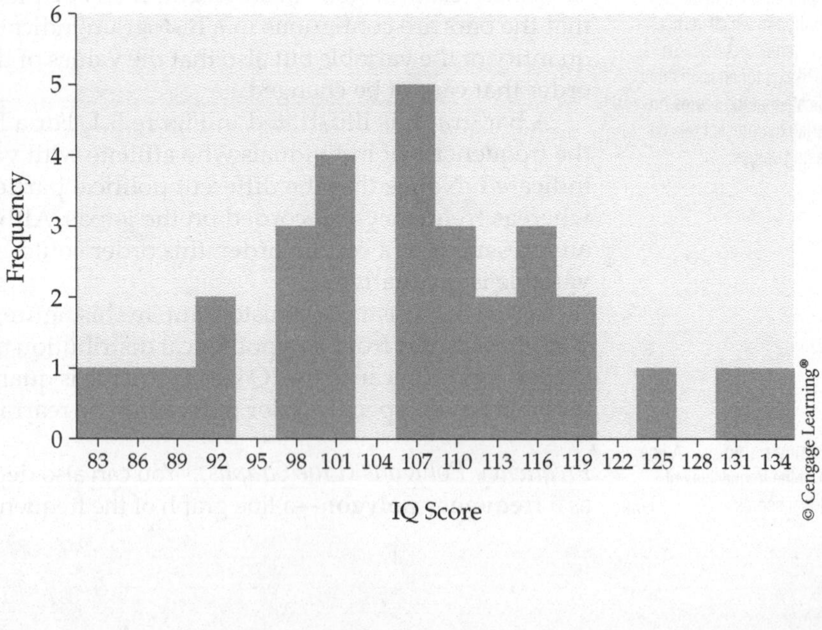

FIGURE 5.2 Histogram representing IQ score data for 30 individuals

FIGURE 5.3 Frequency polygon of IQ score data for 30 individuals

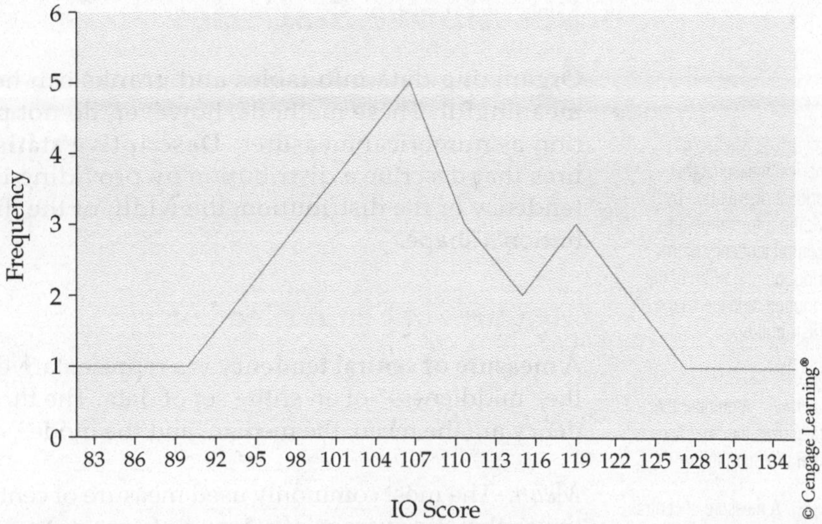

Data Organization — IN REVIEW

TYPES OF ORGANIZATIONAL TOOLS

	FREQUENCY DISTRIBUTION	BAR GRAPH	HISTOGRAM	FREQUENCY POLYGON
Description	A list of all scores occurring in the distribution along with the frequency of each	A pictorial graph with bars representing the frequency of occurrence of items for qualitative variables	A pictorial graph with bars representing the frequency of occurrence of items for quantitative variables	A line graph representing the frequency of occurrence of items for quantitative variables
Use with	Nominal, ordinal, interval, or ratio data	Nominal data	Typically ordinal, interval, or ratio data; most appropriate for discrete data	Typically ordinal, interval, or ratio data; most appropriate for continuous data

CRITICAL THINKING CHECK 5.1

1. What do you think might be the advantage of a graphical representation of data over a frequency distribution?
2. A researcher observes driving behavior on a roadway, noting the gender of the drivers, the types of vehicle driven, and the speeds at which they are traveling. The researcher wants to organize the data in graphs but cannot remember when to use bar graphs, histograms, or frequency polygons. Which type of graph should be used to describe each variable?

Descriptive Statistics

Organizing data into tables and graphs can help make a data set more meaningful. These methods, however, do not provide as much information as numerical measures. **Descriptive statistics** are numerical measures that describe a distribution by providing information on the central tendency of the distribution, the width of the distribution, and the distribution's shape.

descriptive statistics Numerical measures that describe a distribution by providing information on the central tendency of the distribution, the width of the distribution, and the shape of the distribution.

Measures of Central Tendency

A **measure of central tendency** is a representative number that characterizes the "middleness" of an entire set of data. The three measures of central tendency are the mean, the median, and the mode.

measure of central tendency A number that characterizes the "middleness" of an entire distribution.

Mean. The most commonly used measure of central tendency is the **mean**—the arithmetic average of a group of scores. You are probably familiar with this idea. We can calculate the mean for our distribution of exam scores by adding all of the scores together and dividing the sum by the total number of scores. Mathematically, this is

mean A measure of central tendency; the arithmetic average of a distribution.

$$\mu = \frac{\Sigma X}{N}$$

where

μ (pronounced "mu") represents the symbol for the population mean;
Σ represents the symbol for "the sum of";
X represents the individual scores; and
N represents the number of scores in the distribution.

To calculate the mean, we sum all of the *X*s, or scores, and divide by the total number of scores in the distribution (N). You may have also seen this formula represented as

$$\overline{X} = \frac{\Sigma X}{N}$$

This is the formula for calculating a sample mean, where $\overline{X}$ represents the sample mean, and N represents the number of scores in the sample.

We can use either formula (they are the same mathematically) to calculate the mean for the distribution of exam scores. These scores are presented again in Table 5.5, along with a column showing the frequency (f) and another column showing the frequency of the score multiplied by the score (*f times X or fX*). The sum of all the values in the fX column is the sum of all the individual scores (ΣX). Using this sum in the formula for the mean, we have

TABLE 5.5 Frequency Distribution of Exam Scores, Including an *fX* Column

X	*f*	*fx*
45	1	45
47	1	47
54	1	54
56	1	56
59	1	59
60	2	120
63	1	63
65	1	65
69	1	69
70	1	70
74	3	222
75	1	75
76	1	76
77	1	77
78	2	156
80	1	80
82	2	164
85	1	85
86	1	86
87	1	87
90	1	90
92	1	92
93	1	93
94	1	94
95	1	95
	$N = 30$	$\Sigma X = 2,220$

$$\mu = \frac{\Sigma X}{N} = \frac{2,200}{30} = 74.00$$

You can also calculate the mean using Excel, SPSS, or the Stats function on most calculators. As an example, the procedure for calculating the mean using each of these tools is presented in the Statistical Software Resources section at the end of this chapter. The use of the mean is constrained by the nature of the data: The mean is appropriate for interval and ratio data but not for ordinal or nominal data.

TABLE 5.6 Yearly Salaries for 25 Employees

SALARY	FREQUENCY	*fx*
$ 15,000	1	15,000
20,000	2	40,000
22,000	1	22,000
23,000	2	46,000
25,000	5	125,000
27,000	2	54,000
30,000	3	90,000
32,000	1	32,000
35,000	2	70,000
38,000	1	38,000
39,000	1	39,000
40,000	1	40,000
42,000	1	42,000
45,000	1	45,000
1,800,000	1	1,800,000
	$N = 25$	$\Sigma X = 2,498,000$

Median. Another measure of central tendency, the median, is used in situations in which the mean might not be representative of a distribution. Let's use a different distribution of scores to demonstrate when it is appropriate to use the median rather than the mean. Imagine that you are considering taking a job with a small computer company. When you interview for the position, the owner of the company informs you that the mean salary for employees at the company is approximately $100,000 and that the company has 25 employees. Most people would view this as good news. Having learned in a statistics class that the mean might be influenced by extreme scores, however, you ask to see the distribution of the 25 salaries. The distribution is shown in Table 5.6. The calculation of the mean for this distribution is

$$\frac{\Sigma X}{N} = \frac{2,498,000}{25} = 99,920$$

Notice that, as claimed, the mean salary of company employees is very close to $100,000. Notice also, however, that the mean in this case is not very representative of central tendency, or "middleness." The mean is thrown off center or inflated by one extreme score of $1,800,000 (the salary of the company's owner, needless to say). This extremely high salary pulls the mean toward it and thus increases or inflates the mean. Thus, in distributions that have one or a few extreme scores (either high or low), the mean is not a good indicator of central tendency. In such cases, a better measure of central tendency is the median.

median A measure of central tendency; the middle score in a distribution after the scores have been arranged from highest to lowest or lowest to highest.

The **median** is the middle score in a distribution after the scores have been arranged from highest to lowest or lowest to highest. The distribution of salaries in Table 5.6 is already ordered from lowest to highest. To determine the median, we simply have to find the middle score. In this situation, with 25 scores, that is the 13th score. You can see that the median of the distribution is a salary of $27,000, which is far more representative of the central tendency for this distribution of salaries.

Why is the median not as influenced as the mean by extreme scores? Think about the calculation of each of these measures. When calculating the mean, we must add in the atypical income of $1,800,000, thus distorting the calculation. When determining the median, however, we do not consider the size of the $1,800,000 income; it is only a score at one end of the distribution whose numerical value does not have to be considered to locate the middle score in the distribution. The point to remember is that the median is not affected by extreme scores in a distribution because it is only a positional value. The mean is affected by extreme scores because its value is determined by a calculation that has to include the extreme values.

In the salary example, the distribution has an odd number of scores ($N = 25$). Thus, the median is an actual score in the distribution (the 13th score). In distributions that have an even number of observations, the median is calculated by averaging the two middle scores. In other words, we determine the middle point between the two middle scores. Look back at the distribution of exam scores in Table 5.5. This distribution has 30 scores. The median is the average of the 15th and 16th scores (the two middle scores). Thus, the median is 75.5—not an actual score in the distribution, but the middle point nonetheless. Notice that in this distribution, the median (75.5) is very close to the mean (74.00). They are so similar because this distribution contains no extreme scores; both the mean and the median are representative of the central tendency of the distribution.

Like the mean, the median can be used with ratio and interval data and is inappropriate for use with nominal data, but unlike the mean, the median can be used with most ordinal data. In other words, it is appropriate to report the median for a distribution of ranked scores.

mode A measure of central tendency; the score in a distribution that occurs with the greatest frequency.

Mode. The third measure of central tendency is the **mode**—the score in a distribution that occurs with the greatest frequency. In the distribution of exam scores, the mode is 74 (similar to the mean and median). In the distribution of salaries, the mode is $25,000 (similar to the median but not the mean). In some distributions, all scores occur with equal frequency; such a distribution has no mode. In other distributions, several scores occur with equal frequency. Thus, a distribution may have two modes (bimodal), three modes (trimodal), or even more. The mode is the only indicator of central tendency that can be used with nominal data. Although it can also be used with ordinal, interval, or ratio data, the mean and median are more reliable indicators of the central tendency of a distribution, and the mode is seldom used.

Measures of Central Tendency — IN REVIEW

TYPES OF CENTRAL TENDENCY MEASURES

	MEAN	MEDIAN	MODE
Definition	The arithmetic average	The middle score in a distribution of scores organized from highest to lowest or lowest to highest	The score occurring with greatest frequency
Use with	Interval and ratio data	Ordinal, interval, and ratio data	Nominal, ordinal, interval, or ratio data
Cautions	Not for use with distributions with a few extreme scores		Not a reliable measure of central tendency

CRITICAL THINKING CHECK 5.2

1. In the example described in Critical Thinking Check 5.1, a researcher collected data on drivers' gender, type of vehicle, and speed of travel. What is an appropriate measure of central tendency to calculate for each type of data?
2. If one driver was traveling at 100 mph (25 mph faster than anyone else), which measure of central tendency would you recommend against using?

Measures of Variation

measure of variation A number that indicates the degree to which scores are either clustered or spread out in a distribution.

A measure of central tendency provides information about the "middleness" of a distribution of scores but not about the width or spread of the distribution. To assess the width of a distribution, we need a measure of variation or dispersion. A **measure of variation** indicates the degree to which scores are either clustered or spread out in a distribution. As an illustration, consider the two very small distributions of exam scores shown in Table 5.7. Notice that the mean is the same for both distributions. If these data represented two very small classes of students, reporting that the two classes had the same mean on the exam might lead you to conclude that the classes performed essentially the same. Notice, however, how different the distributions are. Providing a measure of variation along with a measure of central tendency conveys the information that even though the distributions have the same mean, their spreads are very different.

TABLE 5.7 Two Distributions of Exam Scores

CLASS 1	CLASS 2
0	45
50	50
100	55
$\Sigma X = 150$	$\Sigma X = 150$
$\mu = 50$	$\mu = 50$

We will discuss three measures of variation: the range, the average deviation, and the standard deviation. The range can be used with ordinal, interval, or ratio data; however, the standard deviation and average deviation are appropriate for only interval and ratio data.

range A measure of variation; the difference between the lowest and the highest scores in a distribution.

Range. The simplest measure of variation is the **range**—the difference between the lowest and the highest scores in a distribution. The range is usually reported with the mean of the distribution. To find the range, we simply subtract the lowest score from the highest score. In our hypothetical distributions of exam scores in Table 5.7, the range for Class 1 is 100 points, whereas the range for Class 2 is 10 points. Thus, the range provides some information concerning the difference in the spreads of the distributions. In this simple measure of variation, however, only the highest and lowest scores enter the calculation, and all other scores are ignored. For example, in the distribution of 30 exam scores in Table 5.5, only 2 of the 30 scores are used in calculating the range (95 − 45 = 50). Thus, the range is easily distorted by one unusually high or low score in a distribution.

Average Deviation and Standard Deviation. More sophisticated measures of variation use all of the scores in the distribution in their calculation. The most commonly used measure of variation is the *standard deviation.* Most people have heard this term before and may even have calculated a standard deviation if they have taken a statistics class. However, many people who know how to calculate a standard deviation do not really appreciate the information it provides.

To begin, let's think about what the phrase *standard deviation* means. Other words that might be substituted for the word *standard* include *average, normal,* and *usual*. The word *deviation* means to *diverge, move away from,* or *digress.* Putting these terms together, we see that the standard deviation means the average movement away from something. But what? It is the average movement away from the middle of the distribution, or the mean.

standard deviation A measure of variation; the average difference between the scores in the distribution and the mean or central point of the distribution, or, more precisely, the square root of the average squared deviation from the mean.

The **standard deviation**, then, is the average distance of all the scores in the distribution from the mean or central point of the distribution—or, as you'll see shortly, the square root of the average squared deviation from the mean. Think about how we would calculate the average distance of all the scores from the mean of the distribution. First, we would have to determine how far each score is from the mean; this is the deviation, or difference, score. Then, we would have to average these scores. This is the basic idea behind calculating the standard deviation.

The data in Table 5.5 are presented again in Table 5.8. Let's use these data to calculate the average distance from the mean. We begin with a calculation that is slightly simpler than the standard deviation, known as the *average deviation.* The **average deviation** is essentially what the name implies—the average distance of all the scores from the mean of the distribution. Referring to Table 5.8, you can see that we begin by determining how much each score deviates from the mean, or

average deviation An alternative measure of variation that, like the standard deviation, indicates the average difference between the scores in a distribution and the mean of the distribution.

$$X - \mu$$

Then we need to sum the deviation scores. Notice, however, that if we were to sum these scores, they would add to zero. Therefore, we first take the absolute value of the deviation scores (the distance from the mean, irrespective of direction), as shown in the last column of Table 5.8. To

TABLE 5.8 Calculations for the Sum of the Absolute Values of the Deviation Scores ($\mu = 74$)

X	$X - \mu$	$\lvert X - \mu \rvert$
45	−29.00	29.00
47	−27.00	27.00
54	−20.00	20.00
56	−18.00	18.00
59	−15.00	15.00
60	−14.00	14.00
60	−14.00	14.00
63	−11.00	11.00
65	−9.00	9.00
69	−5.00	5.00
70	−4.00	4.00
74	0.00	0.00
74	0.00	0.00
74	0.00	0.00
75	1.00	1.00
76	2.00	2.00
77	3.00	3.00
78	4.00	4.00
78	4.00	4.00
80	6.00	6.00
82	8.00	8.00
82	8.00	8.00
85	11.00	11.00
86	12.00	12.00
87	13.00	13.00
90	16.00	16.00
92	18.00	18.00
93	19.00	19.00
94	20.00	20.00
95	21.00	21.00
		$\Sigma\lvert X-\mu \rvert = 332.00$

calculate the average deviation, we sum the absolute value of each deviation score:

$$\Sigma|X - \mu|$$

Then we divide the sum by the total number of scores to find the average deviation:

$$AD = \frac{\Sigma|X - \mu|}{N}$$

Using the data from Table 5.8, we can calculate the average deviation as follows:

$$AD = \frac{\Sigma|X - \mu|}{N} = \frac{332}{30} = 11.07$$

For the exam score distribution, the scores fall an average of 11.07 points from the mean of 74.00.

Although the average deviation is fairly easy to compute, it isn't as useful as the standard deviation because, as we will see in later chapters, the standard deviation is used in many other statistical procedures.

The standard deviation is very similar to the average deviation. The only difference is that rather than taking the absolute value of the deviation scores, we use another method to "get rid of" the negative deviation scores—we square them. This procedure is illustrated in Table 5.9. Notice that this table is very similar to Table 5.8. It includes the distribution of exam scores, the deviation scores, and the squared deviation scores. The formula for the standard deviation is

$$\sigma = \sqrt{\frac{\Sigma(X - \mu)^2}{N}}$$

This formula represents the standard deviation for a population. The symbol for the population standard deviation is σ (pronounced "sigma"). To derive the standard deviation for a sample, the calculation is the same, but the symbols differ. We will discuss this later in the chapter.

Notice that the formula for σ is similar to that for the average deviation. We determine the deviation scores, square the deviation scores, sum the squared deviation scores, and divide by the number of scores in the distribution. Last, we take the square root of that number. Why? Squaring the deviation scores has inflated them. We now need to bring the squared deviation scores back to the same level of measurement as the mean so that the standard deviation is measured on the same scale as the mean.

Now, using the sum of the squared deviation scores (5,580.00) from Table 5.9, we can calculate the standard deviation:

$$\sigma = \sqrt{\frac{\Sigma(X - \mu)^2}{N}} = \sqrt{\frac{5{,}580.00}{30}} = \sqrt{186.00} = 13.64$$

TABLE 5.9 Calculations for the Sum of the Squared Deviation Scores ($\mu = 74$)

X	$X-\mu$	$(X-\mu)^2$
45	−29.00	841.00
47	−27.00	729.00
54	-20.00	400.00
56	-18.00	324.00
59	−15.00	225.00
60	−14.00	196.00
60	−14.00	196.00
63	−11.00	121.00
65	−9.00	81.00
69	−5.00	25.00
70	−4.00	16.00
74	0.00	0.00
74	0.00	0.00
74	0.00	0.00
75	1.00	1.00
76	2.00	4.00
77	3.00	9.00
78	4.00	16.00
78	4.00	16.00
80	6.00	36.00
82	8.00	64.00
82	8.00	64.00
85	11.00	121.00
86	12.00	144.00
87	13.00	169.00
90	16.00	256.00
92	18.00	324.00
93	19.00	361.00
94	20.00	400.00
95	21.00	441.00
		$\Sigma(X-\mu)^2 = 5{,}580.00$

We can compare this number with the average deviation calculated on the same data ($AD = 11.07$). The standard deviation tells us that the exam scores fall an average of 13.64 points from the mean of 74.00. The standard deviation is slightly larger than the average deviation of 11.07 and will always be larger whenever both of these measures of variation are calculated on the same distribution of scores (unless the variability in the distribution is zero, in which case the average deviation and the standard deviation will be the same). This occurs because we are squaring the deviation scores and thus giving more weight to those that are farther from the mean of the distribution. The scores that are lowest and highest have the largest deviation scores; squaring them exaggerates this difference. When all of the squared deviation scores are summed, these large scores necessarily lead to a larger numerator and, even after we divide by N and take the square root, result in a larger number than what we find for the average deviation.

If you have taken a statistics class, you may have used the "raw-score (or computational) formula" to calculate the standard deviation. The raw-score formula is shown in Table 5.10, where it is used to calculate the standard deviation for the same distribution of exam scores. The numerator represents an algebraic transformation from the original formula that is somewhat shorter to use. Although the raw-score formula is slightly easier to use, it is more difficult to equate this formula with what the standard deviation actually is—the average deviation (or distance) from the mean for all the scores in the distribution. Thus, I prefer the definitional formula because it allows you not only to calculate the statistic but also to understand it better.

As mentioned previously, the formula for the standard deviation for a sample (S) differs from the formula for the standard deviation for a population (σ) only in the symbols used to represent each term. The formula for a sample is

$$S = \sqrt{\frac{\Sigma(X - \overline{X})^2}{N}}$$

where

X = each individual score
$\overline{X}$ = sample mean
N = number of scores in the distribution
S = sample standard deviation

TABLE 5.10 Standard Deviation Raw-Score Formula

$$\sigma = \sqrt{\frac{\Sigma X^2 - \frac{(\Sigma X)^2}{N}}{N}} = \sqrt{\frac{169{,}860 - \frac{(2{,}220)^2}{30}}{30}} = \sqrt{\frac{169{,}860 - \frac{4{,}928{,}400}{30}}{30}}$$

$$= \sqrt{\frac{169{,}860 - 164{,}280}{30}} = \sqrt{\frac{5{,}580.00}{30}} = \sqrt{186.00} = 13.64$$

Note that the main difference is in the symbol for the mean ($\overline{X}$ rather than μ). This difference reflects the symbols for the population mean versus the sample mean. However, the calculation is exactly the same as for σ. Thus, if we used the data set in Table 5.9 to calculate S, we would arrive at exactly the same answer that we computed for σ, 13.64.

If, however, we are using sample data to *estimate* the population standard deviation, then the standard deviation formula must be slightly modified. The modification provides what is called an "unbiased estimator" of the population standard deviation based on sample data. The modified formula is

$$s = \sqrt{\frac{\Sigma(X - \overline{X})^2}{N - 1}}$$

Notice that the symbol for the unbiased estimator of the population standard deviation is s (lowercase), whereas the symbol for the sample standard deviation is S (uppercase). The main difference, however, is the denominator: $N-1$ rather than N. The reason is that the standard deviation within a small sample may not be representative of the population; that is, there may not be as much variability in the sample as there actually is in the population. We therefore divide by $N-1$ because dividing by a smaller number increases the standard deviation and thus provides a better estimate of the population standard deviation.

We can use the formula for s to calculate the standard deviation on the same set of exam score data. Before we even begin the calculation, we know that because we are dividing by a smaller number ($N-1$), s should be larger than either σ or S (which were both 13.64). Normally we would not compute σ, S, and s on the same distribution of scores because σ is the standard deviation for the population, S is the standard deviation for a sample, and s is the unbiased estimator of the population standard deviation based on sample data. We are doing so here simply to illustrate the difference in the formulas.

$$s = \sqrt{\frac{\Sigma(X - \overline{X})^2}{N - 1}} = \sqrt{\frac{5580.00}{30 - 1}} = \sqrt{\frac{5580.00}{29}} = \sqrt{192.41} = 13.87$$

Note that s (13.87) is slightly larger than σ and S (13.64). The procedures for calculating σ, S, and S using Excel, SPSS, and the TI-84 calculator are shown in the Statistical Software Resource section at the end of this chapter.

variance The standard deviation squared.

One final measure of variability is called the variance. The **variance** is equal to the standard deviation squared. Thus, the variance for a population is σ^2, for a sample is S^2, and for the unbiased estimator of the population is s^2. Because the variance is not measured in the same level of measurement as the mean (it's the standard deviation squared), it isn't as useful a descriptive statistic as the standard deviation. Thus, we will not discuss it in great detail here; however, the variance is used in more advanced statistical procedures presented later in the text.

The formulas for the average deviation, standard deviation, and variance all use the mean. Thus, it is appropriate to use these measures with interval or ratio data but not with ordinal or nominal data.

Measures of Variation **IN REVIEW**

TYPES OF VARIATION MEASURES

	RANGE	AVERAGE DEVIATION	STANDARD DEVIATION
Definition	The difference between the lowest and highest scores in the distribution	The average distance of the scores from the mean of the distribution	The square root of the average squared deviation from the mean of a distribution
Use With	Primarily interval and ratio data	Primarily interval and ratio data	Primarily interval and ratio data
Cautions	A simple measure that does not use all scores in the distribution in its calculation	A more sophisticated measure in which all scores are used but which may not weight extreme scores adequately	The most sophisticated and most frequently used measure of variation

CRITICAL THINKING CHECK 5.3

1. For a distribution of scores, what information does a measure of variation add that a measure of central tendency does not convey?
2. Today's weather report included information on the normal rainfall for this time of year. The amount of rain that fell today was 1.5 inches above normal. To decide whether this is an abnormally high amount of rain, you need to know that the standard deviation for rainfall is 0.75 of an inch. What would you conclude about how normal the amount of rainfall was today? Would your conclusion be different if the standard deviation were 2 inches rather than 0.75 of an inch?

Types of Distributions

In addition to knowing the central tendency and the width or spread of a distribution, it is important to know about the shape of the distribution.

normal curve A symmetrical, bell-shaped frequency polygon representing a normal distribution.

normal distribution A theoretical frequency distribution that has certain special characteristics.

Normal Distributions. When a distribution of scores is fairly large ($N > 30$), it often tends to approximate a pattern called a *normal distribution*. When plotted as a frequency polygon, a normal distribution forms a symmetrical, bell-shaped pattern often called a **normal curve** (see Figure 5.4). We say that the pattern *approximates* a normal distribution because a true normal distribution is a theoretical construct not actually observed in the real world.

The **normal distribution** is a theoretical frequency distribution that has certain special characteristics. First, it is bell-shaped and symmetrical—the right

FIGURE 5.4
A normal distribution

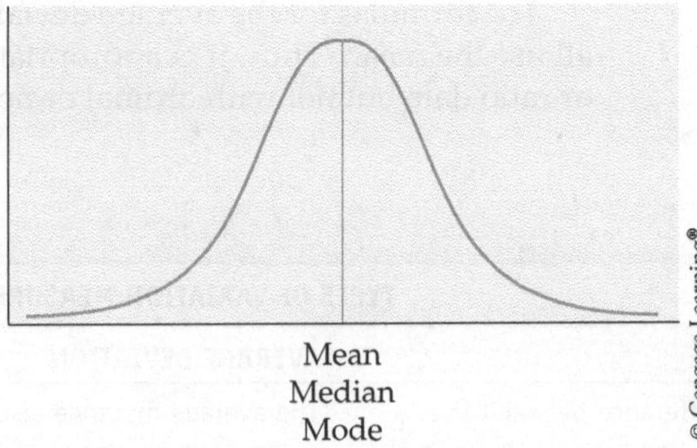

half is a mirror image of the left half. Second, the mean, median, and mode are equal and are located at the center of the distribution. Third, the normal distribution is unimodal—it has only one mode. Fourth, most of the observations are clustered around the center of the distribution, with far fewer observations at the ends or "tails" of the distribution. Last, when standard deviations are plotted on the x-axis, the percentage of scores falling between the mean and any point on the x-axis is the same for all normal curves. This important property of the normal distribution will be discussed more fully later in the chapter.

kurtosis How flat or peaked a normal distribution is.

mesokurtic Normal curves that have peaks of medium height and distributions that are moderate in breadth.

leptokurtic Normal curves that are tall and thin, with only a few scores in the middle of the distribution having a high frequency.

platykurtic Normal curves that are short and more dispersed (broader).

Kurtosis. Although we typically think of the normal distribution as being similar to the curve depicted in Figure 5.4, there are variations in the shape of normal distributions. **Kurtosis** refers to how flat or peaked a normal distribution is. In other words, kurtosis refers to the degree of dispersion among the scores or whether the distribution is tall and skinny or short and fat. The normal distribution depicted in Figure 5.4 and on the far left of Figure 5.5 is called mesokurtic—the term *meso* means middle. **Mesokurtic** (pronounced me-zō **kur**-tik) curves have peaks of medium height, and the distributions are moderate in breadth. Now look at the remaining two distributions depicted in Figure 5.5. The normal distribution in the middle is leptokurtic—the term *lepto* means thin. **Leptokurtic** (pronounced lep-tuh-kur-tik) curves are tall and thin, with only a few scores in the middle of the distribution having a high frequency. Last, see the curve on the right side of Figure 5.5. This is a platykurtic curve—*platy* means broad or flat. **Platykurtic** (pronounced plat-i-**kur**-tik) curves are short and more dispersed

FIGURE 5.5
Types of distributions: mesokurtic, leptokurtic, and platykurtic

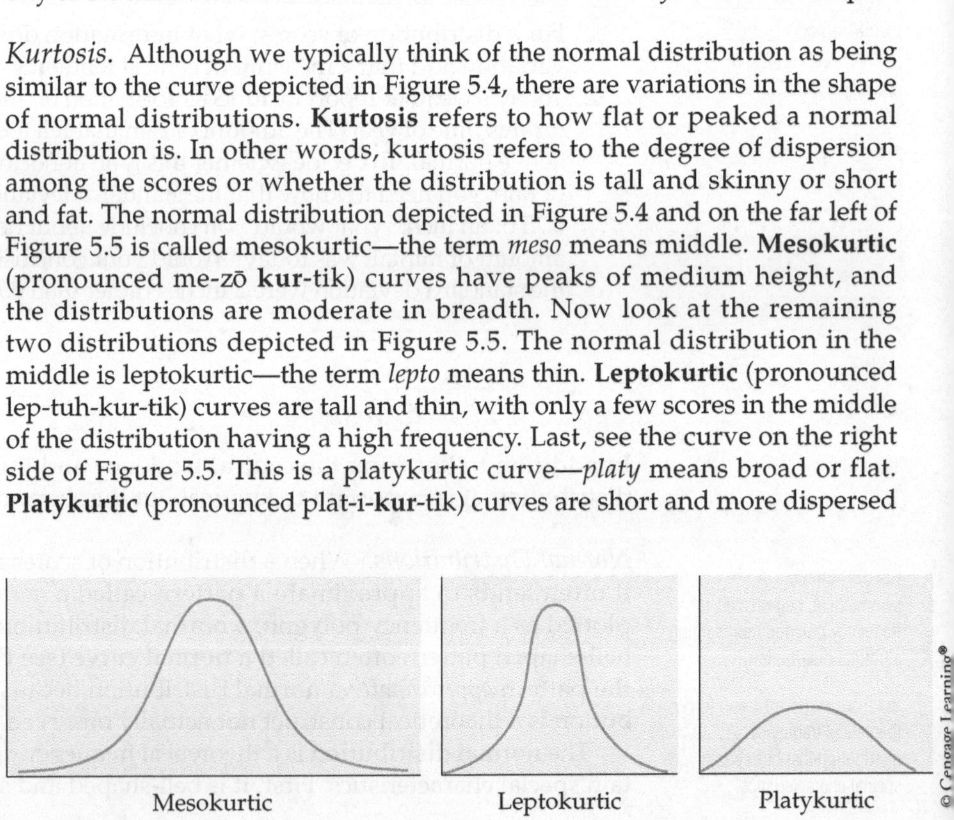

(broader). In a platykurtic curve, there are many scores around the middle score that all have a similar frequency.

Positively Skewed Distributions. Most distributions do not approximate a normal or bell-shaped curve. Instead they are skewed, or lopsided. In a skewed distribution, scores tend to cluster at one end or the other of the *x*-axis, with the tail of the distribution extending in the opposite direction. In a **positively skewed distribution,** the peak is to the left of the center point, and the tail extends toward the right, or in the positive direction (see Figure 5.6).

positively skewed distribution A distribution in which the peak is to the left of the center point, and the tail extends toward the right, or in the positive direction.

Notice that what skews the distribution, or throws it off center, are the scores toward the right, or positive direction. A few individuals have extremely high scores that pull the distribution in that direction. Notice also what this does to the mean, median, and mode. These three measures do not have the same value nor are they all located at the center of the distribution as they are in a normal distribution. The mode—the score with the highest frequency—is the high point on the distribution. The median divides the distribution in half. The mean is pulled in the direction of the tail of the distribution; that is, the few extreme scores pull the mean toward them and inflate it.

Negatively Skewed Distributions. The opposite of a positively skewed distribution is a **negatively skewed distribution**—a distribution in which the peak is to the right of the center point, and the tail extends toward the left, or in the negative direction. The term *negative* refers to the direction of the skew. As can be seen in Figure 5.6, in a negatively skewed distribution, the mean is pulled toward the left by the few extremely low scores in the distribution. As in all distributions, the median divides the distribution in half, and the mode is the most frequently occurring score in the distribution.

negatively skewed distribution A distribution in which the peak is to the right of the center point, and the tail extends toward the left, or in the negative direction.

Knowing the shape of a distribution provides valuable information about the distribution. For example, would you prefer to have a negatively skewed or positively skewed distribution of exam scores for an exam that you have taken? Students frequently answer that they would prefer a positively skewed distribution because they think the term *positive* means good. Keep in mind, though, that *positive* and *negative* describe the skew of the

FIGURE 5.6 Positively and negatively skewed distributions

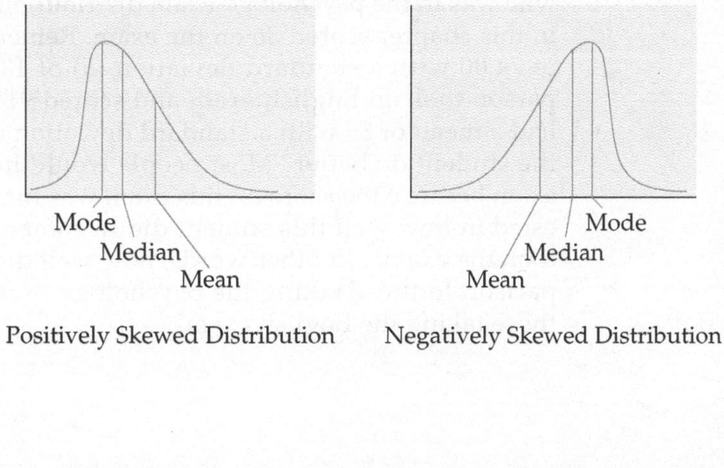

distribution, not whether the distribution is "good" or "bad." Assuming that the exam scores span the entire possible range (say, 0 to 100), you should prefer a negatively skewed distribution—meaning that most people have high scores and only a few have low scores.

Another example of the value of knowing the shape of a distribution is provided by Harvard paleontologist Stephen Jay Gould (1985). Gould was diagnosed in 1982 with a rare form of cancer. He immediately began researching the disease and learned that it was incurable and had a median mortality rate of only 8 months after discovery. Rather than immediately assuming that he would be dead in 8 months, Gould realized this meant that half of the patients lived longer than 8 months. Because he was diagnosed with the disease in its early stages and was receiving high-quality medical treatment, he reasoned that he could expect to be in the half of the distribution that lived beyond 8 months. The other piece of information that Gould found encouraging was the shape of the distribution. Look again at the two distributions in Figure 5.6, and decide which you would prefer in this situation. With a positively skewed distribution, the cases to the right of the median could stretch out for years; this is not true for a negatively skewed distribution. The distribution of life expectancy for Gould's disease was positively skewed, and Gould was obviously in the far right-hand tail of the distribution because he lived and remained professionally active for another 20 years.

z-Scores

The descriptive statistics and types of distributions discussed so far are valuable for describing a sample or group of scores. Sometimes, however, we want information about a single score. For example, in our exam score distribution, we may want to know how one person's exam score compares with those of others in the class. Or we may want to know how an individual's exam score in one class, say psychology, compares with the same person's exam score in another class, say English. Because the two distributions of exam scores are different (different means and standard deviations), simply comparing the raw scores on the two exams does not provide this information. Let's say an individual who was in the psychology exam distribution used as an example earlier in this chapter scored 86 on the exam. Remember, the exam had a mean of 74.00 with a standard deviation (S) of 13.64. Assume that the same person took an English exam and scored 91 and that the English exam had a mean of 85 with a standard deviation of 9.58. On which exam did the student do better? Most people would immediately say the English exam because the score on this exam was higher. However, we are interested in how well this student did in comparison to everyone else who took the exams. In other words, how well did the individual do in comparison to those taking the psychology exam versus in comparison to those taking the English exam?

z-score (standard score) A number that indicates how many standard deviation units a raw score is from the mean of a distribution.

To answer this question, we need to convert the exam scores to a form we can use to make comparisons. A **z-score** or **standard score** is a measure of how many standard deviation units an individual raw score falls from the mean of the distribution. We can convert each exam score to a z-score and then compare the z-scores because they will be in the same unit of measurement. You can think of z-scores as a translation of raw scores into scores of the same language for comparative purposes. The formulas for a z-score transformation are

$$z = \frac{X - \overline{X}}{S}$$

and

$$z = \frac{X - \mu}{\sigma}$$

where z is the symbol for the standard score. The difference between the two formulas is that the first is used when calculating a z-score for an individual in comparison to a sample, and the second is used when calculating a z-score for an individual in comparison to a population. Notice that the two formulas do exactly the same thing; they indicate the number of standard deviations an individual score is from the mean of the distribution.

Conversion to a z-score is a statistical technique that is appropriate for use with data on an interval or ratio scale of measurement (scales for which means are calculated). Let's use the formula to calculate the z-scores for the previously mentioned student's psychology and English exam scores. The necessary information is summarized in Table 5.11.

To calculate the z-score for the English test, we first calculate the difference between the score and the mean and then divide by the standard deviation. We use the same process to calculate the z-score for the psychology exam. These calculations are as follows:

$$z_{\text{English}} = \frac{X-\overline{X}}{S} = \frac{91-85}{9.58} = \frac{6}{9.58} = +0.626$$

$$z_{\text{Psychology}} = \frac{X-\overline{X}}{S} = \frac{86-74}{13.64} = \frac{12}{13.64} = +0.880$$

TABLE 5.11 Raw Score (X), Sample Mean ($\overline{X}$), and Standard Deviation (S) for English and Psychology Exams

	X	$\overline{X}$	S
English	91	85	9.58
Psychology	86	74	13.64

The individual's z-score for the English test is 0.626 standard deviation above the mean, and the z-score for the psychology test is 0.880 standard deviation above the mean. Thus, even though the student answered more questions correctly on the English exam (had a higher raw score) than on the psychology exam, the student performed better on the psychology exam relative to other students in the psychology class than on the English exam in comparison to other students in the English class.

The z-scores calculated in the previous example were both positive, indicating that the individual's scores were above the mean in both distributions. When a score is below the mean, the z-score is negative, indicating that the individual's score is lower than the mean of the distribution. Let's go over another example so that you can practice calculating both positive and negative z-scores.

Suppose you administered a test to a large sample of people and computed the mean and standard deviation of the raw scores, with the following results:

$$\overline{X} = 45$$
$$S = 4$$

Suppose also that four of the individuals who took the test had the following scores:

Person	*Score (X)*
Rich	49
Debbie	45
Pam	41
Henry	39

Let's calculate the z-score equivalents for the raw scores of these individuals, beginning with Rich:

$$z_{\text{Rich}} = \frac{X_{\text{Rich}} - \overline{X}}{S} = \frac{49 - 45}{4} = \frac{4}{4} = +1$$

Notice that we substitute Rich's score (X_{Rich}) and then use the group mean ($\overline{X}$) and the group standard deviation (S). The positive sign (+) indicates that the z-score is positive, or above the mean. We find that Rich's score of 49 is 1 standard deviation above the group mean of 45.

Now let's calculate Debbie's z-score:

$$z_{\text{Debbie}} = \frac{X_{\text{Debbie}} - \overline{X}}{S} = \frac{45 - 45}{4} = \frac{0}{4} = 0$$

Debbie's score is the same as the mean of the distribution. Therefore, her z-score is 0, indicating that she scored neither above nor below the mean. Keep in mind that a z-score of 0 does not indicate a low score—it indicates a score right at the mean or average. See if you can calculate the z-scores for Pam and Henry on your own. Do you get $z_{\text{Pam}} = -1$ and $z_{\text{Henry}} = -1.5$? Good work!

In summary, the *z*-score tells whether an individual raw score is above the mean (a positive *z*-score) or below the mean (a negative *z*-score), and it tells how many standard deviations the raw score is above or below the mean. Thus, *z*-scores are a way of transforming raw scores to standard scores for purposes of comparison in both normal and skewed distributions.

z-Scores, the Standard Normal Distribution, Probability, and Percentile Ranks

standard normal distribution A normal distribution with a mean of 0 and a standard deviation of 1.

If the distribution of scores for which you are calculating *z*-scores is normal (symmetrical and unimodal), then it is referred to as the **standard normal distribution**—a normal distribution with a mean of 0 and a standard deviation of 1. The standard normal distribution is actually a theoretical distribution defined by a specific mathematical formula. All other normal curves approximate the standard normal curve to a greater or lesser extent. The value of the standard normal curve is that it provides information about the proportion of scores that are higher or lower than any other score in the distribution. A researcher can also determine the probability of occurrence of a score that is higher or lower than any other score in the distribution. The proportions under the standard normal curve hold for only normal distributions—not for skewed distributions. Even though *z*-scores may be calculated on skewed distributions, the proportions under the standard normal curve do not hold for skewed distributions.

Take a look at Figure 5.7, which represents the area under the standard normal curve in terms of standard deviations. Based on this figure, we see that approximately 68% of the observations in the distribution fall between −1.0 and +1.0 standard deviations from the mean. This approximate percentage holds for all data that are normally distributed. Notice also that approximately 13.5% of the observations fall between −1.0 and −2.0 and another 13.5% between +1.0 and +2.0, and that approximately 2% of the observations fall between −2.0 and −3.0 and another 2% between +2.0 and +3.0. Only 0.13% of the scores are beyond a *z*-score of ±3.0. If we sum the percentages in Figure 5.7, we have 100%—all of the area under the curve

FIGURE 5.7 Area under the standard normal curve

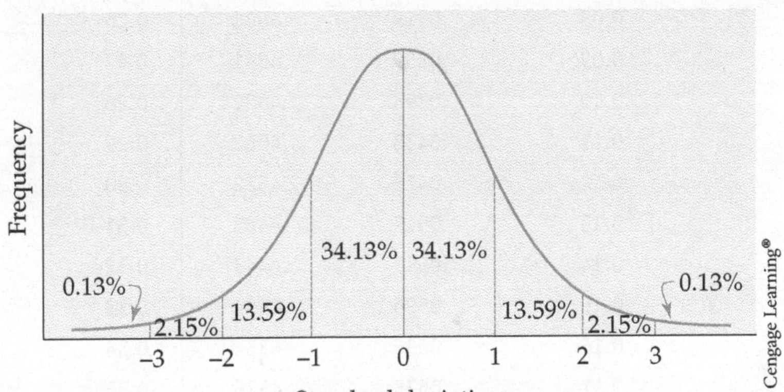

representing everybody in the distribution. If we sum half of the curve, we have 50%—half of the distribution.

With a curve that is normal or symmetrical, the mean, median, and mode are all at the center point; thus, 50% of the scores are above this number and 50% are below this number. This property helps us determine probabilities. A **probability** is defined as the expected relative frequency of a particular outcome. The outcome could be the result of an experiment or any situation in which the result is not known in advance. For example, from the normal curve, what is the probability of randomly choosing a score that falls above the mean? The probability is equal to the proportion of scores in that area, or .50. Figure 5.7 gives a rough estimate of the proportions under the normal curve. Luckily for us, statisticians have determined the exact proportion of scores that will fall between any two z-scores, for example, between z-scores of +1.30 and +1.39. This information is provided in Table A.2 in Appendix A at the back of the text. A small portion of this table is shown in Table 5.12.

probability The expected relative frequency of a particular outcome.

TABLE 5.12 A Portion of the Standard Normal Curve Table

AREAS UNDER THE STANDARD NORMAL CURVE FOR VALUES OF *z*

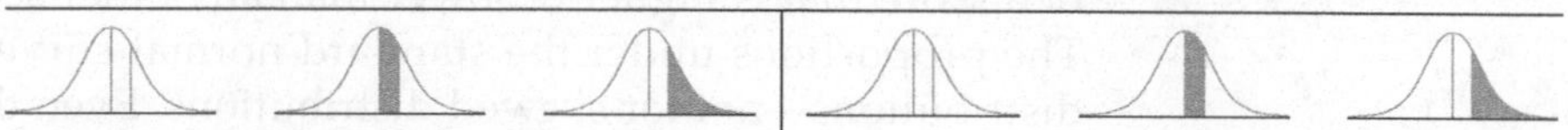

z	AREA BETWEEN MEAN AND *z*	AREA BEYOND *z*	*z*	AREA BETWEEN MEAN AND *z*	AREA BEYOND *z*
0.00	.0000	.5000	0.18	.0714	.4286
0.01	.0040	.4960	0.19	.0753	.4247
0.02	.0080	.4920	0.20	.0793	.4207
0.03	.0120	.4880	0.21	.0832	.4268
0.04	.0160	.4840	0.22	.0871	.4129
0.05	.0199	.4801	0.23	.0910	.4090
0.06	.0239	.4761	0.24	.0948	.4052
0.07	.0279	.4721	0.25	.0987	.4013
0.08	.0319	.4681	0.26	.1026	.3974
0.09	.0359	.4641	0.27	.1064	.3936
0.10	.0398	.4602	0.28	.1103	.3897
0.11	.0438	.4562	0.29	.1141	.3859
0.12	.0478	.4522	0.30	.1179	.3821
0.13	.0517	.4483	0.31	.1217	.3783
0.14	.0557	.4443	0.32	.1255	.3745
0.15	.0596	.4404	0.33	.1293	.3707
0.16	.0636	.4364	0.34	.1331	.3669
0.17	.0675	.4325	0.35	.1368	.3632

(continued)

TABLE 5.12 A Portion of the Standard Normal Curve Table (*continued*)

AREAS UNDER THE STANDARD NORMAL CURVE FOR VALUES OF *z*

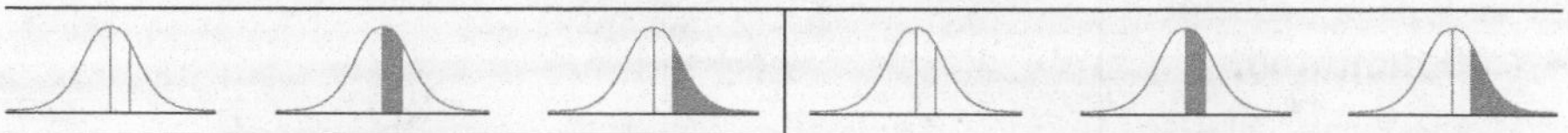

z	AREA BETWEEN MEAN AND *z*	AREA BEYOND *z*	*z*	AREA BETWEEN MEAN AND *z*	AREA BEYOND *z*
0.36	.1406	.3594	0.60	.2257	.2743
0.37	.1443	.3557	0.61	.2291	.2709
0.38	.1480	.3520	0.62	.2324	.2676
0.39	.1517	.3483	0.63	.2357	.2643
0.40	.1554	.3446	0.64	.2389	.2611
0.41	.1591	.3409	0.65	.2422	.2578
0.42	.1628	.3372	0.66	.2454	.2546
0.43	.1664	.3336	0.67	.2486	.2514
0.44	.1770	.3300	0.68	.2517	.2483
0.45	.1736	.3264	0.69	.2549	.2451
0.46	.1772	.3228	0.70	.2580	.2420
0.47	.1808	.3192	0.71	.2611	.2389
0.48	.1844	.3156	0.72	.2642	.2358
0.49	.1879	.3121	0.73	.2673	.2327
0.50	.1915	.3085	0.74	.2704	.2296
0.51	.1950	.3050	0.75	.2734	.2266
0.52	.1985	.3015	0.76	.2764	.2236
0.53	.2019	.2981	0.77	.2794	.2206
0.54	.2054	.2946	0.78	.2823	.2177
0.55	.2088	.2912	0.79	.2852	.2148
0.56	.2123	.2877	0.80	9.2881	.2119
0.57	.2157	.2843	0.81	.2910	.2090
0.58	.2190	.2810	0.82	.2939	.2061
0.59	.2224	.2776	0.83	.2967	.2033

The columns across the top of the table are labeled *z*, Area Between Mean and *z*, and Area Beyond *z*. There are also pictorial representations. The *z* column refers to the *z*-score with which you are working. The Area Between Mean and *z* is the area under the curve between the mean of the distribution (where $z = 0$) and the *z*-score with which you are working, that is, the proportion of scores between the mean and the *z*-score in column 1. The Area Beyond *z* is the area under the curve from the *z*-score out to the tail

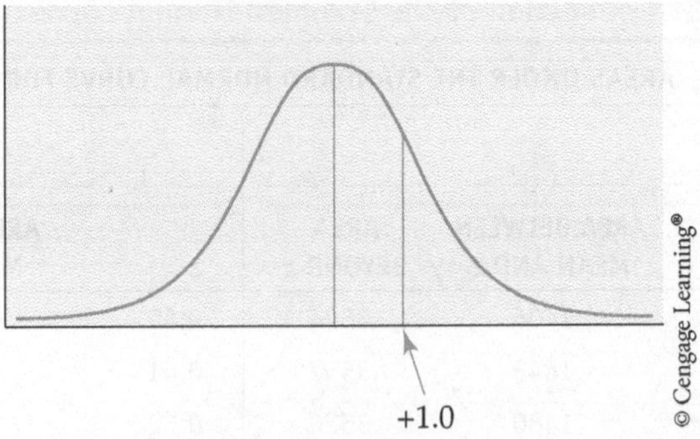

FIGURE 5.8
Standard normal curve with z-score of +1.00 indicated

end of the distribution. Notice that the entire table goes out to only a z-score of 4.00 because it is very unusual for a normally distributed population of scores to include scores larger than this. Notice also that the table provides information about only positive z-scores, even though the distribution of scores actually ranges from approximately −4.00 to +4.00. Because the distribution is symmetrical, the areas between the mean and z and beyond the z-scores are the same whether the z-score is positive or negative.

Let's use some of the examples from earlier in the chapter to illustrate how to use these proportions under the normal curve. Assume that the test data described earlier (with $\bar{X} = 45$ and $S = 4$) are normally distributed, so that the proportions under the normal curve apply. We calculated z-scores for four individuals who took the test—Rich, Debbie, Pam, and Henry. Let's use Rich's z-score to illustrate the use of the normal curve table. Rich had a z-score equal to +1.00—1 standard deviation above the mean. Let's begin by drawing a picture representing the normal curve and then sketch in the z-score. Thus, Figure 5.8 shows a representation of the normal curve, with a line drawn at a z-score of +1.00.

Before we look at the proportions under the normal curve, we can begin to gather information from this picture. We see that Rich's score is above the mean. Using the information from Figure 5.7, we see that roughly 34% of the area under the curve falls between his z-score and the mean of the distribution, whereas approximately 16% of the area falls beyond his z-score. Using Table A.2 to get the exact proportions, we find (from the Area Beyond z column) that the proportion of scores falling above the z-score of +1.0 is .1587. This number can be interpreted to mean that 15.87% of the scores were higher than Rich's score or that the probability of randomly choosing a score with a z-score greater than +1.00 is .1587. To determine the proportion of scores falling below Rich's z-score, we need to use the Area Between Mean and z column and add .50 to this proportion. According to the table, the area between the mean and the z-score is .3413. Why must we add .50 to this number? The table provides information about only one side of the standard normal distribution. We must add in the proportion of scores represented by the other half of the distribution, which is always .50. Look back

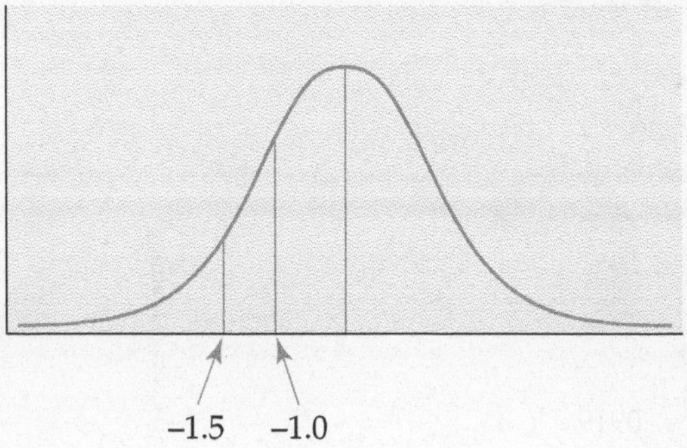

FIGURE 5.9 Standard normal curve with *z*-scores of −1.0 and −1.5 indicated

at Figure 5.8. Rich's score is +1.00 above the mean, which means that he did better than those between the mean and his *z*-score (.3413) and also better than everybody below the mean (.50). Hence, 84.13% of the scores are below Rich's score.

Let's use Debbie's *z*-score to further illustrate the use of the *z* table. Debbie's *z*-score was 0.00—right at the mean. We know that if she is at the mean ($z = 0$), then half of the distribution is below her score and half is above her score. Does this match what Table A.2 tells us? According to the table, .5000 (50%) of scores are beyond this *z*-score, so the information in the table does agree with our reasoning.

Using the *z* table with Pam and Henry's *z*-scores is slightly more difficult because both Pam and Henry had negative *z*-scores. Remember, Pam had a *z*-score of −1.00, and Henry had a *z*-score of −1.50. Let's begin by drawing a normal distribution and then marking where both Pam and Henry fall on that distribution. This information is represented in Figure 5.9.

Before even looking at the *z* table, let's think about what we know from Figure 5.9. We know that both Pam and Henry scored below the mean, that they are in the lower 50% of the class, that the proportion of people scoring higher than them is greater than .50, and that the proportion of people scoring lower than them is less than .50. Keep this overview in mind as we use Table A.2. Using Pam's *z*-score of −1.0, see if you can determine the proportion of scores lying above and below her score. If you determine that the proportion of scores above hers is .8413 and that the proportion below is .1587, then you are correct! Why is the proportion above her score .8413? We begin by looking in the table at a *z*-score of 1.0 (remember, there are no negatives in the table). The Area Between Mean and *z* is .3413, and then we need to add the proportion of .50 in the top half of the curve. Adding these two proportions, we get .8413. The proportion below her score is represented by the area in the tail, the Area Beyond *z* of .1587. Note that the proportion above and the proportion below should sum to 1.0 ($.8413 + .1587 = 1.0$). Now see if you can compute the proportions above and below Henry's *z*-score of −1.5. Do you get .9332 above his score and .0668 below his score? Good work!

FIGURE 5.10
Proportion of scores between z-scores of −1.0 and −1.5

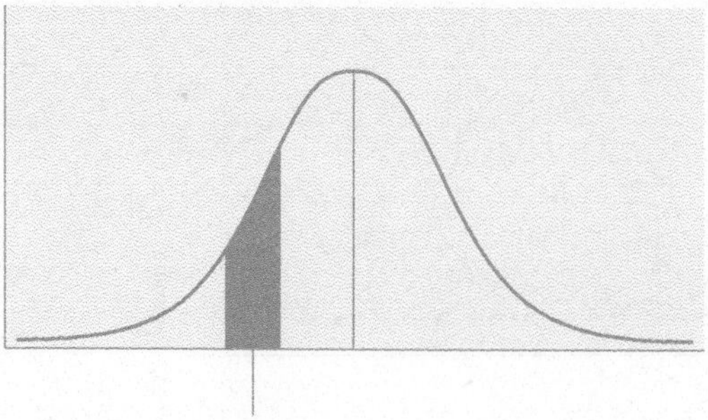

.0919

Now let's try something slightly more difficult by determining the proportion of scores that fall between Henry's z-score of −1.5 and Pam's z-score of −1.0. Referring to Figure 5.9, we see that we are targeting the area between the two z-scores represented on the curve. Again, we use Table A.2 to provide the proportions. The area between the mean and Henry's z-score of −1.5 is .4332, whereas the area between the mean and Pam's z-score of −1.0 is .3413. To determine the proportion of scores that fall between the two, we subtract .3413 from .4332, obtaining a difference of .0919. This result is illustrated in Figure 5.10.

percentile rank A score that indicates the percentage of people who scored at or below a given raw score.

The standard normal curve can also be used to determine an individual's **percentile rank**—the percentage of scores equal to or below the given raw score, or the percentage of scores the individual's score is higher than. To determine a percentile rank, we must first know the individual's z-score.

Let's say we want to calculate an individual's percentile rank based on this person's score on an intelligence test. The scores on the intelligence test are normally distributed, with $\mu = 100$ and $\sigma = 15$. Let's suppose the individual scored 119. Using the z-score formula, we have

$$z = \frac{X - \mu}{\sigma} = \frac{119 - 100}{15} = \frac{19}{15} = +1.27$$

Looking at the Area Between Mean and z column for a score of +1.27, we find the proportion .3980. To determine all of the area below the score, we must add .50 to .3980; the entire area below a z-score of +1.27, then, is .8980. If we multiply this proportion by 100, we can describe the intelligence test score of 119 as being in the 89.80th percentile.

To practice calculating percentile ranks, see if you can calculate the percentile ranks for Rich, Debbie, Pam, and Henry from our previous examples. You should arrive at the following percentile ranks.

Person	*Score (X)*	*z-Score*	*Percentile Rank*
Rich	49	+1.0	84.13th
Debbie	45	0.0	50.00th
Pam	41	−1.0	15.87th
Henry	39	−1.50	6.68th

Students most often have trouble determining percentile ranks from negative z-scores. Always draw a figure representing the normal curve with the z-scores indicated; this will help you determine which column to use from the z table. When the z-score is negative, the proportion of the curve representing those who scored lower than the individual (the percentile rank) is found in the Area Beyond z column. When the z-score is positive, the proportion of the curve representing those who scored lower than the individual (the percentile rank) is found by using the Area Between Mean and z column and adding .50 (the bottom half of the distribution) to this proportion.

What if we know an individual's percentile rank and want to determine this person's raw score? Let's say we know that an individual scored at the 75th percentile on the intelligence test described previously. We want to know what score has 75% of the scores below it. We begin by using Table A.2 to determine the z-score for this percentile rank. If the individual is at the 75th percentile, we know the Area Between Mean and z is .25. How do we know this? The person scored higher than the 50% of people in the bottom half of the curve and .75 − .50 = .25. Therefore, we look in the column labeled Area Between Mean and z and find the proportion that is closest to .25. The closest we come to .25 is .2486, which corresponds to a z-score of 0.67.

Remember, the z-score formula is

$$z = \frac{X - \mu}{\sigma}$$

We know that $\mu = 100$ and $\sigma = 15$, and now we know that $z = 0.67$. What we want to find is the person's raw score, X. So, let's solve the equation for X:

$$z = \frac{X - \mu}{\sigma}$$

$$z\sigma = X - \mu$$

$$z\sigma + \mu = X$$

Substituting the values we have for μ, σ, and z, we find

$$\begin{aligned} X &= z\sigma + \mu \\ X &= 0.67(15) + 100 \\ &= 10.05 + 100 \\ &= 110.05 \end{aligned}$$

As you can see, the standard normal distribution is useful for determining how a single score compares with a population or sample of scores and also for determining probabilities and percentile ranks. Knowing how to use the proportions under the standard normal curve increases the information we can derive from a single score.

Types of Distributions — IN REVIEW

	TYPES OF DISTRIBUTIONS		
	NORMAL	POSITIVELY SKEWED	NEGATIVELY SKEWED
Description	A symmetrical, bell-shaped unimodal curve	A lopsided curve with a tail extending toward the positive or right side	A lopsided curve with a tail extending toward the negative or left side
z-score transformations applicable?	Yes	Yes	Yes
Percentile ranks and proportions under standard normal curve applicable?	Yes	No	No

CRITICAL THINKING CHECK 5.4

1. On one graph, draw two distributions with the same mean but different standard deviations. Draw a second set of distributions on another graph with different means but the same standard deviation.
2. Why is it not possible to use the proportions under the standard normal curve with skewed distributions?
3. Students in the psychology department at General State University consume an average of 7 sodas per day with a standard deviation of 2.5. The distribution is normal.
   a. What proportion of students consumes an amount equal to or greater than 6 sodas per day?
   b. What proportion of students consumes an amount equal to or greater than 8.5 sodas per day?
   c. What proportion of students consumes an amount between 6 and 8.5 sodas per day?
   d. What is the percentile rank for an individual who consumes 5.5 sodas per day?
   e. How many sodas would an individual at the 75th percentile drink per day?
4. Based on what you have learned about *z*-scores, percentile ranks, and the area under the standard normal curve, fill in the missing information in the following table representing performance on an exam that is normally distributed with $\bar{X} = 55$ and $S = 6$.

	X	*z-Score*	*Percentile Rank*
John	63		
Ray		−1.66	
Betty			72

Summary

In this chapter, we discussed data organization and descriptive statistics. We presented several methods of data organization, including a frequency distribution, a bar graph, a histogram, and a frequency polygon. We also discussed the types of data appropriate for each of these methods.

Descriptive statistics that summarize a large data set include measures of central tendency (mean, median, and mode) and measures of variation (range, average deviation, and standard deviation). These statistics provide information about the central tendency or "middleness" of a distribution of scores and about the spread or width of the distribution, respectively. A distribution may be normal, positively skewed, or negatively skewed. The shape of the distribution affects the relationships among the mean, median, and mode.

Finally, we discussed the calculation of *z*-score transformations as a means of standardizing raw scores for comparative purposes. Although *z*-scores may be used with either normal or skewed distributions, the proportions under the standard normal curve can be applied only to data that approximate a normal distribution.

Based on our discussion of these descriptive methods, you can begin to organize and summarize a large data set and also compare the scores of individuals to the entire sample or population.

KEY TERMS

frequency distribution
class interval frequency distribution
qualitative variable
bar graph
quantitative variable
histogram
frequency polygon
descriptive statistics
measure of central tendency
mean
median
mode
measure of variation
range
standard deviation
average deviation
variance
normal curve
normal distribution
kurtosis
mesokurtic
leptokurtic
platykurtic
positively skewed distribution
negatively skewed distribution
z-score (standard score)
standard normal distribution
probability
percentile rank

CHAPTER EXERCISES

(Answers to odd-numbered exercises appear in Appendix C.)

1. The following data represent a distribution of speeds (in miles per hour) at which individuals were traveling on a highway.

64	80	64	70
76	79	67	72
65	73	68	65
67	65	70	62
67	68	65	64

Organize these data into a frequency distribution with frequency (*f*) and relative frequency (*rf*) columns.

2. Organize the data in Exercise 1 into a class interval frequency distribution using 10 intervals with frequency (*f*) and relative frequency (*rf*) columns.
3. Which type of figure should be used to represent the data in Exercise 1—a bar graph, histogram, or frequency polygon? Why? Draw the appropriate figure for these data.
4. Calculate the mean, median, and mode for the data set in Exercise 1. Is the distribution normal or skewed? If it is skewed, what type of skew is it? Which measure of central tendency is most appropriate for this distribution, and why?
5. Calculate the mean, median, and mode for the following four distributions (*a*–*d*):

a	*b*	*c*	*d*
2	1	1	2
2	2	3	3
4	3	3	4
5	4	3	5
8	4	5	6
9	5	5	6
10	5	8	6
11	5	8	7
11	6	8	8
11	6	9	8
	8	10	
	9	11	

6. Calculate the range, average deviation, and standard deviation for the following five distributions:
   a. 1, 2, 3, 4, 5, 6, 7, 8, 9
   b. −4, −3, −2, −1, 0, 1, 2, 3, 4
   c. 10, 20, 30, 40, 50, 60, 70, 80, 90
   d. 0.1, 0.2, 0.3, 0.4, 0.5, 0.6, 0.7, 0.8, 0.9
   e. 100, 200, 300, 400, 500, 600, 700, 800, 900
7. The results of a recent survey indicate that the average new car costs $23,000 with a standard deviation of $3,500. The price of cars is normally distributed.
   a. If someone bought a car for $32,000, what proportion of cars cost an equal amount or more than this?
   b. If someone bought a car for $16,000, what proportion of cars cost an equal amount or more than this?
   c. At what prcentile rank is a car that sold for $30,000?
   d. At what percentile rank is a car that sold for $12,000?
   e. What proportion of cars were sold for an amount between $12,000 and $30,000?
   f. For what price would a car at the 16th percentile have sold?
8. A survey of college students was conducted during final exam week to assess the number of cups of coffee consumed each day. The mean number of cups was 5 with a standard deviation of 1.5 cups. The distribution was normal.
   a. What proportion of students drank 7 or more cups of coffee per day?
   b. What proportion of students drank 2 or more cups of coffee per day?
   c. What proportion of students drank between 2 and 7 cups of coffee per day?
   d. How many cups of coffee would an individual at the 60th percentile rank drink?
   e. What is the percentile rank for an individual who drinks 4 cups of coffee a day?
   f. What is the percentile rank for an individual who drinks 7.5 cups of coffee a day?
9. Fill in the missing information in the following table representing performance on an exam that is normally distributed with $\bar{X} = 72$ and $S = 9$.

	X	*z-Score*	*Percentile Rank*
Ken	73	—	—
Drew	—	1.55	—
Cecil	—	—	82

CRITICAL THINKING CHECK ANSWERS

5.1

1. One advantage is that it is easier to "see" the data set in a graphical representation. A picture makes it easier to determine where the majority of the scores are in the distribution. A frequency distribution requires more reading before a judgment can be made about the shape of the distribution.
2. Gender and type of vehicle driven are qualitative variables, measured on a nominal scale; thus, a bar graph should be used. The speed at which the drivers are traveling is a quantitative variable, measured on a ratio scale. Either a histogram or a frequency polygon could be used. A frequency polygon might be better because of the continuous nature of the variable.

5.2

1. Because gender and type of vehicle driven are nominal data, only the mode can be determined; it is inappropriate to use the median or the mean with these data. Speed of travel is ratio in scale, so the mean, median, or mode could be used. Both the mean and median are better indicators of central tendency than the mode. If the distribution is skewed, however, the mean should not be used.
2. In this case, the mean should not be used because of the single outlier (extreme score) in the distribution.

5.3

1. A measure of variation tells us about the spread of the distribution. In other words, are the scores clustered closely about the mean, or are they spread over a wide range?
2. The amount of rainfall for the indicated day is 2 standard deviations above the mean. I would therefore conclude that the amount of rainfall was well above average. If the standard deviation were 2 rather than 0.75, then the amount of rainfall for the indicated day would be less than 1 standard deviation above the mean—above average but not greatly.

5.4

1.

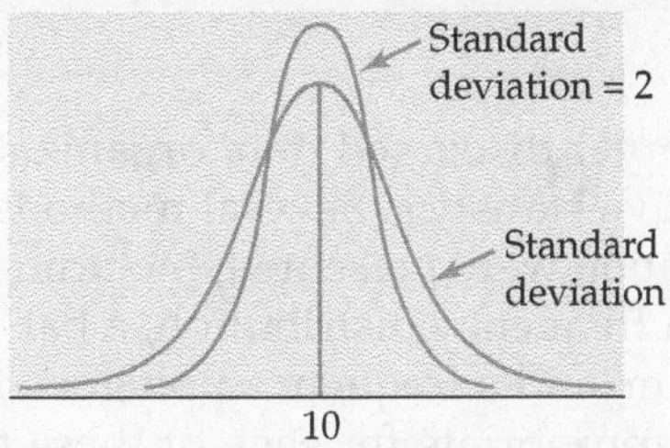

Same Mean, Different Standard Deviations

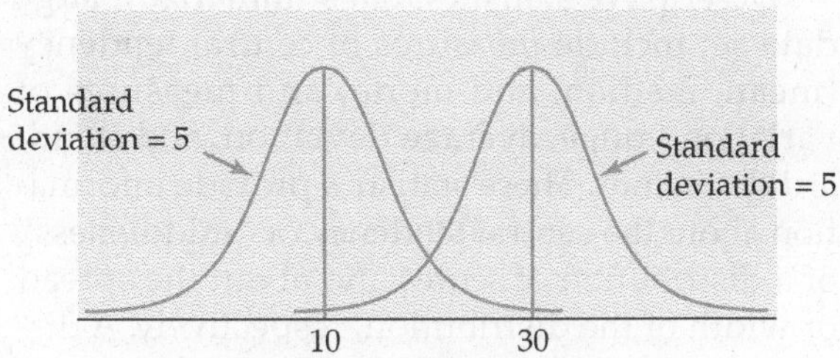

Same Standard Deviation, Different Means

2. The proportions hold for only normal (symmetrical) distributions where one-half of the distribution is equal to the other. If the distribution were skewed, this condition would be violated.
3. a. .6554
   b. .2743
   c. .3811
   d. 27.43rd
   e. 8.68
4.

	X	*z-Score*	*Percentile Rank*
John	63	+1.33	90.82
Ray	45.04	−1.66	4.85
Betty	58.48	+0.58	72.00

WEB RESOURCES

The book-specific website at CengageBrain.com offers students a variety of study tools and useful resources such as glossaries and flashcards.

Chapter 5 ▪ Study Guide

CHAPTER 5 SUMMARY AND REVIEW: DATA ORGANIZATION AND DESCRIPTIVE STATISTICS

This chapter discussed data organization and descriptive statistics. Several methods of data organization were presented, including how to design a frequency distribution, a bar graph, a histogram, and a frequency polygon. The type of data appropriate for each of these methods was also discussed.

Descriptive statistics that summarize a large data set include measures of central tendency (mean, median, and mode) and measures of variation (range, average deviation, and standard deviation). These statistics provide information about the central tendency or "middleness" of a distribution of scores and about the spread or width of the distribution, respectively. A distribution may be normal, positively skewed, or negatively skewed. The shape of the distribution affects the relationship among the mean, median, and mode. Finally, the calculation of *z*-score transformations was discussed as a means of standardizing raw scores for comparative purposes. Although *z*-scores can be used with either normal or skewed distributions, the proportions under the standard normal curve can only be applied to data that approximate a normal distribution.

Based on the discussion of these descriptive methods, you can begin to organize and summarize a large data set and also compare the scores of individuals to the entire sample or population.

CHAPTER 5 REVIEW EXERCISES

(Answers to exercises appear in Appendix C.)

FILL-IN SELF-TEST

Answer the following questions. If you have trouble answering any of the questions, restudy the relevant material before going on to the multiple-choice self test.

1. A ________ is a table in which all of the scores are listed along with the frequency with which each occurs.
2. A categorical variable for which each value represents a discrete category is a ________ variable.
3. A graphical representation of a frequency distribution in which vertical bars centered above scores on the *x*-axis touch each other to indicate that the scores on the variable represent related, increasing values is a ________.
4. Measures of ________ are numbers intended to characterize an entire distribution.
5. The ________ is the middle score in a distribution after the scores have been arranged from highest to lowest or lowest to highest.
6. Measures of ________ are numbers that indicate how dispersed scores are around the mean of the distribution.
7. An alternative measure of variation that indicates the average difference between the scores in a distribution and the mean of the distribution is the ________.

8. When we divide the squared deviation scores by $N-1$ rather than by N, we are using the ______ of the population standard deviation.
9. σ represents the ______ standard deviation, and S represents the ______ standard deviation.
10. A distribution in which the peak is to the left of the center point and the tail extends toward the right is a ______ skewed distribution.
11. A number that indicates how many standard deviation units a raw score is from the mean of a distribution is a ______.
12. The normal distribution with a mean of 0 and a standard deviation of 1 is the ______.

MULTIPLE-CHOICE SELF-TEST

Select the single best answer for each of the following questions. If you have trouble answering any of the questions, restudy the relevant material.

1. A ______ is a graphical representation of a frequency distribution in which vertical bars are centered above each category along the x-axis and are separated from each other by a space indicating that the levels of the variable represent distinct, unrelated categories.
   a. histogram
   b. frequency polygon
   c. bar graph
   d. class interval histogram
2. Qualitative variable is to quantitative variable as ______ is to ______.
   a. categorical variable; numerical variable
   b. numerical variable; categorical variable
   c. bar graph; histogram
   d. categorical variable and bar graph; numerical variable and histogram
3. Seven Girl Scouts reported the following individual earnings from their sale of cookies: \$17, \$23, \$13, \$15, \$12, \$19, and \$13. In this distribution of individual earnings, the mean is ______ the mode and ______ the median.
   a. equal to; equal to
   b. greater than; equal to
   c. equal to; less than
   d. greater than; greater than
4. When Dr. Thomas calculated her students' history test scores, she noticed that one student had an extremely high score. Which measure of central tendency should be used in this situation?
   a. mean
   b. standard deviation
   c. median
   d. either the mean or the median
5. Imagine that 4,999 people who are penniless live in Medianville. An individual whose net worth is \$500,000,000 moves to Medianville. Now the mean net worth in this town is ______ and the median net worth is ______.
   a. 0; 0
   b. \$100,000; 0
   c. 0; \$100,000
   d. \$100,000; \$100,000
6. Middle score in the distribution is to ______ and score occurring with the greatest frequency is to ______.
   a. mean; median
   b. median; mode
   c. mean; mode
   d. mode; median
7. Mean is to ______ and mode is to ______.
   a. ordinal, interval, and ratio data only; nominal data only
   b. nominal data only; ordinal data only
   c. interval and ratio data only; all types of data
   d. none of the above

8. The calculation of the standard deviation differs from the calculation of the average deviation in that the deviation scores are:
   a. squared.
   b. converted to absolute values.
   c. squared and converted to absolute values.
   d. It does not differ.
9. Imagine that distribution A contains the following scores: 11, 13, 15, 18, 20. Imagine that distribution B contains the following scores: 13, 14, 15, 16, 17. Distribution A has a ________ standard deviation and a ________ average deviation in comparison to distribution B.
   a. larger; larger
   b. smaller; smaller
   c. larger; smaller
   d. smaller; larger
10. Which of the following is not true?
    a. All scores in the distribution are used in the calculation of the range.
    b. The average deviation is a more sophisticated measure of variation than the range; however, it may not weight extreme scores adequately.
    c. The standard deviation is the most sophisticated measure of variation because all scores in the distribution are used and because it weights extreme scores adequately.
    d. None of the above.
11. If the shape of a frequency distribution is lopsided, with a long tail projecting longer to the left than to the right, how would the distribution be skewed?
    a. normally
    b. negatively
    c. positively
    d. nominally
12. If Jack scored 15 on a test with a mean of 20 and a standard deviation of 5, what is his *z*-score?
    a. 1.5
    b. −1.0
    c. 0.0
    d. Cannot be determined
13. Faculty in the physical education department at State University consume an average of 2,000 calories per day with a standard deviation of 250 calories. The distribution is normal. What proportion of faculty consumes an amount between 1,600 and 2,400 calories?
    a. .4452
    b. .8904
    c. .50
    d. None of the above
14. If the average weight for women is normally distributed with a mean of 135 pounds and a standard deviation of 15 pounds, then approximately 68% of all women should weigh between ________ and ________ pounds.
    a. 120; 150
    b. 120; 135
    c. 105; 165
    d. Cannot say from the information given
15. Sue's first philosophy exam score is −1 standard deviation from the mean in a normal distribution. The test has a mean of 82 and a standard deviation of 4. Sue's percentile rank would be approximately:
    a. 78%.
    b. 84%.
    c. 16%.
    d. Cannot say from the information given.

SELF-TEST PROBLEMS

1. Calculate the mean, median, and mode for the following distribution.

   1, 1, 2, 2, 4, 5, 8, 9, 10, 11, 11, 11

2. Calculate the range, average deviation, and standard deviation for the following distribution.

   2, 2, 3, 4, 5, 6, 7, 8, 8

3. The results of a recent survey indicate that the average new home costs $100,000 with a standard deviation of $15,000. The price of homes is normally distributed.
   a. If someone bought a home for $75,000, what proportion of homes cost an equal amount or more than this?
   b. At what percentile rank is a home that sold for $112,000?
   c. For what price would a home at the 20th percentile have sold?

Chapter 5 ▪ Statistical Software Resources

If you need help getting started with Excel or SPSS, please see Appendix D: Getting Started with Excel and SPSS.

USING EXCEL TO CALCULATE THE MEAN, MEDIAN, MODE, AND STANDARD DEVIATION

To begin using Excel to conduct data analyses, the data must be entered into an Excel spreadsheet. This simply involves opening Excel and entering the data into the spreadsheet. You can see in the following spreadsheet that I have entered the exam grade data from Table 5.1 in Chapter 5 into an Excel spreadsheet.

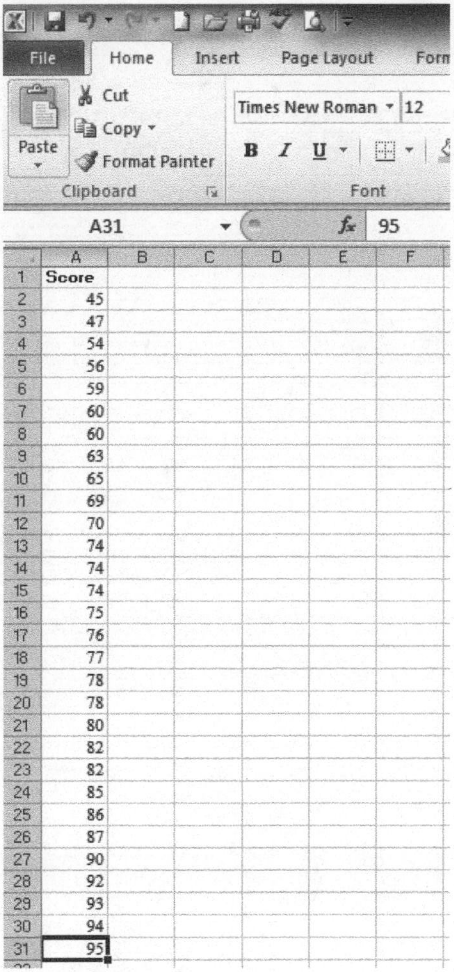

Once the data have been entered, we use the Data Analysis tool to calculate descriptive statistics. This is accomplished by clicking on the **Data** tab or ribbon and then clicking the **Data Analysis** icon on the top right side of the window. Once the Data Analysis tab is active, a dialog box of options will appear (see next).

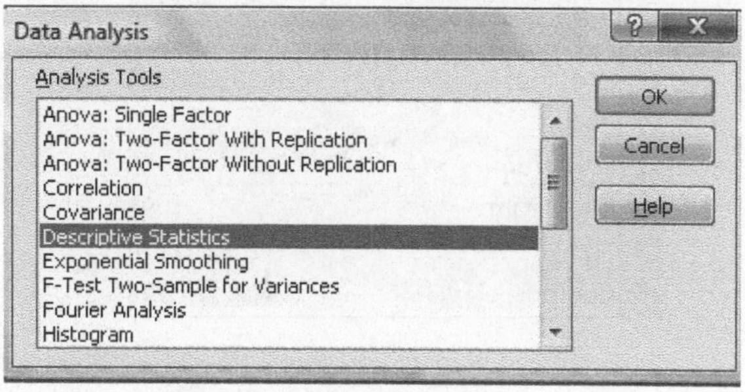

Select **Descriptive Statistics** as is indicated in the preceding box, and then click **OK**. This will lead to the following dialog box.

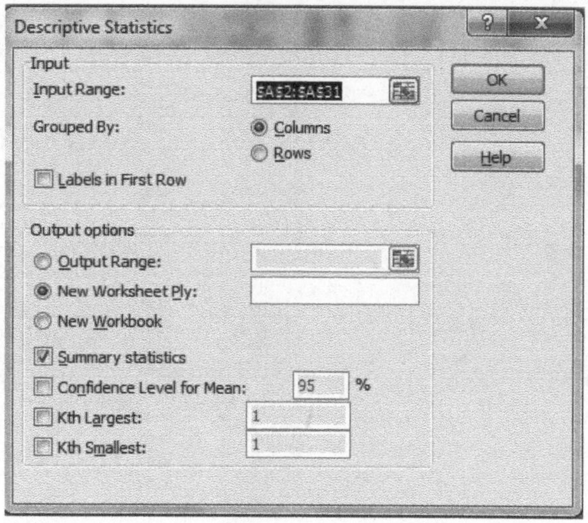

With the cursor in the **Input Range** box, highlight the data that you want analyzed from column A in the Excel spreadsheet so that they appear in the input range. In addition, check the **Summary statistics** box. Once you have done this, click **OK**. The summary statistics will appear in a new Worksheet, as seen next.

	A	B
1	*Column1*	
2		
3	Mean	74
4	Standard Error	2.532546762
5	Median	75.5
6	Mode	74
7	Standard Deviation	13.8713299
8	Sample Variance	192.4137931
9	Kurtosis	-0.60744581
10	Skewness	-0.391850234
11	Range	50
12	Minimum	45
13	Maximum	95
14	Sum	2220
15	Count	30

As you can see, there are several descriptive statistics reported, including all three measures of central tendency (mean, median, and mode).

USING SPSS TO CALCULATE THE MEAN AND STANDARD DEVIATION

As with the Excel exercise above, we will once again be using the data from Table 5.1 in Chapter 5 to calculate descriptive statistics. We begin by entering the data from Table 5.1 into an SPSS spreadsheet. This simply involves opening SPSS and entering the data into the spreadsheet. You can see in the following spreadsheet that I have entered the exam grade data from Table 5.1 into an SPSS spreadsheet.

File Edit View Data Transform Analyze Graphs Utilities Add-ons Window Help

	VAR00001	var	var	var	var	var	var	var	var	var	var
1	45.00										
2	47.00										
3	54.00										
4	56.00										
5	59.00										
6	60.00										
7	60.00										
8	63.00										
9	65.00										
10	69.00										
11	70.00										
12	74.00										
13	74.00										
14	74.00										
15	75.00										
16	76.00										
17	77.00										
18	78.00										
19	78.00										
20	80.00										
21	82.00										
22	82.00										
23	85.00										
24	86.00										
25	87.00										
26	90.00										
27	92.00										
28	93.00										
29	94.00										
30	95.00										
31											

Notice that the variable is simply named VAR0001. To rename the variable to something appropriate for your data set, click on the **Variable View** tab on the bottom left of the screen. You will see the following window.

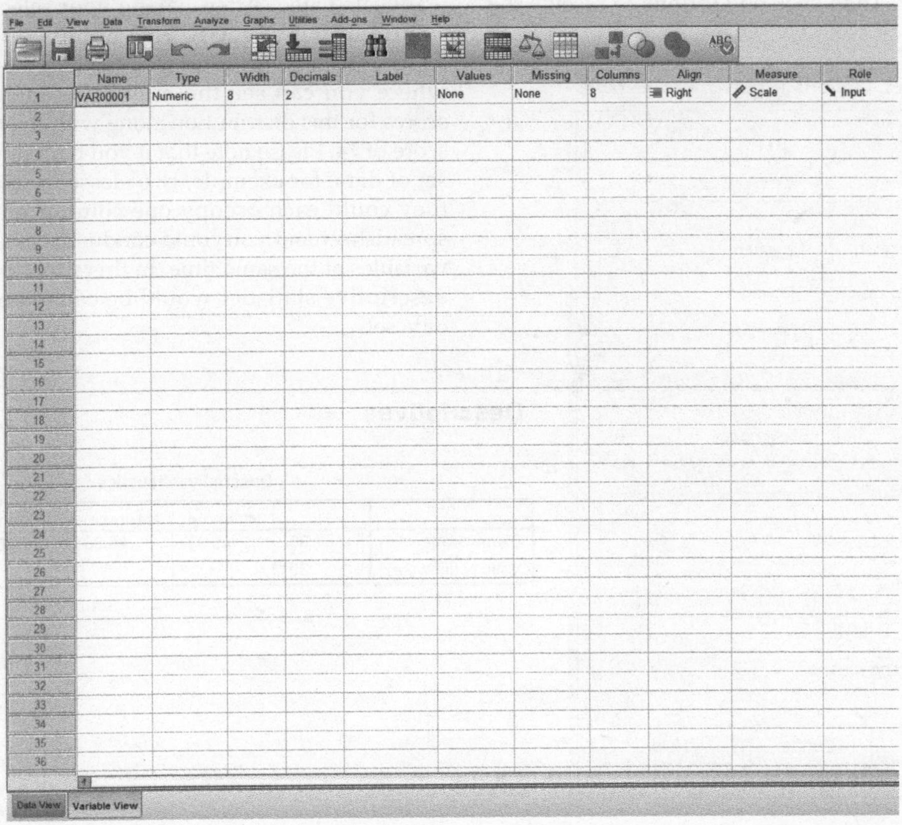

Type the name you wish to give the variable in the highlighted **Name** box. The variable name cannot have any spaces in it. Because these data represent exam grade data, we'll type in **Examgrade**. Note also that the **Type** of data is Numeric. Once the variable is named, highlight the **Data View** tab on the bottom left of the screen in order to get back to the data spreadsheet. Once you've navigated back to the data spreadsheet, click on the **Analyze** tab at the top of the screen and a drop-down menu with various statistical analyses will appear. Select **Descriptive Statistics** and then **Descriptive** The following dialog box will appear.

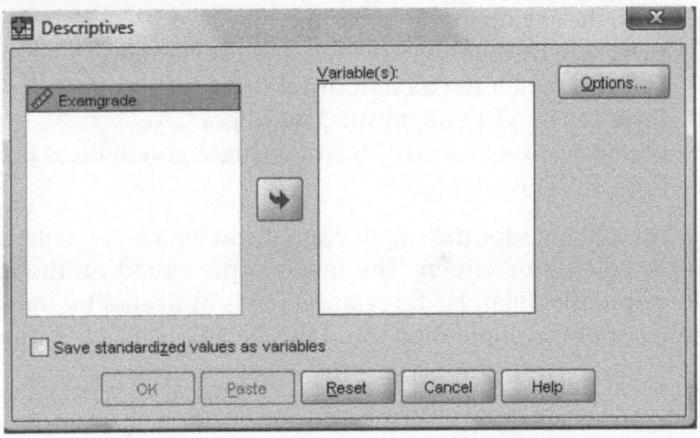

Examgrade will be highlighted, as above. Click on the arrow in the middle of the window and the Examgrade variable will be moved over to the **Variables** box. Then click on **Options** to receive the following dialog box.

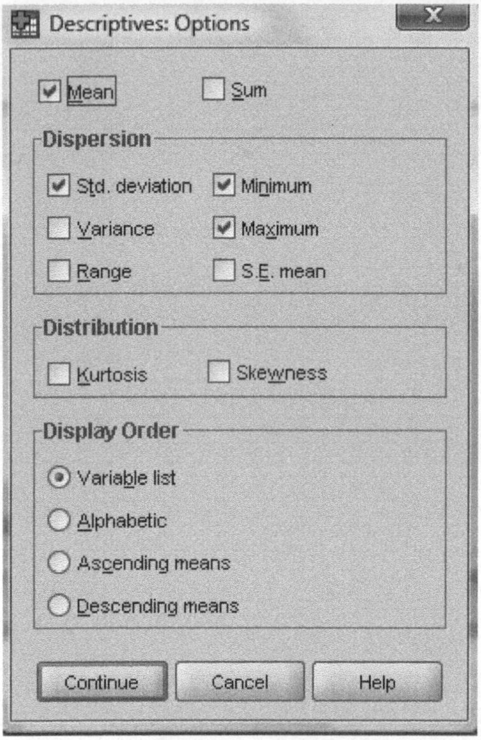

You can see that the Mean, Standard Deviation, Minimum, and Maximum are all checked. However, you could select any of the descriptive statistics you want calculated. After making your selections, click **Continue** and then **OK**. The output will appear on a separate page as an Output file like the one below where you can see the minimum and maximum scores for this distribution along with the mean exam score of 74. Please note that if you had more than one set of data, for example, two classes of exam scores, they could each occupy one column in your SPSS spreadsheet and you could conduct analyses on both variables at the same time. In this situation, separate descriptive statistics would be calculated for each data set.

Descriptives

Descriptive Statistics

	N	Minimum	Maximum	Mean	Std. Deviation
Exam Grade	30	45.00	95.00	74.0000	13.87133
Valid N (listwise)	30				

Using the TI-84 Calculator to Calculate the Mean and Standard Deviation

Follow the steps below to use your TI-84 calculator to calculate the mean for the data set from Table 5.1 in Chapter 5.

1. With the calculator on, press the STAT key.
2. EDIT will be highlighted. Press the ENTER key.
3. Under L1 enter the data from Table 3.1.
4. Press the STAT key again and highlight CALC.
5. Number 1: 1—VAR STATS will be highlighted. Press ENTER.
6. Press ENTER once again.

The statistics for the single variable on which you entered data will be presented on the calculator screen. The mean is presented on the first line of output as $\bar{X}$. The population standard deviation (σ) is indicated by the symbol σ_x. The unbiased estimator of the population standard deviation (s) is indicated by the symbol S_x.

CHAPTER

6 Correlational Methods and Statistics

Learning Objectives

- Describe the differences among strong, moderate, and weak correlation coefficients.
- Draw and interpret scatterplots.
- Explain negative, positive, curvilinear, and no relationship between variables.
- Explain how assuming causality and directionality, the third-variable problem, restrictive ranges, and curvilinear relationships can be problematic when interpreting correlation coefficients.
- Explain how correlations allow us to make predictions.
- Describe when it would be appropriate to use the Pearson product-moment correlation coefficient, the Spearman rank-order correlation coefficient, the point-biserial correlation coefficient, and the phi coefficient.
- Calculate the Pearson product-moment correlation coefficient for two variables.
- Determine and explain r^2 for a correlation coefficient.
- Explain regression analysis.
- Determine the regression line for two variables.

In this chapter, we will discuss correlational research methods and correlational statistics. As a research method, correlational designs allow you to describe the relationship between two measured variables. A correlation coefficient (descriptive statistic) helps by assigning a numerical value to the observed relationship. We will begin with a discussion of how to conduct correlational research, the magnitude and direction of correlations, and graphical representations of correlations. We will then turn to special considerations when interpreting correlations, how to use correlations for predictive purposes, and how to calculate correlation coefficients. Last, we will discuss an advanced correlational technique, regression analysis.

Conducting Correlational Research

When conducting correlational studies, researchers determine whether two variables (for example, height and weight or smoking and cancer) are related to each other. Such studies assess whether the variables are "correlated" in some way: Do people who are taller tend to weigh more, or do those who smoke tend to have a higher incidence of cancer? As we saw in Chapter 1, the correlational method is a type of nonexperimental method that describes the relationship between two measured variables. In addition to describing a relationship, correlations allow us to make predictions from one variable to another. If two variables are correlated, we can predict from one variable to the other with a certain degree of accuracy. For example, knowing that height and weight are correlated allows us to estimate, within a certain range, an individual's weight based on knowing that person's height.

Correlational studies are conducted for a variety of reasons. Sometimes it is impractical or ethically impossible to do an experimental study. For example, it would be ethically impossible to manipulate smoking and assess whether it causes cancer in humans. How would you, as a participant in an experiment, like to be randomly assigned to the smoking condition and be told that you have to smoke a pack of cigarettes a day? Obviously, this is not a viable experiment, so one means of assessing the relationship between smoking and cancer is through correlational studies. In this type of study, we can examine people who have already chosen to smoke and assess the degree of relationship between smoking and cancer.

Sometimes researchers choose to conduct correlational research because they are interested in measuring many variables and assessing the relationships between them. For example, they might measure various aspects of personality and assess the relationship between dimensions of personality.

Magnitude, Scatterplots, and Types of Relationships

magnitude An indication of the strength of the relationship between two variables.

Correlations vary in their **magnitude**—the strength of the relationship. Sometimes there is no relationship between variables, or the relationship may be weak; other relationships are moderate or strong. Correlations can also be represented graphically in a scatterplot or scattergram. In addition, relationships are of different types—positive, negative, none, or curvilinear.

Magnitude

The magnitude or strength of a relationship is determined by the correlation coefficient describing the relationship. As we saw in Chapter 3, a correlation coefficient is a measure of the degree of relationship between two variables; it can vary between −1.00 and +1.00. The stronger the relationship between the variables, the closer the coefficient is to either −1.00 or +1.00. The weaker the relationship between the variables, the closer the coefficient is to 0. You may recall from Chapter 3 that we typically discuss correlation coefficients as assessing a strong, moderate, or weak relationship, or no relationship. Table 6.1 provides general guidelines for assessing the magnitude of a relationship, but these do not necessarily hold for all variables and all relationships.

TABLE 6.1 Estimates for Weak, Moderate, and Strong Correlation Coefficients

CORRELATION COEFFICIENT	STRENGTH OF RELATIONSHIP
±.70–1.00	Strong
±.30–.69	Moderate
±.00–.29	None (.00) to weak

A correlation coefficient of either −1.00 or +1.00 indicates a perfect correlation—the strongest relationship possible. For example, if height and weight were perfectly correlated (+1.00) in a group of 20 people, this would mean that the person with the highest weight was also the tallest person, the person with the second-highest weight was the second-tallest person, and so on down the line. In addition, in a perfect relationship, each individual's score on one variable goes perfectly with his or her score on the other variable, meaning, for example, that for every increase (decrease) in height of 1 inch, there is a corresponding increase (decrease) in weight of 10 pounds. If height and weight had a perfect negative correlation (−1.00), this would mean that the person with the highest weight was the shortest, the person with the second-highest weight was the second shortest, and so on, and that height and weight increased (decreased) by a set amount for each individual. It is very unlikely that you will ever observe a perfect correlation between two variables, but you may observe some very strong relationships between variables (±.70−.99). Whereas a correlation coefficient of ±1.00 represents a perfect relationship, a coefficient of 0.00 indicates no relationship between the variables.

Scatterplots

scatterplot A figure that graphically represents the relationship between two variables.

A **scatterplot** or scattergram, a figure showing the relationship between two variables, graphically represents a correlation coefficient. Figure 6.1 presents a scatterplot of the height and weight relationship for 20 adults.

In a scatterplot, two measurements are represented for each participant by the placement of a marker. In Figure 6.1, the horizontal *x*-axis shows the

FIGURE 6.1 Scatterplot for height and weight

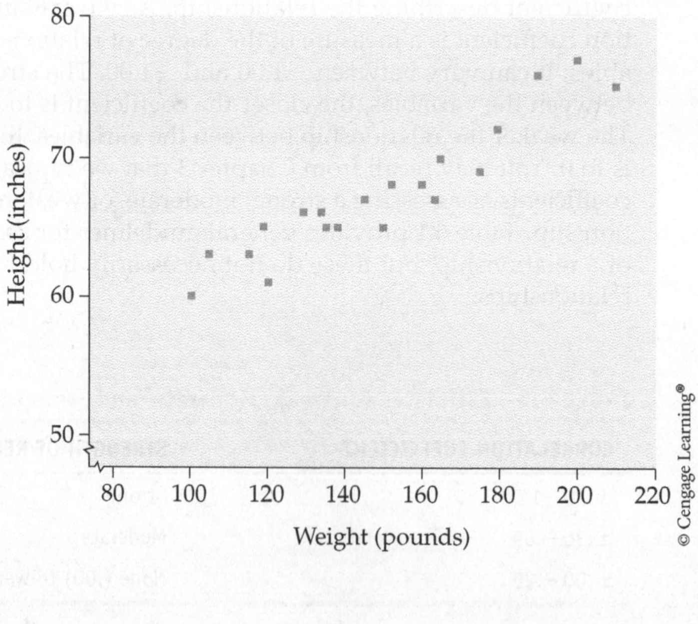

participant's weight, and the vertical y-axis shows height. The two variables could be reversed on the axes, and it would make no difference in the scatterplot. This scatterplot shows an upward trend, and the points cluster in a linear fashion. The stronger the correlation, the more tightly the data points cluster around an imaginary line through their center. When there is a perfect correlation (±1.00), the data points all fall on a straight line. In general, a scatterplot may show four basic patterns: a positive relationship, a negative relationship, no relationship, or a curvilinear relationship.

Positive Relationships

The relationship represented in Figure 6.2a shows a positive correlation, one in which a direct relationship exists between the two variables. This means that an increase in one variable is related to an increase in the other, and a decrease in one is related to a decrease in the other. Notice that this scatterplot is similar to the one in Figure 6.1. The majority of the data points fall along an upward angle (from the lower-left corner to the upper-right corner). In this example, a person who scored low on one variable also scored low on the other; an individual with a mediocre score on one variable had a mediocre score on the other; and those who scored high on one variable also scored high on the other. In other words, an increase (decrease) in one variable is accompanied by an increase (decrease) in the other variable—as variable x increases (or decreases), variable y does the same. If the data in Figure 6.2a represented height and weight measurements, we could say that

FIGURE 6.2 Possible types of correlational relationships: (a) positive; (b) negative; (c) none; (d) curvilinear

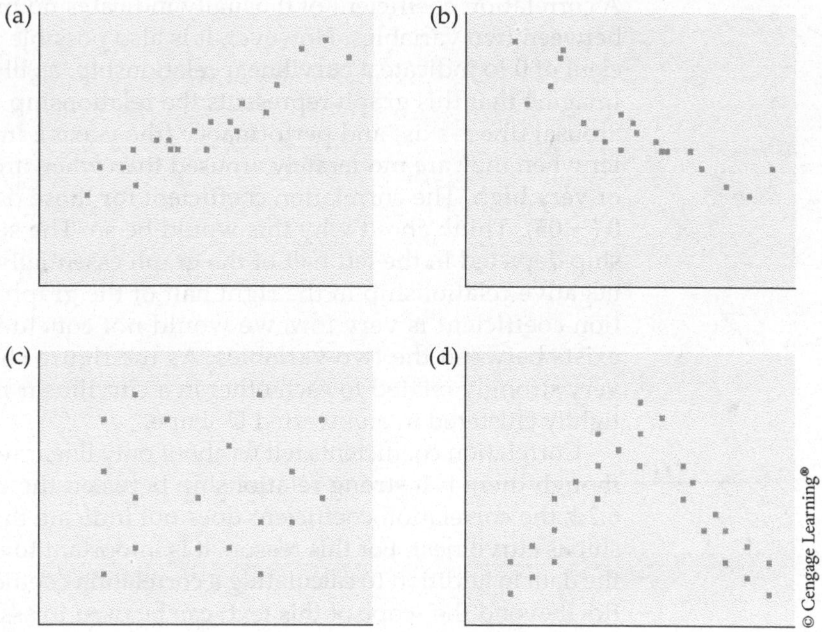

those who are taller also tend to weigh more, whereas those who are shorter tend to weigh less. Notice also that the relationship is linear. We could draw a straight line representing the relationship between the variables, and the data points would all fall fairly close to that line.

Negative Relationships

Figure 6.2b represents a negative relationship between two variables. Notice that in this scatterplot, the data points extend from the upper left to the lower right. This negative correlation indicates that an increase in one variable is accompanied by a *decrease* in the other variable. This represents an inverse relationship: The more of variable x that we have, the less we have of variable y. Assume that this scatterplot represents the relationship between age and eyesight. As age increases, the ability to see clearly tends to decrease—a negative relationship.

No Relationship

As shown in Figure 6.2c, it is also possible to observe no meaningful relationship between two variables. In this scatterplot, the data points are scattered in a random fashion. As you would expect, the correlation coefficient for these data is very close to 0 (−.09).

Curvilinear Relationships

A correlation coefficient of 0 usually indicates no meaningful relationship between two variables. However, it is also possible for a correlation coefficient of 0 to indicate a curvilinear relationship, as illustrated in Figure 6.2d. Imagine that this graph represents the relationship between psychological arousal (the x-axis) and performance (the y-axis). Individuals perform better when they are moderately aroused than when arousal is either very low or very high. The correlation coefficient for these data is also very close to 0 (−.05). Think about why this would be so. The strong positive relationship depicted in the left half of the graph essentially cancels out the strong negative relationship in the right half of the graph. Although the correlation coefficient is very low, we would not conclude that no relationship exists between the two variables. As the figure shows, the variables are very strongly related to each other in a curvilinear manner—the points are tightly clustered in an inverted U shape.

Correlation coefficients tell us about only linear relationships. Thus, even though there is a strong relationship between the two variables in Figure 6.2d, the correlation coefficient does not indicate this because the relationship is curvilinear. For this reason, it is important to examine a scatterplot of the data in addition to calculating a correlation coefficient. Alternative statistics (beyond the scope of this text) can be used to assess the degree of curvilinear relationship between two variables.

Relationships Between Variables — IN REVIEW

	TYPES OF RELATIONSHIPS			
	POSITIVE	**NEGATIVE**	**NONE**	**CURVILINEAR**
Description of Relationship	Variables increase and decrease together	As one variable increases, the other decreases—an inverse relationship	Variables are unrelated and do not move together in any way	Variables increase together up to a point and then, as one continues to increase, the other decreases
Description of Scatterplot	Data points are clustered in a linear pattern extending from lower left to upper right	Data points are clustered in a linear pattern extending from upper left to lower right	There is no pattern to the data points; they are scattered all over the graph	Data points are clustered in a curved linear pattern forming a U shape or an inverted U shape
Example of Variables Related in This Manner	Smoking and cancer	Mountain elevation and temperature	Intelligence and weight	Memory and age

CRITICAL THINKING CHECK 6.1

1. Which of the following correlation coefficients represents the weakest relationship between two variables?
   –.59
   +.10
   –1.00
   +.76
2. Explain why a correlation coefficient of 0.00 or close to 0.00 may not mean that there is no relationship between the variables.
3. Draw a scatterplot representing a strong negative correlation between depression and self-esteem. Make sure you label the axes correctly.

Misinterpreting Correlations

Correlational data are frequently misinterpreted, especially when presented by newspaper reporters, talk-show hosts, and television newscasters. Here we discuss some of the most common problems in interpreting correlations. Remember, a correlation simply indicates that there is a weak, moderate, or strong relationship (either positive or negative) or no relationship between two variables.

The Assumptions of Causality and Directionality

The most common error made when interpreting correlations is assuming that the relationship observed is causal in nature—that a change in variable A *causes* a change in variable B. Correlations simply identify relationships—they do not indicate causality. For example, a recent commercial on television was sponsored by an organization promoting literacy. The statement was made at the beginning of the commercial that a strong positive correlation has been observed between illiteracy and drug use in high school students (those high on the illiteracy variable also tended to be high on the drug use variable). The commercial concluded with a statement like "Let's stop drug use in high school students by making sure they can all read." Can you see the flaw in this conclusion? The commercial did not air for very long, and someone probably pointed out the error in the conclusion.

causality The assumption that a correlation indicates a causal relationship between the two variables.

directionality The inference made with respect to the direction of a causal relationship between two variables.

This commercial made the error of assuming causality and also the error of assuming directionality. **Causality** refers to the assumption that the correlation indicates a causal relationship between two variables, whereas **directionality** refers to the inference made with respect to the direction of a causal relationship between two variables. For example, the commercial assumed that illiteracy was causing drug use (and not that drug use was causing illiteracy); it claimed that if illiteracy were lowered, then drug use would be lowered also. As previously discussed, a correlation between two variables indicates only that they are related—they vary together. Although it is possible that one variable causes changes in the other, we cannot draw this conclusion from correlational data.

As a further example, research on self-esteem and success also illustrates the limitations of correlational data. In the pop psychology literature there are hundreds of books and programs promoting the idea that there is a causal link between self-esteem and success. Schools, businesses, and government offices have implemented programs that offer praise and complements to their students and employees in the hopes of raising self-esteem and, in turn, raising the success of the students and employees. The problem with this is that the relationship between self-esteem and success is correlational. However, people misinterpret these claims and make the error of assuming causality and directionality (i.e., high self-esteem causes success). For example, with respect to success in school, although self-esteem is positively associated with school success, it appears that better school performance contributes to high self-esteem, not the reverse (Mercer, 2010; Baumeister et al., 2003). In other words, focusing on the self-esteem part of the relationship will likely do little to raise school performance.

Research on smoking and cancer illustrates this limitation of correlational data. For research with humans, we have only correlational data indicating a positive correlation between smoking and cancer. Because these data are correlational, we cannot conclude that there is a causal relationship. In this situation, it is probable that the relationship is causal. However, based solely on correlational data, we cannot conclude that it is causal, nor can we assume the direction of the relationship. For example, the tobacco industry could argue that, yes, there is a correlation between smoking and cancer, but maybe cancer causes smoking—maybe those individuals predisposed to cancer are more attracted to smoking cigarettes. Experimental data based on research with laboratory animals do indicate that smoking causes cancer. The tobacco industry, however, frequently denied that this research is applicable to humans and for years continued to insist that no research has produced evidence of a causal link between smoking and cancer in humans.

A classic example of the assumption of causality and directionality with correlational data occurred when researchers observed a strong negative correlation between eye movement patterns and reading ability in children. Poorer readers tended to make more erratic eye movements, more movements from right to left, and more stops per line of text. Based on this correlation, some researchers assumed causality and directionality: They assumed that poor oculomotor skills caused poor reading and proposed programs for "eye movement training." Many elementary school students who were poor readers spent time in such training, supposedly developing oculomotor skills in the hope that this would improve their reading ability. Experimental research later provided evidence that the relationship between eye movement patterns and reading ability is indeed causal, but that the direction of the relationship is the reverse—poor reading causes more erratic eye movements! Children who are having trouble reading need to go back over the information more and stop and think about it more. When children improve their reading skills (improve recognition and comprehension), their eye movements become smoother (Olson & Forsberg, 1993). Because of the errors of assuming causality and directionality, many children never received the appropriate training to improve their reading ability.

The Third-Variable Problem

When we interpret a correlation, it is also important to remember that although the correlation between the variables may be very strong, it may also be that the relationship is the result of some third variable that influences both of the measured variables. The **third-variable problem** results when a correlation between two variables is dependent on another (third) variable.

third-variable problem The problem of a correlation between two variables being dependent on another (third) variable.

A good example of the third-variable problem is a well-cited study conducted by social scientists and physicians in Taiwan (Li, 1975). The researchers attempted to identify the variables that best predicted the use of birth control—a question of interest to the researchers because of overpopulation problems in Taiwan. They collected data on various behavioral and environmental variables and found that the variable most strongly correlated with contraceptive use was the number of electrical appliances (yes, electrical appliances—stereos, toasters, televisions, and so on) in the home. If we take this correlation at face value, it means that individuals with more electrical appliances tend to use contraceptives more, whereas those with fewer electrical appliances tend to use contraceptives less.

It should be obvious to you that this is not a causal relationship (buying electrical appliances does not cause individuals to use birth control nor does using birth control cause individuals to buy electrical appliances). Thus, we probably do not have to worry about people assuming either causality or directionality when interpreting this correlation. The problem here is a third variable. In other words, the relationship between electrical appliances and contraceptive use is not really a meaningful relationship—other variables are tying these two together. Can you think of other dimensions on which individuals who use contraceptives and who have a large number of appliances might be similar? If you thought of education, you are beginning to understand what is meant by third variables. Individuals with a higher education level tend to be better informed about contraceptives and also tend to have a higher socioeconomic status (they get better-paying jobs). Their higher socioeconomic status allows them to buy more "things," including electrical appliances.

partial correlation A correlational technique that involves measuring three variables and then statistically removing the effect of the third variable from the correlation of the remaining two variables.

It is possible statistically to determine the effects of a third variable by using a correlational procedure known as *partial correlation.* **Partial correlation** involves measuring all three variables and then statistically removing the effect of the third variable from the correlation of the remaining two variables. If the third variable (in this case, education) is responsible for the relationship between electrical appliances and contraceptive use, then the correlation should disappear when the effect of education is removed, or partialed out.

Restrictive Range

restrictive range A variable that is truncated and has limited variability.

The idea behind measuring a correlation is that we assess the degree of relationship between two variables. Variables, by definition, must vary. When a variable is truncated, we say that it has a **restrictive range**—the variable does not vary enough. Look at Figure 6.3a that represents a scatterplot of

FIGURE 6.3 Restricted range and correlation

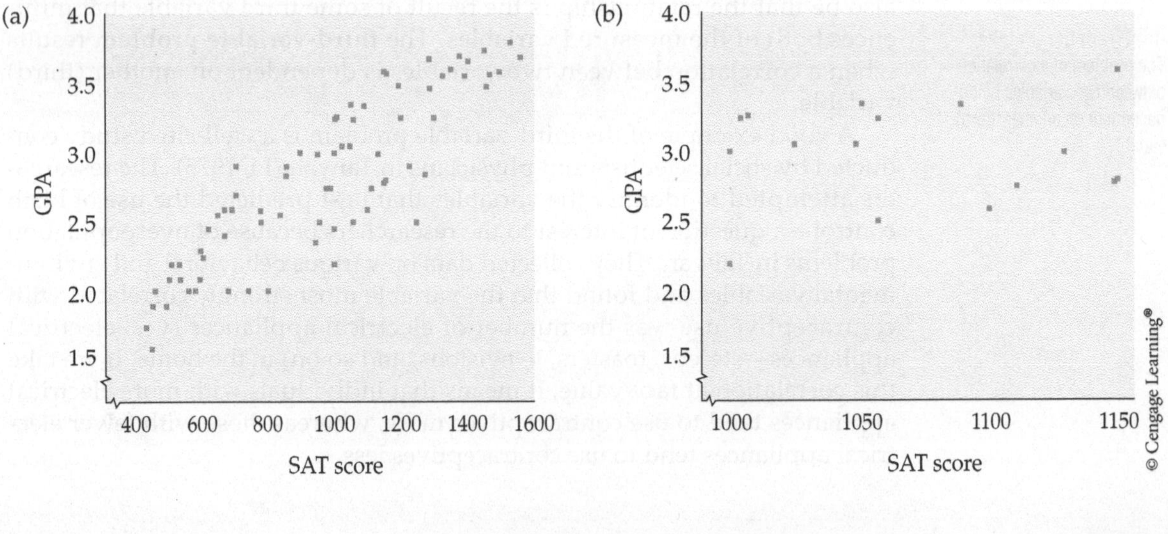

SAT scores and college GPAs for a group of students. SAT scores and GPAs are positively correlated. Neither of these variables is restricted in range (for this group of students, SAT scores vary from 400 to 1600, and GPAs vary from 1.5 to 4.0), so we have the opportunity to observe a relationship between the variables. Now look at Figure 6.3b, which represents the correlation between the same two variables, except that here the range on the SAT variable is restricted to those who scored between 1000 and 1150. The variable has been restricted or truncated and does not "vary" very much. As a result, the opportunity to observe a correlation has been diminished. Even if there were a strong relationship between these variables, we could not observe it because of the restricted range of one of the variables. Thus, when interpreting and using correlations, beware of variables with restricted ranges. For example, colleges that are very selective, such as Ivy League schools, would have a restrictive range on SAT scores—they only accept students with very high SAT scores. Thus, in these situations, SAT scores are not a good predictor of college GPAs because of the restrictive range on the SAT variable.

Curvilinear Relationships

Curvilinear relationships and the caution in interpreting them were discussed earlier in this chapter. Remember, correlations are a measure of linear relationships. When a relationship is curvilinear, a correlation coefficient does not adequately indicate the degree of relationship between the variables. If necessary, look back over the previous section on curvilinear relationships to refresh your memory concerning them.

Misinterpreting Correlations — IN REVIEW

	TYPES OF MISINTERPRETATIONS			
	CAUSALITY AND DIRECTIONALITY	**THIRD VARIABLE**	**RESTRICTIVE RANGE**	**CURVILINEAR RELATIONSHIP**
Description of Misinterpretation	We assume the correlation is causal and that one variable causes changes in the other.	Other variables are responsible for the observed correlation.	One or more of the variables is truncated or restricted and the opportunity to observe a relationship is minimized.	The curved nature of the relationship decreases the observed correlation coefficient.
Examples	We assume that smoking causes cancer or that illiteracy causes drug abuse because a correlation has been observed.	We find a strong positive relationship between birth control and the number of electrical appliances.	If SAT scores are restricted (limited in range), the correlation between SAT and GPA appears to decrease.	As arousal increases, performance increases up to a point; as arousal continues to increase, performance decreases.

> **CRITICAL THINKING CHECK 6.2**
>
> 1. I have recently observed a strong negative correlation between depression and self-esteem. Explain what this means. Make sure you avoid the misinterpretations described previously.
> 2. General State University recently investigated the relationship between SAT scores and GPAs (at graduation) for its senior class. They were surprised to find a weak correlation between these two variables. They know they have a grade inflation problem (the whole senior class graduated with GPAs of 3.0 or higher), but they are unsure how this might help account for the low correlation observed. Can you explain?

Prediction and Correlation

Correlation coefficients not only describe the relationship between variables; they also allow you to make predictions from one variable to another. Correlations between variables indicate that when one variable is present at a certain level, the other also tends to be present at a certain level. Notice the wording used. The statement is qualified by the phrase "tends to." We are not saying that a prediction is guaranteed or that the relationship is causal—but simply that the variables seem to occur together at specific levels. Think about some of the examples used in this chapter. Height and weight are positively correlated. One is not causing the other; nor can we predict exactly what an individual's weight will be based on height (or vice versa). But because the two variables are correlated, we can predict with a certain degree of accuracy what an individual's approximate weight might be if we know the person's height.

Let's take another example. We have noted a correlation between SAT scores and college freshman GPAs. Think about what the purpose of the SAT is. College admissions committees use the test as part of the admissions procedure. Why? Because there is a positive correlation between SAT scores and college GPAs in the general population. Individuals who score high on the SAT tend to have higher college freshman GPAs; those who score lower on the SAT tend to have lower college freshman GPAs. This means that knowing students' SAT scores can help predict, with a certain degree of accuracy, their freshman GPAs and thus their potential for success in college. At this point, some of you are probably saying, "But that isn't true for me—I scored poorly (or very well) on the SAT and my GPA is great (or not so good)." Statistics tell us only what the trend is for most people in the population or sample. There will always be outliers—the few individuals who do not fit the trend, but on average, or for the average person, the prediction will be accurate.

Think about another example. We know there is a strong positive correlation between smoking and cancer, but you may know someone who has smoked for 30 or 40 years and does not have cancer or any other health problems. Does this one individual negate the fact that there is a strong relationship between smoking and cancer? No. To claim that it does would be a classic **person-who argument**—arguing that a well-established statistical trend is invalid because we know a "person who" went against the trend (Stanovich, 2007). A counterexample does not change the fact of a strong statistical relationship between the variables and that you are increasing your chance of getting cancer if you smoke. Because of the correlation between the variables, we can predict (with a fairly high degree of accuracy) who might get cancer based on knowing a person's smoking history.

person-who argument Arguing that a well-established statistical trend is invalid because we know a "person who" went against the trend.

Statistical Analysis: Correlation Coefficients

Now that you understand how to interpret a correlation coefficient, let's turn to the actual calculation of correlation coefficients. The type of correlation coefficient used depends on the type of data (nominal, ordinal, interval, or ratio) that were collected.

Pearson's Product-Moment Correlation Coefficient: What It Is and What It Does

The most commonly used correlation coefficient is the **Pearson product-moment correlation coefficient,** usually referred to as **Pearson's *r*** (*r* is the statistical notation we use to report this correlation coefficient). Pearson's *r* is used for data measured on an interval or ratio scale of measurement. Refer to Figure 6.1, which presents a scatterplot of height and weight data for 20 individuals. Because height and weight are both measured on a ratio scale, Pearson's *r* is applicable to these data.

Pearson product-moment correlation coefficient (Pearson's *r*) The most commonly used correlation coefficient when both variables are measured on an interval or ratio scale.

The development of this correlation coefficient is typically credited to Karl Pearson (hence the name), who published his formula for calculating *r* in 1895. Actually, Francis Edgeworth published a similar formula for calculating *r* in 1892. Not realizing the significance of his work, however, Edgeworth embedded the formula in a statistical paper that was very difficult to follow, and it was not noted until years later. Thus, although Edgeworth had published the formula 3 years earlier, Pearson received the recognition (Cowles, 1989).

Calculations for the Pearson Product-Moment Correlation. Table 6.2 presents the raw scores from which the scatterplot in Figure 6.1 was derived, along with the mean and standard deviation for each distribution. Height is presented in inches and weight in pounds. We'll use these data to demonstrate the calculation of Pearson's *r*.

To calculate Pearson's *r*, we begin by converting the raw scores on the two different variables to the same unit of measurement. This should sound familiar to you from an earlier chapter. In Chapter 5, we used *z*-scores to

TABLE 6.2 Weight and Height Data for 20 Individuals

WEIGHT (IN POUNDS)	HEIGHT (IN INCHES)
100	60
120	61
105	63
115	63
119	65
134	65
129	66
143	67
151	65
163	67
160	68
176	69
165	70
181	72
192	76
208	75
200	77
152	68
134	66
138	65
$\mu = 149.25$ $\sigma = 30.42$	$\mu = 67.4$ $\sigma = 4.57$

convert data measured on different scales to standard scores measured on the same scale (a *z*-score represents the number of standard deviation units a raw score is above or below the mean). High raw scores are always above the mean and have positive *z*-scores; low raw scores are always below the mean and thus have negative *z*-scores.

Think about what happens if we convert our raw scores on height and weight to *z*-scores. If the correlation is strong and positive, we should find that positive *z*-scores on one variable go with positive *z*-scores on the other variable, and negative *z*-scores on one variable go with negative *z*-scores on the other variable. After we calculate *z*-scores, the next step in calculating Pearson's *r* is to calculate what is called a *cross-product*—the *z*-score on one variable multiplied by the *z*-score on the other variable. This is also sometimes referred to as a *cross-product of z-scores.* Once again, think about what happens if both *z*-scores used to calculate the cross-product are positive—the cross-product is positive. What if both *z*-scores are negative? The cross-product is again positive (a negative number multiplied by a negative number results in a positive number). If we sum all of these positive cross-products and divide by the total number of cases (to obtain the average of the cross-products), we end up with a large positive correlation coefficient.

What if we find that when we convert our raw scores to *z*-scores, positive *z*-scores on one variable go with negative *z*-scores on the other variable? These cross-products are negative and, when averaged (i.e., summed and divided by the total number of cases), result in a large negative correlation coefficient.

Last, imagine what happens if no linear relationship exists between the variables being measured. In other words, some individuals who score high on one variable also score high on the other, and some individuals who score low on one variable score low on the other. Each of these situations results in positive cross-products. However, we also find that some individuals with high scores on one variable have low scores on the other variable, and vice versa. These situations result in negative cross-products. When all of the cross-products are summed and divided by the total number of cases, the positive and negative cross-products essentially cancel each other out, and the result is a correlation coefficient close to 0.

Now that you have a basic understanding of the logic behind calculating Pearson's *r*, let's look at the formula for Pearson's *r*:

$$r = \frac{\sum z_X z_Y}{N}$$

Thus, we begin by calculating the *z*-scores for *X* (weight) and *Y* (height). They are shown in Table 6.3. Remember, the formula for a *z*-score is

$$z = \frac{X - \mu}{\sigma}$$

The first two columns list the weight and height raw scores for the 20 individuals. As a general rule of thumb, when calculating a correlation

TABLE 6.3 Calculating the Pearson Correlation Coefficient

X (WEIGHT IN POUNDS)	Y (HEIGHT IN INCHES)	z_X	z_Y	$z_X z_Y$
100	60	−1.62	−1.62	2.62
120	61	−0.96	−1.40	1.34
105	63	−1.45	−0.96	1.39
115	63	−1.13	−0.96	1.08
119	65	−0.99	−0.53	0.52
134	65	−0.50	−0.53	0.27
129	66	−0.67	−0.31	0.21
143	67	−0.21	−0.09	0.02
151	65	0.06	−0.53	−0.03
163	67	0.45	−0.09	−0.04
160	68	0.35	0.13	0.05
176	69	0.88	0.35	0.31
165	70	0.52	0.57	0.30
181	72	1.04	1.01	1.05
192	76	1.41	1.88	2.65
208	75	1.93	1.66	3.20
200	77	1.67	2.10	3.51
152	68	0.09	0.13	0.01
134	66	−0.50	−0.31	0.16
138	65	−0.37	−0.53	0.20
				$\Sigma = +18.82$

coefficient, we should have at least 10 participants per variable. Thus, with two variables, we need a minimum of 20 individuals, which we have. Following the raw scores for variable X (weight) and variable Y (height) are columns representing z_X, z_Y, and $z_X z_Y$ (the cross-product of z-scores). The cross-products column has been summed (Σ) at the bottom of the table. Now, let's use the information from the table to calculate r:

$$r = \frac{\sum z_X z_Y}{N} = \frac{18.82}{20} = +.94$$

There are alternative formulas to calculate Pearson's r, one of which is the computational formula. If your instructor prefers that you use this formula, it is presented in Table 6.4.

TABLE 6.4 Computational Formula for Pearson's Product-Moment Correlation Coefficient

$$r = \frac{\sum XY - \frac{(\sum X)(\sum Y)}{N}}{\sqrt{\left(\sum X^2 - \frac{(\sum X)^2}{N}\right)\left(\sum Y^2 - \frac{(\sum Y)^2}{N}\right)}}$$

Interpreting the Pearson Product-Moment Correlation. The obtained correlation between height and weight for the 20 individuals represented in Table 6.3 is +.94. Can you interpret this correlation coefficient? The positive sign tells us that the variables increase and decrease together. The large magnitude (close to 1.00) tells us that there is a strong relationship between height and weight: Those who are taller tend to weigh more, whereas those who are shorter tend to weigh less. You can see how to use either Excel, SPSS, or the TI-84 calculator to calculate Pearson's *r* in the Statistical Software Resources section at the end of this chapter.

coefficient of determination (r^2) A measure of the proportion of the variance in one variable that is accounted for by another variable; calculated by squaring the correlation coefficient.

In addition to interpreting the correlation coefficient, it is important to calculate the coefficient of determination. Calculated by squaring the correlation coefficient, the **coefficient of determination (r^2)** is a measure of the proportion of the variance in one variable that is accounted for by another variable. In our group of 20 individuals, there is variation in both the height and weight variables, and some of the variation in one variable can be accounted for by the other variable. We could say that some of the variation in the weights of these 20 individuals can be explained by the variation in their heights. Some of the variation in their weights, however, cannot be explained by the variation in height. It might be explained by other factors such as genetic predisposition, age, fitness level, or eating habits. The coefficient of determination tells us how much of the variation in weight is accounted for by the variation in height. Squaring the obtained correlation coefficient of +.94, we have $r^2 = .8836$. We typically report r^2 as a percentage. Hence, 88.36% of the variance in weight can be accounted for by the variance in height—a very high coefficient of determination. Depending on the research area, the coefficient of determination may be much lower and still be important. It is up to the researcher to interpret the coefficient of determination.

Alternative Correlation Coefficients

As noted previously, the type of correlation coefficient used depends on the type of data collected in the research study. Pearson's correlation coefficient is used when both variables are measured on an interval or ratio scale. Alternative correlation coefficients can be used with ordinal and nominal scales of measurement. We will mention three such correlation coefficients, but we will not present the formulas because our coverage of statistics is necessarily selective. All of the formulas are based on Pearson's formula and can be found in a more comprehensive statistics text. Each of these coefficients is reported on a scale of −1.00 to +1.00. Thus, each is interpreted in a fashion similar to Pearson's r. Last, like Pearson's r, the coefficient of determination (r^2) can be calculated for each of these correlation coefficients to determine the proportion of variance in one variable accounted for by the other variable.

Spearman's rank-order correlation coefficient The correlation coefficient used when one (or more) of the variables is measured on an ordinal (ranking) scale.

point-biserial correlation coefficient The correlation coefficient used when one of the variables is measured on a dichotomous nominal scale and the other is measured on an interval or ratio scale.

phi coefficient The correlation coefficient used when both measured variables are dichotomous and nominal.

When one or more of the variables is measured on an ordinal (ranking) scale, the appropriate correlation coefficient is **Spearman's rank-order correlation coefficient**. If one of the variables is interval or ratio in nature, it must be ranked (converted to an ordinal scale) before the calculations are done. If one of the variables is measured on a dichotomous (having only two possible values, such as gender) nominal scale and the other is measured on an interval or ratio scale, the appropriate correlation coefficient is the **point-biserial correlation coefficient**. Last, if both variables are dichotomous and nominal, the **phi coefficient** is used.

Although both the point-biserial and phi coefficients are used to calculate correlations with dichotomous nominal variables, you should refer back to one of the cautions mentioned earlier in the chapter concerning potential problems when interpreting correlation coefficients—specifically, the caution regarding restricted ranges. Clearly, a variable with only two levels has a restricted range. What would the scatterplot for such a correlation look like? The points would have to be clustered in columns or groups, depending on whether one or both of the variables were dichotomous.

Correlation Coefficients — IN REVIEW

	TYPES OF COEFFICIENTS			
	PEARSON	SPEARMAN	POINT-BISERIAL	PHI
Type of Data	Both variables must be interval or ratio	Both variables are ordinal (ranked)	One variable is interval or ratio, and one variable is nominal and dichotomous	Both variables are nominal and dichotomous
Correlation Reported	±.0–1.0	±.0–1.0	±.0–1.0	±.0–1.0
r^2 Applicable?	Yes	Yes	Yes	Yes

CRITICAL THINKING CHECK 6.3

1. Calculate and interpret r^2 for an observed correlation coefficient between SAT scores and college GPAs of +.72.
2. In a recent study, researchers were interested in determining the relationship between gender and the amount of time spent studying for a group of college students. Which correlation coefficient should be used to assess this relationship?
3. If I wanted to correlate class rank with SAT scores for a group of 50 individuals, which correlation coefficient would I use?

Advanced Correlational Techniques: Regression Analysis

regression analysis A procedure that allows us to predict an individual's score on one variable based on knowing one or more other variables.

regression line The best-fitting straight line drawn through the center of a scatterplot that indicates the relationship between the variables.

As you have seen, the correlational procedure allows us to predict from one variable to another, and the degree of accuracy with which we can predict depends on the strength of the correlation. A tool that enables us to predict an individual's score on one variable based on knowing one or more other variables is **regression analysis**. For example, imagine that you are an admissions counselor at a university, and you want to predict how well a prospective student might do at your school based on both SAT scores and high school GPA. Or imagine that you work in a human resources office, and you want to predict how well future employees might perform based on test scores and performance measures. Regression analysis allows you to make such predictions by developing a regression equation.

To illustrate regression analysis, let's use the height and weight data presented in Figure 6.1 and Table 6.2. When we used these data to calculate Pearson's r, we determined that the correlation coefficient was +.94. Also, we can see in Figure 6.1 that the relationship between the variables is *linear,* meaning that a straight line can be drawn through the data to represent the relationship between the variables. This **regression line** is shown in Figure 6.4; it is the best-fitting straight line drawn through the center of the scatterplot that indicates the relationship between the variables height and weight for this group of individuals.

Regression analysis involves determining the equation for the best-fitting line for a data set. This equation is based on the equation for representing a line that you may remember from algebra class: $y = mx + b$ where m is the slope of the line and b is the y-intercept (the point where the line crosses the y-axis). For a linear regression analysis, the formula is essentially the same, although the symbols differ:

$$Y' = bX + a$$

where Y' is the predicted value on the Y variable, b is the slope of the line, X represents an individual's score on the X variable, and a is the y-intercept. Using this formula, then, we can predict an individual's approximate score on variable Y based on that person's score on variable X. With the height and weight data, for example, we can predict an individual's approximate height based on knowing that person's weight. You can picture what we are talking about by looking at Figure 6.4. Given the regression line in Figure 6.4, if we know an individual's weight (read from the x-axis), we can predict the person's height (by finding the corresponding value on the y-axis).

To use the regression line formula, we need to determine both b and a. Let's begin with the slope (b). The formula for computing b is

$$b = r\left(\frac{\sigma_Y}{\sigma_X}\right)$$

FIGURE 6.4 The relationship between height and weight with the regression line indicated

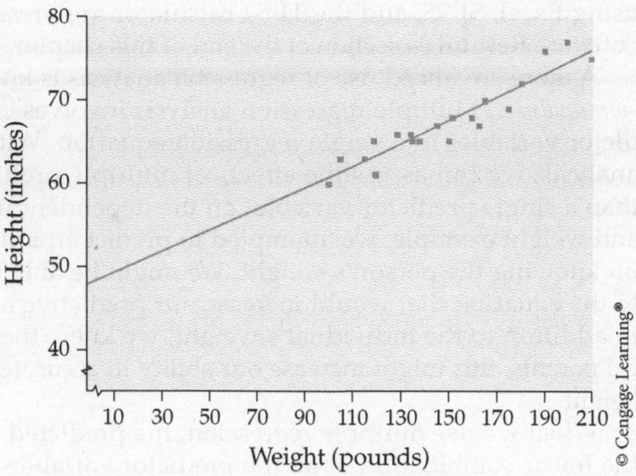

This should look fairly simple to you. We have already calculated r and the standard deviations (σ) for both height and weight (see Table 6.2). Using these calculations, we can compute b as follows:

$$b = .94\left(\frac{4.57}{30.42}\right) = .94(0.150) = 0.141$$

Now that we have computed b, we can compute a. The formula for a is

$$a = \bar{Y} - b(\bar{X})$$

Once again, this should look fairly simple because we have just calculated b, and $\bar{Y}$ and $\bar{X}$ are presented in Table 6.2 as μ for each variable. Using these values in the formula for a, we have

$$\begin{aligned} a &= 67.40 - 0.141(149.25) \\ &= 67.40 - 21.04 \\ &= 46.36 \end{aligned}$$

Thus, the regression equation for the line for the data in Figure 6.4 is

$$Y' \text{ (height)} = 0.141X\text{(weight)} + 46.36$$

where 0.141 is the slope, and 46.36 is the y-intercept. Thus, if we know that an individual weighs 110 pounds, we can predict the person's height using this equation:

$$\begin{aligned} Y' &= 0.141(110) + 46.36 \\ &= 15.51 + 46.36 \\ &= 61.87 \textit{ inches} \end{aligned}$$

Determining the regression equation for a set of data thus allows us to predict from one variable to the other. The calculations for regression analysis using Excel, SPSS, and the TI-84 calculator are presented in the Statistical Software Resources section at the end of this chapter.

A more advanced use of regression analysis is known as *multiple regression analysis*. Multiple regression analysis involves combining several predictor variables in a single regression equation. With multiple regression analysis, we can assess the effects of multiple predictor variables (rather than a single predictor variable) on the dependent measure. In our height and weight example, we attempted to predict an individual's height based on knowing the person's weight. We might be able to add other variables to the equation that would increase our predictive ability. For example, if, in addition to the individual's weight, we knew the height of the biological parents, this might increase our ability to accurately predict the person's height.

When we use multiple regression, the predicted value of Y' represents the linear combination of all the predictor variables used in the equation. The rationale behind using this more advanced form of regression analysis is that in the real world, it is unlikely that one variable is affected by only one other variable. In other words, real life involves the interaction of many variables on other variables. Thus, to more accurately predict variable A, it makes sense to consider all possible variables that might influence variable A. In our example, it is doubtful that height is influenced by weight alone. There are many other variables that might help us to predict height, such as the variable mentioned previously—the height of each biological parent. The calculation of multiple regression is beyond the scope of this book. For further information, consult a more advanced statistics text.

Summary

After reading this chapter, you should have an understanding of the correlational research method that allows researchers to observe relationships between variables and of correlation coefficients, the statistics that assess that relationship. Correlations vary in type (positive, negative, none, or curvilinear) and magnitude (weak, moderate, or strong). The pictorial representation of a correlation is a scatterplot. A scatterplot allows us to see the relationship, facilitating its interpretation.

Several errors are commonly made when interpreting correlations, including assuming causality and directionality, overlooking a third variable, having a restrictive range on one or both variables, and assessing a curvilinear relationship. Knowing that two variables are correlated allows researchers to make predictions from one variable to the other.

We introduced four different correlation coefficients (Pearson's, Spearman's, point-biserial, and phi) along with when each should be used. Also discussed were the coefficient of determination and regression analysis, which provides a tool for predicting from one variable to another.

KEY TERMS

magnitude
scatterplot
causality
directionality
third-variable problem
partial correlation
restrictive range
person-who argument
Pearson product-moment correlation coefficient (Pearson's r)
coefficient of determination (r^2)
Spearman's rank-order correlation coefficient
point-biserial correlation coefficient
phi coefficient
regression analysis
regression line

CHAPTER EXERCISES

(Answers to odd-numbered exercises appear in Appendix C.)

1. A health club recently conducted a study of its members and found a positive relationship between exercise and health. It was claimed that the correlation coefficient between the variables of exercise and health was +1.25. What is wrong with this statement? In addition, it was stated that this proved that an increase in exercise increases health. What is wrong with this statement?
2. Draw a scatterplot indicating a strong negative relationship between the variables of income and mental illness. Be sure to label the axes correctly.
3. We have mentioned several times that there is a fairly strong positive correlation between SAT scores and freshman GPAs. The admissions process for graduate school is based on a similar test, the GRE, which also has a potential 400 to 1600 total point range. If graduate schools do not accept anyone who scores below 1000 and if a GPA below 3.00 represents failing work in graduate school, what would we expect the correlation between GRE scores and graduate school GPAs to be like in comparison to the correlation between SAT scores and college GPAs? Why would we expect this?
4. In a study on caffeine and stress, college students indicated how many cups of coffee they drink per day and their stress level on a scale of 1 to 10. The data are provided in the following table.

Number of Cups of Coffee	*Stress Level*
3	5
2	3
4	3
6	9
5	4
1	2
7	10
3	5
2	3
4	8

Calculate a Pearson's r to determine the type and strength of the relationship between caffeine and stress level. How much of the variability in stress scores is accounted for by the number of cups of coffee consumed per day?

5. Given the following data, determine the correlation between IQ scores and psychology exam scores, between IQ scores and statistics exam scores, and between psychology exam scores and statistics exam scores.

Student	*IQ Score*	*Psychology Exam Score*	*Statistics Exam Score*
1	140	48	47
2	98	35	32
3	105	36	38
4	120	43	40
5	119	30	40
6	114	45	43
7	102	37	33
8	112	44	47
9	111	38	46
10	116	46	44

Calculate the coefficient of determination for each of these correlation coefficients, and explain what it means. In addition, calculate the regression equation for each pair of variables.

6. Assuming that the regression equation for the relationship between IQ score and psychology exam score is $Y' = 9 + 0.274X$, what would you expect the psychology exam scores to be for the following individuals given their IQ exam scores?

Individual	IQ Score (X)	Psychology Exam Score (Y)
Tim	118	
Tom	98	
Tina	107	
Tory	103	

CRITICAL THINKING CHECK ANSWERS

6.1

1. +.10
2. A correlation coefficient of .00 or close to .00 may indicate no relationship or a weak relationship. However, if the relationship is curvilinear, the correlation coefficient could also be .00 or close to this. In this case, there is a relationship between the two variables, but because the relationship is curvilinear, the correlation coefficient does not truly represent the strength of the relationship.
3.

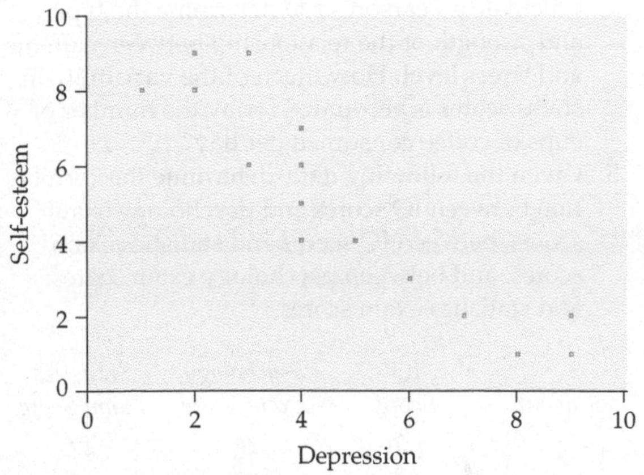

6.2

1. A strong negative correlation between depression and self-esteem means that individuals who are more depressed also tend to have lower self-esteem, whereas individuals who are less depressed tend to have higher self-esteem. It does not mean that one variable causes changes in the other, but simply that the variables tend to move together in a certain manner.
2. General State University observed such a weak correlation between GPAs and SAT scores because of a restrictive range on the GPA variable. Because of grade inflation, the whole senior class graduated with a GPA of 3.0 or higher. This restriction on one of the variables lessens the opportunity to observe a correlation.

6.3

1. r^2=.52. Although the correlation coefficient between SAT scores and GPAs is strong, the coefficient of determination shows us that SAT scores account for only 52% of the variability in GPAs.
2. In this study, gender is nominal in scale, and the amount of time spent studying is ratio in scale. Thus, a point-biserial correlation coefficient is appropriate.
3. Because class ranks are an ordinal scale of measurement and SAT scores are measured on an interval/ratio scale, you would have to convert SAT scores to an ordinal scale and use the Spearman rank-order correlation coefficient.

WEB RESOURCES

The book-specific website at CengageBrain .com offers students a variety of study tools and useful resources such as glossaries and flashcards.

Chapter 6 ▪ Study Guide

CHAPTER 6 SUMMARY AND REVIEW: CORRELATIONAL METHODS AND STATISTICS

After reading this chapter, you should have an understanding of the correlational research method that allows researchers to observe relationships between variables and correlation coefficients, the statistics that assess that relationship. Correlations vary in type (positive or negative) and magnitude (weak, moderate, or strong). The pictorial representation of a correlation is a scatterplot. Scatterplots allow us to see the relationship, facilitating the interpretation of a relationship.

When interpreting correlations, several errors are commonly made. These include assuming causality and directionality, the third-variable problem, having a restrictive range on one or both variables, and assessing a curvilinear relationship. Knowing that two variables are correlated allows researchers to make predictions from one variable to another.

Four different correlation coefficients (Pearson's, Spearman's, point-biserial, and phi) and when each should be used were discussed. The coefficient of determination was also discussed with respect to more fully understanding correlation coefficients. Lastly, regression analysis, which allows us to predict from one variable to another, was described.

CHAPTER 6 REVIEW EXERCISES

(Answers to exercises appear in Appendix C.)

FILL-IN SELF-TEST

Answer the following questions. If you have trouble answering any of the questions, restudy the relevant material before going on to the multiple-choice self test.

1. A ________ is a figure showing the relationship between two variables that graphically represents the relationship between the variables.
2. When an increase in one variable is related to a decrease in the other variable and vice versa, we have observed an inverse or ________ relationship.
3. When we assume that because we have observed a correlation between two variables, one variable must be causing changes in the other variable, we have made the errors of ________ and ________.
4. A variable that is truncated and does not vary enough is said to have a ________.
5. The ________ correlation coefficient is used when both variables are measured on an interval/ratio scale.
6. The ________ correlation coefficient is used when one variable is measured on an interval/ratio scale and the other on a nominal scale.
7. To measure the proportion of variance accounted for in one of the variables by the other variable, we use the ________.
8. ________ is a procedure that allows us to predict an individual's score on one variable based on knowing their score on a second variable.

MULTIPLE-CHOICE SELF-TEST

Select the single best answer for each of the following questions. If you have trouble answering any of the questions, restudy the relevant material.

1. The magnitude of a correlation coefficient is to _______ and the type of correlation is to _______.
   a. slope; absolute value
   b. sign; absolute value
   c. absolute value; sign
   d. none of the above
2. Strong correlation coefficient is to weak correlation coefficient as _______ is to _______.
   a. −1.00; +1.00
   b. −1.00; −.10
   c. +1.00; −1.00
   d. +.10; −1.00
3. Which of the following correlation coefficients represents the variables with the weakest degree of relationship?
   a. +.89
   b. −1.00
   c. +.10
   d. −.47
4. A correlation coefficient of +1.00 is to _______ and a correlation coefficient of −1.00 is to _______.
   a. no relationship; weak relationship
   b. weak relationship; perfect relationship
   c. perfect relationship; perfect relationship
   d. perfect relationship; no relationship
5. If the points on a scatterplot are clustered in a pattern that extends from the upper left to the lower right, this would suggest that the two variables depicted are:
   a. normally distributed.
   b. positively correlated.
   c. regressing toward the average.
   d. negatively correlated.
6. We would expect the correlation between height and weight to be _______, whereas we would expect the correlation between age in adults and hearing ability to be _______.
   a. curvilinear; negative
   b. positive; negative
   c. negative; positive
   d. positive; curvilinear
7. When we argue against a statistical trend based on one case we are using a:
   a. third-variable.
   b. regression analysis.
   c. partial correlation.
   d. person-who argument.
8. If a relationship is curvilinear, we would expect the correlation coefficient to be:
   a. close to 0.00.
   b. close to +1.00.
   c. close to −1.00.
   d. an accurate representation of the strength of the relationship.
9. The _______ is the correlation coefficient that should be used when both variables are measured on an ordinal scale.
   a. Spearman rank-order correlation coefficient
   b. coefficient of determination
   c. point-biserial correlation coefficient
   d. Pearson product-moment correlation coefficient
10. Suppose that the correlation between age and hearing ability for adults is −.65. What proportion (or percent) of the variability in hearing ability is accounted for by the relationship with age?
    a. 65%
    b. 35%
    c. 42%
    d. unable to determine
11. Drew is interested in assessing the degree of relationship between belonging to a Greek organization and the number of alcoholic drinks consumed per week. Drew should use the _______ correlation coefficient to assess this.
    a. partial
    b. point-biserial
    c. phi
    d. Pearson product-moment
12. Regression analysis allows us to:
    a. predict an individual's score on one variable based on knowing the individual's score on another variable.
    b. determine the degree of relationship between two interval/ratio variables.
    c. determine the degree of relationship between two nominal variables.
    d. predict an individual's score on one variable based on knowing that the variable is interval/ratio in scale.

Chapter 6 ▪ Statistical Software Resources

If you need help getting started with Excel or SPSS, please see Appendix D: Getting Started with Excel and SPSS.

CORRELATION COEFFICIENTS

The data we'll be using to illustrate how to calculate correlation coefficients are the weight and height data presented in the Table 6.2 Chapter 6.

Using Excel

To illustrate how Excel can be used to calculate a correlation coefficient, let's use the data from Table 6.2, on which we will calculate Pearson's product-moment correlation coefficient. In order to do this, we begin by entering the data from Table 6.2 into Excel. The following figure illustrates this—the weight data were entered into column A and the height data into column B.

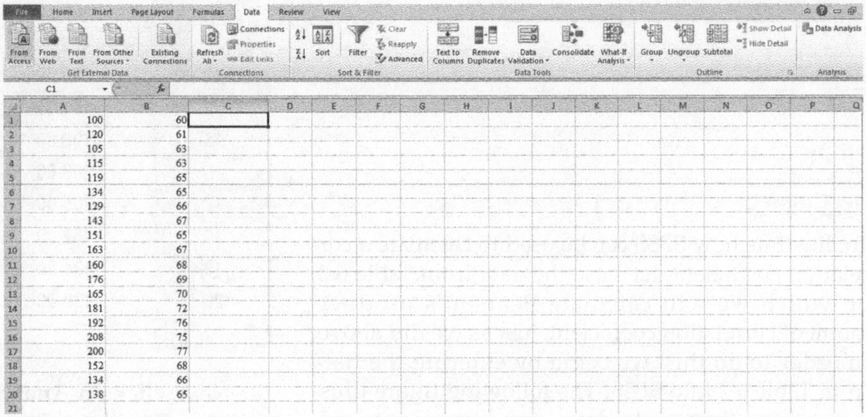

Next, with the **Data** ribbon active, as in the preceding window, click on **Data Analysis** in the upper right corner. The following dialog box will appear.

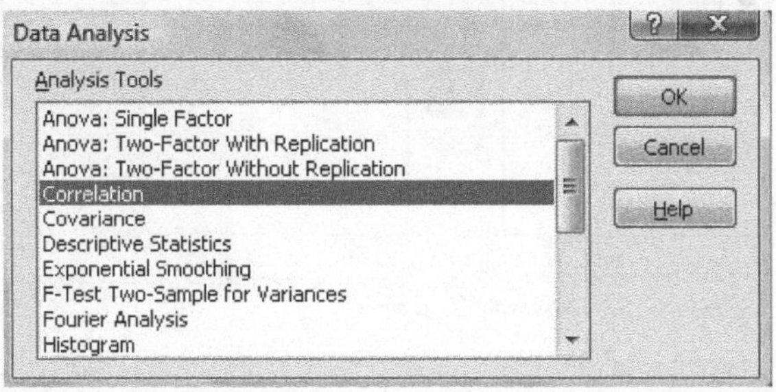

Highlight **Correlation** and then click **OK**. The subsequent dialog box will appear.

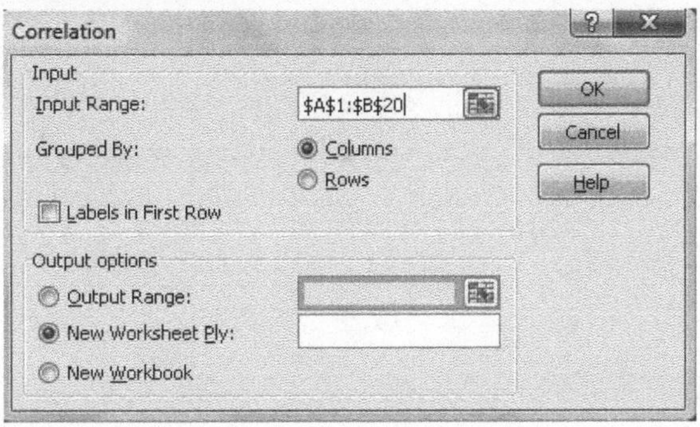

With the cursor in the **Input Range** box, highlight the data in Columns A and B and click **OK**. The output worksheet generated from this is very small and simply reports the correlation coefficient of +.94, as seen next.

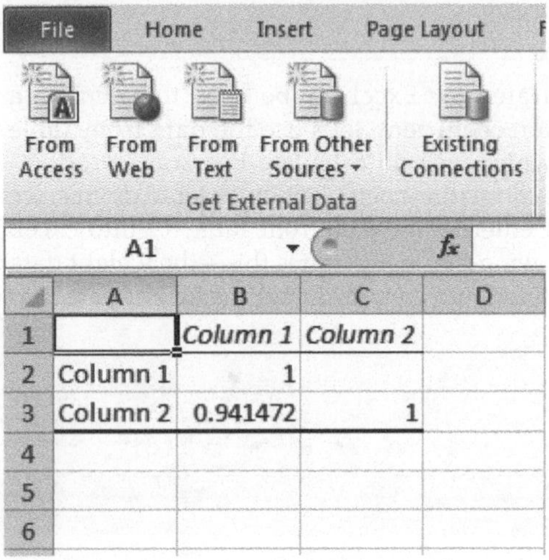

Using SPSS

To illustrate how SPSS can be used to calculate a correlation coefficient, let's use the data from Table 6.2, on which we will calculate Pearson's product-moment correlation coefficient, just as we did above. In order to do this, we begin by entering the data from Table 6.2 into SPSS. The following figure illustrates this—the weight data were entered into column A and the height data into column B.

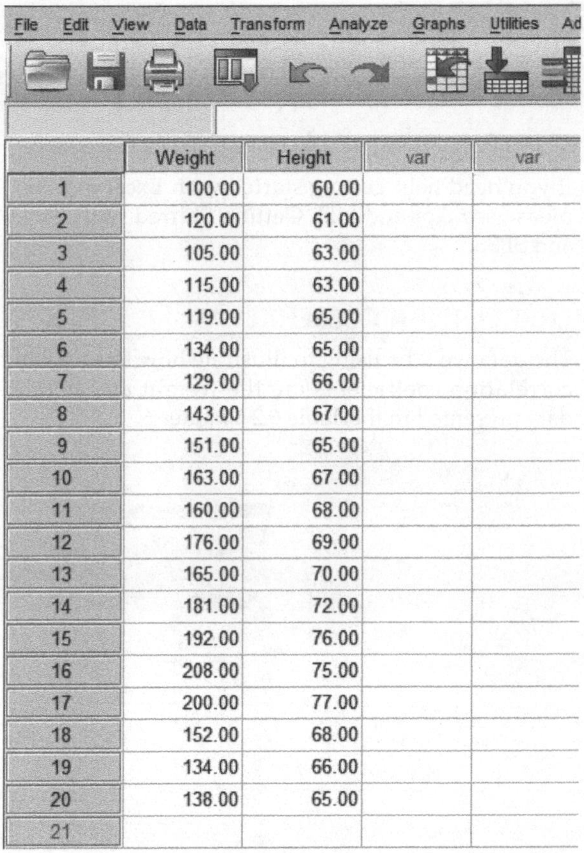

Next, click on **Analyze,** followed by **Correlate**, and then **Bivariate**. The dialog box that follows will be produced.

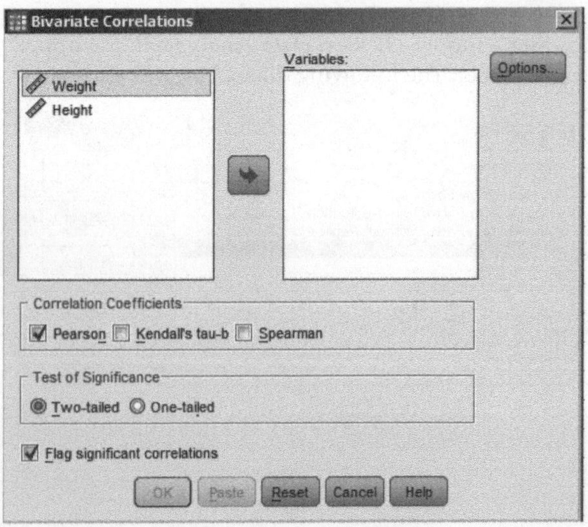

Move the two variables you want correlated (Weight and Height) into the Variables box. In addition, click **One-tailed** because this was a one-tailed test, and lastly, click on Options and select **Means and standard deviations**, thus letting SPSS know that you want descriptive statistics on the two variables. The dialog box should now appear as follows.

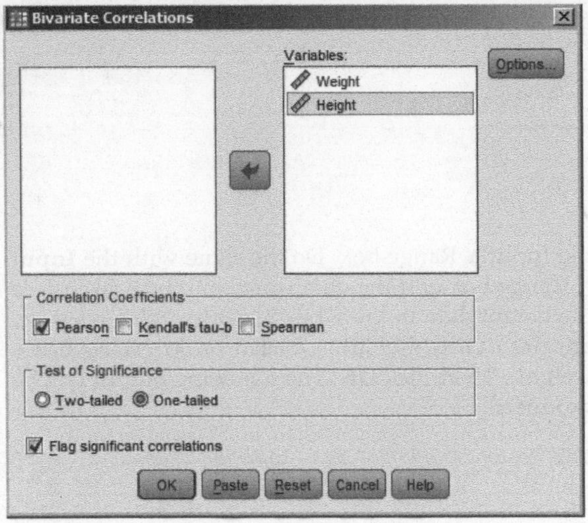

Click **OK** to receive the following output.

Correlations

Descriptive Statistics

	Mean	Std. Deviation	N
Weight	149.2500	31.21213	20
Height	67.4000	4.68368	20

Correlations

		Weight	Height
Weight	Pearson Correlation	1	.941**
	Sig. (1-tailed)		.000
	N	20	20
Height	Pearson Correlation	.941**	1
	Sig. (1-tailed)	.000	
	N	20	20

**. Correlation is significant at the 0.01 level (1-tailed).

The correlation coefficient of +.941 is provided along with the one-tailed significance level and the mean and standard deviation for each of the variables.

Using the TI84

Let's use the data from Table 6.2 to conduct the analyses using the TI84 calculator.

1. With the calculator on, press the STAT key.
2. EDIT will be highlighted. Press the ENTER key.
3. Under L1 enter the weight data from Table 6.2.
4. Under L2 enter the height data from Table 6.2.
5. Press the 2nd key and 0 [catalog] and scroll down to DiagnosticOn and press ENTER. Press ENTER once again. (The message DONE should appear on the screen.)
6. Press the STAT key and highlight CALC. Scroll down to 8:LinReg(a+bx) and press ENTER.
7. Type L_1(by pressing the 2nd key followed by the 1 key) followed by a comma and L_2 (by pressing the 2nd key followed by the 2 key) next to LinReg(a+bx). It should appear as follows on the screen: LinReg(a+bx) L_1,L_2
8. Press ENTER.

The values of a (46.31), b (0.141), r^2 (.89), and r (.94) should appear on the screen. You can see that r (the correlation coefficient) is the same as that calculated by Excel and SPSS.

REGRESSION ANALYSIS

The data we'll be using to illustrate how to calculate a regression analysis are the weight and height data presented in the Table 6.2 in Chapter 6.

Using Excel

To illustrate how Excel can be used to calculate a regression analysis, let's use the data from Table 6.2, on which we will calculate a regression line. In order to do this, we begin by entering the data from Table 6.2 into Excel. The following figure illustrates this—the weight data were entered into column A and the height data into column B.

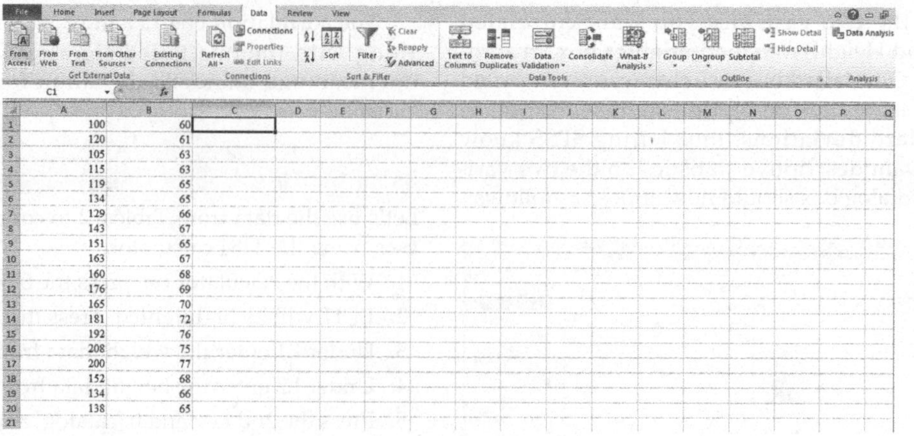

Next, with the **Data** ribbon active, as in the preceding window, click on **Data Analysis** in the upper right corner. The following drop-down box will appear.

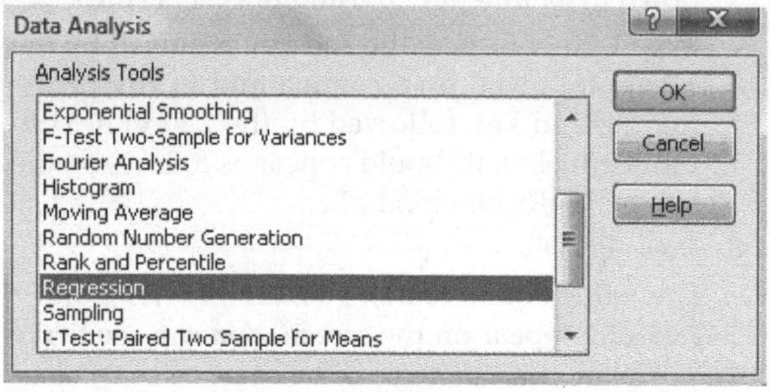

Highlight **Regression** and then click **OK**. The dialog box that follows will appear.

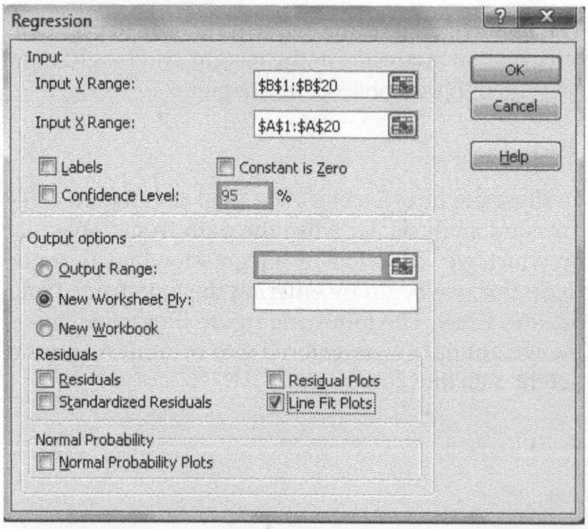

With the cursor in the **Input Y Range** box, highlight the height data in column B so that it appears in the Input Y Range box. Do the same with the **Input X Range** box and the data from column A (we place the height data in the Y box because this is what we are predicting—height—based on knowing one's weight). Then click **OK**. The following output will be produced.

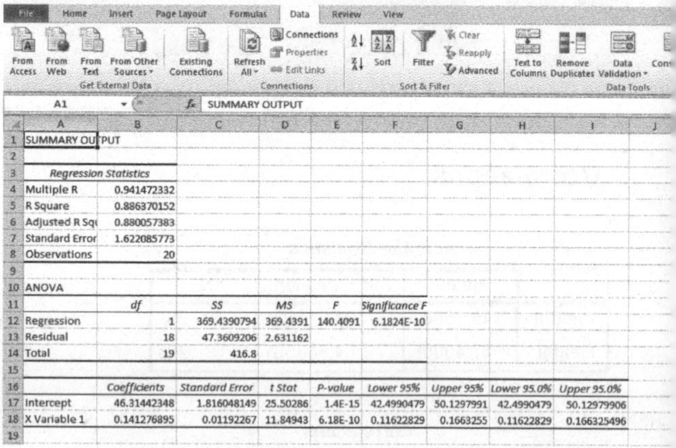

SUMMARY OUTPUT								
Regression Statistics								
Multiple R	0.941472332							
R Square	0.886370152							
Adjusted R Sq	0.880057383							
Standard Error	1.622085773							
Observations	20							
ANOVA								
	df	*SS*	*MS*	*F*	*Significance F*			
Regression	1	369.4390794	369.4391	140.4091	6.1824E-10			
Residual	18	47.3609206	2.631162					
Total	19	416.8						
	Coefficients	*Standard Error*	*t Stat*	*P-value*	*Lower 95%*	*Upper 95%*	*Lower 95.0%*	*Upper 95.0%*
Intercept	46.31442348	1.816048149	25.50286	1.4E-15	42.4990479	50.1297991	42.4990479	50.12979906
X Variable 1	0.141276895	0.01192267	11.84943	6.18E-10	0.11622829	0.1663255	0.11622829	0.166325496

We are primarily interested in the data necessary to create the regression line—the *Y*-intercept and the slope. This can be found on lines 17 and 18 of the output worksheet in the first column labeled Coefficients. We see that the *Y*-intercept is 46.31 and the slope is .141. Thus, the regression equation would be $Y' = .141(X) + 46.31$.

Using SPSS

To illustrate how SPSS can be used to calculate a regression analysis, let's again use the data from Table 6.2, on which we will calculate a regression line, just as we did with Excel. In order to do this, we begin by entering the data from Table 6.2 into SPSS. The following figure illustrates this.

Next, click on **Analyze,** followed by **Regression,** and then **Linear** as in the following dialog box.

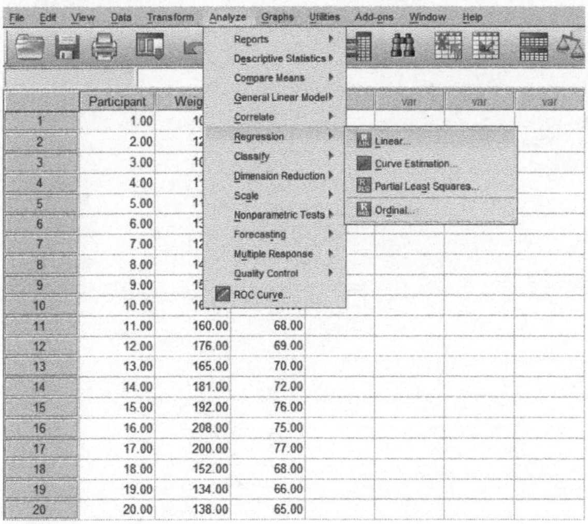

The dialog box that follows will be produced.

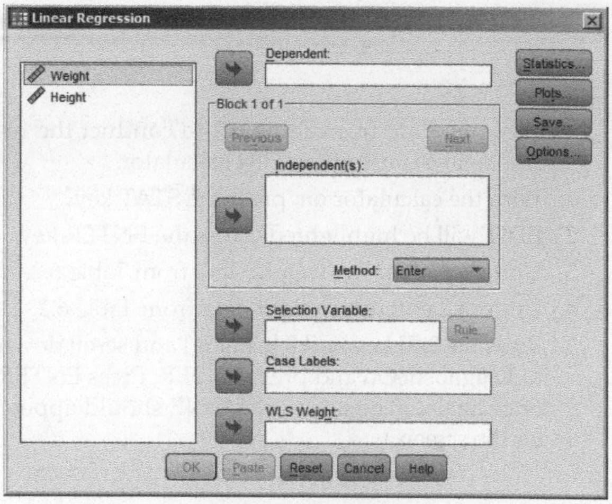

For this regression analysis, we are attempting to predict height based on knowing an individual's weight. Thus, we are using height as the dependent measure in our model and weight as the independent measure. Enter Height into the **Dependent** box and Weight into the **Independent** box by using the appropriate arrows. Then click **OK**. The output will be generated in the output window.

Regression

Variables Entered/Removed[b]

Model	Variables Entered	Variables Removed	Method
1	Weight[a]	.	Enter

a. All requested variables entered.

b. Dependent Variable: Height

Model Summary

Model	R	R Square	Adjusted R Square	Std. Error of the Estimate
1	.941[a]	.886	.880	1.62209

a. Predictors: (Constant), Weight

Coefficients[a]

Model		Unstandardized Coefficients B	Unstandardized Coefficients Std. Error	Standardized Coefficients Beta	t	Sig.
1	(Constant)	46.314	1.816		25.503	.000
	Weight	.141	.012	.941	11.849	.000

a. Dependent Variable: Height

We are most interested in the data necessary to create the regression line—the *Y*-intercept and the slope. This can be found in the box labeled

Coefficients. We see that the *Y*-intercept (Constant) is 46.314 and the slope is 0.141. Thus, the regression equation would be $Y' = 0.141(X) + 46.31$.

Using the TI84

Let's use the data from Table 6.2 to conduct the regression analysis using the TI84 calculator.

1. With the calculator on, press the STAT key.
2. EDIT will be highlighted. Press the ENTER key.
3. Under L1 enter the weight data from Table 6.2.
4. Under L2 enter the height data from Table 6.2.
5. Press the 2nd key and 0 [catalog] and scroll down to DiagnosticOn and press ENTER. Press ENTER once again. (The message DONE should appear on the screen.)
6. Press the STAT key and highlight CALC. Scroll down to 8:LinReg(a+bx) and press ENTER.
7. Type L_1(by pressing the 2nd key followed by the 1 key) followed by a comma and L_2 (by pressing the 2nd key followed by the 2 key) next to LinReg(a+bx). It should appear as follows on the screen: LinReg(a+bx) L_1,L_2
8. Press ENTER.

The values of *a* (46.31), *b* (0.141), r^2 (.89), and *r* (.94) should appear on the screen. (Please note: Any differences between the numbers calculated on the TI84 and those calculated previously by hand are due to rounding.)

CHAPTER 7

Probability and Hypothesis Testing

Learning Objectives

- Understand how probability is used in everyday life.
- Know how to compute a probability.
- Understand and be able to apply the multiplication rule.
- Understand and be able to apply the addition rule.
- Understand the relationship between the standard normal curve and probability.
- Differentiate null and alternative hypotheses.
- Differentiate one- and two-tailed hypothesis tests.
- Explain how Type I and Type II errors are related to hypothesis testing.
- Explain what statistical significance means.

---

probability The study of likelihood and uncertainty; the number of ways a particular outcome can occur, divided by the total number of outcomes.

hypothesis testing The process of determining whether a hypothesis is supported by the results of a research study.

In this chapter you will be introduced to the concepts of probability and hypothesis testing. **Probability** is the study of likelihood and uncertainty. Most decisions that we make are probabilistic in nature.

Thus, probability plays a critical role in most professions and in our everyday decisions. We will discuss basic probability concepts along with how to compute probabilities and the use of the standard normal curve in making probabilistic decisions.

Hypothesis testing is the process of determining whether a hypothesis is supported by the results of a research project. Our introduction to hypothesis testing will include a discussion of the null and alternative hypotheses, Type I and Type II errors, and one- and two-tailed tests of hypotheses as well as an introduction to statistical significance and probability as they relate to inferential statistics.

Probability

In order to better understand the nature of probabilistic decisions, consider the following court case of *The People v. Collins*, 1968. In this case, the robbery victim was unable to identify his assailant. All that the victim could recall was that the assailant was female with a blonde ponytail. In addition, he remembered that she fled the scene in a yellow convertible that was driven by an African American male who had a full beard. The suspect in the case fit the description given by the victim, so the question was "Could the jury be sure, beyond a reasonable doubt, that the woman on trial was the robber?" The evidence against her was as follows: She was blonde and often wore her hair in a ponytail; her codefendant friend was an African American male with a moustache, beard, and a yellow convertible. The attorney for the defense stressed the fact that the victim could not identify this woman as the woman who robbed him; therefore, there should be reasonable doubt on the part of the jury.

The prosecutor, on the other hand, called an expert in probability theory who testified to the following: The probability of all of the above conditions (being blonde and often having a ponytail and having an African American male friend and his having a full beard and his owning a yellow convertible) co-occurring when these characteristics are independent was one in 12 million. The expert further testified that the combination of characteristics was so unusual that the jury could in fact be certain "beyond a reasonable doubt" that the woman was the robber. The jury returned a verdict of "guilty" (Arkes & Hammond, 1986; Halpern, 1996).

As can be seen in the previous example, the legal system operates on probability and recognizes that we can never be absolutely certain when deciding whether an individual is guilty. Thus the standard of "beyond a reasonable doubt" was established and jurors base their decisions on probability, whether they realize it or not. Most decisions that we make on a daily basis are, in fact, based on probabilities. Diagnoses made by doctors, verdicts produced by juries, decisions made by business executives regarding expansion and what products to carry, decisions regarding whether individuals are admitted to colleges, and most everyday decisions all involve using probability. In addition, all games of chance (for example, cards, horse racing, the stock market) involve probability.

If you think about it, there is very little in life that is certain. Therefore, most of our decisions are probabilistic and having a better understanding of probability will help you with those decisions. In addition, because probability also plays an important role in science, that is another important reason for us to have an understanding of it. As we will see in later chapters, the laws of probability are critical in the interpretation of research findings.

Basic Probability Concepts

Probability refers to the number of ways a particular outcome (event) can occur divided by the total number of outcomes (events). (Please note that the words *outcome* and *event* will be used interchangeably in this chapter.) Probabilities are often presented or expressed as proportions. Proportions vary between 0.0 and 1.0, where a probability of 0.0 means the event certainly will not occur and a probability of 1.0 means that the event is certain to occur. Thus, any probability between 0.0 and 1.0 represents an event with some degree of uncertainty to it. How much uncertainty depends on the exact probability with which we are dealing. For example, a probability close to 0.0 represents an event that is almost certain not to occur, and a probability close to 1.0 represents an event that is almost certain to occur. On the other hand, a probability of .50 represents maximum uncertainty. In addition, keep in mind that probabilities tell us about the likelihood of events in the long run, not the short run.

Let's start with a simplistic example of probability. What is the probability of getting a "head" when tossing a coin? In this example we have to consider how many ways there are to get a "head" on a coin toss (there is only one way, the coin lands heads up) and how many possible outcomes there are (there are two possible outcomes, either a "head" or a "tail"). So, the probability of a "head" in a coin toss is:

$$p(Head) = \frac{\textit{Number of ways to get a head}}{\textit{Number of possible outcomes}} = \frac{1}{2} = .50$$

This means that in the long run, we can expect a coin to land heads up 50% of the time.

Let's consider some other examples. How likely would it be for an individual to roll a 2 in one roll of a die? Once again, let's put this into basic probability terms. There is only one way to roll a 2, the die lands with the 2 side up. How many possible outcomes are there in a single roll of a die? There are six possible outcomes (any number between 1 and 6 could appear on the die). Hence, the probability of rolling a 2 on a single roll of a die would be 1/6, or about .17. Represented as a formula as we did for the previous example this would be:

$$p(2) = \frac{\textit{Number of ways to get a 2}}{\textit{Number of possible outcomes}} = \frac{1}{6} = .17$$

Let's make it a little more difficult. What is the probability of rolling an odd number in a single roll of a die? Well, there are three odd numbers on any single die (1, 3, and 5). Thus, there are three ways that an odd number can occur. Once again, how many possible outcomes are there in a single roll of a die? Six (any number between 1 and 6). Therefore, the probability of rolling an odd number on a single roll is 3/6, or .50. Represented as a formula this would be:

$$p(odd\ number) = \frac{\textit{Number of ways to get an odd number}}{\textit{Number of possible outcomes}} = \frac{3}{6} = .50$$

What if I asked you what the probability of rolling a single-digit number is in a single roll of a die? A die has six numbers on it, and each is a single-digit number. Thus, there are six ways to get a single-digit number. How many possible outcomes are there in a single roll of a die? Once again, six. Hence, the probability of rolling a single-digit number is 6/6, or 1.0. If someone asked you to place a bet on this occurring, you could not lose on this bet! Once again, as a formula this would be:

$$p(\textit{single-digit number}) = \frac{\textit{Number of ways to get a single-digit number}}{\textit{Number of possible outcomes}}$$

$$= \frac{6}{6} = 1.0$$

Now that you have a basic idea of where probabilities come from, let's talk a little bit more about how we use probabilities. Keep in mind that probabilities tell us something about what will happen in the long run. Therefore, when we think about using some of the probabilities that we just calculated, we have to think about using them in the long run. For example, we determined that the probability of rolling a 2 on a single roll of a die was .17. This means that over many rolls of the die, it will land with the 2 side up about 17% of the time. We cannot predict what will happen on any single roll of the die, but over many rolls of the die, we will roll a 2 with a probability of .17. This means that with a very large number of trials, we can predict with great accuracy what proportion of the rolls will end up as 2s. However, we cannot predict which particular roll will yield a 2. So when we think about using probabilities, we need to think about using them for predictions in the long run, not the short run.

CRITICAL THINKING CHECK 7.1

1. What is the probability of pulling a king from a standard (52-card) deck of playing cards?
2. What is the probability of pulling a spade from a standard deck of playing cards?
3. What is the probability of rolling an even number on a single roll of a die?
4. Imagine that you have a bag that contains four black poker chips and seven red poker chips. What is the probability of pulling a black poker chip from the bag?

The Rules of Probability

Often we are concerned with the probability of two or more events occurring and not just the probability of a single event occurring. For example, what is the probability of rolling at least one 4 in two rolls of a die, or what is the probability of getting two tails in two flips of a coin?

FIGURE 7.1
Tree diagram of possible coin toss outcomes

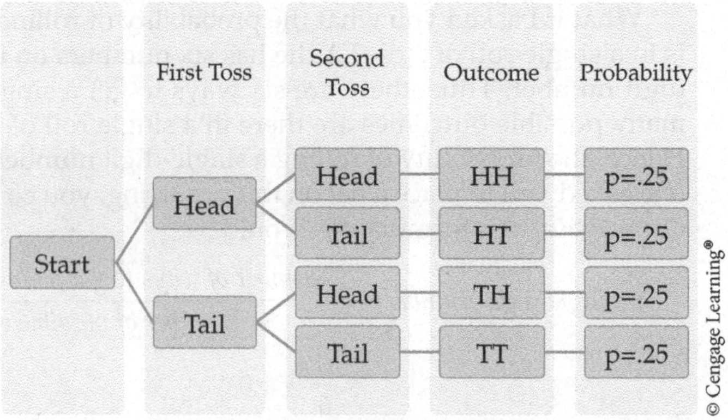

Let's use the coin-toss example to determine the probability of two tails occurring in two flips of a coin. Based on what we discussed in the previous section, we know that the probability of a tail on one flip of a coin is ½, or .50. The same is true for the second toss; the probability of a tail is ½, or .50. However, let's think about the possible outcomes for two tosses of a coin. One outcome is a head on the first toss and a head on the second toss (HH). The other outcomes would be a head followed by a tail (HT), a tail followed by a head (TH), and a tail followed by a tail (TT). These four possible outcomes are illustrated in the tree diagram in Figure 7.1.

Notice that the probability of two tails or any one of the other three possible outcomes is ¼, or .25. But how are these probabilities calculated? The general rule that we apply here is known as the multiplication rule, or the *and* rule. When the events are independent and we want to know the probability of one event "and" another event, we use this rule.

multiplication rule A probability rule stating that the probability of a series of outcomes occurring on successive trials is the product of their individual probabilities, when the sequence of outcomes is independent.

The **multiplication rule** says that the probability of a series of out comes occurring on successive trials is the product of their individual probabilities when the events are independent (do not impact one another). Thus, when using the multiplication rule, we multiply the probability of the first event by the probability of the second event. Therefore, for the present problem, the probability of a tail in the first toss is ½, or .50, and the probability of a tail in the second toss is ½, or .50. When we multiply these two probabilities, we have $.50 \times .50 = .25$. This should make some sense to you because the probability of both events occurring should be less than that of either event alone. We can represent the problem as follows:

$$p(\text{tail on first toss } \textit{and} \text{ tail on second toss}) = p(\text{tail on first toss}) \times p(\text{tail on second toss})$$

Let's try another example. Assuming that the probabilities of having a girl and having a boy are both .50 for single-child births, what is the probability that a couple planning a family of three children would have the children in the following order: girl, girl, boy?

You can see in the tree diagram in Figure 7.2 that the probability of girl, girl, boy is .125. Let's use the *and* rule to double-check this probability. The

FIGURE 7.2
Tree diagram of possible birth orders

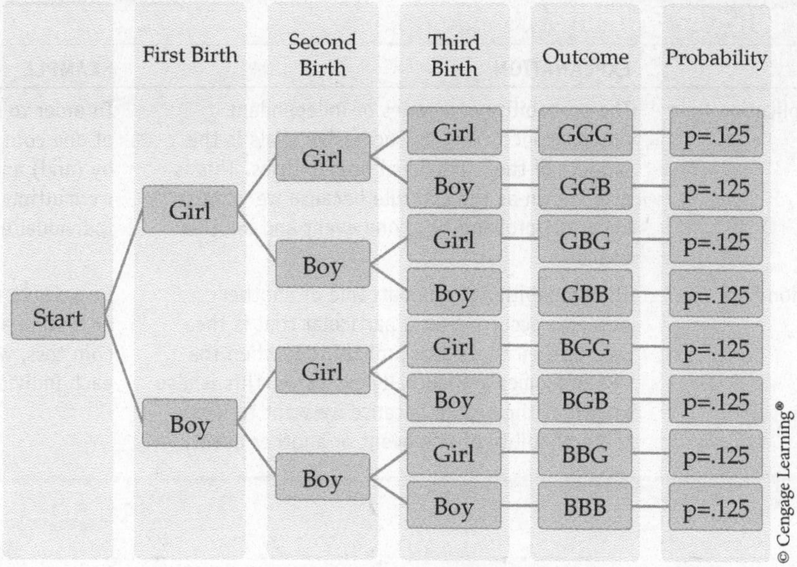

probability of a girl as the first child is ½, or .50. The same is true for the probability of a girl as the second child (.50) and the probability of a boy as the third child (.50). In order to determine the probability of this sequence of births, we multiply: .50 × .50 × .50 = .125.

In addition to being able to calculate probabilities based on a series of independent events (as in the preceding examples), we can also calculate the probability of one event or another event occurring on a single trial when the events are mutually exclusive. *Mutually exclusive* means that only one of the events can occur on a single trial. For example, a coin toss can either be heads or tails on a given trial, but not both. When dealing with mutually exclusive events, we apply what is known as the **addition rule**, which states that the probability of one outcome or the other outcome occurring on a particular trial is the sum of their individual probabilities. In other words, we are adding the two probabilities together. Thus, the probability of having either a girl or a boy when giving birth would be:

addition rule A probability rule stating that the probability of one outcome or another outcome occurring on a particular trial is the sum of their individual probabilities, when the outcomes are mutually exclusive.

$$p(\text{girl } or \text{ boy}) = p(\text{girl}) + p(\text{boy}) = .50 + .50 = 1.00$$

This is sometimes referred to as the *or* rule because we are determining the probability of one event or the other event.

Let's try another problem using the *or* rule. What is the probability of drawing either a club or a heart when drawing one card from a deck of cards? The probability of drawing a club is 13/52, or .25. The same holds for drawing a heart (13/52 = .25). Thus, the probability of drawing either a club or a heart card on a single draw would be .25 + .25 = .50.

$$p(\text{club or heart}) = p(\text{club}) + p(\text{heart}) = .25 + .25 = .50$$

The Rules of Probability — IN REVIEW

RULE	EXPLANATION	EXAMPLE
The Multiplication Rule	The probability of a series of independent outcomes occurring on successive trials is the product of their individual probabilities. This is also known as the *and* rule because we want to know the probability of one event and another event.	In order to determine the probability of one coin toss of a head followed by (and) another coin toss of a head, we multiply the probability of each individual event: $.50 \times .50 = .25$
The Addition Rule	The probability of one outcome or another outcome occurring on a particular trial is the sum of their individual probabilities when the two outcomes are mutually exclusive. This is also known as the *or* rule because we want to know the probability of one event or another event.	In order to determine the probability of tossing a head or a tail on a single coin toss, we sum the probability of each individual event: $.50 + .50 = 1.0$

CRITICAL THINKING CHECK 7.2

1. Which rule, the multiplication rule or the addition rule, would be applied in each of the following situations?
   a. What is the probability of a couple having a girl as their first child followed by a boy as their second child?
   b. What is the probability of pulling a spade or a diamond from a standard deck of cards on a single trial?
   c. What is the probability of pulling a spade (and then putting it back in the deck) followed by pulling a diamond from a standard deck of cards?
   d. What is the probability of pulling a jack or a queen from a standard deck of cards on a single trial?
2. Determine the probability for each of the examples in exercise 1.

Probability and the Standard Normal Distribution

As you might remember from Chapter 5, *z* scores can be used to determine proportions under the standard normal curve. In that chapter, we used *z* scores and the area under the standard normal curve to determine percentile ranks. We will now use *z* scores and the area under the standard normal curve (Table A.2) to determine probabilities. As you might remember, the standard normal curve has a mean of 0 and a standard deviation of 1. In addition, as discussed in Chapter 5, the standard normal curve is symmetrical and bell-shaped, and the mean, median, and mode are all the same. Take a look at Figure 7.3, which represents the area under the standard normal curve in terms of standard deviations. We've already looked at this

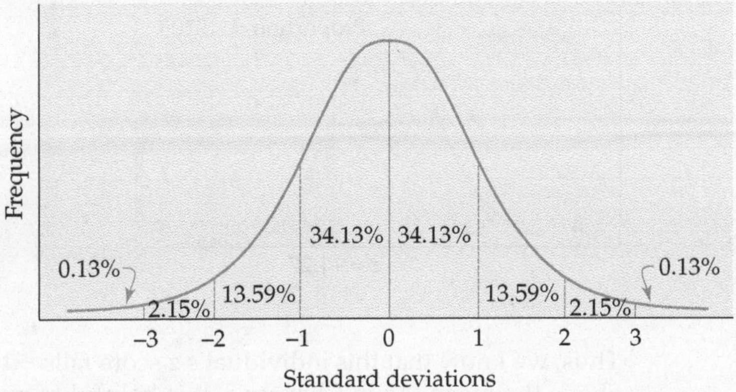

FIGURE 7.3
Area under the standard normal curve

figure in Chapter 5, and, based on this figure, we see that approximately 68% of the observations in the distribution fall between −1.0 and +1.0 standard deviations from the mean. This approximate percentage holds for all data that are normally distributed. Notice also that approximately 13.5% of the observations fall between –1.0 and –2.0, another 13.5% between +1.0 and +2.0, approximately 2% between −2.0 and −3.0, and another 2% between +2.0 and +3.0. Only .13% of the scores are beyond a *z* score of either ±3.0. If you sum the percentages in Figure 7.3, you will have 100%—all of the area under the curve, representing everybody in the distribution. If you sum half of the curve, you will have 50%—half of the distribution.

We can use the areas under the standard normal curve to determine the probability that an observation falls within a certain area under the curve. Let's use a distribution that is normal to illustrate what we mean. Intelligence test scores are normally distributed with a mean of 100 and a standard deviation of 15. We could use the standard normal curve to determine the probability of randomly selecting someone from the population who had an intelligence score as high or higher than a certain amount. For example, if a school psychologist wanted to know the probability of selecting a student from the general population who had an intelligence test score of 119 or higher, we could use the area under the standard normal curve to determine this. First, we have to convert the intelligence test score to a *z* score. As you might remember, the formula for a *z* score is:

$$z = \frac{X - \mu}{\sigma}$$

where X represents the individual's score on the intelligence test, μ represents the population mean, and σ represents the population standard deviation. Using this formula, we can calculate the individual's *z* score as follows:

$$z = \frac{X - \mu}{\sigma} = \frac{119 - 100}{15} = \frac{19}{15} = +1.27$$

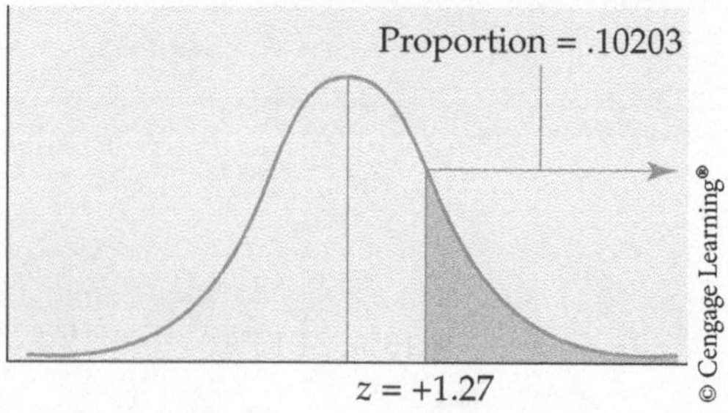

FIGURE 7.4 Standard normal curve with $z = +1.27$ indicated

Thus, we know that this individual's *z* score falls +1.27 standard deviations above the mean. As in Chapter 5, it is helpful to represent this on a figure where the *z* score of +1.27 is indicated. This is illustrated in Figure 7.4.

Now, in order to determine the probability of selecting a student with an intelligence test score of 119 or higher, we need to turn to Table A.2 in Appendix A. We begin by looking up a *z* score of 1.27 and find that for this *z* score, a proportion of .39797 of the intelligence test scores fall between the *z* score and the mean of the distribution, and a proportion of .10203 of the intelligence test scores fall beyond the *z* score. Referring to Figure 7.4, we see that the proportion of the curve in which we are interested is the area beyond the score, or .10203. This means that the probability of randomly selecting a student with an intelligence test score of 119 or higher is .10203, or just slightly higher than 10%. We can represent this problem in standard probability format as follows:

$$p(X \geq 119) = .10203$$

Let's try a couple more probability problems using the intelligence test score distribution. First, what is the probability of the school psychologist randomly selecting a student with an intelligence test score of 85 or higher? Second, what is the probability of the school psychologist selecting a student with an intelligence test score of 70 or lower?

Let's begin with the first problem. We need to convert the intelligence test score to a *z* score and then consult Table A.2.

$$z = \frac{X - \mu}{\sigma} = \frac{85 - 100}{15} = \frac{-15}{15} = -1.0$$

When we consult Table A.2, we find that for a *z* score of −1.0, .15866 of the scores fall below this score and .34134 of the scores fall between this score and the mean of the distribution. This *z* score is illustrated in Figure 7.5 along with the area in which we are interested—the probability of a student with an intelligence test score of 85 or higher being selected.

In order to determine the probability of selecting a student with an intelligence test score this high or higher, we take the area between the mean and the *z* score (.34134) and add the .50 from the other half of the distribution to it. Hence, the probability of selecting a student with an intelligence test score of 85 or higher is .84134, or approximately 84%. You should see

FIGURE 7.5
Standard normal curve with $z = -1.0$ indicated

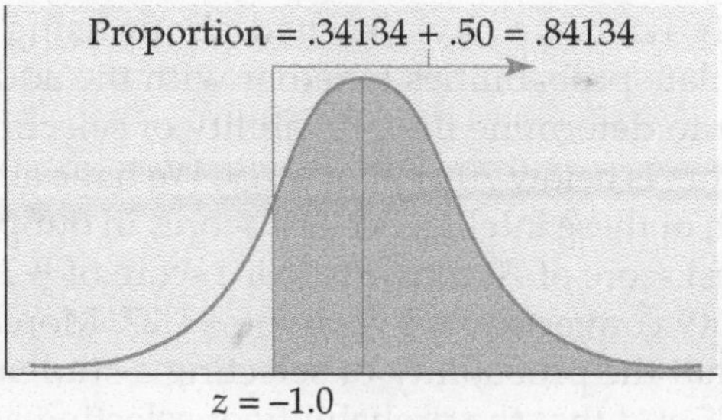

that the probability of this happening is fairly high because when we look at Figure 7.5 we are talking about a large proportion of people who fit this description. This can be represented as follows:

$$p(X \geq 85) = .84134$$

Let's work the second problem, the probability of selecting a student with an intelligence test score of 70 or lower. Once again we begin by converting this score into a z score.

$$z = \frac{X - \mu}{\sigma} = \frac{70 - 100}{15} = \frac{-30}{15} = 2.0$$

Next, we represent this on a figure with the z score indicated along with the area in which we are interested (anyone with this score or a lower score). This is illustrated in Figure 7.6.

Consulting Table A.2, we find that for a z score of -2.0, .02275 of the scores are below the score (beyond it) and .47725 of the scores are between the score and the mean of the distribution. We are interested in the probability of selecting a student with an intelligence test score of 70 or lower. Can you figure out what that would be? If you answered .02275, you are correct. Therefore, there is slightly more than a 2% chance of selecting a student with an intelligence test score this low or lower—a fairly low-probability event. This can be represented as follows:

$$p(X \leq 70) = .02275$$

FIGURE 7.6
Standard normal curve with $z = -2.0$ indicated

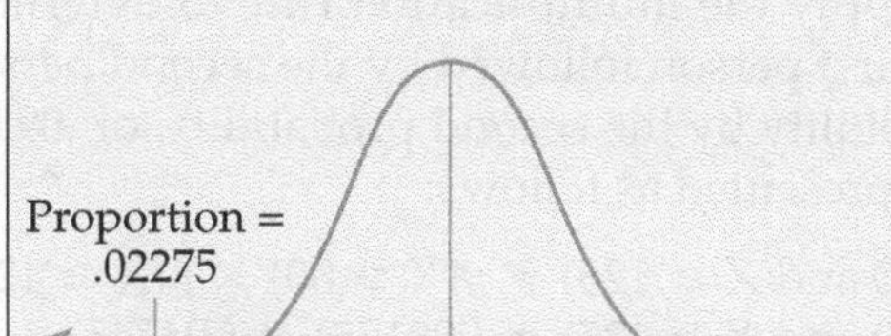

Let's apply what we have learned about using the standard normal curve to calculate probabilities together with the addition rule from earlier in the chapter to determine the probability of selecting a child whose intelligence test score is below 70 or above 119. We have already determined the z scores for each of these intelligence test scores in our previous problems. The intelligence test score of 70 converts to a z score of -2.0, and the intelligence test score of 119 converts to a z score of $+1.27$. Moreover, we have already determined that the probability of selecting a student with a score of 70 or lower is .02275 and that the probability of selecting a student with an intelligence test score of 119 or higher is .10203. Thus, applying the addition rule, the probability of selecting a student with a score that is 70 or lower or 119 or higher would be the sum of these two probabilities, or .02275 + .10203. These two probabilities sum to .12478, or just about 12.5%. This can be represented as follows:

$$p(X \leq 70 \text{ or } X \geq 119) = p(X \leq 70) + p(X \geq 119)$$
$$= p(X \leq 70 \text{ or } X \geq 119) = (.02275) + (.10203)$$
$$= p(X \leq 70 \text{ or } X \geq 119) = .12478$$

Now let's turn to using the multiplication rule, discussed earlier in the chapter, with the area under the standard normal curve (Table A.2). In this case, we want to determine the probability of selecting two students who fit different descriptions. For example, what is the probability of selecting one student with an intelligence test score equal to or below 80, followed by another student with an intelligence test score equal to or above 125? Once again, we begin by converting the scores to z scores.

$$z = \frac{X - \mu}{\sigma} = \frac{80 - 100}{15} = \frac{-20}{15} = -1.33$$

$$z = \frac{X - \mu}{\sigma} = \frac{125 - 100}{15} = \frac{25}{15} = +1.67$$

Consequently, the intelligence test scores convert to z scores of -1.33 and $+1.67$, respectively. Next we use Table A.2 to determine the probability of each of these events. Consulting Table A.2, we find that the probability of selecting a student with a score of 80 or lower is .09175, and the probability of selecting a student with a score of 125 or higher is .04745. These z scores and proportions are represented in Figure 7.7.

We now apply the multiplication rule to determine the probability of selecting the first person followed by the second person. Thus, we multiply the first probability by the second probability, or .09175 × .04745 = .00435. This can be represented as follows:

$$p(X \leq 80 \text{ and } X \geq 125) = p(X \leq 80) \times p(X \geq 125)$$
$$= p(X \leq 80 \text{ and } X \geq 125) = (.09175) \times (.04745)$$
$$= p(X \leq 80 \text{ and } X \geq 125) = .00435$$

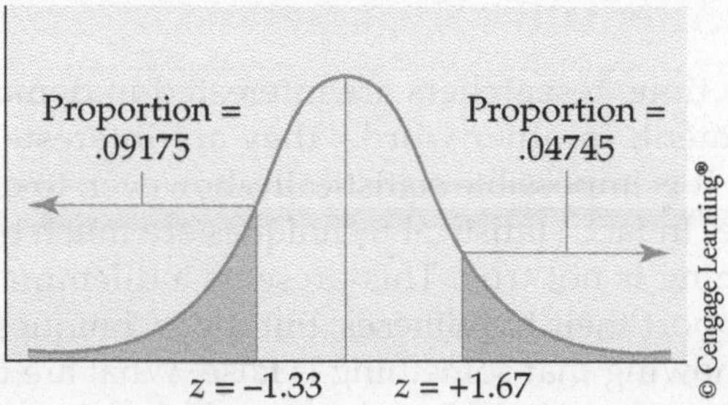

FIGURE 7.7 Standard normal curve with $z = -1.33$ and $z = +1.67$ indicated

Thus, the probability of the first event followed by the second event has a very low probability of less than 1%.

> **CRITICAL THINKING CHECK 7.3**
>
> 1. If SAT scores are normally distributed with a mean of 1,000 and a standard deviation of 200, what is the probability of a student scoring 1,100 or higher on the SAT?
> 2. For this hypothetical SAT distribution, what is the probability of a student scoring 910 or lower on the SAT?
> 3. For this hypothetical SAT distribution, what is the probability of a student scoring 910 or lower or 1,100 or higher?
> 4. For this hypothetical SAT distribution, what is the probability of selecting a student who scored 910 or lower followed by a student who scored 1,100 or higher on the SAT?

Hypothesis Testing

Research is usually designed to answer a specific question—for example, Do science majors score differently on tests of intelligence than students in the general population? The process of determining whether this statement is supported by the results of the research project is referred to as *hypothesis testing*.

Suppose a researcher wants to examine the relationship between the type of after-school program attended by a child and the child's intelligence level. The researcher is interested in whether students who attend after-school programs that are academically oriented (math, writing, computer use) score differently on an intelligence test than students who do not attend such programs. The researcher will form a hypothesis. The hypothesis might be that children in academic after-school programs have different IQ scores than children in the general population. Because most intelligence tests are standardized with a mean score (μ) of 100 and a standard deviation (σ) of 15, the students in academic after-school programs must score higher or lower than 100 for the hypothesis to be supported.

Null and Alternative Hypotheses

Most of the time, researchers are interested in demonstrating the truth of some statement. In other words, they are interested in supporting their hypothesis. It is impossible statistically, however, to demonstrate that something is true. In fact, statistical techniques are much better at demonstrating that something is not true. This presents a dilemma for researchers. They want to support their hypotheses, but the techniques available to them are better for showing that something is false. What are they to do? The logical route is to propose exactly the opposite of what they want to demonstrate to be true and then disprove or falsify that hypothesis. What is left (the initial hypothesis) must then be true (Kranzler & Moursund, 1995).

Let's use our sample hypothesis to demonstrate what we mean. We want to show that children who attend academic after-school programs have different IQ scores than those who do not. We understand that statistics cannot demonstrate the truth of this statement. We therefore construct what is known as a null hypothesis (H_0). Whatever the research topic, the **null hypothesis** predicts the opposite of that. In this case, the opposite of the research hypothesis would be that there is no difference between the groups being compared. This is typically what the researcher does not expect to find. Think about the meaning of *null*—nothing or zero. The null hypothesis means we have found nothing—no difference between the groups.

null hypothesis The hypothesis predicting that no difference exists between the groups being compared.

For the sample study, the null hypothesis is that children who attend academic after-school programs have the same intelligence level as other children. Remember, we said that statistics allow us to disprove or falsify a hypothesis. Therefore, if the null hypothesis is not supported, then our original hypothesis—that children who attend academic after-school programs have different IQs than other children—is all that is left. In statistical notation, the null hypothesis for this study is

$$H_0: \mu_0 = \mu_1; \text{ or } \mu_{\text{academic program}} = \mu_{\text{general population}}$$

The purpose of the study, then, is to decide whether H_0 is probably true or probably false.

The hypothesis that the researcher wants to support is known as the **alternative hypothesis** (H_a), or the **research hypothesis** (H_1). The statistical notation for H_a is

alternative hypothesis The hypothesis that the researcher wants to support, predicting that a significant difference exists between the groups being compared.

$$H_a: \mu_1 \neq \mu_2; \text{ or } \mu_{\text{academic program}} \neq \mu_{\text{general population}}$$

When we use inferential statistics, we are trying to reject H_0, which means that H_a is supported.

Two-Tailed and One-Tailed Hypothesis Tests

two-tailed hypothesis An alternative hypothesis in which the researcher predicts that the groups being compared differ but does not predict the direction of the difference.

The manner in which the previous alternative hypothesis (H_a) was stated reflects what is known statistically as a **two-tailed hypothesis**, or a **nondirectional hypothesis**—an alternative hypothesis in which the researcher expects to find differences between the groups but is unsure what the differences will be. In this case, the researcher would predict a difference in IQ scores between children in academic after-school programs and those in the general population, but the direction of the difference would not be predicted. Those in academic programs would be expected to have either higher or lower IQs but not the same IQs as the general population of children. The statistical notation for a two-tailed test is

$$H_0: \mu_0 = \mu_1; \text{ or } \mu_{\text{academic program}} = \mu_{\text{general population}}$$
$$H_a: \mu_0 \neq \mu_1; \text{ or } \mu_{\text{academic program}} \neq \mu_{\text{general population}}$$

one-tailed hypothesis An alternative hypothesis in which the researcher predicts the direction of the expected difference between the groups.

The alternative to a two-tailed or nondirectional test is a **one-tailed hypothesis**, or a **directional hypothesis**—an alternative hypothesis in which the researcher predicts the direction of the expected difference between the groups. In our example, the researcher would predict the direction of the difference—namely, that children in academic after-school programs will be more intelligent than children in the general population. Thus, the alternative hypothesis would be written as

$$H_a: \mu_0 > \mu_1; \text{ or } \mu_{\text{academic program}} > \mu_{\text{general population}}$$

When we use a directional alternative hypothesis, the null hypothesis is also, in some sense, directional. If the alternative hypothesis is that children in academic after-school programs will have higher intelligence test scores, then the null hypothesis is that being in academic after-school programs either will have no effect on intelligence test scores or will decrease intelligence test scores. Thus, the null hypothesis for the one-tailed directional test might more appropriately be written as

$$H_0: \mu_0 \leq \mu_1; \text{ or } \mu_{\text{academic program}} \leq \mu_{\text{general population}}$$

In other words, if the alternative hypothesis for a one-tailed test is $\mu_0 > \mu_1$, then the null hypothesis is $\mu_0 \leq \mu_1$, and to reject H_0, the children in academic after-school programs have to have intelligence test scores higher than those in the general population. In our example, the one-tailed hypothesis makes more sense.

Assume that the researcher has selected a random sample of children from academic after-school programs to compare their IQs with the IQs of children in the general population (as noted previously, we know that the mean IQ for the population is 100). If we collected data and found that the mean intelligence level of the children in academic after-school programs is "significantly" (a term that will be discussed shortly) higher than the mean intelligence level for the population, we could reject the null hypothesis. Remember that the null hypothesis states that no difference exists between the sample and the population. Thus, the researcher concludes that the null hypothesis—that there is no difference or that children performed more poorly—is not supported. When the null hypothesis is rejected, the alternative hypothesis—that those in academic programs have higher IQ scores than those in the general population—is supported. We can say that the evidence suggests that the sample of children in academic after-school programs represents a specific population that scores higher on the IQ test than the general population.

If, on the other hand, the mean IQ scores of the children in academic after-school programs are not significantly different from the population mean score, then the researcher has failed to reject the null hypothesis and, by default, has failed to support the alternative hypothesis. In this case, the alternative hypothesis—that the children in academic programs have higher IQs than the general population—is not supported.

Type I and II Errors in Hypothesis Testing

Anytime we make a decision using statistics, four outcomes are possible (see Table 7.1). Two of the outcomes represent correct decisions, whereas two represent errors. Let's use our example to illustrate these possibilities.

If we reject the null hypothesis (that there is no IQ difference between groups), we may be correct in our decision, or we may be incorrect. If our decision to reject H_0 is correct, that means there truly is a difference in IQ between children in academic after-school programs and the general population of children. However, our decision could be incorrect. The result may have been due to chance. Even though we observed a significant difference in IQs between the children in our study and the general population, the result might have been a fluke—maybe the children in our sample just happened to guess correctly on a lot of the questions. In this case, we have made what is known as a **Type I error**—we rejected H_0, when in reality, we should have failed to reject it (it is true that there really is no IQ difference between the sample and the population). Type I errors can be thought of as false alarms—we said there was a difference, but in reality, there is no difference.

Type I error An error in hypothesis testing in which the null hypothesis is rejected when it is true.

What if our decision is to not reject H_0, meaning we conclude that there is no difference in IQs between the children in academic after-school programs and children in the general population? This decision could be correct, meaning that in reality, there is no IQ difference between the sample and the population. However, it could also be incorrect. In this case, we would be making a **Type II error**—saying there is no difference between groups when, in reality, there is a difference. Somehow we have missed the difference that really exists and have failed to reject the null hypothesis when it is false. These possibilities are summarized in Table 7.1.

Type II error An error in hypothesis testing in which there is a failure to reject the null hypothesis when it is false.

TABLE 7.1 The Four Possible Outcomes in Statistical Decision Making

	THE TRUTH (UNKNOWN TO THE RESEARCHER)	
THE RESEARCHER'S DECISION	**H_0 IS TRUE**	**H_0 IS FALSE**
Reject H_0 (say it is false)	Type I error	Correct decision
Fail to reject H_0 (say it is true)	Correct decision	Type II error

Statistical Significance and Errors

Suppose we actually do the study on IQ levels and academic after-school programs. In addition, suppose we find that there is a difference between the IQ levels of children in academic after-school programs and children in the general population (those in academic programs score higher). Last, suppose this difference is statistically significant at the .05 (or the 5%) level (also known as the .05 alpha level). To say that a result has **statistical significance** at the .05 level means that a difference as large as or larger than what we observed between the sample and the population could have occurred by chance only 5 times or less out of 100. In other words, the likelihood that this result is due to chance is small. If the result is not due to chance, then it is most likely due to a true or real difference between the groups. If our result is statistically significant, we can reject the null hypothesis and conclude that we have observed a significant difference in IQ scores between the sample and the population.

statistical significance An observed difference between two descriptive statistics (such as means) that is unlikely to have occurred by chance.

Remember, however, that when we reject the null hypothesis, we could be correct in our decision, or we could be making a Type I error. Maybe the null hypothesis is true, and this is one of those 5 or less times out of 100 when the observed differences between the sample and the population did occur by chance. This means that when we adopt the .05 level of significance (the .05 alpha level), as often as 5 times out of 100, we could make a Type I error. The *alpha level*, then, is the probability of making a Type I error (for this reason, it is also referred to as a *p value*, which means *probability value*—the probability of a Type I error). In the social and behavioral sciences, alpha is typically set at .05 (as opposed to .01, .08, or anything else). This means that researchers in these areas are willing to accept up to a 5% risk of making a Type I error.

What if you want to reduce your risk of making a Type I error and decide to use the .01 alpha level—reducing the risk of a Type I error to 1 out of 100 times? This seems simple enough: Simply reduce alpha to .01, and you have reduced your chance of making a Type I error. By doing this, however, you have now increased your chance of making a Type II error. Do you see why? If I reduce my risk of making a false alarm—saying a difference is there when it really is not—I increase my risk of missing a difference that really is there. When we reduce the alpha level, we are insisting on more stringent conditions for accepting our research hypothesis, making it more likely that we could miss a significant difference when it is present. We will return to Type I and II errors in Chapter 8 when we cover statistical power and discuss alternative ways of addressing this problem.

Which type of error, Type I or Type II, do you think is considered more serious by researchers? Most researchers consider a Type I error more serious. They would rather miss a result (Type II error) than conclude that there is a meaningful difference when there really is not (Type I error). What about in other arenas, for example, in the courtroom? A jury could make a correct decision in a case (find guilty when truly guilty or find innocent when truly innocent). They could also make either a Type I error (say guilty when innocent) or a Type II error (say innocent when guilty). Which is more serious here? Most people believe that a Type I error is worse in this situation also. How about in the medical profession? Imagine a doctor attempting to determine whether or not a patient has cancer. Here again, the doctor could make one of the two correct decisions or one of the two types of errors. What would the Type I error be? This would be saying that cancer is present when in fact it is not. What about the Type II error? This would be saying that there is no cancer when in fact there is. In this situation, most people would consider a Type II error to be more serious.

Hypothesis Testing — IN REVIEW

CONCEPT	DESCRIPTION	EXAMPLE
Null Hypothesis	The hypothesis stating that the independent variable has no effect and that there will be no difference between the two groups.	$H_0: \mu_0 = \mu_1$ (two-tailed) $H_0: \mu_0 \leq \mu_1$ (one-tailed) $H_0: \mu_0 \geq \mu_1$ (one-tailed)
Alternative Hypothesis or Research Hypothesis	The hypothesis stating that the independent variable has an effect and that there will be a difference between the two groups.	$H_a: \mu_0 \neq \mu_1$ (two-tailed) $H_a: \mu_0 > \mu_1$ (one-tailed) $H_a: \mu_0 < \mu_1$ (one-tailed)
Two-Tailed or Nondirectional Test	An alternative hypothesis stating that a difference is expected between the groups, but there is no prediction as to which group will perform better or worse.	The mean of the sample will be different from or unequal to the mean of the general population.
One-Tailed or Directional Test	An alternative hypothesis stating that a difference is expected between the groups, and it is expected to occur in a specific direction.	The mean of the sample will be greater than the mean of the population, or the mean of the sample will be less than the mean of the population.
Type I Error	The error of rejecting H_0 when we should have failed to reject it.	This error in hypothesis testing is equivalent to a "false alarm," saying that there is a difference when in reality there is no difference between the groups.
Type II Error	The error of failing to reject H_0 when we should have rejected it.	This error in hypothesis testing is equivalent to a "miss," saying that there is not a difference between the groups when in reality there is.
Statistical Significance	When the probability of a Type I error is low (.05 or less).	The difference between the groups is so large that we conclude it is due to something other than chance.

CRITICAL THINKING CHECK 7.4

1. A researcher hypothesizes that children in the South weigh less (because they spend more time outside) than the national average. Identify H_0 and H_a. Is this a one- or two-tailed test?
2. A researcher collects data on children's weights from a random sample of children in the South and concludes that children in the South weigh less than the national average. The researcher, however, does not realize that the sample includes many children who are small for their age and that in reality there is no difference in weight between children in the South and the national average. What type of error is the researcher making?
3. If a researcher decides to use the .10 level rather than the conventional .05 level of significance, what type of error is more likely to be made? Why? If the .01 level is used, what type of error is more likely? Why?

Single-Sample Research and Inferential Statistics

single-group design A research study in which there is only one group of participants.

Now that you understand the concept of hypothesis testing, we can begin to discuss how hypothesis testing can be applied to research. The simplest type of study involves only one group and is known as a **single-group design**. The single-group design lacks a comparison group—there is no control group of any sort. We can, however, compare the performance of the group (the sample) with the performance of the population (assuming that population data are available).

Earlier in the chapter, we illustrated hypothesis testing using a single-group design—comparing the IQ scores of children in academic after-school programs (the sample) with the IQ scores of children in the general population. The null and alternative hypotheses for this study were

$$H_0: \mu_0 \leq \mu_1; \text{ or } \mu_{\text{academic program}} \leq \mu_{\text{general population}}$$
$$H_a: \mu_0 > \mu_1; \text{ or } \mu_{\text{academic program}} > \mu_{\text{general population}}$$

To compare the performance of the sample with that of the population, we need to know the population mean (μ) and the population standard deviation (σ). We know that for IQ tests, $\mu = 100$ and $\sigma = 15$. We also need to decide who will be in the sample. As noted in previous chapters, random selection increases our chances of getting a representative sample of children enrolled in academic after-school programs. How many children do we need in the sample? You will see in the next chapter that the larger the sample, the greater the power of the study. We will also see that one of the assumptions of the statistical procedure we will be using to test our hypothesis is a sample size of 30 or more.

After we have chosen our sample, we need to collect the data. We have discussed data collection in several earlier chapters. It is important to make sure that the data are collected in a nonreactive manner as discussed in Chapter 4. To collect IQ score data, we could either administer an intelligence test to the children or look at their academic files to see whether they have already taken such a test.

Inferential statistics Procedures for drawing conclusions about a population based on data collected from a sample.

parametric tests A statistical test that involves making assumptions about estimates of population characteristics, or parameters.

nonparametric tests A statistical test that does not involve the use of any population parameters, μ and σ are not needed, and the underlying distribution does not have to be normal.

After the data are collected, we can begin to analyze them using inferential statistics. **Inferential statistics** involve the use of procedures for drawing conclusions based on the scores collected in a research study and going beyond them to make inferences about a population. In the following chapter, we will describe two inferential statistical tests. These tests, the *z* test and the *t* test, are **parametric tests**—tests that require us to make certain assumptions about estimates of population characteristics, or parameters. These assumptions typically involve knowing the mean (μ) and standard deviation (σ) of the population and that the population distribution is normal. Parametric tests are generally used with interval or ratio data. **Nonparametric tests**—that is, tests that do not involve the use of any population parameters (in other words, μ and σ are not needed and the underlying distribution does not have to be normal) will be discuss in Chapter 14. Nonparametric tests are most often used with ordinal or nominal data.

Inferential Statistical Tests — IN REVIEW

CONCEPT	DESCRIPTION	EXAMPLE
Parametric Inferential Statistics	Inferential statistical procedures that require certain assumptions about the parameters of the population represented by the sample data, such as knowing μ and σ, and that the distribution is normal. Most often used with interval or ratio data.	*z* test *t* test
Nonparametric Inferential Statistics	Inferential procedures that do not require assumptions about the parameters of the population represented by the sample data; μ and σ are not needed, and the underlying distribution does not have to be normal. Most often used with ordinal or nominal data.	Chi-square tests Wilcoxon tests (both discussed in Chapter 14)

CRITICAL THINKING CHECK 7.5

1. How do inferential statistics differ from descriptive statistics?
2. How does single-sample research involve the use of hypothesis testing? In other words, in a single-group design, what hypothesis is tested?

Summary

This chapter consisted of an introduction to probability and hypothesis testing. There was a discussion of how to calculate basic probabilities, how to use the multiplication and addition rules, and lastly how to use the area under the normal curve to calculate probabilities. We also introduced hypothesis testing and inferential statistics. The discussion of hypothesis testing included the null and alternative hypotheses, one-and two-tailed hypothesis tests, and Type I and Type II errors in hypothesis testing. In addition, we defined the concept of statistical significance. The simplest type of hypothesis testing—a single-group design in which the performance of a sample is compared with that of the general population—was used to illustrate the use of inferential statistics in hypothesis testing.

KEY TERMS

probability
hypothesis testing
multiplication rule
addition rule
null hypothesis
alternative hypothesis (research hypothesis)
two-tailed hypothesis (nondirectional hypothesis)
one-tailed hypothesis (directional hypothesis)
Type I error
Type II error
statistical significance
single-group design
inferential statistics
parametric test
nonparametric test

CHAPTER EXERCISES

(Answers to odd-numbered exercises appear in Appendix C.)

1. Imagine that I have a jar that contains 50 blue marbles and 20 red marbles.
   a. What is the probability of selecting a red marble from the jar?
   b. What is the probability of selecting a blue marble from the jar?
   c. What is the probability of selecting either a red or a blue marble from the jar?
   d. What is the probability of selecting a red marble (with replacement) followed by a blue marble?
2. What is the probability of a couple having children in the following birth order: boy, boy, boy, boy?
3. What is the probability of selecting either a 2 or a 4 (of any suit) from a standard deck of cards?
4. If height is normally distributed with a mean of 68 inches and a standard deviation of 5 inches, what is the probability of selecting someone who is 70 inches or taller?
5. For the distribution described in exercise 4, what is the probability of selecting someone who is 64 inches or shorter?
6. For the distribution described in exercise 4, what is the probability of selecting someone who is 70 inches or taller or 64 inches or shorter?
7. For the distribution described in exercise 4, what is the probability of selecting someone who is 70 inches or taller followed by someone who is 64 inches or shorter?
8. The admissions counselors at Brainy University believe that the freshman class they have just recruited is the brightest yet. If they want to test this belief (that the freshmen are brighter than the other classes), what are the null and alternative hypotheses? Is this a one- or two tailed hypothesis test?

9. To test the hypothesis in exercise 8, the admissions counselors select a random sample of freshmen and compare their scores on the SAT with those of the population of upperclassmen. They find that the freshmen do in fact have a higher mean SAT score. However, they are unaware that the sample of freshmen was not representative of all freshmen at Brainy University. In fact, the sample overrepresented those with high scores and underrepresented those with low scores. What type of error (Type I or Type II) did the counselors make?
10. A researcher believes that family size has increased in the past decade in comparison to the previous decade—that is, people are now having more children than they were before. What are the null and alternative hypotheses in a study designed to assess this? Is this a one- or two-tailed hypothesis test?
11. What are the appropriate H_0 and H_a for each of the following research studies? In addition, note whether the hypothesis test is one- or two-tailed.
    a. A study in which researchers want to test whether there is a difference in spatial ability between left- and right-handed people
    b. A study in which researchers want to test whether nurses who work 8-hour shifts deliver higher-quality care than those who work 12-hour shifts
    c. A study in which researchers want to determine whether crate-training puppies is superior to training without a crate
12. Assume that each of the following conclusions represents an error in hypothesis testing. Indicate whether each of the statements is a Type I or II error.
    a. Based on the data, the null hypothesis is rejected.
    b. There is no significant difference in quality of care between nurses who work 8- and 12-hour shifts.
    c. There is a significant difference between right- and left-handers in their ability to perform a spatial task.
    d. The researcher fails to reject the null hypothesis based on these data.
13. How do inferential statistics differ from descriptive statistics?

CRITICAL THINKING CHECK ANSWERS

7.1

1. 4/52 = .077
2. 13/52 = .25
3. 3/6 = .50
4. 4/11 = .36

7.2

1. (a) Multiplication rule
   (b) Addition rule
   (c) Multiplication rule
   (d) Addition rule
2. (a) .50 × .50 = .25
   (b) (13/52) + (13/52) = .25 + .25 = .50
   (c) (13/52) × (13/52) = .25 × .25 = .0625
   (d) (4/52) + (4/52) = .077 + .077 = .154

7.3

1. $z = +.50, p = .30854$
2. $z = -.45, p = .32634$
3. .32634 + .30854 = .63488
4. .32634 × .30854 = .101

7.4

1. $$H_0: \mu_{\text{southern children}} \geq \mu_{\text{children in general}}$$
   $$H_a: \mu_{\text{southern children}} < \mu_{\text{children in general}}$$

   This is a one-tailed test.
2. The researcher concluded that there was a difference when, in reality, there was no difference between the sample and the population. This is a Type I error.
3. With the .10 level of significance, the researcher is willing to accept a higher probability that the result may be due to chance. Therefore, a Type I error is more likely to be made than if the researcher used the more traditional .05 level of significance. With a .01 level of significance, the researcher is willing to accept only a .01 probability that the result may be due to chance. In this case, a true result is more likely to be missed, meaning that a Type II error is more likely.

7.5

1. Inferential statistics allow researchers to make inferences about a population based on sample data. Descriptive statistics simply describe a data set.
2. Single-sample research allows researchers to compare sample data with population data. The hypothesis tested is whether the sample performs similarly to the population or whether the sample differs significantly from the population and thus represents a different population.

WEB RESOURCES

The book-specific website at CengageBrain.com offers students a variety of study tools and useful resources such as glossaries and flashcards.

Chapter 7 ■ Study Guide

CHAPTER 7 SUMMARY AND REVIEW: PROBABILITY AND HYPOTHESIS TESTING

This chapter consisted of an introduction to probability and hypothesis testing. There was a discussion of how to calculate basic probabilities, how to use the multiplication and addition rules, and lastly how to use the area under the normal curve to calculate probabilities. With respect to hypothesis testing, there was a discussion of the null and alternative hypotheses, two- and one-tailed hypothesis tests, and Type I and Type II errors in hypothesis testing. In addition, the concept of statistical significance was defined. The most simplistic use of hypothesis testing—a single-group design—in which the performance of a sample is compared to the general population was presented to illustrate the use of inferential statistics in hypothesis testing.

CHAPTER 7 REVIEW EXERCISES

(Answers to exercises appear in Appendix B.)

FILL-IN SELF-TEST

Answer the following questions. If you have trouble answering any of the questions, restudy the relevant material before going on to the multiple-choice self-test.

1. ______________ is the study of likelihood and uncertainty.
2. The rule that says that the probability of a series of outcomes occurring on successive trials is the product of their individual probabilities is the ______________ rule.
3. The rule that says that the probability of one out come or the other outcome occurring on a particular trial is the sum of their individual probabilities is the ______________ rule.
4. The hypothesis predicting that no difference exists between the groups being compared is the ______________.
5. An alternative hypothesis in which the researcher predicts the direction of the expected difference between the groups is a ______________.
6. An error in hypothesis testing in which the null hypothesis is rejected when it is true is a ______________.
7. When an observed difference, say between two means, is unlikely to have occurred by chance, we say that the result has ______________.
8. ______________ tests are statistical tests that do not involve the use of any population parameters.

MULTIPLE-CHOICE SELF-TEST

Select the single best answer for each of the following questions. If you have trouble answering any of the questions, restudy the relevant material.

1. The study of likelihood and uncertainty is to _______________ and the process or determining whether a hypothesis is supported by the results of a research project is to _______________.
   a. hypothesis testing; probability
   b. hypothesis testing; inferential statistics
   c. probability; hypothesis testing
   d. inferential statistics; probability
2. The *and* rule is to _______________ and the *or* rule is to _______________.
   a. multiplication rule; addition rule
   b. addition rule; multiplication rule
   c. multiplication rule; multiplication rule
   d. addition rule; addition rule
3. The probability of rolling a 5 on one roll of a standard die is
   a. .25
   b. .50
   c. .20
   d. .17
4. The probability of rolling either a 2 or a 5 on one roll of a standard die is
   a. .34
   b. .25
   c. .50
   d. .03
5. The probability of rolling a 2 followed by a 6 on a standard die is:
   a. .34
   b. .25
   c. .50
   d. .03
6. If a psychology exam is normally distributed with a mean of 75 and a standard deviation of 5, what is the probability of someone scoring 80 or higher on the exam?
   a. .15866
   b. .34134
   c. .84134
   d. .30598
7. If a psychology exam is normally distributed with a mean of 75 and a standard deviation of 5, what is the probability of someone scoring 65 or higher on the exam?
   a. .02275
   b. .47725
   c. .52275
   d. .97725
8. Inferential statistics allow us to infer something about the _______________ based on the _______________.
   a. sample; population
   b. population; sample
   c. sample; sample
   d. population; population
9. The hypothesis predicting that differences exist between the groups being compared is the _______________ hypothesis.
   a. null
   b. alternative
   c. one-tailed
   d. two-tailed
10. Null hypothesis is to alternative hypothesis as _______________ is to _______________.
    a. effect; no effect
    b. Type I error; Type II error
    c. no effect; effect
    d. None of the alternatives is correct.
11. A one-tailed hypothesis is to a directional hypothesis as _______________ hypothesis is to _______________ hypothesis.
    a. null; alternative
    b. alternative; null
    c. two-tailed; nondirectional
    d. two-tailed; one-tailed
12. When using a one-tailed hypothesis, the researcher predicts
    a. the direction of the expected difference between the groups.
    b. that the groups being compared will differ in some way.
    c. nothing.
    d. only one thing.

13. In a study of the effects of caffeine on driving performance, researchers predict that those in the group that is given more caffeine will exhibit worse driving performance. The researchers are using a ______________ hypothesis.
    a. two-tailed
    b. directional
    c. one-tailed
    d. both directional and one-tailed
14. In a recent study, researchers concluded that caffeine significantly increased anxiety levels. What the researchers were unaware of, however, was that several of the participants in the no-caffeine group were also taking antianxiety medications. The researchers' conclusion is a(n) ______________ error.
    a. Type II
    b. Type I
    c. null hypothesis
    d. alternative hypothesis
15. When alpha is .05, this means that
    a. the probability of a Type II error is .95.
    b. the probability of a Type II error is .05.
    c. the probability of a Type I error is .95.
    d. the probability of a Type I error is .05.

CHAPTER 8

Introduction to Inferential Statistics

Learning Objectives

- Explain what a *z* test is and what it does.
- Calculate a *z* test.
- Explain what statistical power is and how to make statistical tests more powerful.
- List the assumptions of the *z* test.
- Calculate confidence intervals using the *z* distribution.
- Explain what a *t* test is and what it does.
- Calculate a *t* test.
- List the assumptions of the *t* test.
- Calculate confidence intervals using the *t* distribution.

In this chapter, you will be introduced to inferential statistics—procedures for drawing conclusions about a population based on data collected from a sample. We will address two statistical tests: the *z* test and the *t* test. After reading this chapter, engaging in the critical thinking checks, and working through the problems at the end of the chapter, you should understand the differences between these tests, when to use each test, how to use each to test a hypothesis, and the assumptions of each test.

The *z* Test: What It Is and What It Does

z test A parametric inferential statistical test of the null hypothesis for a single sample where the population variance is known.

The *z* **test** is a parametric statistical test that allows us to test the null hypothesis for a single sample when the population variance is known. This procedure allows us to compare a sample with a population to assess whether the sample differs significantly from the population. If the sample was drawn randomly from a certain population (children in academic after-school programs) and we observe a difference between the sample and a broader population (all children), we can then conclude that the population represented by the sample differs significantly from the comparison population. Let's return to our example from Chapter 7 and assume that we have actually collected IQ scores from 75 students enrolled in academic after-school programs. We want to determine whether the sample of children in academic after-school programs represents a population with a mean IQ higher than the mean IQ of the general population of children. We already know μ (100) and σ (15) for the general population of children. The null and alternative hypotheses for a one-tailed test are

$$H_0: \mu_0 \leq \mu_1; \text{ or } \mu_{\text{academic program}} \leq \mu_{\text{general population}}$$
$$H_a: \mu_0 > \mu_1; \text{ or } \mu_{\text{academic program}} > \mu_{\text{general population}}$$

In Chapter 5, you learned how to calculate a *z*-score for a single data point (or a single individual's score). To review, the formula for a *z*-score is

$$z = \frac{X - \mu}{\sigma}$$

Remember that a *z*-score tells us how many standard deviations above or below the mean of the distribution an individual score falls. When using the *z* test, however, we are not comparing an individual score with the population mean. Instead, we are comparing a sample mean with the population mean. We therefore cannot compare the sample mean with a population distribution of individual scores. We must compare it instead with a distribution of sample means, known as the sampling distribution.

The Sampling Distribution

sampling distribution A distribution of sample means based on random samples of a fixed size from a population.

If you are becoming confused, think about it this way: A **sampling distribution** is a distribution of sample means based on random samples of a fixed size from a population. Imagine that we have drawn many different samples of the same size (say, 75) from the population (children on whom we can measure IQ). For each sample that we draw, we calculate the mean; then we plot the means of all the samples. What do you think the distribution will look like? Most of the sample means will probably be similar to the population mean of 100. Some of the sample means will be slightly lower than 100, some will be slightly higher than 100, and others will be right at 100. A few of the sample means, however, will not be similar to the population mean. Why? Based on chance, some samples will contain some of the rare individuals with either very high IQ scores or very low IQ scores. Thus, the means for these samples will be much higher than 100 or much lower than 100. Such samples, however, will be few in number. Thus, the sampling distribution (the distribution of sample means) will be normal (bell-shaped), with most of the sample means clustered around 100 and a few sample means in the tails or the extremes. Therefore, the mean for the sampling distribution will be the same as the mean for the distribution of individual scores (100).

The Standard Error of the Mean

standard error of the mean The standard deviation of the sampling distribution.

Here is a more difficult question: Will the standard deviation of the sampling distribution, known as the **standard error of the mean**, be the same as that for a distribution of individual scores? We know that $\sigma = 15$ for the distribution of individual IQ test scores. Will the variability in the sampling distribution be as great as it is in a distribution of individual scores? Let's think about it. The sampling distribution is a distribution of sample means. In our example, each sample has 75 people in it. Now, the mean for a sample of 75 people can never be as low or as high as the lowest or highest individual score. Why? Most people have IQ scores around 100. This means that in each of the samples, most people will have scores around 100. A few people will have very low scores, and when they are included in the sample, they will pull down the mean for that sample. A few others will have very high scores, and these scores will raise the mean for the sample in which they are included. A few people in a sample of 75, however, can never pull the mean for the sample as low as a single individual's score might be or as high as a single individual's score might be. For this reason, the standard error of the mean (the standard deviation of the sampling distribution) can never be as large as σ (the standard deviation for the distribution of individual scores).

How does this relate to the z test? A z test uses the mean and standard deviation of the sampling distribution to determine whether the sample mean is significantly different from the population mean. Thus, we need to know the mean (μ) and the standard error of the mean ($\sigma_{\overline{X}}$) for the sampling distribution. We have already said that μ for the sampling distribution is the same as μ for the distribution of individual scores—100. How will we determine what $\sigma_{\overline{X}}$ is? To find the standard error of the mean, we need to draw a number of samples from the population, determine the mean for each sample, and then calculate the standard deviation for this distribution of sample means. This is hardly feasible. Luckily for us, there is a way to find the standard error of the mean without doing all of this. It is based on the central limit theorem. The central limit theorem is a precise description of the distribution that would be obtained if you selected every possible sample, calculated every sample mean, and constructed the distribution of sample means. The **central limit theorem** states that for any population with a mean μ and standard deviation σ, the distribution of sample means for sample size N will have a mean of μ, a standard deviation of $\sigma/\sqrt{N}$, and will approach a normal distribution as N approaches infinity. Thus, according to the central limit theorem, to determine the standard error of the mean (the standard deviation for the sampling distribution), we take the standard deviation for the population (σ) and divide by the square root of the sample size ($\sqrt{N}$):

central limit theorem A theorem that states that for any population with a mean μ and a standard deviation σ, the distribution of sample means for sample size N will have a mean of μ, a standard deviation of $\sigma/\sqrt{N}$, and will approach a normal distribution as N approaches infinity.

$$\sigma_{\overline{X}} = \frac{\sigma}{\sqrt{N}}$$

We can now use this information to calculate z. The formula for z is

$$z = \frac{\overline{X} - \mu}{\sigma_{\overline{X}}}$$

where

$\overline{X}$ = sample mean,
μ = mean of the sampling distribution, and
$\sigma_{\overline{X}}$ = standard deviation of the sampling distribution, or standard error of the mean.

The z Test (Part I) **IN REVIEW**

CONCEPT	DESCRIPTION	USE
Sampling Distribution	A distribution of sample means where each sample is the same size (*N*)	Used for comparative purposes for *z* tests—a sample mean is compared with the sampling distribution to assess the likelihood that the sample is part of the sampling distribution
Standard Error of the Mean ($\sigma_{\overline{X}}$)	The standard deviation of a sampling distribution, determined by dividing σ by $\sqrt{N}$	Used in the calculation of *z*
z Test	An indication of the number of standard deviation units the sample mean is from the mean of the sampling distribution	An inferential test that compares a sample mean with the sampling distribution to determine the likelihood that the sample is part of the sampling distribution

CRITICAL THINKING CHECK 8.1

1. Explain how a sampling distribution differs from a distribution of individual scores.
2. Explain the difference between $\sigma_{\overline{X}}$ and σ.
3. How is a z test different from a z-score?

Calculations for the One-Tailed *z* Test

You can see that the formula for a *z* test represents finding the difference between the sample mean ($\overline{X}$) and the population mean (μ) and then dividing by the standard error of the mean ($\sigma_{\overline{X}}$). This will tell us how many standard deviation units a sample mean is from the population mean, or the likelihood that the sample is from that population. We already know μ and σ, so we need to find the mean for the sample ($\overline{X}$) and to calculate $\sigma_{\overline{X}}$ based on a sample size of 75.

Suppose we find that the mean IQ score for the sample of 75 children enrolled in academic after-school programs is 103.5. We can calculate $\sigma_{\overline{X}}$ based on knowing the sample size and σ:

$$\sigma_{\overline{X}} = \frac{\sigma}{\sqrt{N}} = \frac{15}{\sqrt{75}} = \frac{15}{8.66} = 1.73$$

We now use $\sigma_{\overline{X}}$ (1.73) in the *z*-test formula:

$$z = \frac{\overline{X} - \mu}{\sigma_{\overline{X}}} = \frac{103.5 - 100}{1.73} = \frac{3.5}{1.73} = +2.02$$

Interpreting the One-Tailed *z* Test

Figure 8.1 shows where the sample mean of 103.5 lies with respect to the population mean of 100. The *z*-test score of +2.02 can be used to test our

FIGURE 8.1
The obtained mean in relation to the population mean

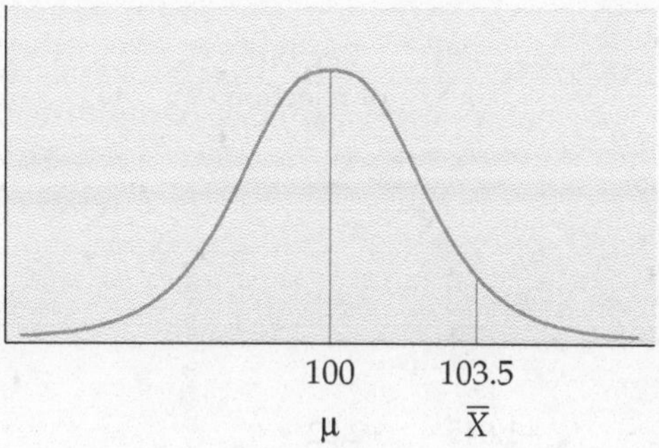

hypothesis that the sample of children in academic after-school programs represents a population with a mean IQ higher than the mean IQ for the general population. To do this, we need to determine whether the probability is high or low that a sample mean as large as 103.5 would be found from this sampling distribution. In other words, is a sample mean IQ score of 103.5 far enough away from, or different enough from, the population mean of 100 for us to say that it represents a significant difference with an alpha level of .05 or less?

How do we determine whether a *z*-score of 2.02 is statistically significant? Because the sampling distribution is normally distributed, we can use the area under the normal curve (Table A.2 in Appendix A). When we discussed *z*-scores in Chapter 5, we saw that Table A.2 provides information on the proportion of scores falling between μ and the *z*-score and the proportion of scores beyond the *z*-score. To determine whether a *z* test is significant, we can use the area under the curve to determine whether the chance of a given score occurring is 5% or less. In other words, is the score far enough away from (above or below) the mean that only 5% or less of the scores are as far or farther away?

critical value The value of a test statistic that marks the edge of the region of rejection in a sampling distribution, where values equal to it or beyond it fall in the region of rejection.

region of rejection The area of a sampling distribution that lies beyond the test statistic's critical value; when a score falls within this region, H_0 is rejected.

Using Table A.2, we find that the *z*-score that marks off the top 5% of the distribution is 1.645. This is referred to as the ***z* critical value**, or z_{cv}—the value of a test statistic that marks the edge of the region of rejection in a sampling distribution. The **region of rejection** is the area of a sampling distribution that lies beyond the test statistic's critical value; when a score falls within this region, H_0 is rejected. For us to conclude that the sample mean is significantly different from the population mean, the sample mean must be at least ± 1.645 standard deviations (z units) from the mean. The critical value of ± 1.645 is illustrated in Figure 8.2. The *z* we obtained for our sample mean (z_{obt}) is $+2.02$, and this value falls within the region of rejection for the null hypothesis. We therefore reject H_0 that the sample mean represents the general population mean and support our alternative hypothesis that the sample mean represents a population of children in academic after-school programs whose mean IQ is higher than 100. We make this decision because the *z*-test score for the sample is greater than (farther out in the tail than) the critical value of ± 1.645. In APA style (discussed in detail in Chapter 15), the result is reported as

FIGURE 8.2
The z-critical value and the z-obtained for the z test example

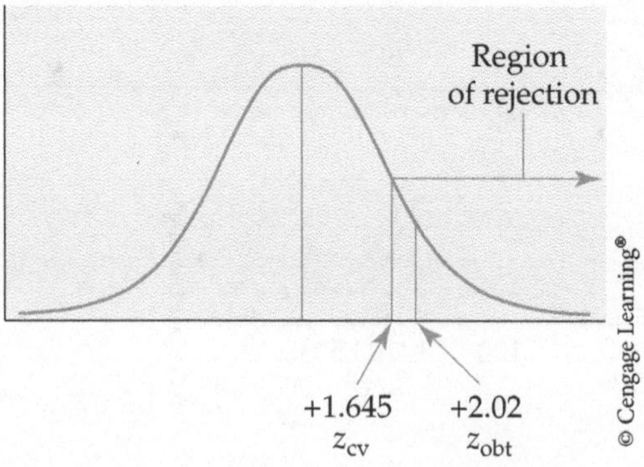

$$z(N = 75) = +2.02, p < .05 \text{ (one-tailed)}$$

This style conveys in a concise manner the z-score, the sample size, that the results are significant at the .05 level, and that we used a one-tailed test.

The test just conducted was a one-tailed test because we predicted that the sample would score higher than the population. What if this were reversed? For example, imagine I am conducting a study to see whether children in athletic after-school programs weigh less than children in the general population. What are H_0 and H_a for this example?

$$H_0: \mu_0 \geq \mu_1, \text{or } \mu_{\text{athletic programs}} \geq \mu_{\text{general population}\sigma}$$
$$H_a: \mu_0 < \mu_1, \text{or } \mu_{\text{athletic programs}} < \mu_{\text{general population}}$$

Assume that the mean weight of children in the general population (μ) is 90 pounds, with a standard deviation (σ) of 17 pounds. Let's imagine we take a random sample ($N = 50$) of children in athletic after-school programs and find that their mean weight ($\overline{X}$) is 86 pounds. Given this information, you can test the hypothesis that the sample of children in athletic after-school programs represents a population with a mean weight that is lower than the mean weight for the general population of children.

First, we calculate the standard error of the mean ($\sigma_{\overline{X}}$):

$$\sigma_{\overline{X}} = \frac{\sigma}{\sqrt{N}} = \frac{17}{\sqrt{50}} = \frac{17}{7.07} = 2.40$$

Now, we enter $\sigma_{\overline{X}}$ into the z-test formula:

$$z = \frac{\overline{X} - \mu}{\sigma_{\overline{X}}} = \frac{86 - 90}{2.40} = \frac{-4}{2.40} = -1.67$$

The z-score for this sample mean is -1.67, meaning that it falls 1.67 standard deviations below the mean. The critical value for a one-tailed test is ± 1.645 standard deviations. This means the z-score has to be at least 1.645 standard deviations away from (above or below) the mean to fall in the region of rejection. Is our z-score at least that far away from the mean? It is, but just barely. Therefore, we reject H_0 and support H_a—that children in athletic after-school programs weigh significantly less than children in the general population and hence represent a population of children who weigh less. In APA style, the result is reported as $z(N = 50) = -1.67, p < .05$ (one-tailed). Instructions on using the TI-84 calculator to conduct these one-tailed z tests appear in the Statistical Software Resources section at the end of the chapter.

Calculations for the Two-Tailed z Test

So far, we have completed two z tests, both one-tailed. Let's turn now to a two-tailed z test. Remember that a two-tailed test is also known as a nondirectional test—a test in which the prediction is simply that the sample will perform differently from the population, with no prediction as to whether the sample mean will be lower or higher than the population mean.

Suppose that in the previous example, we used a two-tailed rather than a one-tailed test. We expect the weight of children in athletic after-school programs to differ from the weight of children in the general population, but we are not sure whether they will weigh less (because of the activity) or more (because of greater muscle mass). H_0 and H_a for this two-tailed test appear next. See if you can determine what they would be before you continue reading.

$$H_0: \mu_0 = \mu_1; \text{or } \mu_{\text{athletic programs}} = \mu_{\text{general population}}$$
$$H_a: \mu_0 \neq \mu_1; \text{or } \mu_{\text{athletic programs}} \neq \mu_{\text{general population}}$$

Let's use the same data as before: The mean weight of children in the general population (μ) is 90 pounds, with a standard deviation (σ) of 17 pounds; for children in the sample ($N = 50$), the mean weight ($\overline{X}$) is 86 pounds. Using this information, we can now test the hypothesis that children in athletic after-school programs differ in weight from those in the general population. Notice that the calculations will be exactly the same for this z test; that is, $\sigma_{\overline{X}}$ and the z-score will be exactly the same as before. Why? All of the measurements are exactly the same. To review:

$$\sigma_{\overline{X}} = \frac{\sigma}{\sqrt{N}} = \frac{17}{\sqrt{50}} = \frac{17}{7.07} = 2.40$$

$$z = \frac{\overline{X} - \mu}{\sigma_{\overline{X}}} = \frac{86 - 90}{2.40} = \frac{-4}{2.40} = -1.67$$

Interpreting the Two-Tailed z Test

If we end up with the same z-score, how does a two-tailed test differ from a one-tailed test? The difference is in the z critical value (z_{cv}). In a two-tailed test, both halves of the normal distribution have to be taken into account. Remember that with a one-tailed test, z_{cv} was ± 1.645; this z-score was so far away from the mean (either above or below) that only 5% of the scores were beyond it. How does the z_{cv} for a two-tailed test differ? With a two-tailed test, z_{cv} has to be so far away from the mean that a total of only 5% of the scores are beyond it (both above and below the mean). A z_{cv} of ±1.645 leaves 5% of the scores above the positive z_{cv} and 5% below the negative z_{cv}. If we take both sides of the normal distribution into account (which we do with a two-tailed test because we do not predict whether the sample mean will be above or below the population mean), then 10% of the distribution will fall beyond the two critical values. Thus, ±1.645 cannot be the critical value for a two-tailed test because this leaves too much chance (10%) operating.

To determine z_{cv} for a two-tailed test, we need to find the z-score that is far enough away from the population mean that only 5% of the distribution—taking into account both halves of the distribution—is beyond the score. Because Table A.2 (in Appendix A) represents only half of the distribution, we need to look for the z-score that leaves only 2.5% of the distribution beyond it. Then, when we take into account both halves of the distribution, 5% of the distribution will be accounted for (2.5% + 2.5% = 5%). Can you determine this z-score using Table A.2? If you find that it is ±1.96, you are correct. This is the z-score that is far enough away from the population mean (using both halves of the distribution) that only 5% of the distribution is beyond it. The critical values for both one- and two-tailed tests are illustrated in Figure 8.3.

Okay, what do we do with this critical value? We use it exactly the same way we used z_{cv} for a one-tailed test. In other words, z_{obt} has to be as large as or larger than z_{cv} for us to reject H_0. Is our z_{obt} as large as or larger than ±1.96? No, our z_{obt} is -1.67. We therefore fail to reject H_0 and conclude that the weight of children in athletic after-school programs does not differ significantly from the weight of children in the general population. Instructions on using the TI-84 calculator to conduct this two-tailed z test appear in the Statistical Software Resources section at the end of the chapter.

FIGURE 8.3
Regions of rejection and critical values for one-tailed versus two-tailed tests

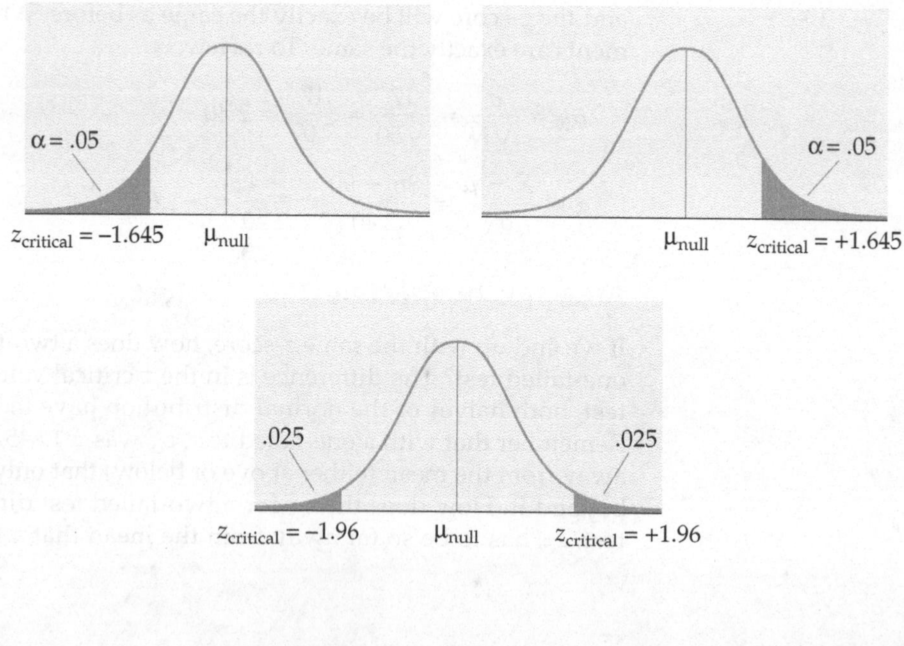

With exactly the same data (sample size, μ, σ, $\overline{X}$, and $\sigma_{\overline{X}}$), we rejected H_0 using a one-tailed test and failed to reject H_0 with a two-tailed test. How can this be? The answer is that a one-tailed test is statistically a more powerful test than a two-tailed test. **Statistical power** refers to the probability of correctly rejecting a false H_0. With a one-tailed test, we are more likely to reject H_0 because z_{obt} does not have to be as large (as far away from the population mean) to be considered significantly different from the population mean. (Remember, z_{cv} for a one-tailed test is ± 1.645, but for a two-tailed test, it is ± 1.96.)

Statistical power The probability of correctly rejecting a false H_0.

Statistical Power

Let's think back to the discussion of Type I and II errors. We said that to reduce the risk of a Type I error, we need to lower the alpha level—for example, from .05 to .01. We also noted, however, that lowering the alpha level increases the risk of a Type II error. How, then, can we reduce the risk of a Type I error but not increase the risk of a Type II error? As we just noted, a one-tailed test is more powerful—we do not need as large a z_{cv} to reject H_0. Here, then, is one way to maintain an alpha level of .05 but increase our chances of correctly rejecting H_0. Of course, ethically we cannot simply choose to adopt a one-tailed test for this reason. The one-tailed test should be adopted only because we truly believe that the sample will perform above (or below) the mean.

By what other means can we increase statistical power? Look back at the *z*-test formula. We know that the larger z_{obt} is, the greater the chance that it will be significant (as large as or larger than z_{cv}), and we can therefore reject H_0. What could we change in our study that might increase z_{obt}? Well, if the denominator in the *z* formula were a smaller number, then z_{obt} would be larger and more likely to fall in the region of rejection. How can we make the denominator smaller? The denominator is $\sigma_{\overline{X}}$. Do you remember the formula for $\sigma_{\overline{X}}$?

$$\sigma_{\overline{X}} = \frac{\sigma}{\sqrt{N}}$$

It is very unlikely that we can change or influence the standard deviation of the population (σ). The part of the $\sigma_{\overline{X}}$ formula that we can influence is the sample size (N). If we increase the sample size, what will happen to $\sigma_{\overline{X}}$? Let's see. We can use the same example as before: a two-tailed test with all of the same measurements. The only difference will be the sample size. Thus, the null and alternative hypotheses are

$$H_0: \mu_0 = \mu_1; \text{or } \mu_{\text{athletic programs}} = \mu_{\text{general population}}$$
$$H_a: \mu_0 \neq \mu_1; \text{or } \mu_{\text{athletic programs}} \neq \mu_{\text{general population}}$$

The mean weight (μ) of children in the general population is once again 90 pounds with a standard deviation (σ) of 17 pounds, and the sample of children in after-school programs again has a mean weight ($\overline{X}$) of 86 pounds.

The only difference is the sample size. In this case, our sample has 100 children in it. Let's test the hypothesis (conduct the z test) for these data:

$$\sigma_{\bar{X}} = \frac{17}{\sqrt{100}} = \frac{17}{10} = 1.70$$

$$z = \frac{86 - 90}{1.70} = \frac{-4}{1.70} = -2.35$$

Do you see what happened when we increased the sample size? The standard error of the mean ($\sigma_{\bar{X}}$) decreased (we will discuss why in a minute), and z_{obt} increased—in fact, it increased to the extent that we can now reject H_0 with this two-tailed test because our z_{obt} of -2.35 is larger than the z_{cv} of ±1.96. Therefore, another way to increase statistical power is to increase the sample size.

Why does increasing the sample size decrease $\sigma_{\bar{X}}$? Well, you can see why based on the formula, but let's think back to our earlier discussion about $\sigma_{\bar{X}}$. We said that it is the standard deviation of a sampling distribution—a distribution of sample means. If you recall the IQ example we used in our discussion of $\sigma_{\bar{X}}$ and the sampling distribution, we said that $\mu = 100$ and $\sigma = 15$. We discussed what $\sigma_{\bar{X}}$ is for a sampling distribution in which each sample mean is based on a sample size of 75. We further noted that $\sigma_{\bar{X}}$ is always smaller (has less variability) than σ because it represents the standard deviation of a distribution of sample means, not a distribution of individual scores. What, then, does increasing the sample size do to $\sigma_{\bar{X}}$? If each sample in the sampling distribution has 100 people in it rather than 75, what do you think this will do to the distribution of sample means? As we noted earlier, most people in a sample will be close to the mean (100), with only a few people in each sample representing the tails of the distribution. If we increase the sample size to 100, we will have 25 more people in each sample. Most of them will probably be close to the population mean of 100; therefore, each sample mean will probably be closer to the population mean of 100. Thus, a sampling distribution based on samples of $N = 100$ rather than $N = 75$ will have less variability, which means that $\sigma_{\bar{X}}$ will be smaller. In sum, as the sample size increases, the standard error of the mean decreases.

Assumptions and Appropriate Use of the z Test

As noted earlier in the chapter, the z test is a parametric inferential statistical test for hypothesis testing. Parametric tests involve the use of parameters, or population characteristics. With a z test, the parameters, such as μ and σ, are known. If they are not known, the z test is not appropriate. Because the z test involves the calculation and use of a sample mean, it is appropriate for use with interval or ratio data. In addition, because we use the area under the normal curve (see Table A.2 in Appendix A), we are assuming that the distribution of random samples is normal. Small samples often fail to form a normal distribution. Therefore, if the sample size is small ($N < 30$), the z test may not be appropriate. In cases where the sample size is small or where σ is not known, the appropriate test is the t test, discussed later in the chapter.

The z Test (Part II) **IN REVIEW**

CONCEPT	DESCRIPTION	EXAMPLE
One-Tailed z Test	A directional inferential test in which a prediction is made that the population represented by the sample will be either above or below the general population.	$H_a: \mu_0 < \mu_1$ or $H_a: \mu_0 > \mu_1$
Two-Tailed z Test	A nondirectional inferential test in which the prediction is made that the population represented by the sample will differ from the general population, but the direction of the difference is not predicted.	$H_a: \mu_0 \neq \mu_1$
Statistical Power	The probability of correctly rejecting a false H_0.	One-tailed tests are more powerful; increasing sample size increases power.

CRITICAL THINKING CHECK 8.2

1. Imagine that I want to compare the intelligence level of psychology majors with the intelligence level of the general population of college students. I predict that psychology majors will have higher IQ scores. Is this a one- or two-tailed test? Identify H_0 and H_a.
2. Conduct the z test for the preceding example. Assume that $\mu = 100$, $\sigma = 15$, $\overline{X} = 102.75$, and $N = 60$. Should we reject H_0 or fail to reject H_0?

Confidence Intervals Based on the z Distribution

In this text, hypothesis tests such as the previously described z test are the main focus. However, sometimes social and behavioral scientists use estimation of population means based on confidence intervals rather than statistical hypothesis tests. For example, imagine that you want to estimate a population mean based on sample data (a sample mean). This differs from the previously described z test in that we are not determining whether the sample mean differs significantly from the population mean; rather, we are estimating the population mean based on knowing the sample mean. We can still use the area under the normal curve to accomplish this—we simply use it in a slightly different way.

Let's use the previous example in which we know the sample mean weight of children enrolled in athletic after-school programs ($\overline{X} = 86$), $\sigma(17)$, and the sample size ($N = 100$). However, imagine that we do not know the population mean (μ). In this case, we can calculate a confidence interval based on knowing the sample mean and σ. A **confidence interval** is an interval of a certain width, which we feel "confident" will contain μ. We want a confidence interval wide enough that we feel fairly certain it contains the population mean. For example, if we want to be 95% confident, we want a 95% confidence interval.

confidence interval An interval of a certain width that we feel confident will contain μ.

How can we use the area under the standard normal curve to determine a confidence interval of 95%? We use the area under the normal curve to determine the *z*-scores that mark off the area representing 95% of the scores under the curve. If you consult Table A.2 again, you will find that 95% of the scores will fall between ±1.96 standard deviations above and below the mean. Thus, we could determine which scores represent ±1.96 standard deviations from the sample mean of 86. This seems fairly simple, but remember that we are dealing with a distribution of sample means (the sampling distribution) and not with a distribution of individual scores. Thus, we must convert the standard deviation (σ) to the standard error of the mean ($\sigma_{\overline{X}}$, the standard deviation for a sampling distribution) and use the standard error of the mean in the calculation of a confidence interval. Remember, we calculate $\sigma_{\overline{X}}$ by dividing σ by the square root of N.

$$\sigma_{\overline{X}} = \frac{17}{\sqrt{100}} = \frac{17}{10} = 1.7$$

We can now calculate the 95% confidence interval using the following formula:

$$CI = \overline{X} \pm z(\sigma_{\overline{X}})$$

where

$\overline{X}$ = the sample mean,
$\sigma_{\overline{X}}$ = the standard error of the mean, and
z = the *z*-score representing the desired confidence interval.

Thus,

$$\begin{aligned} CI &= 86 \pm 1.96(1.7) \\ &= 86 \pm 3.332 \\ &= 82.668 - 89.332 \end{aligned}$$

Thus, the 95% confidence interval ranges from 82.67 to 89.33. We would conclude, based on this calculation, that we are 95% confident that the population mean lies within this interval.

What if we want to have greater confidence that our population mean is contained in the confidence interval? In other words, what if we want to be 99% confident? We would have to construct a 99% confidence interval. How would we go about doing this? We would do exactly what we did for the 95% confidence interval. First, we would consult Table A.2 to determine what z-scores mark off 99% of the area under the normal curve. We find that z-scores of ±2.58 mark off 99% of the area under the curve. We then apply the same formula for a confidence interval used previously.

$$CI = \overline{X} \pm z(\sigma_{\overline{X}})$$
$$CI = 86 \pm 2.58(1.7)$$
$$= 86 \pm 4.386$$
$$= 81.614 - 90.386$$

Thus, the 99% confidence interval ranges from 81.61 to 90.39. We would conclude, based on this calculation, that we are 99% confident that the population mean lies within this interval.

Typically, statisticians recommend using a 95% or a 99% confidence interval. However, using Table A.2 (the area under the normal curve), you could construct a confidence interval of 55%, 70%, or any percentage you desire.

It is also possible to do hypothesis testing with confidence intervals. For example, if you construct a 95% confidence interval based on knowing a sample mean and then determine that the population mean is not in the confidence interval, the result is significant. For example, the 95% confidence interval we constructed earlier of 82.67 – 89.33 did not include the actual population mean reported earlier in the chapter ($\mu = 90$). Thus, there is less than a 5% chance that this sample mean could have come from this population—the same conclusion we reached when using the z test earlier in the chapter.

The *t* Test: What It Is and What It Does

***t* test** A parametric inferential statistical test of the null hypothesis for a single sample where the population variance is not known.

The ***t* test** for a single sample is similar to the z test in that it is also a parametric statistical test of the null hypothesis for a single sample. As such, it is a means of determining the number of standard deviation units a score is from the mean (μ) of a distribution. With a t test, however, the population variance is not known. Another difference is that t distributions, although symmetrical and bell-shaped, do not fit the standard normal distribution because the t test typically involves using smaller samples ($N < 30$). However, we assume that the populations from which the samples are drawn are normal. This means that the areas under the normal curve that apply for the z test do not apply for the t test, unless the sample is quite large.

Student's *t* Distribution

Student's *t* distribution A set of distributions that, although symmetrical and bell shaped, are not normally distributed.

The t distribution, known as **Student's *t* distribution**, was developed by William Sealey Gosset, a chemist who worked for the Guinness Brewing Company of Dublin, Ireland, at the beginning of the 20th century. Gosset noticed that for small samples of beer ($N < 30$) chosen for quality-control testing, the sampling distribution of the means was symmetrical and bell-shaped but not normal. In other words, with small samples, the curve was symmetrical, but it was not the standard normal curve; therefore, the proportions under the standard normal curve did not apply. As the size of the samples in the sampling distribution increased, the sampling distribution approached the normal distribution, and the proportions under the curve became more similar to those under the standard normal curve. He eventually published his finding under the pseudonym "Student," and with the help of Karl Pearson, a mathematician, he developed a general formula for the t distributions (Peters, 1987; Stigler, 1986; Tankard, 1984).

We refer to t distributions in the plural because unlike the z distribution, of which there is only one, the t distributions are a family of symmetrical distributions that differ for each sample size. As a result, the critical value indicating the region of rejection changes for samples of different sizes. As the size of the samples increases, the t distribution approaches the z or normal distribution. Table A.3 in Appendix A provides the critical values (t_{cv}) for both one- and two-tailed tests for various sample sizes and alpha levels. Notice, however, that although we have said that the critical value depends on sample size, there is no column in the table labeled N for sample size. Instead, there is a column labeled df, which stands for **degrees of freedom**—the number of scores in a sample that are free to vary. The degrees of freedom are related to the sample size. For example, assume that you are given six numbers: 2, 5, 6, 9, 11, and 15. The mean of these numbers is 8. If you are told that you can change the numbers as you like but that the mean of the distribution must remain 8, you can change five of the six numbers arbitrarily. After you have changed five of the numbers arbitrarily, the sixth number is determined by the qualification that the mean of the distribution must equal 8. Therefore, in this distribution of six numbers, five are free to vary. Thus, there are five degrees of freedom. For any single distribution then, $df = N - 1$.

degrees of freedom (df) The number of scores in a sample that are free to vary.

Look again at Table A.3, and notice what happens to the critical values as the degrees of freedom increase. Look at the column for a one-tailed test with alpha equal to .05 and degrees of freedom equal to 10. The critical value is ± 1.812. This is larger than the critical value for a one-tailed z test, which was ± 1.645. Because we are dealing with smaller, nonnormal distributions when using the t test, the t-score must be farther away from the mean for us to conclude that it is significantly different from the mean. What happens as the degrees of freedom increase? Look in the same column—one-tailed test, alpha = .05—for 20 degrees of freedom. The critical value is ± 1.725, which is smaller than the critical value for 10 degrees of freedom. Continue to scan down the same column, one-tailed test and alpha = .05, until you reach the bottom where $df = \infty$. Notice that the critical value is ± 1.645, which is the same as it is for a one-tailed z test. Thus, when the sample size is large, the t distribution is the same as the z distribution.

Calculations for the One-Tailed t Test

Let's illustrate the use of the single-sample t test to test a hypothesis. Assume the mean SAT score of students admitted to General University is 1090. Thus, the university mean of 1090 is the population mean (μ). The population

TABLE 8.1 SAT scores for a sample of 10 biology majors

X
1010
1200
1310
1075
1149
1078
1129
1069
1350
1390
$\Sigma X = 11{,}760$
$\overline{X} = \frac{\Sigma X}{N} = \frac{11{,}760}{10}$
$= 1{,}760.00$

standard deviation is unknown. The members of the biology department believe that students who decide to major in biology have higher SAT scores than the general population of students at the university. The null and alternative hypotheses are

$$H_0: \mu \leq \mu_1, \text{ or } \mu_{\text{biology students}} \leq \mu_{\text{general population}}$$
$$H_a: \mu_0 > \mu_1, \text{ or } \mu_{\text{biology students}} > \mu_{\text{general population}}$$

Notice that this is a one-tailed test because the researchers predict that the biology students have higher SAT scores than the general population of students at the university. The researchers now need to obtain the SAT scores for a sample of biology majors. SAT scores for 10 biology majors are provided in Table 8.1, which shows that the mean SAT score for the sample is 1176. This represents our estimate of the population mean SAT score for biology majors.

The Estimated Standard Error of the Mean

The t test tells us whether this mean differs significantly from the university mean of 1090. Because we have a small sample ($N = 10$) and because we do not know σ, we must conduct a t test rather than a z test. The formula for the t test is

$$t = \frac{\overline{X} - \mu}{s_{\overline{X}}}$$

This looks very similar to the formula for the z test that we used earlier in the chapter. The only difference is the denominator, where $s_{\overline{X}}$ (the **estimated standard error of the mean**)—an estimate of the standard deviation of the sampling distribution based on sample data—has been substituted for $\sigma_{\overline{X}}$. We use $s_{\overline{X}}$ rather than $\sigma_{\overline{X}}$ because we do not know σ (the standard deviation for the population) and thus cannot calculate $\sigma_{\overline{X}}$. We can, however, determine s (the unbiased estimator of the population standard deviation) and, based on this, we can determine $s_{\overline{X}}$. The formula for $s_{\overline{X}}$ is

estimated standard error of the mean An estimate of the standard deviation of the sampling distribution.

$$s_{\overline{X}} = \frac{s}{\sqrt{N}}$$

We must first calculate s (the estimated standard deviation for a population, based on sample data) and then use s to calculate the estimated standard error of the mean ($s_{\overline{X}}$). The formula for s, which you learned in Chapter 5, is

$$s = \sqrt{\frac{\Sigma(X - \overline{X})^2}{N-1}}$$

Using the information in Table 8.1, we can use this formula to calculate s:

$$s = \sqrt{\frac{156{,}352}{9}} = \sqrt{17{,}372.44} = 131.80$$

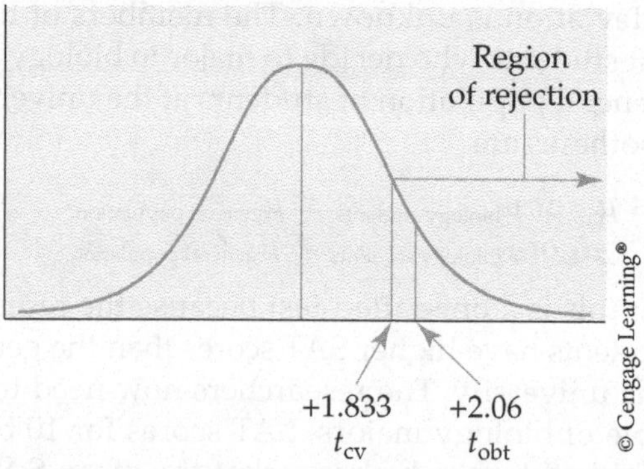

FIGURE 8.4
The *t* critical value and the *t* obtained for the single-sample one-tailed *t* test example

Thus, the unbiased estimator of the standard deviation (s) is 131.80. We can now use this value to calculate $s_{\overline{X}}$, the estimated standard error of the sampling distribution:

$$s_{\overline{X}} = \frac{s}{\sqrt{N}} = \frac{131.80}{\sqrt{10}} = \frac{131.80}{3.16} = 41.71$$

Finally, we can use this value for $s_{\overline{X}}$ to calculate t:

$$t = \frac{\overline{X} - \mu}{s_{\overline{X}}} = \frac{1176 - 1090}{41.71} = \frac{86}{41.71} = +2.06$$

Interpreting the One-Tailed *t* Test

Our sample mean falls 2.06 standard deviations above the population mean of 1090. We must now determine whether this is far enough away from the population mean to be considered significantly different. In other words, is our sample mean far enough away from the population mean that it lies in the region of rejection? Because the alternative hypothesis is one-tailed, the region of rejection is in only one tail of the sampling distribution. Consulting Table A.3 (in Appendix A) for a one-tailed test with alpha $= .05$ and $df = N - 1 = 9$, we see that $t_{cv} = \pm 1.833$. The t_{obt} of 2.06 is therefore within the region of rejection. We reject H_0 and support H_a. In other words, we have sufficient evidence to allow us to conclude that biology majors have significantly higher SAT scores than the rest of the students at General University. Figure 8.4 illustrates the obtained t in relation to the region of rejection. In APA style, the result is reported as

$$t(9) = 2.06, p < .05 \text{ (one-tailed)}$$

This form conveys in a concise manner the t-score, the degrees of freedom, that the result is significant at the .05 level, and that a one-tailed test was used. Instructions on using Excel, SPSS, or the TI-84 calculator to conduct this one-tailed single-sample t test can be found in the Statistical Software Resources section at the end of the chapter.

Calculations for the Two-Tailed *t* Test

What if the biology department made no directional prediction concerning the SAT scores of its students? In other words, suppose the members of the department are unsure whether their students' SAT scores are higher or lower than those of the general population of students and are simply interested in whether biology students differ from the population. In this case, the test of the alternative hypothesis is two-tailed, and the null and alternative hypotheses are

$$H_0: \mu_0 = \mu_1, \text{ or } \mu_{\text{biology students}} = \mu_{\text{general population}}$$
$$H_a: \mu_0 \neq \mu_1; \text{ or } \mu_{\text{biology students}} \neq \mu_{\text{general population}}$$

If we assume that the sample of biology students is the same, then $\overline{X}$, s, and $s_{\overline{X}}$ are all the same. The population at General University is also the same, so μ is still 1090. Using all of this information to conduct the t test, we end up with exactly the same t-test score of ± 2.06. What, then, is the difference for the two-tailed t test? It is the same as the difference between the one- and two-tailed z tests—the critical values differ.

Interpreting the Two-Tailed *t* Test

Remember that with a two-tailed alternative hypothesis, the region of rejection is divided evenly between the two tails (the positive and negative ends) of the sampling distribution. Consulting Table A.3 for a two-tailed test with alpha $= .05$ and $df = N - 1 = 9$, we see that $t_{cv} = 2.262$. The t_{obt} of 2.06 is therefore not within the region of rejection. We do not reject H_0 and thus cannot support H_a. In other words, we do not have sufficient evidence to allow us to conclude that the population of biology majors differs significantly on SAT scores from the rest of the students at General University. Thus, with exactly the same data, we rejected H_0 with a one-tailed test but failed to reject H_0 with a two-tailed test, illustrating once again that one-tailed tests are more powerful than two-tailed tests. Figure 8.5 illustrates the obtained t for the two-tailed test in relation to the region of rejection.

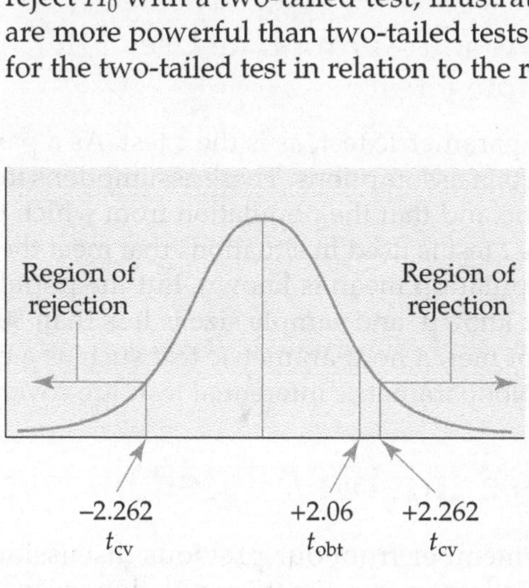

FIGURE 8.5
The *t* critical value and the *t* obtained for the single-sample two-tailed *t* test example

The t Test — IN REVIEW

CONCEPT	DESCRIPTION	USE/EXAMPLE
Estimated standard error of the mean ($s_{\bar{X}}$)	The estimated standard deviation of a sampling distribution, calculated by dividing s by $\sqrt{N}$	Used in the calculation of a t test
t Test	Indicator of the number of standard deviation units the sample mean is from the mean of the sampling distribution.	An inferential statistical test that differs from the z test in that the sample size is small (usually < 30) and σ is not known
One-tailed t Test	A directional inferential test in which a prediction is made that the population represented by the sample will be either above or below the general population.	$H_a: \mu_0 < \mu_1$ or $H_a: \mu_0 > \mu_1$
Two-tailed t Test	A nondirectional inferential test in which the prediction is made that the population represented by the sample will differ from the general population, but the direction of the difference is not predicted.	$H_a: \mu_0 \neq \mu_1$

CRITICAL THINKING CHECK 8.3

1. Explain the difference in use and computation between the z test and the t test.
2. Test the following hypothesis using the t test: Researchers are interested in whether the pulses of long-distance runners differ from those of other athletes. They suspect that the runners' pulses will be slower. They obtain a random sample ($N = 8$) of long-distance runners, measure their resting pulses, and obtain the following data: 45, 42, 64, 54, 58, 49, 47, 55 beats per minute. The average resting pulse of athletes in the general population is 60 beats per minute.

Assumptions and Appropriate Use of the Single-Sample t Test

The t test is a parametric test, as is the z test. As a parametric test, the t test must meet certain assumptions. These assumptions include that the data are interval or ratio and that the population from which the samples are drawn is normal. The t test is used in situations that meet these assumptions and in which the population mean is known, but the population standard deviation (σ) is not known, and sample size is less than 30. In cases where these criteria are not met, a nonparametric test such as a chi-square test is more appropriate. Nonparametric inferential tests are covered in Chapter 14.

Confidence Intervals Based on the t Distribution

You might remember from our previous discussion of confidence intervals that they allow us to estimate population means based on sample data (a sample mean). Thus, when using confidence intervals, rather than determining whether the sample mean differs significantly from the population mean, we are estimating the population mean based on knowing the sample mean. We can use confidence intervals with the t distribution just as we did with the z distribution (the area under the normal curve).

Let's use the previous example in which we know the sample mean SAT score for the biology students ($\overline{X} = 1176$), the estimated standard error of the mean ($s_{\overline{X}} = 41.71$), and the sample size ($N = 10$). We can calculate a confidence interval based on knowing the sample mean and $s_{\overline{X}}$. Remember that a confidence interval is an interval of a certain width, which we feel "confident" will contain μ. We are going to calculate a 95% confidence interval—in other words, an interval that we feel 95% confident contains the population mean. To calculate a 95% confidence interval using the t distribution, we use Table A.3 "Critical Values for the Student's t Distribution" (in Appendix A) to determine the critical value of t at the .05 level. We use the .05 level because 1 minus alpha tells us how confident we are, and, in this case, $1 - \alpha$ is $1 - .05 = .95$, or 95% when converted to a percentage.

For a one-sample t test, the confidence interval is determined with the following formula:

$$CI = \overline{X} \pm t_{cv}(s_{\overline{X}})$$

We already know $\overline{X}$ (1176) and $s_{\overline{X}}$ (41.71), so all we have left to determine is t_{cv}. We use Table A.3 to determine the t_{cv} for the .05 level and a two-tailed test. We always use the t_{cv} for a two-tailed test because we are describing values both above and below the mean of the distribution. Using Table A.3, we find that the t_{cv} for 9 degrees of freedom (remember $df = N - 1$) is 2.262. We now have all of the values we need to determine the confidence interval.

Let's begin by calculating the lower limit of the confidence interval:

$$\begin{aligned} CI &= 1176 - 2.262\,(41.71) \\ &= 1176 - 94.35 = 1081.65 \end{aligned}$$

The upper limit of the confidence interval is

$$\begin{aligned} CI &= 1176 + 2.262\,(41.71) \\ &= 1176 + 94.35 = 1270.35 \end{aligned}$$

Thus, we can conclude that we are 95% confident that the interval of SAT scores from 1081.65 to 1270.35 contains the population mean (μ).

As with the z distribution, we can calculate confidence intervals for the t distribution that give us greater or less confidence (for example, a 99% confidence interval or a 90% confidence interval). Typically, statisticians recommend using either the 95% or 99% confidence interval (the intervals corresponding to the .05 and .01 alpha levels in hypothesis testing). You have likely encountered such intervals in real life. They are usually phrased in terms of "plus or minus" some amount called the margin of error. For example, when a newspaper reports that a sample survey showed that 53% of the viewers support a particular candidate, the margin of error is typically also reported—for example, "with a ±3% margin of error." This means that the researcher who conducted the survey created a confidence interval around the 53% and that if they actually surveyed the entire population, would be within ±3% of the 53%. In other words, they believe that between 50% and 56% of the viewers support this particular candidate.

Correlation Coefficients and Statistical Significance

You may remember from Chapter 6 that correlation coefficients are used to describe the strength of a relationship between two variables. For example, we learned how to calculate the Pearson product-moment correlation coefficient, which is used when the variables are of interval or ratio scale. At that time, however, we did not discuss the idea of statistical significance. In this case, the null hypothesis (H_0) is that the true population correlation is .00—the variables are not related. The alternative hypothesis (H_a) is that the observed correlation is not equal to .00—the variables are related. But what if we obtain a rather weak correlation coefficient, such as +.33? Determining the statistical significance of the correlation coefficient will allow us to decide whether or not to reject H_0.

To test the null hypothesis that the population correlation coefficient is .00, we must consult a table of critical values for *r* (the Pearson product-moment correlation coefficient) as we have done for the other statistics discussed in this chapter. Table A.4 in Appendix A shows critical values for both one- and two-tailed tests of *r*. A one-tailed test of a correlation coefficient means that we have predicted the expected direction of the correlation coefficient (i.e., predicted either a positive or negative correlation), whereas a two-tailed test means that we have not predicted the direction of the correlation coefficient.

To use this table, we first need to determine the degrees of freedom, which for the Pearson product-moment correlation are equal to $N - 2$, where *N* represents the total number of pairs of observations. If the correlation coefficient of +.33 is based on 20 pairs of observations, then the degrees of freedom are $20 - 2 = 18$. After the degrees of freedom are determined, we can consult the critical values table. For 18 degrees of freedom and a two-tailed test at alpha = .05, r_{cv} is ±.4438. This means that r_{obt} must be that large or larger to be statistically significant at the .05 level. Because our r_{obt} is not that large, we fail to reject H_0. In other words, the observed correlation coefficient is not statistically significant. You might remember that the correlation coefficient calculated in Chapter 6 between height and weight was +.94. This was a one-tailed test (we expected a positive relationship) and there were 20 participants in the study. Thus, the degrees of freedom are 18. Consulting Table A.4 in Appendix A, we find that the r_{cv} is ±.3783. Because the r_{obt} is larger than this, we can conclude that the observed correlation coefficient is statistically significant. In APA style, the result is reported as

$$r(18) = +.94, p < .05(\text{one-tailed})$$

Summary

In this chapter, we introduced inferential statistics. We described two parametric statistical tests: the *z* test and the *t* test. Each compares a sample mean with the general population. Because both are parametric tests, the distributions should be bell-shaped, and certain parameters should be known (in the case of the *z* test, μ and σ must be known; for the *t* test, only μ is needed). In addition, because the tests are parametric, the data should be interval or ratio in scale. These tests use the sampling distribution (the distribution of sample means). They also use the standard error of the mean (or estimated standard error of the mean for the *t* test), which is the standard deviation of the sampling distribution. Both *z* tests and *t* tests can test one- or two-tailed alternative hypotheses, but one-tailed tests are more powerful statistically.

Last, we revisited correlation coefficients with respect to significance testing. We learned how to determine whether an observed correlation coefficient is statistically significant by using a critical values table.

In Chapters 10 to 12 and 14 we will continue our discussion of inferential statistics, looking at statistical procedures appropriate for experimental designs with two or more equivalent groups and those appropriate for designs with more than one independent variable.

KEY TERMS

z test	critical value	*t* test
sampling distribution	region of rejection	Student's *t* distribution
standard error of the mean	statistical power	degrees of freedom (*df*)
central limit theorem	confidence interval	estimated standard error of the mean

CHAPTER EXERCISES

(Answers to odd-numbered exercises appear in Appendix C.)

1. A researcher is interested in whether students who attend private high schools have higher average SAT scores than students in the general population. A random sample of 90 students at a private high school is tested and has a mean SAT score of 1050. The average score for public high school students is 1000 ($\sigma = 200$).
   a. Is this a one- or two-tailed test?
   b. What are H_0 and H_a for this study?
   c. Compute z_{obt}.
   d. What is z_{cv}?
   e. Should H_0 be rejected? What should the researcher conclude?
   f. Determine the 95% confidence interval for the population mean, based on the sample mean.
2. The producers of a new toothpaste claim that it prevents more cavities than other brands of toothpaste. A random sample of 60 people used the new toothpaste for 6 months. The mean number of cavities at their next checkup is 1.5. In the general population, the mean number of cavities at a 6-month checkup is 1.73 ($\sigma = 1.12$).
   a. Is this a one- or two-tailed test?
   b. What are H_0 and H_a for this study?
   c. Compute z_{obt}.
   d. What is z_{cv}?
   e. Should H_0 be rejected? What should the researcher conclude?
   f. Determine the 95% confidence interval for the population mean, based on the sample mean.
3. Why does t_{cv} change when the sample size changes? What must be computed to determine t_{cv}?
4. Henry performed a two-tailed test for an experiment in which $N = 24$. He could not find his table of *t* critical values, but he remembered the t_{cv} at $df = 13$. He decided to compare his t_{obt} with this t_{cv}. Is he more likely to make a Type I or a Type II error in this situation?

5. A researcher hypothesizes that people who listen to music via headphones have greater hearing loss and will thus score lower on a hearing test than those in the general population. On a standard hearing test, the overall mean is 22.5. The researcher gives this same test to a random sample of 12 individuals who regularly use headphones. Their scores on the test are 16, 14, 20, 12, 25, 22, 23, 19, 17, 17, 21, 20.
   a. Is this a one- or two-tailed test?
   b. What are H_0 and H_a for this study?
   c. Compute t_{obt}.
   d. What is t_{cv}?
   e. Should H_0 be rejected? What should the researcher conclude?
   f. Determine the 95% confidence interval for the population mean, based on the sample mean.
6. A researcher hypothesizes that individuals who listen to classical music will score differently from the general population on a test of spatial ability. On a standardized test of spatial ability, $\mu = 58$. A random sample of 14 individuals who listen to classical music is given the same test. Their scores on the test are 52, 59, 63, 65, 58, 55, 62, 63, 53, 59, 57, 61, 60, 59.
   a. Is this a one- or two-tailed test?
   b. What are H_0 and H_a for this study?
   c. Compute t_{obt}.
   d. What is t_{cv}?
   e. Should H_0 be rejected? What should the researcher conclude?
   f. Determine the 95% confidence interval for the population mean, based on the sample mean.

CRITICAL THINKING CHECK ANSWERS

8.1

1. A sampling distribution is a distribution of sample means. Thus, rather than representing scores for individuals, the sampling distribution plots the means of samples of a set size.
2. $\sigma_{\overline{X}}$ is the standard deviation for a sampling distribution. It therefore represents the standard deviation for a distribution of sample means. σ is the standard deviation for a population of individual scores rather than sample means.
3. A z test compares the performance of a sample with the performance of the population by indicating the number of standard deviation units the sample mean is from the population mean. A z-score indicates how many standard deviation units an individual score is from the population mean.

8.2

1. Predicting that psychology majors will have higher IQ scores makes this a one-tailed test.

$$H_0: \mu_{\text{psychology majors}} \leq \mu_{\text{general population}}$$

$$H_a: \mu_{\text{psychology majors}} > \mu_{\text{general population}}$$

2. $$\sigma_{\overline{X}} = \frac{15}{\sqrt{60}} = \frac{15}{7.75} = 1.94$$

$$z = \frac{102.75 - 100}{1.94} = \frac{2.75}{1.94} = 1.42$$

Because this is a one-tailed test, $z_{cv} = \pm 1.645$. The $z_{obt} = +1.42$. We therefore fail to reject H_0 and conclude that psychology majors do not differ significantly on IQ scores from the general population of college students.

8.3

1. The z test is used when the sample size is greater than 30, normally distributed, and s is known. The t test is used when the sample size is smaller than 30, bell-shaped but not normal, and s is not known.
2. $H_0: \mu_{\text{runners}} \geq \mu_{\text{other athletes}}$

$H_a: \mu_{\text{runners}} < \mu_{\text{other athletes}}$

$\overline{X} = 51.75$

$s = 7.32$

$\mu = 60$

$$s_{\overline{X}} = \frac{7.32}{\sqrt{8}} = \frac{7.32}{2.83} = 2.59$$

$$t = \frac{51.75 - 60}{2.59} = \frac{-8.25}{2.59} = -3.19$$

$$df = 8 - 1 = 7$$

$$t_{cv} = \pm 1.895$$

$$t_{obt} = -3.19$$

Reject H_0. The runners' pulses are significantly slower than the pulses of athletes in general.

WEB RESOURCES

The book-specific website at CengageBrain .com offers students a variety of study tools and useful resources such as glossaries and flashcards.

Chapter 8 ■ Study Guide

CHAPTER 8 SUMMARY AND REVIEW: HYPOTHESIS TESTING AND INFERENTIAL STATISTICS

This chapter consisted of an introduction to inferential statistics. Two parametric statistical tests were described—the *z* test and the *t* test. Each compares a sample mean to the general population. Because both are parametric tests, the distributions should be bell-shaped, and certain parameters should be known (in the case of the *z* test, μ and σ must be known; for the *t* test, only μ is needed). In addition, because these are parametric tests, the data should be interval or ratio in scale. These tests involve the use of the sampling distribution (the distribution of sample means). They also involve the use of the standard error of the mean (or estimated standard error of the mean for the *t* test), which is the standard deviation of the sampling distribution. Both *z* tests and *t* tests can test one- or two-tailed alternative hypotheses, but one-tailed tests are more powerful statistically.

Lastly, the concept of correlation coefficients was revisited with respect to significance testing. This involved learning how to determine whether an observed correlation coefficient is statistically significant by using a critical values table.

CHAPTER 8 REVIEW EXERCISES

(Answers to exercises appear in Appendix C.)

FILL-IN SELF-TEST

Answer the following questions. If you have trouble answering any of the questions, restudy the relevant material before going on to the multiple-choice self-test.

1. A ________ is a distribution of sample means based on random samples of a fixed size from a population.
2. The ________ is the standard deviation of the sampling distribution.
3. The set of distributions that, although symmetrical and bell-shaped, are not normally distributed is called the ________.
4. The ________ is a parametric statistical test of the null hypothesis for a single sample where the population variance is not known.

MULTIPLE-CHOICE SELF-TEST

Select the single best answer for each of the following questions. If you have trouble answering any of the questions, restudy the relevant material.

1. Inferential statistics allow us to infer something about the ________ based on the ________.
   a. sample; population
   b. population; sample
   c. sample; sample
   d. population; population
2. The sampling distribution is a distribution of:
   a. sample means.
   b. population mean.
   c. sample standard deviations.
   d. population standard deviations.

3. A one-tailed z test is to ________ and a two-tailed z test is to________.
   a. ± 1.645 (at alpha = .05); ± 1.96 (at alpha = .05)
   b. ± 1.96 (at alpha = .05); ± 1.645 (at alpha = .05)
   c. Type I error; Type II error
   d. Type II error; Type I error

4. Which of the following is an assumption of the t test?
   a. The data should be ordinal or nominal.
   b. The sample size is typically more than 30.
   c. The population mean (μ) and standard deviation (σ) are known.
   d. The population distribution of scores from which the sample is drawn should be normal.

SELF-TEST PROBLEMS

1. A researcher is interested in whether students who play chess have higher average SAT scores than students in the general population. A random sample of 75 students who play chess is tested and has a mean SAT score of 1070. The average (μ) is 1000 (σ = 200).
   a. Is this a one- or two-tailed test?
   b. What are H_0 and H_a for this study?
   c. Compute z_{obt}.
   d. What is z_{cv}?
   e. Should H_0 be rejected? What should the researcher conclude?
   f. Calculate the 95% confidence interval for the population mean, based on the sample mean.
2. A researcher hypothesizes that people who listen to classical music have higher concentration skills than those in the general population. On a standard concentration test, the overall mean is 15.5. The researcher gave this same test to a random sample of 12 individuals who regularly listen to classical music. Their scores on the test follow: 16, 14, 20, 12, 25, 22, 23, 19, 17, 17, 21, 20
   a. Is this a one- or two-tailed test?
   b. What are H_0 and H_a for this study?
   c. Compute t_{obt}.
   d. What is t_{cv}?
   e. Should H_0 be rejected? What should the researcher conclude?
   f. Calculate the 95% confidence interval for the population mean, based on the sample mean.

Chapter 8 ▪ Statistical Software Resources

THE Z TEST

One-Tailed z Test

Using the TI-84

1. With the calculator on, press the STAT key.
2. Highlight TESTS.
3. 1: Z-Test will be highlighted. Press ENTER.
4. Highlight STATS. Press ENTER.
5. Scroll down to μ_0: and enter the mean for the population (100).
6. Scroll down to σ: and enter the standard deviation for the population (15).
7. Scroll down to $\overline{X}$: and enter the mean for the sample (103.5).
8. Scroll down to n: and enter the sample size (75).

9. Lastly, scroll down to μ: and select the type of test (one-tailed), indicating that we expect the sample mean to be greater than the population mean (select $> \mu_0$). Press ENTER.
10. Highlight CALCULATE and press ENTER.

The z-score of 2.02 should be displayed followed by the significance level of .02. If you would like to see where the z-score falls on the normal distribution, repeat Steps 1–9, then highlight DRAW, and press ENTER.

Two-Tailed *z* Test

Using the TI-84

1. With the calculator on, press the STAT key.
2. Highlight TESTS.
3. 1: Z-Test will be highlighted. Press ENTER.
4. Highlight STATS. Press ENTER.
5. Scroll down to μ_0: and enter the mean for the population (90).
6. Scroll down to σ: and enter the standard deviation for the population (17).
7. Scroll down to $\overline{X}$: and enter the mean for the sample (86).
8. Scroll down to n: and enter the sample size (50).
9. Lastly, scroll down to μ: and select the type of test (two-tailed), indicating that we expect the sample mean to differ from the population mean (select $\neq \mu_0$). Press ENTER.
10. Highlight CALCULATE and press ENTER.

The z-score of −1.66 should be displayed followed by the alpha level of .096, indicating that this test was not significant. We can therefore conclude that the weight of children in the athletic after-school program does not differ significantly from the weight of children in the general population.

If you would like to see where the z-score falls on the normal distribution, repeat Steps 1–9, then highlight DRAW, and press ENTER.

The Single-Sample *t* Test

Using Excel

To demonstrate how to use Excel to calculate a single-sample *t* test, we'll use the data from Table 8.1 in this chapter, which represent SAT scores for 10 biology majors at General University. We are testing whether biology majors have higher average SAT scores than the population of students at General University. We begin by entering the data into Excel. We enter the sample data into the A column and the population mean of 1090 into the B column. We enter the population mean next to the score for each individual in the sample. Thus, you can see that I've entered 1090 in Column B ten times, one time for each individual in our sample of 10 biology majors.

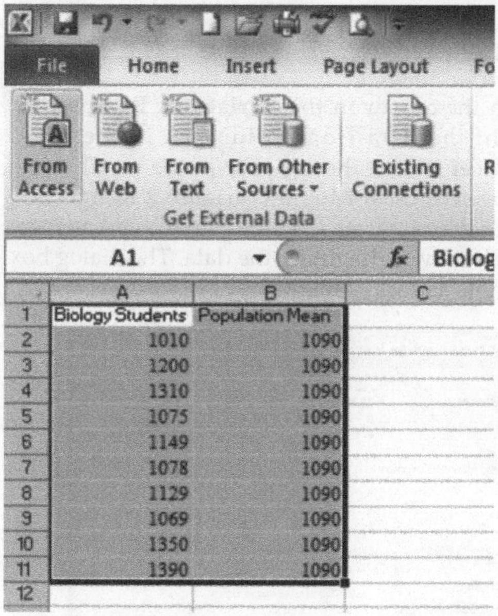

Next highlight the **Data** ribbon, and then click on **Data Analysis** in the top right-hand corner. You should now have the following pop-up window:

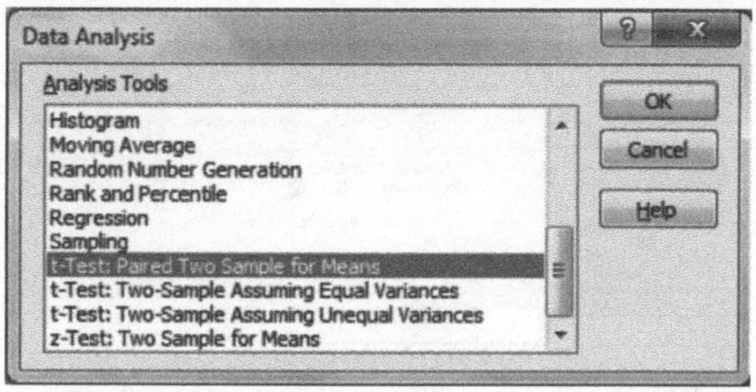

Scroll down to **t-Test: Paired Two Sample for Means**, which is the procedure we'll be using to determine the single-sample *t* test. Then click **OK**. You'll be presented with the following dialog box:

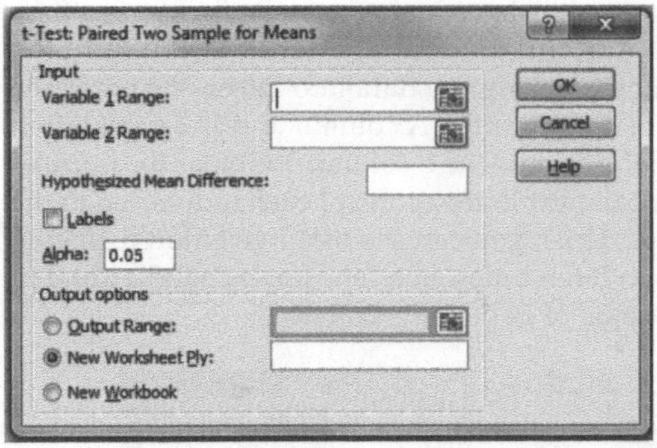

With the cursor in the **Variable 1 Range**: box, highlight the data from Column A in the Excel spreadsheet so that they appear in the input range box. Move the cursor to the **Variable 2 Range**: box and enter the data from Column B in the spreadsheet into this box by highlighting the data. The dialog box should now appear as follows:

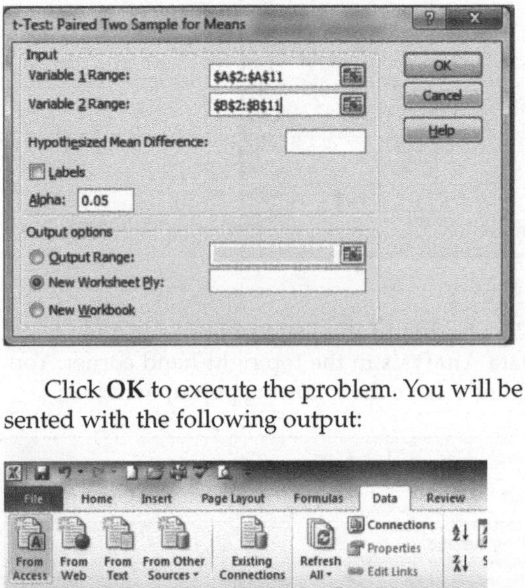

Click **OK** to execute the problem. You will be presented with the following output:

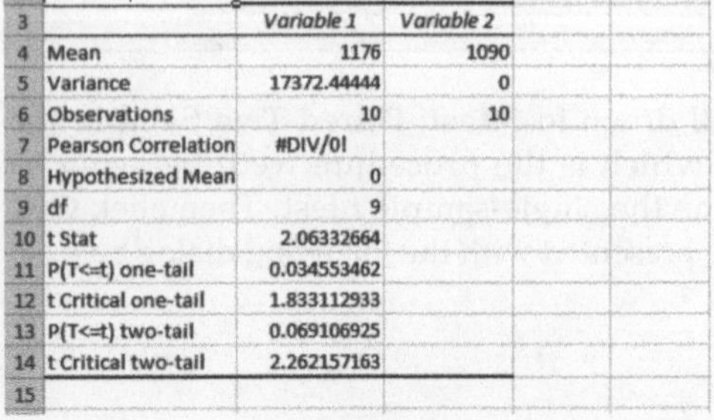

We can see the t test score of 2.063 and the one-tailed significance level of $p = .035$. Thus, our sample mean falls 2.06 standard deviations above the population mean of 1090. We must now determine whether this is far enough away from the population mean to be considered significantly different. Because our obtained alpha level (significance level) is .035 and is less than .05, the result is significant. We reject H_0 and support H_a. In other words, we have sufficient evidence to allow us to conclude that biology majors have significantly higher SAT scores than the rest of the students at General University. In APA style, this would be reported as $t(9) = 2.06$, $p = .035$ (one-tailed).

Using SPSS

To demonstrate how to use SPSS to calculate a single-sample t test, we'll use the data from Table 8.1, which represent SAT scores for 10 biology majors at General University. We are testing whether biology majors have higher average SAT scores than the population of students at General University. We begin by entering the data into SPSS and naming the variable (if you've forgotten how to name a variable, please refer back to Module 1), as follows:

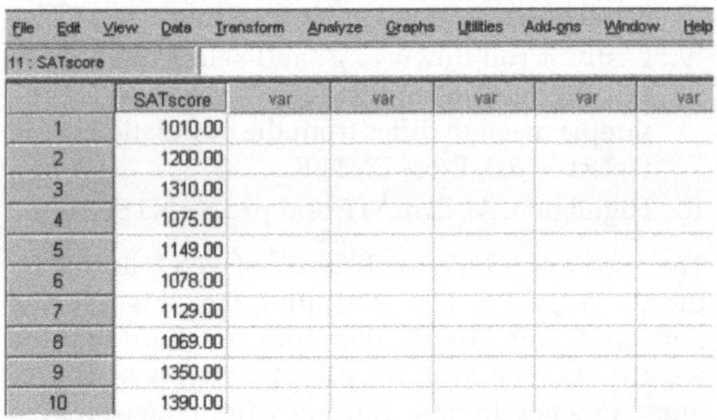

Then select the **Analyze** tab and, from the drop-down menu, **Compare Means** followed by **One-Sample T Test**. The following dialog box will appear:

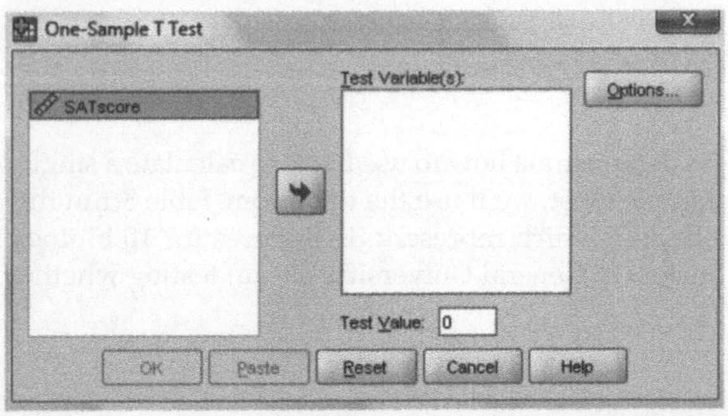

Place the SATscore variable into the **Test Variable** box by utilizing the arrow in the middle of the window. Then let SPSS know what the population mean SAT score is. We can find this earlier in this module where the problem is described—it is 1,090. We enter this population mean in the **Test Value** box as in the following window:

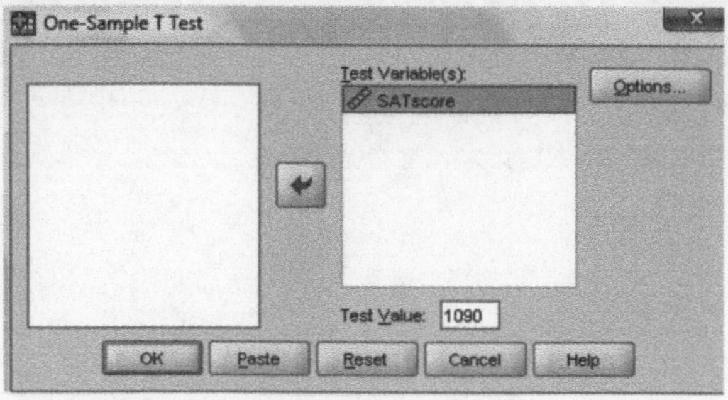

Then click **OK**, and the output for the single-sample t test will be produced in an output window as follows:

T-Test

One-Sample Statistics

	N	Mean	Std. Deviation	Std. Error Mean
SATscore	10	1176.0000	131.80457	41.68026

One-Sample Test

	Test Value = 1090					
					95% Confidence Interval of the Difference	
	t	df	Sig. (2-tailed)	Mean Difference	Lower	Upper
SATscore	2.063	9	.069	86.00000	-8.2873	180.2873

We can see the t test score of 2.063 and the two-tailed significance level. Thus, our sample mean falls 2.06 standard deviations above the population mean of 1090. We must now determine whether this is far enough away from the population mean to be considered significantly different. This was a one-tailed test; thus when using SPSS you will need to divide the significance level in half to obtain a one-tailed significance level because SPSS reports only two-tailed significance levels. Our alpha level (significance level) is .035 and is less than .05, meaning the result is significant. We reject H_0 and support H_a. In other words, we have sufficient evidence to allow us to conclude that biology majors have significantly higher SAT scores than the rest of the students at General University. In APA style, this would be reported as $t(9) = 2.06, p = .035$ (one-tailed).

Using the TI-84

Let's use the data from Table 8.1 to conduct the test using the TI-84 calculator.

1. With the calculator on, press the STAT key.
2. EDIT will be highlighted. Press the ENTER key.
3. Under L1 enter the SAT data from Table 6.1.
4. Press the STAT key once again and highlight TESTS.
5. Scroll down to T-Test. Press the ENTER key.
6. Highlight DATA and press ENTER. Enter 1090 (the mean for the population) next to μ_0: Enter L_1 next to List (to do this press the 2nd key followed by the 1 key).
7. Scroll down to μ: and select $> \mu_0$ (for a one-tailed test in which we predict that the sample mean will be greater than the population mean). Press ENTER.
8. Scroll down to and highlight CALCULATE. Press ENTER.

The t score of 2.06 should be displayed followed by the significance level of .035. In addition, descriptive statistics will be shown. If you would like to see where the t score falls on the distribution, repeat Steps 1–7, then highlight DRAW, and press ENTER.

CHAPTER 9

Experimental Design and Analysis I: Between-Subjects Designs

Learning Objectives

- Explain a between-subjects design.
- Differentiate an independent variable and a dependent variable.
- Differentiate a control group and an experimental group.
- Explain random assignment.
- Explain the relationship between confounds and internal validity.
- Describe the confounds of history, maturation, testing, regression to the mean, instrumentation, mortality, and diffusion of treatment.
- Explain what experimenter effects and subject effects are and how double-blind and single-blind experiments relate to these concepts.
- Differentiate floor and ceiling effects.
- Explain external validity.
- Explain when the *t* test for independent groups should be used.
- Calculate an independent-groups *t* test.
- Interpret an independent-groups *t* test.
- Calculate and interpret Cohen's *d* and r^2.
- Explain the assumptions of the independent-groups *t* test.

In this chapter, we will begin our discussion with the logic of a well-designed experiment and the statistics used to analyze such a study. This discussion will continue in Chapters 10–12. Pick up any newspaper or watch any news program and you will be confronted with results and claims based on scientific research. Some people dismiss or ignore many of the claims because they do not understand how a study or a series of studies can lead to a single conclusion. In other words, they do not understand the concept of control in experiments and that when control is maximized, the conclusion is most likely reliable and valid. Other people accept everything they read, assuming that whatever is presented in a newspaper must be true. They too are not able to assess whether the research was conducted in a reliable and valid manner. This chapter will enable you to understand how to do so.

In previous chapters, we looked at nonexperimental designs. Most recently, in Chapter 6 we discussed correlational designs and the problems and limitations associated with using this type of design. In this chapter, we'll discuss between-subjects designs in their most simplistic form—a two group design. We'll look at other options for experimental designs in Chapters 10–12.

Two-Group Between-Subjects Designs

between-subjects design An experiment in which different subjects are assigned to each group.

In a **between-subjects design**, the subjects in each group are different; that is, different people serve in the control and experimental groups. The idea behind experimentation, you should recall from Chapter 1, is that the researcher manipulates at least one variable (the independent variable) and measures at least one variable (the dependent variable). The independent variable has at least two groups or conditions. In other words, one of the most basic ideas behind an experiment is that there are at least two groups to compare. We typically refer to these two groups or conditions as the control group and the experimental group. The control group is the group that serves as the baseline or "standard" condition. The experimental group is the group that receives some level of the independent variable. Although we describe the two groups in an experiment as the experimental and control groups, an experiment may involve the use of two experimental groups with no control group. As you will see in later chapters, an experiment can also use the same people in the experimental and control groups and it can have more than two groups—in other words, there can be multiple experimental groups in an experiment.

Experimentation involves control. First, we have to control who is in the study. We want to have a sample that is representative of the population about whom we are trying to generalize. Ideally, we accomplish this through the use of random sampling. We also need to control who participates in each condition, so we should use random assignment of subjects to the two conditions. By randomly assigning participants to conditions, we are trying to make the two groups as equivalent as possible. In addition to controlling who serves in the study and in which condition, we need to control what happens during the experiment, so that the only difference between the conditions is in the level of the independent variable that subjects receive. If, after controlling all of this, we observe behavioral changes when the independent variable is manipulated, we can then conclude that the independent variable caused these changes in the dependent variable.

Let's consider the example from Chapter 6 on smoking and cancer to examine the difference between correlational research and experimental research. Remember, we said that there was a positive correlation between smoking and cancer. We also noted that no experimental evidence with humans supported a causal relationship between smoking and cancer. Why is this the case? Let's think about actually trying to design an experiment to determine whether smoking causes cancer in humans. Keep in mind potential ethical problems that might arise as we design this experiment.

Let's first determine the independent variable. If you identified smoking behavior as the independent variable, you are correct. The control group would be the group that does not smoke, and the experimental group would be the group that does smoke. To prevent confounding of our study by previous smoking behavior, we could use only nonsmokers. We would then randomly assign them to either the smoking or the nonsmoking group. In addition to assigning subjects to one of the two conditions, we would control all other aspects of their lives. This means that all participants in the study must be treated exactly the same for the duration of the study, except that half of them would smoke on a regular basis (we would decide when and how much) and half of them would not smoke at all. We would then determine the length of time for which the study should run. In this case, subjects would have to smoke for many years for us to assess any potential differences between groups. During this time, all aspects of their lives

FIGURE 9.1 Experimental study of the effects of smoking on cancer rates

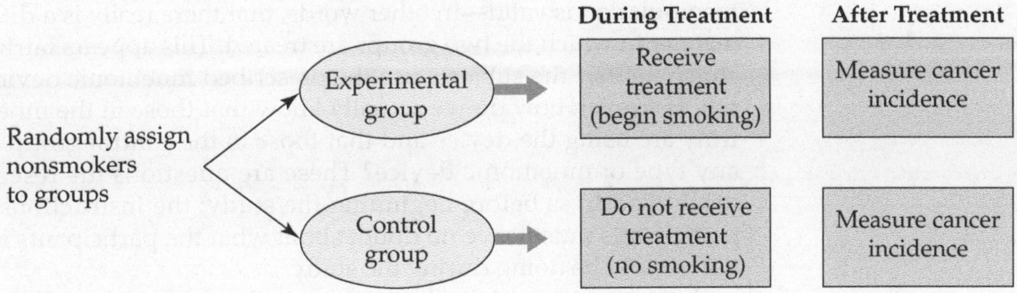

that might contribute to cancer would have to be controlled—held constant between the groups.

What would the dependent variable be? The dependent variable would be the incidence of cancer. After several years had passed, we would begin to take measures on the two groups to determine whether there were any differences in cancer rates. Thus, the cancer rate would be the dependent variable. If control was maximized, and the experimental group and control group were treated exactly the same except for the level of the independent variable that they received, then any difference observed between the groups in cancer rate would have to be due to the only difference that existed between the groups—the independent variable of smoking. This experimental study is illustrated in Figure 9.1.

You should begin to appreciate the problems associated with designing a true experiment to test the effects of smoking on cancer. First, it is not ethical to determine for people whether or not they smoke. Second, it is not feasible to control all aspects of these individuals' lives for the period of time that is needed to conduct this study. For these reasons, there is no experimental study indicating that smoking causes cancer in humans.

It is perfectly feasible, however, to conduct experimental studies on other topics. For example, if we wanted to study the effects of a certain type of mnemonic device (a study strategy) on memory, we could have one group use the device while studying and another group not use the device while studying. We could then give each person a memory test and look for a difference in performance between the two groups. Assuming that everything else was held constant (controlled), any difference observed would have to be due to the independent variable. If the mnemonic group performed better, we could conclude that the mnemonic device caused memory to improve.

posttest-only control group design An experimental design in which the dependent variable is measured after the manipulation of the independent variable.

This memory study is known as a simple **posttest-only control group design**. We start with a control group and an experimental group made up of equivalent subjects; we administer the treatment (mnemonic or no mnemonic); and we take a posttest (after-treatment) measure. It is very important that the experimental and control groups are equivalent because we want to be able to conclude that any differences observed between the two groups are due to the independent variable and not to some other difference between the groups. We help to ensure equivalency of groups by using random assignment.

When we manipulate the independent variable, we must ensure that the manipulation is valid—in other words, that there really is a difference in the manner in which the two groups are treated. This appears fairly easy for this study—either the subjects use the prescribed mnemonic device, or they do not. However, how do we actually know that those in the mnemonic group truly are using the device and that those in the control group are not using any type of mnemonic device? These are questions the researcher would need to address before beginning the study; the instructions given to the participants must leave no doubt about what the participants in each condition should be doing during the study.

Last, the researcher must measure the dependent variable (memory) to assess any effects of the independent variable. To compare performance across the two groups, the same measurement device must be used for both groups. If the groups were equivalent at the beginning of the study and if the independent variable was adequately manipulated and was the only difference between the two groups, then any differences observed in the dependent variable must be attributable to the independent variable.

pretest/posttest control group design An experimental design in which the dependent variable is measured both before and after manipulation of the independent variable.

We could make the preceding design slightly more sophisticated by using a **pretest/posttest control group design**, which involves adding a pretest to the design. This new design has the added advantage of ensuring that the subjects are equivalent at the beginning of the study. This precaution is usually not considered necessary if subjects are randomly assigned and if the researcher uses a sufficiently large sample of subjects. The issue of how many subjects are sufficient will be discussed in greater detail later in the chapter when we discuss the appropriate statistical analysis for this design; however, as a general rule, 20 to 30 subjects per condition are considered adequate. There are disadvantages to pretest/posttest control group designs, including the possibility of increasing demand characteristics and experimenter effects (both discussed later in the chapter). The subjects might guess before the posttest what is being measured in the study. If the participants make an assumption (either correct or incorrect) about the intent of the study, their behavior during the study may change from what would "normally" happen. With multiple testings, there is also more opportunity for an experimenter to influence the subjects. It is up to the researchers to decide which of these designs best suits their needs.

Solomon four-group design A design with four groups that is a combination of the posttest only control group design and the pretest/posttest control group design.

An alternative to each of the previously described designs is a merger between these two designs. This alternative design is called the **Solomon four-group design** and it is a combination of the posttest only control group design and the pretest/posttest control group design. Thus, as the name implies, there are four groups in this design. The groups are as follows:

Group 1:	Pretest	Treatment	Posttest
Group 2:	Pretest		Posttest
Group 3:		Treatment	Posttest
Group 4:			Posttest

By merging the two designs, the disadvantages of each individual design are minimized and the advantages are maximized.

Control and Confounds

confound An uncontrolled extraneous variable or flaw in an experiment.

Obviously, one of the most critical elements of an experiment is control. It is imperative that control be maximized. If a researcher fails to control for something, then the study is open to confounds. A **confound** is an uncontrolled extraneous variable or flaw in an experiment. If a study is confounded, then it is impossible to say whether changes in the dependent variable were caused by the independent variable or by the uncontrolled extraneous variable.

The problem for most psychologists is that maximizing control with human subjects can be very difficult. In other disciplines, control is not as difficult. For example, marine biologists do not need to be as concerned about preexisting differences between the sea snails they may be studying because sea snails do not vary on as many dimensions as do humans (personality, intelligence, and rearing issues, for example, are not relevant as they are for humans). Because of the great variability among humans on all dimensions, psychologists need to be very concerned about preexisting differences. Consider the previously described study on memory and mnemonic devices. A problem could occur if the differences in performance on the memory test resulted from the fact that, based on chance, the more educated subjects made up the experimental group and the less educated subjects made up the control group. In this case, we might have observed a difference in memory performance even if the experimental group had not used the mnemonic strategy.

Even when we use random assignment as a means of minimizing differences between the experimental and control groups, we still need to think about control in the study. For example, if we were to conduct the study on memory and mnemonic devices, we should consider administering some pretests as a means of assuring that the participants in the two groups are equivalent on any dimension (variable) that might affect memory performance. It is imperative that psychologists working with humans understand control and potential confounds due to human variability. If the basis of experimentation is that the control group and the experimental group (or the two experimental groups being compared) are as similar as possible except for differences in the independent variable, then the researcher must make sure that this is indeed the case. In short, the researcher needs to maximize the **internal validity** of the study—the extent to which the results can be attributed to the manipulation of the independent variable rather than to some confounding variable. A study with good internal validity has no confounds and offers only one explanation for the results.

internal validity The extent to which the results of an experiment can be attributed to the manipulation of the independent variable rather than to some confounding variable.

Threats to Internal Validity

We will now consider several potential threats to the internal validity of a study. The confounds described here are those most commonly encountered in psychological research; depending on the nature of the study, other confounds more specific to the type of research being conducted may arise. The confounds presented here will give you an overview of some potential problems and an opportunity to begin developing the critical thinking skills involved in designing a sound study. These confounds are most problematic for nonexperimental designs but may also pose a threat to experimental designs. Taking the precautions described here should indicate whether or not the confound is present in a study.

Nonequivalent Control Group. One of the most basic concerns in an experiment is that the subjects in the control and experimental groups are equivalent at the beginning of the study. For example, if you wanted to test the effectiveness of a smoking cessation program and you compared a group of smokers who voluntarily signed up for the program to a group of smokers who did not, the groups would not be equivalent. They are not equivalent because one group chose to seek help, and this makes them different from the group of smokers who did not seek help. They might be different in a number of ways. For example, they might be more concerned with their health, they might be under doctors' orders to stop smoking, or they may have smoked for a longer time than those who did not seek help. The point is that they differ, and thus, the groups are not equivalent. Using random sampling and random assignment is typically considered sufficient to address the potential problem of a nonequivalent control group. When random sampling and random assignment are not used, subject selection or assignment problems may result. In this case, we would have a quasi-experimental design (discussed in Chapter 13), not a true experiment.

history effect A threat to internal validity in which an outside event that is not a part of the manipulation of the experiment could be responsible for the results.

History. Changes in the dependent variable may be due to historical events that occur outside of the study, leading to the confound known as a **history effect**. These events are most likely unrelated to the study but may nonetheless affect the dependent variable. Imagine that you are conducting a study of the effects of a certain program on stress reduction in college students. The study covers a 2-month period during which students participate in your stress-reduction program. If your posttest measures were taken during midterms or final exams, you might notice an increase in stress even though subjects were involved in a program that was intended to reduce stress. Not taking the historical point in the semester into account might lead you to an erroneous conclusion concerning the stress-reduction program. Notice also that a control group of equivalent subjects would have helped reveal the confound in this study.

maturation effect A threat to internal validity in which naturally occurring changes within the subjects could be responsible for the observed results.

Maturation. In research in which subjects are studied over a period of time, a **maturation effect** can frequently be a problem. Subjects mature physically, socially, and cognitively during the course of the study. Any changes in the dependent variable that occur across the course of the study, therefore, may be due to maturation and not to the independent variable in the study. Using a control group with equivalent subjects will indicate whether changes in the dependent variable are due to maturation; if they are, the subjects in the control group will change on the dependent variable during the course of the study even though they did not receive the treatment.

testing effect A threat to internal validity in which repeated testing leads to better or worse scores.

Testing. In studies in which participants are measured numerous times, a **testing effect** may be a problem—repeated testing may lead to better or worse performance. Many studies involve pretest and posttest measures. Other studies involve taking measures on an hourly, daily, weekly, or monthly basis. In these cases, subjects are exposed to the same or similar "tests" numerous times. As a result, changes in performance on the test may be due to prior experience with the test and not to the independent variable. If, for example, subjects took the same math test before and after participating in a special math course, the improvement observed in scores might be due to the participants' familiarity with and practice on the test items. This type of testing confound is sometimes referred to as a *practice effect*. Testing can also result in the opposite of a practice effect, a *fatigue effect* (sometimes referred to as a *negative practice effect*). Repeated testing fatigues the subjects, and their performance declines as a result. Once again, having a control group of equivalent subjects will help to control for testing confounds because researchers will be able to see practice or fatigue effects in the control group.

Regression to the Mean. Statistical regression occurs when individuals are selected for a study because their scores on some measure were extreme—either extremely high or extremely low. If we were studying students who scored in the top 10% on the SAT and we retested them on the SAT, then we would expect them to do well again. Not all students, however, would score as well as they did originally because of statistical regression, often referred to as **regression to the mean**—a threat to internal validity in which extreme scores, upon retesting, tend to be less extreme, moving toward the mean. In other words, some of the students did well the first time due to chance or luck. What is going to happen when they take the test a second time? They will not be as lucky, and their scores will regress toward the mean.

regression to the mean A threat to internal validity in which extreme scores, upon retesting, tend to be less extreme, moving toward the mean.

Regression to the mean occurs in many situations other than research studies. Many people think that a hex is associated with being on the cover of *Sports Illustrated* and that an athlete's performance will decline after appearing on the cover. This can be explained by regression to the mean. Athletes most likely appear on the cover of *Sports Illustrated* after a very successful season or at the peak of their careers. What is most likely to happen after athletes have been performing exceptionally well over a period of time? They are likely to regress toward the mean and perform in a more average manner (Cozby, 2001). In a research study, having an equivalent control group of subjects with extreme scores will indicate whether changes in the dependent measure are due to regression to the mean or to the effects of the independent variable.

instrumentation effect A threat to internal validity in which changes in the dependent variable may be due to changes in the measuring device.

Instrumentation. An **instrumentation effect** occurs when the measuring device is faulty. Problems of consistency in measuring the dependent variable are most likely to occur when the measuring instrument is a human observer. The observer may become better at taking measures during the course of the study or may become fatigued with taking measures. If the measures taken during the study are not taken consistently, then any change in the dependent variable may be due to these measurement changes and not to the independent variable. Once again, having a control group of equivalent subjects will help to identify this confound.

mortality (attrition) A threat to internal validity in which differential dropout rates may be observed in the experimental and control groups, leading to inequality between the groups.

Mortality or Attrition. Most research studies have a certain amount of **mortality** or **attrition** (dropout). Most of the time, the attrition is equal across experimental and control groups. It is of concern to researchers, however, when attrition is not equal across the groups. Assume that we begin a study with two equivalent groups of participants. If more subjects leave one group than the other, then the two groups of subjects are most likely no longer equivalent, meaning that comparisons cannot be made between the groups. Why might we have differential attrition between the groups? Imagine we are conducting a study to test the effects of a program aimed at reducing smoking. We randomly select a group of smokers and then randomly assign half to the control group and half to the experimental group. The experimental group participates in our program to reduce smoking, but the heaviest smokers just cannot take the demands of the program and quit. When we take a posttest measure on smoking, only those participants who were originally light-to-moderate smokers are left in the experimental group. Comparing them to the control group would be pointless because the groups are no longer equivalent. Having a control group allows us to determine whether there is differential attrition across groups.

diffusion of treatment A threat to internal validity in which observed changes in the behaviors or responses of subjects may be due to information received from other subjects in the study.

Diffusion of Treatment. When subjects in a study are in close proximity to one another, a potential threat to internal validity is **diffusion of treatment**—observed changes in the behaviors of subjects may be due to information received from other subjects. For example, college students are frequently used as participants in research studies. Because many students live near one another and share classes, some students may discuss an experiment in which they participated. If other students were planning to participate in the study in the future, the treatment has now been compromised because they know how some of the subjects were treated during the study. They know what is involved in one or more of the conditions in the study, and this knowledge may affect how they respond in the study regardless of the condition to which they are assigned. To control for this confound, researchers might try to test the subjects in a study in large groups or within a short time span so they do not have time to communicate with one another. In addition, researchers should stress to subjects the importance of not discussing the experiment with anyone until it has ended.

Experimenter and Subject Effects. When researchers design experiments, they invest considerable time and effort in the endeavor. Often this investment leads the researcher to consciously or unconsciously affect or bias the results of the study. For example, a researcher may unknowingly smile more when subjects are behaving in the predicted manner and frown or grimace when subjects are behaving in a manner undesirable to the researcher. This type of **experimenter effect** is also referred to as *experimenter bias* or *expectancy effects* (see Chapter 4) because the results of the study are biased by the experimenter's expectations.

experimenter effect A threat to internal validity in which the experimenter, consciously or unconsciously, affects the results of the study.

One of the most famous cases of experimenter effects is Clever Hans. Clever Hans was a horse that was purported to be able to do mathematical computations. Pfungst (1911) demonstrated that Hans's answers were based on experimenter effects. Hans supposedly solved mathematical problems by tapping out the answers with his hoof. A committee of experts who claimed Hans was receiving no cues from his questioners verified Hans's abilities. Pfungst later demonstrated that this was not so and that tiny head and eye movements were Hans's signals to begin and to end his tapping. When Hans was asked a question, the questioner would look at Hans's hoof as he tapped out the answer. When Hans approached the correct number of taps, the questioner would unknowingly make a subtle

"IT WAS MORE OF A 'TRIPLE-BLIND' TEST. THE PATIENTS DIDN'T KNOW WHICH ONES WERE GETTING THE REAL DRUG, THE DOCTORS DIDN'T KNOW, AND, I'M AFRAID, NOBODY KNEW."

head or eye movement in an upward direction. This was a cue to Hans to stop tapping. If a horse was clever enough to pick up on cues as subtle as these, imagine how human subjects might respond to similar subtle cues provided by an experimenter. For this reason, many researchers choose to combat experimenter effects by conducting blind experiments. There are two types of blind experiments: a single-blind experiment and a double-blind experiment. In a **single-blind experiment**, either the experimenter or the subjects are blind to the manipulation being made. The experimenter being blind in a single-blind experiment would help to combat experimenter effects. In a **double-blind experiment**, neither the experimenter nor the subject knows the condition in which the subject is serving—both parties are blind. Obviously, the coordinator of the study has this information; however, the researcher responsible for interacting with the subjects does not know and therefore cannot provide any cues.

single-blind experiment An experimental procedure in which either the subjects or the experimenters are blind to the manipulation being made.

double-blind experiment An experimental procedure in which neither the experimenter nor the subject knows the condition to which each subject has been assigned; both parties are blind to the manipulation.

subject effect A threat to internal validity in which the subject, consciously or unconsciously, affects the results of the study.

Sometimes subjects in a study bias the results based on their own expectations. They know they are being observed and hence may not behave naturally, or they may simply behave differently than when they are in more familiar situations. This type of confound is referred to as a **subject effect**. This is similar to the concept of reactivity discussed in Chapter 3. However, reactivity can occur even in observational studies when people (or other animals) do not even realize they are subjects in a study. Subject effects, on the other hand, are usually more specialized in nature. For example, many subjects try to be "good subjects," meaning that they try to determine what the researcher wants and to adjust their behavior accordingly. Such subjects may be very sensitive to real or imagined cues from the researcher, referred to as **demand characteristics**. The subjects are trying to guess what characteristics the experimenter is in effect "demanding." In this case, using a single-blind experiment in which the subjects are blind or using a double-blind experiment would help to combat subject effects.

demand characteristics A type of subject effect in which subjects try to guess what characteristics the experimenter is in effect "demanding."

Hawthorne effect A type of reactivity in which subjects improve or change an aspect of their behavior because they know that they are being studied, rather than in response to the experimental manipulation.

A classic example of subject effects is known as the **Hawthorne effect**. The Hawthorne effect is named after the Hawthorne plant in Chicago, Illinois, which was part of Western Electric. The Hawthorne plant was the site of a series of experiments in the 1930s on how lighting conditions affected worker productivity. The subjects in the experiment were a group of specially chosen women who worked at the plant. Researchers were interested in what factors might influence worker productivity. What they discovered was that worker productivity tended to increase no matter how the lighting variable was manipulated. Even having the women work in lighting conditions that were poorer than those in the main factory led to greater productivity. The researchers finally concluded that productivity increased simply because the women knew they were part of an experiment and that they were being observed. More contemporary researchers now believe that the Hawthorne effect may not completely explain the original results due to other confounding variables. However, all researchers agree that subjects may act differently when they believe that they are receiving a treatment.

A special type of subject effect is often present in research on the effects of drugs and medical treatments. Most people report improvement when they are receiving a drug or other medical treatment. Some of this improvement may be caused by a *placebo effect*; that is, the improvement may be due not to the effects of the treatment but to the subject's expectation that the treatment will have an effect. For this reason, drug and medical research must use a special placebo condition, or **placebo group**—a group of subjects who believe that they are receiving treatment but in reality are not. Instead, they are given an inert pill or substance called a **placebo**. The placebo condition helps to distinguish between the actual effects of the drug and the placebo effects. For example, in a study on the effects of "ionized" wrist bracelets on musculoskeletal pain, researchers at the Mayo Clinic used a double-blind procedure in which half of the subjects wore an "ionized" bracelet and half of the subjects wore a placebo bracelet. Both groups were told that they were wearing "ionized" bracelets intended to help with musculoskeletal pain. At the end of 4 weeks of treatment, both groups showed significant improvement in pain scores in comparison to baseline scores. No significant differences were observed between the groups. In other words, those wearing the placebo bracelet reported as much relief from pain as those wearing the "ionized" bracelet (Bratton et al., 2002).

placebo group A group or condition in which subjects believe they are receiving treatment but are not.

placebo An inert substance that subjects believe is a treatment.

Floor and Ceiling Effects. When conducting research, researchers must choose a measure for the dependent variable that is sensitive enough to detect differences between groups. If the measure is not sensitive enough, real differences may be missed. Although this confound does not involve an uncontrolled extraneous variable, it does represent a flaw in the experiment. For example, measuring the weights of rats in an experiment in pounds rather than ounces or grams is not advisable because no differences will be found. In this case, the insensitivity of the dependent variable is called a **floor effect**. All of the rats would be at the bottom of the measurement scale because the measurement scale is not sensitive enough to differentiate between scores at the bottom. Similarly, attempting to weigh elephants on a bathroom scale would also lead to sensitivity problems; however, this is a **ceiling effect**. All of the elephants would weigh at the top of the scale (300 or 350 pounds, depending on the bathroom scale used), and any changes that might occur in weight as a result of the treatment variable would not be reflected in the dependent variable. The use of a pretest can help to identify whether a measurement scale is sensitive enough. Subjects should receive different scores on the dependent measure on the pretest. If all subjects are scoring about the same (either very low or very high), then a floor or ceiling effect may be present.

floor effect A limitation of the measuring instrument that decreases its capability to differentiate between scores at the bottom of the scale.

ceiling effect A limitation of the measuring instrument that decreases its capability to differentiate between scores at the top of the scale.

Threats to Internal Validity — IN REVIEW

MAJOR CONFOUNDING VARIABLES

TYPE OF CONFOUND	DESCRIPTION	MEANS OF CONTROLLING/ MINIMIZING
Nonequivalent control group	Problems in subject selection or assignment may lead to important differences between the subjects assigned to the experimental and control groups.	Use random sampling and random assignment of subjects.
History effect	Changes in the dependent variable may be due to outside events that take place during the course of the study.	Use an equivalent control group.
Maturation effect	Changes in the dependent variable may be due to subjects maturing (growing older) during the course of the study.	Use an equivalent control group.
Testing effect	Changes in the dependent variable may be due to participants being tested repeatedly and getting either better or worse because of these repeated testings.	Use an equivalent control group.
Regression to the mean	Subjects who are selected for a study because they are extreme (either high or low) on some variable may regress toward the mean and be less extreme at a later testing.	Use an equivalent group of subjects with extreme scores.
Instrumentation effect	Changes in the dependent variable may be due to changes in the measuring device, either human or machine.	Use an equivalent control group.
Mortality or attrition	Differential attrition or dropout in the experimental and control groups may lead to inequality between the groups.	Monitor for differential loss of subjects in experimental and control groups.
Diffusion of treatment	Changes in the behaviors or responses of participants may be due to information they have received from others participating in the study.	Attempt to minimize by testing subjects all at once or as close together in time as possible.
Experimenter and subject effects	Either experimenters or subjects consciously or unconsciously affect the results of the study.	Use a double-blind or single-blind procedure.
Floor and ceiling effects	The measuring instrument used is not sensitive enough to detect differences.	Ensure that the measuring instrument is reliable and valid before beginning the study.

CRITICAL THINKING CHECK 9.1

1. We discussed the history effect with respect to a study on stress reduction. Review that section, and explain how having a control group of equivalent subjects would help to reveal the confound of history.
2. Imagine that a husband and wife who are very tall (well above the mean for their respective height distributions) have a son. Would you expect the child to be as tall as his father? Why or why not?
3. While grading a large stack of essay exams, Professor Hyatt becomes tired and hence more lax in her grading standards. Which confound is relevant in this example? Why?

Threats to External Validity

External validity The extent to which the results of an experiment can be generalized.

A study must have internal validity for the results to be meaningful. However, it is also important that the study have external validity. **External validity** is the extent to which the results can be generalized beyond the subjects used in the experiment and beyond the laboratory in which the experiment was conducted.

Generalization to Populations. Generalization to the population being studied can be accomplished by randomly sampling subjects from the population. Generalization to other populations can be problematic, however, given that most psychology research is conducted on college students, especially freshmen and sophomores—hardly a representative sample from the population at large. This problem—sometimes referred to as the **college sophomore problem** (Stanovich, 2007)—means that most conclusions are based on studies of young people with a late adolescent mentality who are still developing self-identities and attitudes (Cozby, 2001).

college sophomore problem An external validity problem that results from using mainly college sophomores as subjects in research studies.

Are research ideals compromised by using college students as subjects in most research? There are three responses to the college sophomore criticism (Stanovich, 2007). First, using college sophomores as subjects in a study does not negate the findings of the study. It simply means that the study needs to be replicated with subjects from other populations to aid in overcoming this problem. Second, in the research conducted in many areas of psychology (for example, sensory research), the college sophomore problem is not an issue. The auditory and visual systems of college sophomores, for example, function in the same manner as do those of the rest of the population. Third, the population of college students today is varied. They come from different socioeconomic backgrounds and geographic areas. They have varied family histories and educational experiences. Hence, in terms of the previously mentioned variables, it is likely that college sophomores may be fairly representative of the general population.

Generalization from Laboratory Settings. Conducting research in a laboratory setting enables us to maximize control. We have discussed at several points the advantages of maximizing control, but control also has the potential disadvantage of creating an artificial environment. This means that we need to exercise some caution when generalizing from the laboratory setting to the real world. This problem is often referred to in psychology as the *artificiality criticism* (Stanovich, 2007). Keep in mind, however, that the whole point of experimentation is to create a situation in which control is maximized to determine cause-and-effect relationships. Obviously, we cannot relax our control in an experiment to counter this criticism.

exact replication Repeating a study using the same means of manipulating and measuring the variables as in the original study.

How, then, can we address the artificiality criticism and the generalization issue? One way is through replication of the experiment to demonstrate that the result is reliable. A researcher might begin with an **exact replication**—repeating the study in exactly the same manner. However, to more adequately address a problem such as the artificiality criticism, one should consider a conceptual or systematic replication (Mitchell & Jolley, 2004). A **conceptual replication** tests the same concepts in a different way. For example, we could use a different manipulation to assess its effect on the same dependent variable, or we could use the same manipulation and a different measure (dependent variable). A conceptual replication might also involve using other research methods to test the result. For example, we might conduct an observational study (see Chapter 4) in addition to a true experiment to assess the generalizability of a finding. A **systematic replication** systematically changes one thing at a time and observes the effect, if any, on the results. For example, a study could be replicated with more or different subjects, in a more realistic setting or with more levels of the independent variable.

conceptual replication A study based on another study that uses different methods, a different manipulation, or a different measure.

systematic replication A study that varies from an original study in one systematic way—for example, by using a different number or type of subjects, a different setting, or more levels of the independent variable.

Parametric Inferential Statistics: Two-Group Designs

As we've just discussed, in the simplest version of the two-group design, two samples (representing two populations) are compared by having one group receive nothing (the control group) and the second group receive some level of the independent variable (the experimental group). As noted, it is also possible to have two experimental groups and no control group. In this case, members of each group receive a different level of the independent variable. The null hypothesis tested in a two-group design using a two-tailed test is that the populations represented by the two groups do not differ:

$$H_0 : \mu_1 = \mu_2$$

The alternative hypothesis is that we expect differences in performance between the two populations, but we are unsure which group will perform better or worse:

$$H_a : \mu_1 \neq \mu_2$$

As discussed in Chapter 8, for a one-tailed test, the null hypothesis is either

$$H_0 : \mu_1 \leq \mu_2 \text{ or } H_0 : \mu_1 \geq \mu_2$$

depending on which alternative hypothesis is being tested:

$$H_a : \mu_1 > \mu_2 \text{ or } H_a : \mu_1 < \mu_2\text{; respectively.}$$

A significant difference between the two groups (samples representing populations) depends on the critical value for the statistical test being conducted. As with the statistical tests described in Chapter 8, alpha is typically set at .05 ($\alpha = .05$).

Remember from Chapter 8 that parametric tests, such as the *t* test, are inferential statistical tests designed for sets of data that meet certain requirements. The most basic requirement is that the data fit a bell-shaped distribution. In addition, parametric tests involve data for which certain parameters are known, such as the mean (μ) and the standard deviation (σ). Finally, parametric tests use interval-ratio data.

t test for Independent Groups (Samples): What It Is and What It Does

independent-groups *t* test A parametric inferential test for comparing sample means of two independent groups of scores.

The **independent-groups *t* test** is a parametric statistical test that compares the means of two different samples of participants. It indicates whether the two samples perform so similarly that we conclude they are likely from the same population or whether they perform so differently that we conclude they represent two different populations.

Imagine, for example, that a researcher wants to study the effects on exam performance of massed versus spaced study. All subjects in the experiment study the same material for the same amount of time. The difference between the groups is that one group studies for 6 hours all at once (massed study), whereas the other group studies for 6 hours broken into three 2-hour blocks (spaced study). Because the researcher believes that the spaced study method will lead to better performance, the null and alternative hypotheses are

H_0: Spaced Study ≤ Massed Study or $\mu_1 \leq \mu_2$
H_a: Spaced Study > Massed Study or $\mu_1 > \mu_2$

The 20 subjects are chosen by random sampling and assigned to the groups randomly. Because of the random assignment of subjects, we are confident that there are no major differences between the two groups prior to the study. The dependent variable is the subjects' scores on a 30-item test of the material; these scores are listed in Table 9.1.

TABLE 9.1 Numbers of Items Answered Correctly by Each Participant Under Spaced- versus Massed-Study Conditions Using a Between-Subjects Design ($N = 20$)

SPACED STUDY	MASSED STUDY
23	15
18	20
25	21
22	15
20	14
24	16
21	18
24	19
21	14
22	17
$\bar{X}_1 = 22$	$\bar{X}_2 = 16.9$

Notice that the mean score of the spaced-study group ($\overline{X}_1 = 22$) is higher than the mean score of the massed-study group ($\overline{X}_2 = 16{:}9$). However, we want to be able to say more than this. We need to statistically analyze the data to determine whether the observed difference is statistically significant. As you may recall from Chapter 8, statistical significance indicates that an observed difference between two descriptive statistics (such as means) is unlikely to have occurred by chance. For this analysis, we will use an independent-groups t test.

Calculations for the Independent-Groups t *Test.* The formula for an independent-groups t test is

$$t_{obt} = \frac{\overline{X}_1 - \overline{X}_2}{s_{\overline{X}_1 - \overline{X}_2}}$$

This formula resembles that for the single-sample t test discussed in Chapter 8. However, rather than comparing a single-sample mean to a population mean, we are comparing two sample means. The denominator in the equation represents the **standard error of the difference between means**—the estimated standard deviation of the sampling distribution of differences between the means of independent samples in a two-sample experiment. When conducting an independent-groups t test, we are determining how far the difference between the sample means falls from the difference between the population means. Based on the null hypothesis, we expect the difference between the population means to be zero. If the difference between the sample means is large, it will fall in one of the tails of the distribution (far from the difference between the population means).

standard error of the difference between means The standard deviation of the sampling distribution of differences between the means of independent samples in a two-sample experiment.

To determine how far the difference between the sample means is from the difference between the population means, we convert the mean differences to standard errors. The formula for this conversion is similar to the formula for the standard error of the mean introduced in Chapter 8:

$$s_{\overline{X}_1 - \overline{X}_2} = \sqrt{\frac{s_1^2}{n_1} + \frac{s_2^2}{n_2}}$$

The standard error of the difference between the means does have a logical meaning. If we took thousands of pairs of samples from these two populations and found $\overline{X}_1 - \overline{X}_2$ for each pair, those differences between means would not all be the same. They would form a distribution. The mean of that distribution would be the difference between the means of the populations ($\mu_1 - \mu_2$), and its standard deviation would be $S_{\overline{X}_1 - \overline{X}_2}$.

Putting all of this together, we see that the formula for determining t is

$$t_{obt} = \frac{\overline{X}_1 - \overline{X}_2}{\sqrt{\frac{s_1^2}{n_1} + \frac{s_2^2}{n_2}}}$$

where

t_{obt} = value of t obtained

$\overline{X}_1$ and $\overline{X}_2$ = means for the two groups

s_1^2 and s_2^2 = variances of the two groups

n_1 and n_2 = number of participants in each of the two groups (we use n to refer to the subgroups and N to refer to the total number of people in the study)

Let's use this formula to determine whether there are any significant differences between the spaced- and massed-study groups. We use the formulas for the mean and variance that we learned in Chapter 5 to do the preliminary calculations:

$$\overline{X}_1 = \frac{\Sigma X_1}{n_1} = \frac{220}{10} = 22 \qquad \overline{X}_2 = \frac{\Sigma X_2}{n_2} = \frac{169}{10} = 16.9$$

$$s_1^2 = \frac{\Sigma(X_1 - \overline{X}_1)^2}{n_1 - 1} = \frac{40}{9} = 4.44 \qquad s_2^2 = \frac{\Sigma(X_2 - \overline{X}_2)^2}{n_2 - 1} = \frac{56.9}{9} = 6.32$$

$$t = \frac{\overline{X}_1 - \overline{X}_2}{\sqrt{\frac{s_1^2}{n_1} + \frac{s_2^2}{n_2}}} = \frac{22 - 16.9}{\sqrt{\frac{4.44}{10} + \frac{6.32}{10}}} = \frac{5.1}{\sqrt{1.076}} = \frac{5.1}{1.037} = 4.92$$

Interpreting the t test. We get $t_{obt} = 4.92$. We now consult Table A.3 in Appendix A to determine the critical value for $t(t_{cv})$. We need to determine the degrees of freedom, which for an independent-groups t test are $(n_1 - 1) + (n_2 - 1)$ or $n_1 + n_2 - 2$. In the present study, with 10 participants in each group, there are 18 degrees of freedom $(10 + 10 - 2 = 18)$. The alternative hypothesis was one-tailed, and $\alpha = .05$.

Consulting Table A.3, we find that for a one-tailed test with 18 degrees of freedom, the critical value of t is 1.734. Our t_{obt} falls beyond the critical value (is larger than the critical value). Thus, the null hypothesis is rejected, and the alternative hypothesis that subjects in the spaced-study condition performed better on a test of the material than did subjects in the massed-study condition is supported. This result is pictured in Figure 9.2. In APA style (discussed in detail in Chapter 15), the result is reported as

$t(18) = 4.92$, $p < .05$ (one-tailed)

This form conveys in a concise manner the t-score, the degrees of freedom, and that the results are significant at the .05 level. Keep in mind that when a result is significant, the p value is reported as less than (<) .05 (or some smaller probability), not greater than (>)—an error commonly made by students. Remember that the p value, or alpha level, indicates the probability of a Type I error. We want this probability to be small, meaning we are confident that there is only a small probability that our results were due to chance. This means it is highly probable that the observed difference between the groups is a meaningful difference—that it is actually due to the independent variable. Instructions on using Excel, SPSS, or the TI-84 calculator to conduct

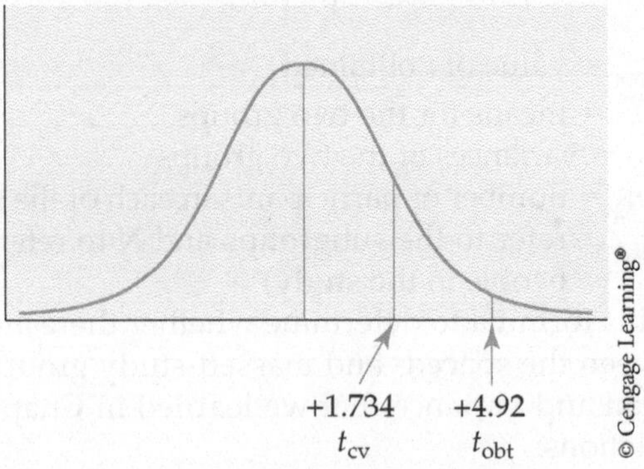

FIGURE 9.2 The obtained *t*-score in relation to the *t* critical value

this independent-groups *t* test appear in the Statistical Software Resources section at the end of the chapter.

Look back at the formula for *t*, and think about what will affect the size of the *t*-score. We would like the *t*-score to be large to increase the chance that it will be significant. What will increase the size of the *t*-score? Anything that increases the numerator or decreases the denominator in the equation. What will increase the numerator? A larger difference between the means for the two groups (a greater difference produced by the independent variable). This difference is somewhat difficult to influence. However, if we minimize chance in our study and the independent variable truly does have an effect, then the means should be different. What will decrease the size of the denominator? Because the denominator is the standard error of the difference between the means ($s_{\bar{X}_1 - \bar{X}_2}$) and is derived by using *s* (the unbiased estimator of the population standard deviation), we can decrease ($s_{\bar{X}_1 - \bar{X}_2}$) by decreasing the variability within each condition or group or by increasing the sample size. Look at the formula and think about why this would be so. In summary, then, three aspects of a study can increase power:

- Greater differences produced by the independent variable
- Less variability of raw scores in each condition
- Increased sample size

Graphing the Means. Typically, when a significant difference is found between two means, the means are graphed to provide a pictorial representation of the difference. In creating a graph, we place the independent variable on the *x*-axis and the dependent variable on the *y*-axis. As noted in Chapter 5, the *y*-axis should be 60 to 75% of the length of the *x*-axis. For a line graph, we plot each mean and connect them with a line. For a bar graph, we draw separate bars whose heights represent the means. Figure 9.3 shows a bar graph representing the data from the spaced- versus massed-study experiment. Recall that the mean number of items answered correctly by those in the spaced-study condition was 22, compared with a mean of 16.9 for those in the massed-study condition.

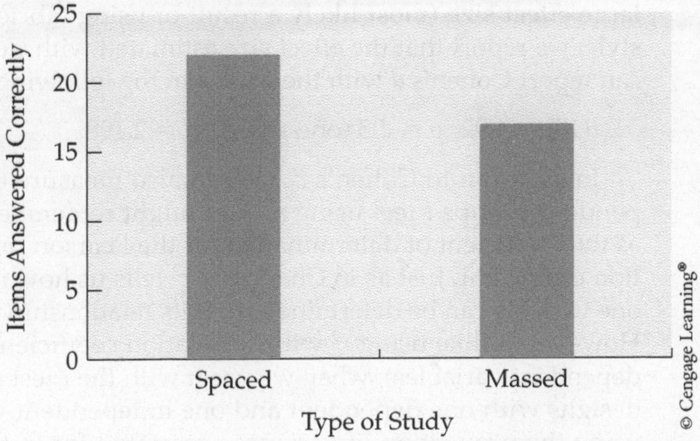

FIGURE 9.3 Mean number of items answered correctly under spaced- and massed-study conditions

effect size The proportion of variance in the dependent variable that is accounted for by the manipulation of the independent variable.

Cohen's *d* An inferential statistic for measuring effect size.

Effect Size: Cohen's d *and* r^2. In addition to the reported statistic, alpha level, and graph, the American Psychological Association (2001a) recommends that we also look at **effect size**—the proportion of variance in the dependent variable that is accounted for by the manipulation of the independent variable. Effect size indicates how large a role the conditions of the independent variable play in determining scores on the dependent variable. Thus, it is an estimate of the effect of the independent variable, regardless of sample size. The larger the effect size, the more consistent is the influence of the independent variable. In other words, the greater the effect size, the more that knowing the conditions of the independent variable improves our accuracy in predicting subjects' scores on the dependent variable. For the *t* test, one formula for effect size, known as **Cohen's *d***, is

$$d = \frac{\overline{X}_1 - \overline{X}_2}{\sqrt{\frac{s_1^2}{2} + \frac{s_2^2}{2}}}$$

Let's begin by working on the denominator, using the data from the spaced- versus massed-study experiment:

$$\sqrt{\frac{s_1^2}{2} + \frac{s_2^2}{2}} = \sqrt{\frac{4.44}{2} + \frac{6.32}{2}} = \sqrt{2.22 + 3.16} = \sqrt{5.38} = 2.32$$

We can now put this denominator into the formula for Cohen's *d*:

$$d = \frac{22 - 16.9}{2.32} = \frac{5.1}{2.32} = 2.198$$

According to Cohen (1988, 1992), a small effect size is one of at least 0.20, a medium effect size is at least 0.50, and a large effect size is at least 0.80. Obviously, our effect size of 2.198 is far greater than 0.80, indicating a very large effect size (most likely a result of using fabricated data). Using APA style, we report that the effect size estimated with Cohen's *d* is 2.198, or you can report Cohen's *d* with the *t*-score in the following manner:

$t(18) = 4.92, p < .05$ (one-tailed), $d = 2.198$

In addition to Cohen's *d*, we can also measure effect size for the independent-groups *t* test using r^2. You might remember using r^2 in Chapter 6 as the coefficient of determination for the Pearson product-moment correlation coefficient. Just as in Chapter 6, r^2 tells us how much of the variance in one variable can be determined from its relationship with the other variable. However, unlike using r^2 with correlation coefficients (which measure two dependent variables), when we use it with the *t* test (based on experimental designs with one dependent and one independent variable), we are measuring the proportion of variance accounted for in the dependent variable based on knowing which treatment group the participants were assigned to for the independent variable. To calculate r^2, use the following formula:

$$r^2 = \frac{t^2}{t^2 + df}$$

Thus, in our example this would be:

$$r^2 = \frac{4.92^2}{4.92^2 + 18} = \frac{24.21}{24.21 + 18} = \frac{24.21}{42.21} = .57$$

According to Cohen (1988), if r^2 is .01, the effect size is small; if it is .09, it is medium; and if it is .25, it is large. Thus, our effect size based on r^2 is large—just as it was when we used Cohen's *d*.

The preceding example illustrates a *t* test for independent groups with equal *n* values (sample sizes). In situations where the *n* values are unequal, a modified version of the previous formula is used. If you need this formula, you can find it in more advanced undergraduate statistics texts.

Confidence Intervals. As with the single-sample *z* test and *t* test discussed in Chapter 8, we can also compute confidence intervals for the independent-groups *t* test. We use the same basic formula we did for computing confidence intervals for the single-sample *t* test in Chapter 8, except that rather than using the sample mean and the standard error of the mean, we use the difference between the means and the standard error of the difference between means. The formula for the 95% confidence interval would be

$$CI_{.95} = \overline{X}_1 - \overline{X}_2 \pm t_{CV}(s_{\overline{X}_1 - \overline{X}_2})$$

We have already calculated the means for the two study conditions ($\overline{X}_1$ and $\overline{X}_2$) and the standard error of the difference between means ($s_{\overline{X}_1 - \overline{X}_2}$) as part of the previous *t* test problem. Thus, we simply need to determine t_{CV} to complete the confidence interval, which should contain the difference between the means for the two conditions. Because we are determining a

95% confidence interval, we use t_{cv} at the .05 level, and just as in Chapter 8, we always use t_{cv} for a two-tailed test because we are determining a confidence interval that contains values both above and below the difference between the means. Consulting Table A.3 in Appendix A for the t_{cv} for 18 degrees of freedom and a two-tailed test, we find that it is 2.101. We can now determine the 95% confidence interval for this problem.

$$\begin{aligned} CI_{.95} &= 22 - 16.9 \pm 2.101(1.037) \\ &= 5.1 \pm 2.18 \\ &= 2.92 - 7.28 \end{aligned}$$

Thus, the 95% confidence interval that should contain the difference in mean test scores between the spaced and the massed groups is 2.92 – 7.28. This means that if someone asked us how large a difference study type makes on test performance, we could answer that we are 95% confident that the difference in performance on the 30-item test between the spaced- versus massed-study groups would be between 2.92 and 7.28 correct answers.

Assumptions of the Independent-Groups t *test.* The assumptions of the independent-groups *t* test are similar to those of the single-sample *t* test. They are as follows:

- The data are interval-ratio scale.
- The underlying distributions are normal.
- The observations are independent.
- If we could compute the true variance of the population represented by each sample, the variances in each population would be the same, which is called homogeneity of variance.

If any of these assumptions is violated, it is appropriate to use another statistic. For example, if the scale of measurement is not interval-ratio or if the underlying distribution is not bell-shaped, then it may be more appropriate to use a nonparametric statistic (described in Chapter 14). If the observations are not independent, then it is appropriate to use a statistic for within- or matched-subjects designs (described in Chapter 10).

Independent-Groups *t* Tests — IN REVIEW

	INDEPENDENT-GROUPS *t* TEST
What It Is	A parametric test for a two-group between-subjects design
What It Does	Compares performance of the two groups to determine whether they represent the same population or different populations
Assumptions	Interval-ratio data Normal distribution Homogeneity of variance Independent observations

> **CRITICAL THINKING CHECK 9.2**
>
> 1. How is effect size different from significance level? In other words, how is it possible to have a significant result yet a small effect size?
> 2. How does increasing the sample size affect a *t* test? Why does it affect a *t* test in this manner?
> 3. How does decreasing variability affect a *t* test? Why does it affect a *t* test in this manner?

Summary

Researchers need to consider several factors when designing and evaluating a true experiment. First, they need to address the issues of control and possible confounds. The study needs to be designed with strong control and no confounds to maximize internal validity. Second, researchers need to consider external validity to ensure that the study is as generalizable as possible while maintaining control. Lastly, we discussed the appropriate parametric statistic for a two-group between subjects design—the independent-groups *t* test.

KEY TERMS

between-subjects design
posttest-only control group design
pretest/posttest control group design
Solomon four-group design
confound
internal validity
history effect
maturation effect
testing effect
regression to the mean
instrumentation effect
mortality (attrition)
diffusion of treatment
experimenter effect
single-blind experiment
double-blind experiment
subject effect
demand characteristics
Hawthorne effect
placebo group
placebo
floor effect
ceiling effect
external validity
college sophomore problem
exact replication
conceptual replication
systematic replication
independent-groups *t* test
standard error of the difference between means
effect size
Cohen's *d*

CHAPTER EXERCISES

(Answers to odd-numbered exercises appear in Appendix C.)

1. You read in a health magazine about a study in which a new therapy technique for depression was examined. A group of depressed individuals volunteered to participate in the study, which lasted 9 months. There were 50 subjects at the beginning of the study and 29 at the end of the 9 months. The researchers claimed that of those who completed the program, 85% improved. What possible confounds can you identify in this study?
2. On the most recent exam in your biology class, every student earned an A. The professor claims that he must really be a good teacher for all of the students to have done so well. Given the confounds discussed in this chapter, what alternative explanation can you offer for this result?
3. What are internal validity and external validity, and why are they so important to researchers?
4. A college student is interested in whether there is a difference between male and female students in the amount of time they spend studying each week. The student gathers information from a random sample of male and female students on campus. The amounts of time spent studying are normally distributed. The data are:

Males	*Females*
27	25
25	29
19	18
10	23
16	20
22	15
14	19

a. What statistical test should be used to analyze these data?
b. Identify H_0 and H_a for this study.
c. Conduct the appropriate analysis.
d. Should H_0 be rejected? What should the researcher conclude?
e. If significant, compute and interpret the effect size.
f. If significant, draw a graph representing the data.
g. Determine the 95% confidence interval.

5. A student is interested in whether students who study with music playing devote as much attention to their studies as do students who study under quiet conditions (he believes that studying under quiet conditions leads to better attention). He randomly assigns participants to either the music or no-music condition and has them read and study the same passage of information for the same amount of time. Subjects are given the same 10-item test on the material. Their scores appear next. Scores on the test represent interval-ratio data and are normally distributed.

Music	*No Music*
6	10
5	9
6	7
5	7
6	6
6	6
7	8
8	6
5	9

a. What statistical test should be used to analyze these data?
b. Identify H_0 and H_a for this study.
c. Conduct the appropriate analysis.
d. Should H_0 be rejected? What should the researcher conclude?
e. If significant, compute and interpret the effect size.
f. If significant, draw a graph representing the data.
g. Determine the 95% confidence interval.

CRITICAL THINKING CHECK ANSWERS

9.1

1. Having a control group in the stress-reduction study would help to reveal the confound of history because if this confound were present, we would expect the control group to also increase in stress level, possibly more so than the experimental group. Having a control group informs a researcher about the effects of treatment versus no treatment and about the effects of historical events.
2. Based on what we have learned about regression to the mean, the son would probably not be as tall as his father. Because the father represents an extreme score on height, the son would most likely regress toward the mean and not be as tall as his father. However, because his mother is also extremely tall, genetics may overcome regression to the mean.
3. This example is similar to an instrumentation effect. The way the measuring device is used has changed over the course of the "study."

9.2

1. Effect size indicates the magnitude of the influence of the experimental treatment, regardless of the sample size. A result can be statistically significant because the sample size is very large, even if the effect of the independent variable is not so large. Effect size indicates whether this is the case because, in this situation, effect size should be small.
2. In the long run, it means that the obtained t is more likely to be significant. In terms of the formula used to calculate t, increasing the sample size will decrease the standard error of

the difference between means ($s_{\bar{X}_1 - \bar{X}_2}$). This, in turn, will increase the size of the obtained *t*. A larger obtained *t* means that the obtained value is more likely to exceed the critical value and be significant.

3. Decreasing variability also makes a *t* test more powerful (likely to be significant) because decreasing variability also means that $s_{\bar{X}_1 - \bar{X}_2}$ (the standard error of the difference between means) will be smaller. Again, this increases the size of the obtained *t*, and a larger obtained *t* means that the obtained value is more likely to exceed the critical value and be significant.

WEB RESOURCES

The book-specific website at CengageBrain .com offers students a variety of study tools and useful resources such as glossaries and flashcards.

Chapter 9 ▪ Study Guide

CHAPTER 9 SUMMARY AND REVIEW: EXPERIMENTAL DESIGN AND ANALYSIS I

Several factors need to be considered when designing and evaluating a true experiment. First, the issues of control and possible confounds need to be addressed. The study needs to be designed with strong control and no confounds to maximize internal validity. Second, external validity needs to be considered to ensure that the study is as generalizable as possible while maintaining control. Lastly, the statistics most appropriate to the design must be used. For a two-group design in which parametric statistics are appropriate, the independent-groups *t* test would be used.

CHAPTER 9 REVIEW EXERCISES

(Answers to exercises appear in Appendix C.)

FILL-IN SELF-TEST

Answer the following questions. If you have trouble answering any of the questions, restudy the relevant material before going on to the multiple-choice self test.

1. An experiment in which different subjects are assigned to each group is a ________.
2. When we use ________, we randomly determine who serves in each group in an experiment.
3. When the dependent variable is measured both before and after manipulation of the independent variable, we are using a ________ design.
4. ________ is the extent to which the results of an experiment can be attributed to the manipulation of the independent variable, rather than to some confounding variable.
5. A(n) ________ is a threat to internal validity where the possibility of naturally occurring changes within the subjects is responsible for the observed results.
6. If there is a problem with the measuring device, then there may be a(n) ________ effect.

7. If subjects talk to each other about an experiment, then there may be ________.
8. When neither the experimenter nor the subject know the condition to which each subject has been assigned, a ________ experiment is being used.
9. When the measuring device is limited in such a way that scores at the top of the scale cannot be differentiated, there is a ________ effect.
10. The extent to which the results of an experiment can be generalized is called ________.
11. When a study is based on another study but uses different methods, a different manipulation, or a different measure, we are conducting a ________ replication.
12. A(n) ________ is a parametric inferential test for comparing sample means of two independent groups of scores.
13. ________ is an inferential statistic for measuring effect size with *t* tests.

MULTIPLE-CHOICE SELF-TEST

Select the single best answer for each of the following questions. If you have trouble answering any of the questions, restudy the relevant material.

1. Manipulate is to measure as ________ is to ________.
   a. independent variable; dependent variable
   b. dependent variable; independent variable
   c. control group; experimental group
   d. experimental group; control group
2. In an experimental study of the effects of stress on appetite, stress is the:
   a. dependent variable.
   b. independent variable.
   c. control group.
   d. experimental group.
3. In an experimental study of the effects of stress on appetite, subjects are randomly assigned to either the no-stress group or the stress group. These groups represent the ________ and the ________, respectively.
   a. independent variable; dependent variable
   b. dependent variable; independent variable
   c. control group; experimental group
   d. experimental group; control group
4. The extent to which the results of an experiment can be attributed to the manipulation of the independent variable, rather than to some confounding variable refers to:
   a. external validity.
   b. generalization to populations.
   c. internal validity.
   d. both b and c.
5. Joann conducted an experiment to test the effectiveness of an antianxiety program. The experiment took place over a 1-month time period. Subjects in the control group and the experimental group (those who participated in the antianxiety program) recorded their anxiety levels several times each day. Joann was unaware that midterm exams also happened to take place during the 1-month time period of her experiment. Joann's experiment is now confounded by:
   a. a maturation effect.
   b. a history effect.
   c. regression to the mean.
   d. a mortality effect.
6. Joe scored very low on the SAT the first time he took it. Based on the confound of ________, if Joe were to retake the SAT, his score should ________.
   a. instrumentation; increase
   b. instrumentation; decrease
   c. regression to the mean; increase
   d. regression to the mean; decrease
7. When the confound of mortality occurs:
   a. subjects are lost equally from both the experimental and control groups.
   b. subjects die as a result of participating in the experiment.
   c. subjects boycott the experiment.
   d. subjects are lost differentially from the experimental and control groups.
8. Controlling subject effects is to controlling both subject and experimenter effects as ________ is to ________.
   a. fatigue effects; practice effects
   b. practice effects; fatigue effects
   c. double-blind experiment; single-blind experiment
   d. single-blind experiment; double-blind experiment

9. If you were to use a bathroom scale to weigh mice in an experimental setting, your experiment would most likely suffer from a:
   a. ceiling effect.
   b. floor effect.
   c. practice effect.
   d. fatigue effect.
10. If we were to conduct a replication in which we increased the number of levels of the independent variable, we would be using a(n) _____ replication.
    a. exact
    b. conceptual
    c. nonexperimental
    d. systematic
11. Most psychology experiments suffer from the _____ problem because of the type of subjects used.
    a. diffusion of treatment problem
    b. college sophomore problem
    c. regression to the mean problem
    d. mortality problem
12. The value of the *t* test will _____ as sample variance decreases.
    a. increase
    b. decrease
    c. stay the same
    d. not be affected
13. Which of the following *t* test results has the greatest chance of statistical significance?
    a. $t(28) = 3.12$
    b. $t(14) = 3.12$
    c. $t(18) = 3.12$
    d. $t(10) = 3.12$
14. If the null hypothesis is false, then the *t* test should be:
    a. equal to 0.00.
    b. greater than 1.
    c. greater than .05.
    d. greater than .95.
15. Imagine that you conducted an independent-groups *t* test with 10 participants in each group. For a one-tailed test, the t_{cv} at $\alpha = .05$ would be:
    a. ±1.729.
    b. ±2.101.
    c. ±1.734.
    d. ±2.093.
16. If a researcher reported for an independent-groups *t* test that $t(26) = 2.90$, $p < .005$, how many subjects were there in the study?
    a. 13
    b. 26
    c. 27
    d. 28
17. Cohen's *d* is a measure of _____ for a _____.
    a. significance; *t* test
    b. significance; X^2 test
    c. effect size; *t* test
    d. effect size; X^2 test
18. $t_{cv} = \pm 2.15$ and $t_{obt} = -2.20$. Based on these results we:
    a. reject H_0.
    b. fail to reject H_0.
    c. accept H_0.
    d. reject H_a.

SELF-TEST PROBLEM

1. A college student is interested in whether there is a difference between male and female students in the amount of time spent doing volunteer work each week. The student gathers information from a random sample of male and female students on her campus. The amount of time volunteering (in minutes) is normally distributed. The data appear next. They are measured on an interval-ratio scale and are normally distributed.

Males	*Females*
20	35
25	39
35	38
40	43
36	50
24	49

   a. What statistical test should be used to analyze these data?
   b. Identify H_0 and *Ha* for this study.
   c. Conduct the appropriate analysis.
   d. Should H_0 be rejected? What should the researcher conclude?
   e. If significant, compute and interpret the effect size.
   f. If significant, draw a graph representing the data.
   g. Calculate the 95% confidence interval.

Chapter 9 ▪ Statistical Software Resources

INDEPENDENT-GROUPS *t* TEST

Using Excel

We'll use the data from Table 9.1 to illustrate how to use Excel to calculate an independent-groups *t* test. The data represent the number of items answered correctly for two groups of participants when one group used a spaced-study technique and the other used a massed-study technique. The researcher predicted that those in the spaced-study condition would perform better. The data from Table 9.1 have been entered into the following Excel worksheet with the data from the spaced condition in Column A and the data from the massed condition in Column B.

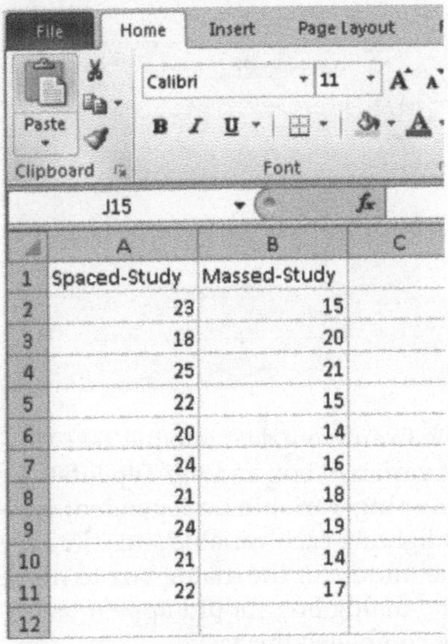

Next, with the **Data Ribbon** active, we click on **Data Analysis** in the top right corner of the screen and the following dialog box appears:

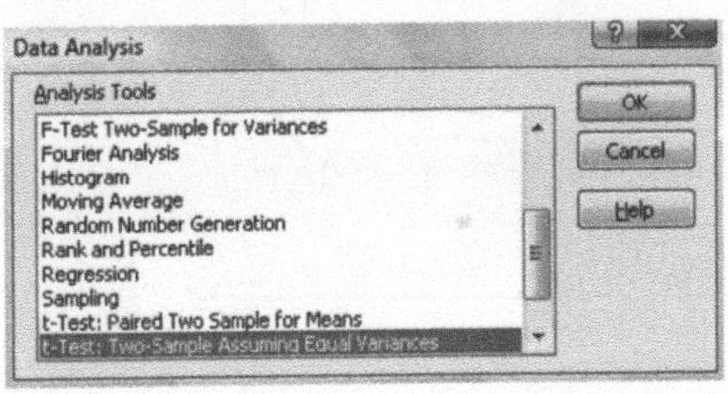

You can see that I have selected **t-test: Two-Sample Assuming Equal Variances**. After you have done the same, click **OK**, and you will then see the following dialog box:

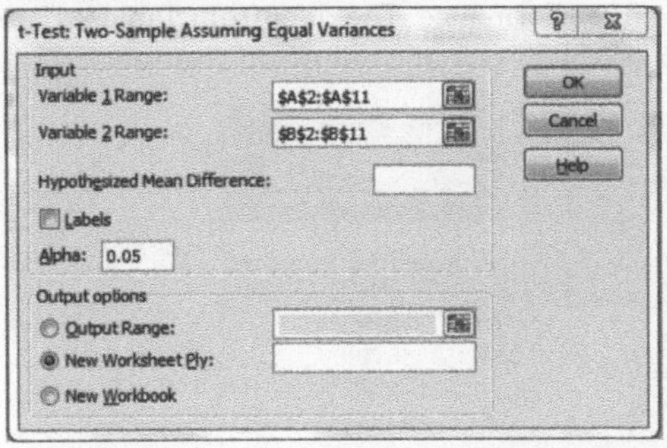

With the cursor in the **Variable 1 Range** box, highlight the data in Column A in the Excel spreadsheet so that they are entered in to the **Variable 1 Range** box (do not highlight the column heading of **Spaced Study**). Do the same for Column B and enter these data into the **Variable 2 Range** box. Then click **OK**. You will see the following output:

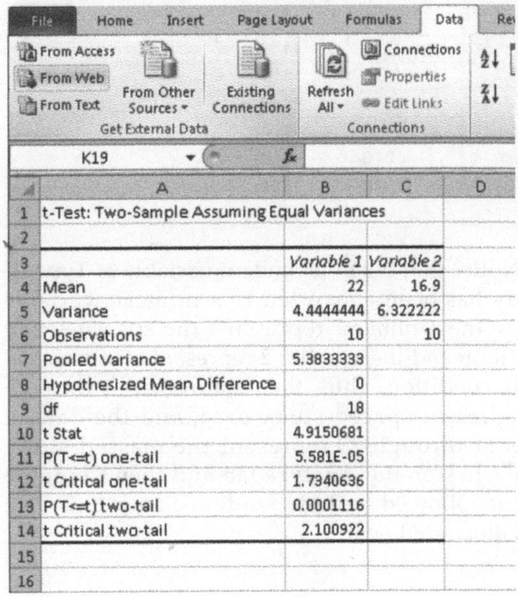

We are provided with the t test statistic of 4.92 along with the probability and critical values for both one- and two-tailed tests. We can see based on the one-tailed critical value of t that the test is significant at $p < .000056$. This would be reported in APA style as $t(18) = 4.92$, $p = .000056$ (one-tailed).

Using SPSS

We'll employ the same problem to illustrate the use of SPSS for an independent-groups t test. As above, researchers have participants use one of two types of study, spaced or massed, and then they measured exam performance. The data from Table 9.1 are entered into SPSS as in the following window:

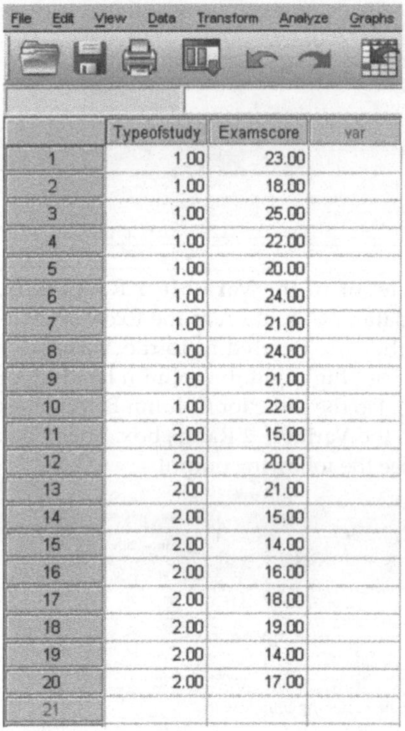

Notice that the independent variable of **TypeofStudy** has been converted to a numeric variable where the number 1 represents the spaced-study condition and the number 2 represents the massed-study condition. Thus, the data in rows 1 through 10 represent spaced-study data, and the data in rows 11 through 20 represent the massed-study data. Click on the **Analyze** tab and then **Compare Means** followed by **Independent-Samples T Test** as is illustrated next.

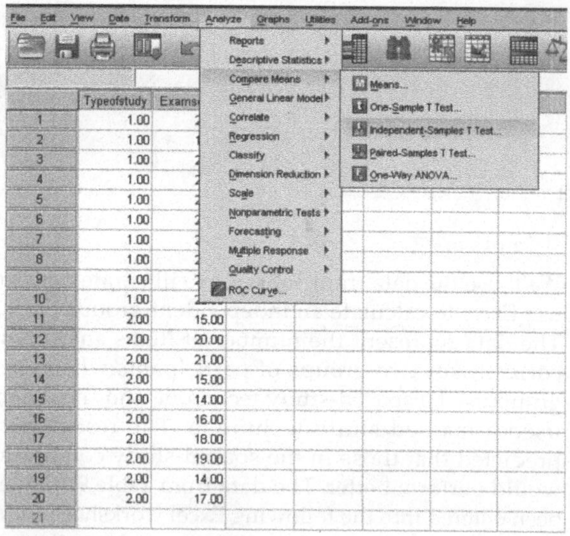

The following dialog box will appear

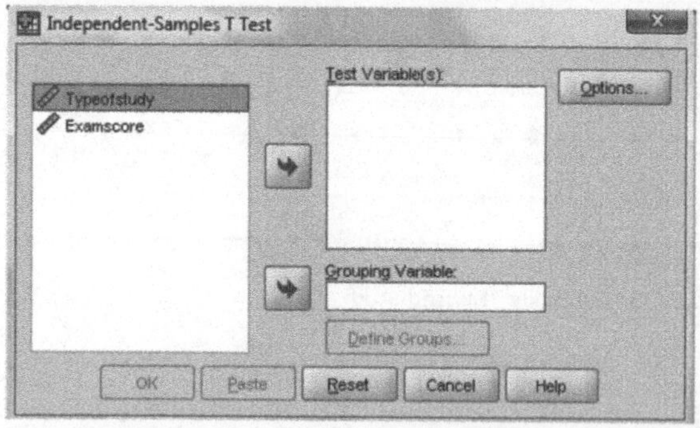

We'll place the Examscore data into the **Test Variable** (dependent variable) box and the **Typeofstudy** data into the **Grouping Variable** (independent variable) box by highlighting each variable and using the arrow keys in the middle of the dialog box to move the variables. The dialog box should appear as follows once you've completed this task.

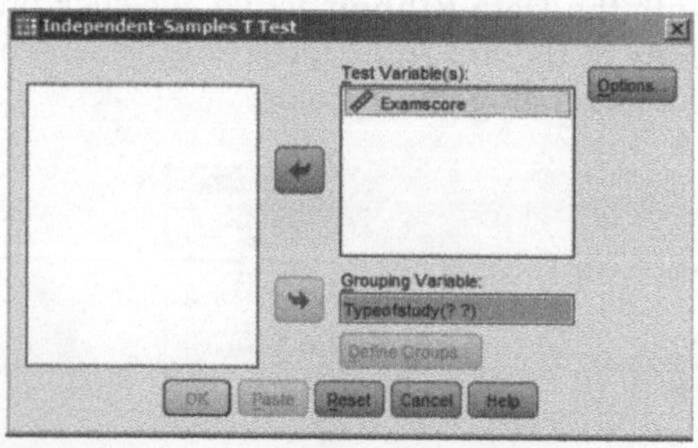

Once you have done this operation, click on the Grouping Variable box and the Define Groups box below it, which will become active, and you will receive a dialog box as follows:

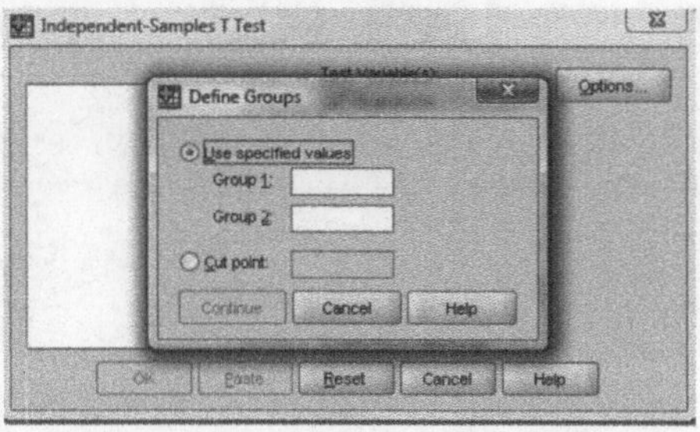

T-Test

[DataSet0]

Group Statistics

	Typeofstudy	N	Mean	Std. Deviation	Std. Error Mean
Examscore	1.00	10	22.0000	2.10819	.66667
	2.00	10	16.9000	2.51440	.79512

Independent Samples Test

		Levene's Test for Equality of Variances		t-test for Equality of Means					95% Confidence Interval of the Difference	
		F	Sig.	t	df	Sig. (2-tailed)	Mean Difference	Std. Error Difference	Lower	Upper
Examscore	Equal variances assumed	.827	.375	4.915	18	.000	5.10000	1.03763	2.92003	7.27997
	Equal variances not assumed			4.915	17.469	.000	5.10000	1.03763	2.91527	7.28473

We have to let SPSS know what values we used to designate the spaced- versus the massed-study groups. Thus, enter a 1 into the **Group 1** box and a 2 into the **Group 2** box and click **Continue**. Then click **OK** in the **Independent-Samples T Test** dialog box. You should receive output similar to the following:

Descriptive statistics for the two conditions are reported in the first table followed by the *t* test score of 4.915. Because we are assuming equal variances, we use the *df*, *t*-score, and other data from that row in the table. Moreover, the two-tailed significance level is provided, so we would have to divide this number in half to obtain the one-tailed significance level. However, because SPSS is reporting only the first three numbers, the significance level is reported as .000. Remember from the Excel example earlier that the significant level when carried out several decimal places is .0000132. We are also provided with the 95% confidence interval for the *t* test.

Using the TI-84

Let's use the data from Table 9.1 to conduct the test using the TI-84 calculator:

1. With the calculator on, press the **STAT** key.
2. **EDIT** will be highlighted. Press the **ENTER** key.
3. Under **L1** enter the data from Table 9.1 for the spaced-study group.
4. Under **L2** enter the data from Table 9.1 for the massed-study group.
5. Press the **STAT** key once again and highlight **TESTS**.
6. Scroll down to **2-SampTTest**. Press the **ENTER** key.
7. Highlight **DATA**. Enter **L1** next to **List1** (by pressing the 2nd key followed by the **1** key). Enter **L2** next to **List2** (by pressing the 2nd key followed by the **2** key).
8. Scroll down to **µ1**: and select > **µ2** (for a one-tailed test in which we predict that the spaced-study group will do better than the massed-study group). Press **ENTER**.
9. Scroll down to **Pooled:** and highlight **YES**. Press **ENTER**.
10. Scroll down to and highlight **CALCULATE**. Press **ENTER**.

The *t*-score of 4.915 should be displayed followed by the significance level of .000056 and the *df* of 18. In addition, descriptive statistics for both variables on which you entered data will be shown.

CHAPTER 10

Experimental Design and Analysis II: Correlated-Groups Designs

Learning Objectives

- Explain correlated-groups designs.
- Describe order effects and how counterbalancing is related to this concept.
- Explain what a Latin square design is.
- Explain when the t test for correlated-groups should be used.
- Calculate a correlated-groups t test.
- Interpret a correlated-groups t test.
- Calculate and interpret Cohen's d and r^2.
- Explain the assumptions of the correlated-groups t test.

Correlated-Groups Designs

correlated-groups design An experimental design in which the subjects in the experiment a land control groups are related in some way.

The designs described in the previous chapter were between-subjects designs—the subjects in each condition were different. We will now consider the use of **correlated-groups designs**—designs in which the subjects in the experimental and control groups are related. There are two types of correlated-groups designs: within-subjects designs and matched-subjects designs.

Within-Subjects Experimental Designs

within-subjects design A type of correlated-groups design in which the same subjects are used in each condition.

In a **within-subjects design**, the same subjects are used in all conditions. Within-subjects designs are often referred to as *repeated-measures designs* because we are repeatedly taking measures on the same individuals. A random sample of participants is selected, but random assignment is not relevant or necessary because all subjects serve in all conditions. Within subjects designs are popular in psychological research for several reasons.

First, within-subjects designs typically require fewer subjects than between-subjects designs. For example, suppose we were conducting the study mentioned in the previous chapter on the effects of mnemonic devices on memory. We could conduct this study using a between-subjects design and randomly assign different people to the control condition (no mnemonic device) and the experimental condition (those using a mnemonic device). If we wanted 20 participants in each condition, we would need a minimum of 20 people to serve in the control condition and 20 people to serve in the experimental condition, for a total of 40 subjects. If we conducted the experiment using a within-subjects design, we would need only 20 subjects who would serve in both the control and experimental conditions. Because subjects for research studies are difficult to recruit, using a within-subjects design to minimize the number of subjects needed is advantageous.

Second, within-subjects designs usually require less time to conduct than between-subjects designs. The study is conducted more quickly because subjects can usually participate in all conditions in one session; thus, unlike in a between subjects design, the experimenter does not test a subject in one condition and then wait around for the next subject to participate in another condition. In addition, the instructions need to be given to each subject only once. If there are 10 subjects in a within-subjects design and subjects are tested individually, this means explaining the experiment only 10 times. If there are 10 subjects in each condition in a between subjects design in which subjects are tested individually, this means explaining the experiment 20 times.

Third, and most important, within-subjects designs increase statistical power. When the same individuals participate in multiple conditions, individual differences between those conditions are minimized. This in turn reduces variability and increases the chances of achieving statistical significance. Think about it this way. In a between-subjects design, the differences between the groups or conditions may be mainly due to the independent variable. Some of the difference in performance between the two groups, however, is due to the fact that the individuals in one group are different from the individuals in the other group. This is referred to as *variability due to individual differences*. In a within-subjects design, however, most variability between the two conditions (groups) must come from the manipulation of the independent variable because the same participants produce both groups of scores. The differences between the groups cannot be caused by individual differences because the scores in both conditions come from the same person. Because of the reduction in individual differences (variability), a within-subjects design has greater statistical power than a between-subjects design. It provides a purer measure of the true effects of the independent variable.

Although the within-subjects design has advantages, it also has weaknesses. First, within-subjects designs are open to most of the confounds described in the previous chapter (see Chapter 9). As with between-subjects designs, internal validity is a concern for within-subjects designs. In fact, several of the confounds described earlier are especially troublesome for within-subjects designs. For example, testing effects—called **order effects** in a within-subjects design—are more problematic because all participants are measured at least twice—in the control condition and in the experimental condition. Because of this multiple testing, both practice and fatigue effects are common. However, these effects can be equalized across conditions in a within-subjects design by **counterbalancing**—systematically varying the order of the conditions for subjects in a within-subjects experiment. For example, if our memory experiment were counterbalanced, half of the people would participate in the control condition first, whereas the other half would participate in the experimental condition first. In this manner, practice and fatigue effects would be evenly distributed across conditions. When experimental designs are more complicated (i.e., they have three, four, or more conditions), counterbalancing can become more cumbersome. For example, a design with three conditions has 6 possible orders ($3! = 3 \times 2 \times 1$) in which to present the conditions, a design with four conditions has

order effects A problem for within-subjects designs in which the order of the conditions has an effect on the dependent variable.

counterbalancing A mechanism for controlling order effects either by including all orders of treatment presentation or by randomly determining the order for each subject.

24 possible orderings for the conditions (4! = 4 × 3 × 2 × 1), and a design with five conditions has 120 possible orderings (5! = 5 × 4 × 3 × 2 × 1). Given that most research studies use a limited number of subjects in each condition (usually 20 to 30), it is not possible to use all of the orderings of conditions (called *complete counterbalancing*) in studies with four or more conditions. Luckily, there are alternatives to complete counterbalancing known as partial counterbalancing. One partial counterbalancing alternative is to randomize the order of presentation of the conditions for each subject. Another alternative is to randomly select the number of orders that matches the number of subjects. For example, in a study with four conditions and 24 possible orderings, if we had 15 subjects, we could randomly select 15 of the 24 possible orderings.

Latin square A counterbalancing technique to control for order effects without using all possible orders.

A more formal way to use partial counterbalancing is to construct a Latin square. A **Latin square** uses a limited number of orders. When using a Latin square, we have the same number of orders as we have conditions. Thus, a Latin square for a design with four conditions uses 4 orders rather than the 24 orders used in the complete counterbalancing of a design with four conditions. Another criterion that must be met when constructing a Latin square is that each condition should be presented at each order. In other words, for a study with four conditions, each condition should appear once in each ordinal position. In addition, in a Latin square, each condition should precede and follow every other condition once. A Latin square for a study with four conditions appears in Table 10.1. The conditions are designated A, B, C, and D so that you can see how the order of conditions changes in each of the four orders used; however, once the Latin square is constructed using the letter symbols, each of the four conditions is randomly assigned to one of the letters to determine which condition will be A, B, and so on. A more complete discussion of Latin square designs can be found in Keppel (1991).

carryover effects A type of testing effect often present in within-subjects designs in which subjects "carry" something with them from one condition to another.

Another type of testing effect often present in within-subjects designs is known as a **carryover effect**; that is, subjects "carry" something with them from one condition to another. As a result of participating in one condition, they experience a change that they now carry with them to the second condition. Some drug research may involve carryover effects. The effects of the drug received in one condition will be present for a while and may be carried to the next condition. If the study described in Chapter 9 on memory and mnemonic devices were conducted using a within-subjects design, there would likely be a carryover effect. If individuals participate in the control condition first and then the experimental condition (using a mnemonic device), there probably would not be a carryover effect. If some individuals participate in the experimental condition first, however, it will be difficult not to continue using the mnemonic device after they have learned it. What they learned in one condition is carried with them to the next condition and alters their performance in that condition. Counterbalancing enables the experimenter to assess the extent of carryover effects by comparing performance in the experimental condition when presented first versus second. However, using a matched-subjects design (to be discussed next) will eliminate carryover effects.

TABLE 10.1 A Latin Square for a Design with Four Conditions

ORDER OF CONDITIONS			
A	B	D	C
B	C	A	D
C	D	B	A
D	A	C	B

NOTE: The four conditions in this experiment were randomly given the letter designations A, B, C, and D.

Finally, within-subjects designs are more open to *demand characteristics*—the information the participants infer about what the researcher wants. Because individuals participate in all conditions, they know how the instructions vary by condition and how each condition differs from the previous ones. This gives them information about the study that a subject in a between-subjects design would not have. This information, in turn, may enable them to determine the purpose of the investigation, which could lead to a change in their performance.

Not all research can be conducted using a within-subjects design. For example, most drug research is conducted using different subjects in each condition because drugs often permanently affect or change an individual. Thus, subjects cannot serve in more than one condition. In addition, researchers who study reasoning and problem solving often cannot use within-subjects designs because after a subject has solved a problem, that person cannot then serve in another condition and attempt to solve the same problem again. Where possible, however, many psychologists choose to use within-subjects designs because they believe the added strengths of the design outweigh the weaknesses.

Matched-Subjects Experimental Designs

matched-subjects design A type of correlated-groups design in which subjects are matched between conditions on variable(s) that the researcher believes is (are) relevant to the study.

The second type of correlated-groups design is a **matched-subjects design**. Matched-subjects designs share certain characteristics with both between and within-subjects designs. As in a between-subjects design, different participants are used in each condition. However, for each subject in one condition, there is a subject in the other condition(s) who matches him or her on some relevant variable or variables. For example, if weight is a concern in a study and the researchers want to ensure that for each subject in the control condition there is a subject in the experimental condition of the same weight, they match subjects on weight. Matching the subjects on one or more variables makes the matched-subjects design similar to the within subjects design. A within-subjects design has perfect matching because the same people serve in each condition; with the matched-subjects design, we are attempting to achieve as much equivalence between the groups as we can.

Why, then, do we not simply use a within-subjects design? The answer is usually carryover effects. Participating in one condition changes the subjects to such an extent that they cannot also participate in the second condition.

For example, drug research usually uses between-subjects designs or matched-subjects designs but rarely a within-subjects design. Subjects cannot take both the placebo and the real drug as part of an experiment; hence, this type of research requires that different people serve in each condition. But to ensure equivalency between groups, the researcher may choose to use a matched-subjects design.

The matched-subjects design has advantages over both between-subjects and within-subjects designs. First, because different people are in each group, testing effects and demand characteristics are minimized in comparison to a within-subjects design. Second, the groups are more equivalent than those in a between-subjects design and almost as equivalent as those in a within-subjects design. Third, because participants have been matched on variables of importance to the study, the same types of statistics used for the within-subjects designs are used for the matched-subjects designs. In other words, data from a matched-subjects design are treated like data from a within-subjects design. This means that a matched-subjects design is as powerful statistically as a within-subjects design because individual differences have been minimized.

Of course, matched-subjects designs also have weaknesses. First, more subjects are needed than in a within-subjects design. Also, if one subject in a matched-subjects design drops out, the entire pair is lost. Thus, mortality is even more of an issue in matched-subjects designs. The biggest weakness of the matched-subjects design, however, is the matching itself. Finding an individual willing to participate in an experiment who exactly (or very closely) matches another participant on a specific variable can be difficult. If the researcher is matching subjects on more than one variable (for example, height and weight), it becomes even more difficult. Because subjects are hard to find, it is very difficult to find enough subjects who are matches to take part in a matched-subjects study.

Comparison of Designs — IN REVIEW

	BETWEEN-SUBJECTS DESIGN	WITHIN-SUBJECTS DESIGN	MATCHED-SUBJECTS DESIGN
Description	Different subjects are randomly assigned to each condition.	The same subjects are used in all conditions.	Subjects are randomly assigned to each condition after they are matched on relevant variables.
Strengths	Testing effects are minimized. Demand characteristics are minimized.	Fewer participants are needed. Less time-consuming. Equivalency of groups is ensured. More powerful statistically.	Testing effects are minimized. Demand characteristics are minimized. Groups are fairly equivalent. More powerful statistically.
Weaknesses	More participants are needed. More time-consuming. Groups may not be equivalent. Less powerful statistically.	Probability of testing effects is high. Probability of demand characteristics is high.	Matching is very difficult. More participants are needed.

CRITICAL THINKING CHECK 10.1

1. If a researcher wants to conduct a study with four conditions and 15 subjects in each condition, how many subjects will be needed for a between-subjects design? For a within-subjects design?
2. People with anxiety disorders are selected to participate in a study on a new drug for the treatment of this disorder. The researchers know that the drug is effective in treating the disorder, but they are concerned with possible side effects. In particular, they are concerned with the effects of the drug on cognitive abilities. Therefore, they ask each subject in the experiment to identify a family member or friend who is the same gender as the subject and who is of a similar age as the subject (within 5 years) but who does not have an anxiety disorder. The researchers then administer the drug to those with the disorder and measure cognitive functioning in both groups. What type of design is this? Would you suggest measuring cognitive functioning more than once? When and why?

Parametric Inferential Statistics: Two-Group Designs

In this chapter, we will discuss the common type of parametric statistical analyses used with correlated-groups designs with two-groups. Nonparametric statistics for correlated-groups designs with two groups are discussed in Chapter 14. For the statistic presented in this chapter, the experimental design is similar—a two-group correlated-groups (within-subjects or matched-subjects) design. Remember that a matched-subjects design is analyzed statistically the same way as a within-subjects design. Thus, the parametric test presented in this chapter is the correlated-groups equivalent of the *t* test described in Chapter 9. As you might remember, the *t* test covered in the previous chapter was the independent-groups *t* test, and was used with between-subjects designs. Thus, in this chapter we cover the correlated-groups *t* test, which is used with correlated-groups designs. As with the previously discussed *t* test, the correlated-groups *t* test is designed to test differences between two equivalent groups or treatment conditions.

t Test for Correlated Groups: What It Is and What It Does

correlated-groups *t* test A parametric inferential test used to compare the means of two related (within- or matched-subjects) samples.

The **correlated-groups *t* test**, like the previously discussed independent-groups *t* test, compares the means of subjects in two-groups. In this case, however, the same people are used in each group (a within-subjects design) or different participants are matched between groups (a matched-subjects design). The test indicates whether there is a difference in the sample means and whether this difference is greater than would be expected based on chance. In a correlated-groups design, the sample includes two scores for each person, instead of just one. To conduct the *t* test for correlated groups (also called the *t* test for dependent groups or samples), we must convert the two scores for each person into one score. That is, we compute a difference score for each person by subtracting one score from the other for that person (or for the two individuals in a matched pair). Although this may sound confusing, the dependent-groups *t* test is actually easier to compute than the independent-groups *t* test. The two samples are related, so the analysis becomes easier because we work with pairs of scores. The null hypothesis is that there is no difference between the two scores; that is, a person's score in one condition is the same as that (or a matched) person's score in the second condition. The alternative hypothesis is that there is a difference between the paired scores—that the individuals (or matched pairs) performed differently in each condition.

To illustrate the use of the correlated-groups *t* test, imagine that we conduct a study in which subjects are asked to learn two lists of words. One list is composed of 20 concrete words (for example, *desk, lamp, bus*); the other is 20 abstract words (for example, *love, hate, deity*). Each subject is tested twice, once in each condition. (Think back to the discussion of weaknesses in within-subjects designs from earlier in this chapter, and identify how you would control for practice and fatigue effects in this study.)

Because each subject provides one pair of scores, a correlated-groups *t* test is the appropriate way to compare the means of the two conditions. We expect to find that recall performance is better for the concrete words. Thus, the null hypothesis is $H_0 = \mu_1 - \mu_2 = 0$ because the null hypothesis states that subjects should perform the same in each of the treatment conditions. Thus, the expected difference between the performance the abstract and concrete conditions would be zero. The alternative hypothesis on the other hand predicts that subjects will perform better in the concrete conditions (i.e., they will remember more words in the concrete condition). Thus, the alternative hypothesis is $H_a = \mu_1 - \mu_2 > 0$ indicating that the difference between the means for the abstract and concrete conditions will be greater than zero, and representing a one-tailed test of the null hypothesis. The null and alternative hypotheses could also be written as they were for the independent-groups *t* test in Chapter 9.

$$H_0 = \mu_{\text{concrete}} \leq \mu_{\text{abstract}}$$

$$H_a = \mu_{\text{concrete}} > \mu_{\text{abstract}}$$

To better understand the correlated-groups *t* test, consider the sampling distribution for the test. This is a sampling distribution of the differences between pairs of sample means. Imagine the population of people who must recall abstract words versus the population of people who must recall concrete words. Further, imagine that samples of eight participants are chosen

TABLE 10.2 Numbers of Abstract and Concrete Words Recalled by Each Participant Using a Correlated-Groups (Within-Subjects) Design

PARTICIPANT	CONCRETE	ABSTRACT
1	13	10
2	11	9
3	19	13
4	13	12
5	15	11
6	10	8
7	12	10
8	13	13

(the eight subjects in each individual sample come from one population), and each sample's mean score in the abstract condition is subtracted from the mean score in the concrete condition. We do this repeatedly until the entire population has been sampled. If the null hypothesis is true, the differences between the sample means should be zero, or very close to zero. If, as the researcher suspects, subjects remember more concrete words than abstract words, the difference between the sample means should be significantly greater than zero.

The data representing each subject's performance are presented in Table 10.2. Notice that we have two sets of scores, one for the concrete word list and one for the abstract list. The calculations for the correlated-groups t test involve transforming the two sets of scores into one set by determining difference scores. **Difference scores** represent the difference between subjects' performance in one condition and their performance in the other condition. The difference scores for our study are shown in Table 10.3.

difference scores Scores representing the difference between subjects' performance in one condition and their performance in a second condition.

Calculations for the Correlated-Groups t *Test.* After calculating the difference scores, we have one set of scores representing the performance of subjects in both conditions. We can now compare the mean of the difference scores with zero (based on the null hypothesis stated previously). The computations from this point on for the dependent-groups t test are similar to those for the single-sample t test in Chapter 8:

$$t = \frac{\overline{D} - 0}{s_{\overline{D}}}$$

where

$\overline{D}$ = mean of the difference scores, and
$s_{\overline{D}}$ = standard error of the difference scores:

standard error of the difference scores The standard deviation of the sampling distribution of mean differences between dependent samples in a two-group experiment.

The **standard error of the difference scores** ($s_{\overline{D}}$) is the standard deviation of the sampling distribution of mean differences between dependent

TABLE 10.3 Numbers of Concrete and Abstract Words Recalled by Each Participant, with Different Scores

PARTICIPANT	CONCRETE	ABSTRACT	*D* (DIFFERENCE SCORE)
1	13	10	3
2	11	9	2
3	19	13	6
4	13	12	1
5	15	11	4
6	10	8	2
7	12	10	2
8	13	13	0
			$\Sigma = 20$

samples in an experiment with two conditions. It is calculated in a similar manner to the estimated standard error of the mean ($s_{\overline{X}}$) that you learned how to calculate in Chapter 8:

$$s_{\overline{D}} = \frac{s_D}{\sqrt{N}}$$

where s_D is the unbiased estimator of the standard deviation of the difference scores. The standard deviation of the difference scores is calculated in the same manner as the standard deviation for any set of scores:

$$s_D = \sqrt{\frac{\Sigma(D - \overline{D})^2}{N - 1}}$$

where

D = each difference score

$\overline{D}$ = mean of the difference scores, and

N = the sample size

Or, if you prefer, you may use the computational formula for the standard deviation:

$$s_D = \sqrt{\frac{\Sigma D^2 - \frac{(\Sigma D)^2}{N}}{N - 1}}$$

Let's use the definitional formula to determine s_D, $s_{\overline{D}}$, and the final *t*-score. We begin by determining the mean of the difference scores ($\overline{D}$), which is $20/8 = 2.5$, and then use this to determine the deviation scores, the squared

TABLE 10.4 Difference Scores and Squared Difference Scores for Numbers of Concrete and Abstract Words Recalled

D (DIFFERENCE SCORE)	$D - \bar{D}$	$(D - \bar{D})^2$
3	0.5	0.25
2	−0.5	0.25
6	3.5	12.25
1	−1.5	2.25
4	1.5	2.25
2	−0.5	0.25
2	−0.5	0.25
0	−2.5	6.25
		Σ = 24

deviation scores, and the sum of the squared deviation scores as shown in Table 10.4. We then use this sum (24) to determine s_D, which is 1.85.

$$s_D = \sqrt{\frac{24}{7}} = \sqrt{3.429} = 1.85$$

Next, we use the standard deviation ($s_D = 1.85$) to calculate the standard error of the difference scores ($s_{\bar{D}}$), which is 0.65.

$$S_{\bar{D}} = \frac{S_D}{\sqrt{N}} = \frac{1.85}{\sqrt{8}} = \frac{1.85}{2.83} = 0.65$$

FIGURE 10.1
The obtained *t*-score in relation to the t-critical value

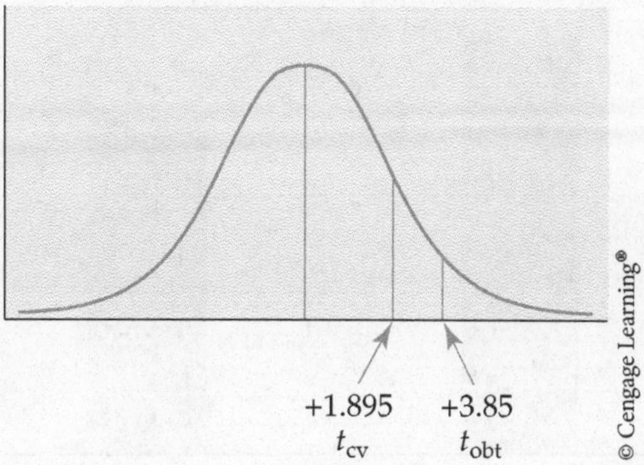

Finally, we use the standard error of the difference scores ($s_{\overline{D}} = 0.65$) and the mean of the difference scores (2.5) in the *t*-test formula:

$$t = \frac{\overline{D} - 0}{s_{\overline{D}}} = \frac{2.5 - 0}{0.65} = \frac{2.5}{0.65} = 3.85$$

Interpreting the Correlated-Groups t *Test and Graphing the Means.* The degrees of freedom for a correlated-groups *t* test are equal to $N - 1$—in this case, $8 - 1 = 7$. We can use Table A.3 in Appendix A to determine t_{cv} for a one-tailed test with $\alpha = .05$ and $df = 7$. We find that $t_{cv} = 1.895$. Our $t_{obt} = 3.85$ and therefore falls in the region of rejection. Figure 10.1 shows this t_{obt} in relation to t_{cv}. In APA style, this is reported as $t(7) = 3.85, p < .05$ (one-tailed), indicating that there is a significant difference in the number of words recalled in the two conditions. Instructions on using Excel, SPSS, or the TI-84 calculator to conduct this correlated-groups *t* test appear in the Statistical Software Resources section at the end of the chapter.

This difference is illustrated in Figure 10.2, in which the mean numbers of concrete and abstract words recalled by the subjects have been graphed. Thus, we can conclude that subjects performed significantly better in the concrete word condition, which supports the alternative (research) hypothesis.

Effect Size: Cohen's d *and* r^2. As with the independent-groups *t* test, we should also compute Cohen's *d* (the proportion of variance in the dependent variable that is accounted for by the manipulation of the independent variable) for the correlated-groups *t* test. Remember, effect size indicates how large a role the conditions of the independent variable play in determining scores on the dependent variable. For the correlated-groups *t* test, the formula for Cohen's *d* is

$$d = \frac{\overline{D}}{s_D}$$

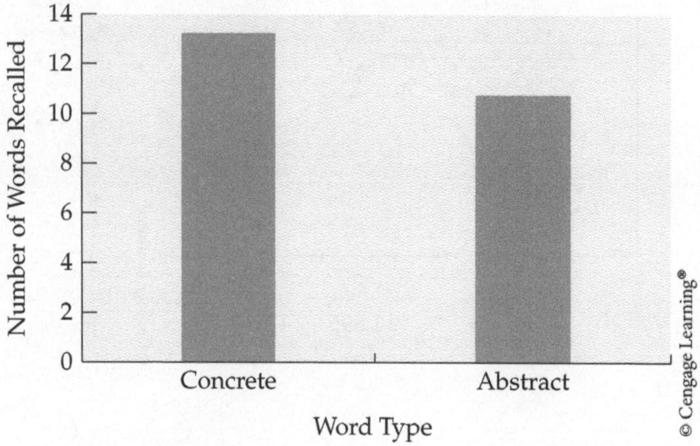

FIGURE 10.2 Mean number of words recalled correctly under concrete and abstract word conditions

where $\overline{D}$ is the mean of the difference scores, and s_D is the standard deviation of the difference scores. We have already calculated each of these as part of the *t* test. Thus,

$$d = \frac{2.5}{1.85} = 1.35$$

Cohen's *d* for a correlated-groups design is interpreted in the same manner as *d* for an independent-groups design. That is, a small effect size is one of at least 0.20, a medium effect size is at least 0.50, and a large effect size is at least 0.80. Obviously, our effect size of 1.35 is far greater than 0.80, indicating a very large effect size.

We can also compute r^2 for the correlated-groups *t* test just as we did for the independent-groups *t* test using the same formula we did in Chapter 9.

$$r^2 = \frac{t^2}{t^2 + df} = \frac{3.85^2}{3.85^2 + 7} = \frac{14.82}{14.82 + 7} = \frac{14.82}{21.82} = .68$$

Using the guidelines established by Cohen (1988) and noted in Chapter 9, this is a large effect size.

Confidence Intervals. Just as with the independent-groups *t* test, we can calculate confidence intervals based on a correlated-groups *t* test. In this case, we use a formula very similar to that used for the single-sample *t* test from Chapter 8 :

$$CI_{.95} = \overline{D} \pm t_{cv}(s_{\overline{D}})$$

We have already calculated $\overline{D}$ and $s_{\overline{D}}$ as part of the previous *t*-test problem. Thus, we only need to determine t_{cv} to calculate the 95% confidence interval. Once again, we consult Table A.3 in Appendix A for a two-tailed test (remember, we are determining values both above and below the mean, so we use the t_{cv} for a two-tailed test) with 7 degrees of freedom. We find that the t_{cv} is 2.365. Using this, we calculate the confidence interval as follows:

$$CI_{.95} = 2.5 \pm 2.365(0.65)$$
$$= 2.5 \pm 1.54$$
$$= 0.96 - 4.04$$

Thus, the 95% confidence interval that should contain the difference in mean test scores between concrete and abstract words is 0.96 – 4.04. This means that if someone asked us how large a difference word type makes on memory performance, we could answer that we are 95% confident that the difference in performance on the 20-item memory test between the two word-type conditions would be between 0.96 and 4.04 words recalled correctly.

Assumptions of the Correlated-Groups t *Test.* The assumptions for the correlated-groups *t* test are the same as those for the independent-groups *t* test, except for the assumption that the observations are independent. In this case, the observations are not independent—they are correlated.

- The data are interval-ratio scale.
- The underlying distributions are normal.
- The observations are dependent or related.
- If we could compute the true variance of the population represented by each sample, the variances in each population would be the same, which is called homogeneity of variance.

Correlated-Groups *t* Tests — IN REVIEW

	CORRELATED-GROUPS *T* TESTS
What It Is	A parametric test for a two-group within subjects or matched-subjects design
What It Does	Analyzes whether each individual performed in a similar or different manner across conditions
Assumptions	Interval-ratio data Normal distribution Homogeneity of variance Dependent or related observations

CRITICAL THINKING CHECK 10.2

1. What are difference scores with respect to the correlated-groups *t* test and how are difference scores calculated?
2. When calculating the correlated-groups *t* test, why does the numerator for the equation involve subtracting zero from the mean of the difference scores?

Summary

Correlated-groups designs and the parametric statistic appropriate for analyzing these designs were covered. This coverage included the difference between within-subjects and matched-subjects designs along with the advantages and disadvantages of each. In addition, this discussion included how to calculate a correlated-groups t test and the appropriate measures of effect size for this test.

KEY TERMS

correlated-groups designs
within-subjects design
order effects
counterbalancing
Latin square
carryover effects
matched-subjects design
correlated-groups t test
difference scores
standard error of the difference scores

CHAPTER EXERCISES

(Answers to odd-numbered exercises appear in Appendix C.)

1. A researcher is interested in whether listening to classical music improves spatial ability. She randomly assigns subjects to either a classical music condition or a no-music condition. Is this a between-subjects or a within-subjects design?
2. How does using a Latin square aid a researcher in counterbalancing a study?
3. What are the similarities and differences between within-subjects and matched-subjects designs?
4. A researcher is interested in whether participating in sports positively influences self-esteem in young girls. She identifies a group of girls who have not played sports before but are now planning to begin participating in organized sports. The researcher gives them a 50-item self-esteem inventory before they begin playing sports and administers the same test again after 6 months of playing sports. The self-esteem inventory is measured on an interval scale, with higher numbers indicating higher self-esteem. In addition, scores on the inventory are normally distributed. The scores follow.

Before	After
44	46
40	41
39	41
46	47
42	43
43	45

   a. What statistical test should be used to analyze these data?
   b. Identify H_0 and H_a for this study.
   c. Conduct the appropriate analysis.
   d. Should H_0 be rejected? What should the researcher conclude?
   e. If significant, compute and interpret the effect size.
   f. If significant, draw a graph representing the data.
   g. Determine the 95% confidence interval.
5. The researcher in exercise 5 in Chapter 9 decides to conduct the same study using a within-subjects design to control for differences in cognitive ability. He selects a random sample of subjects and has them study different material of equal difficulty in both the music and no-music conditions. The study is completely counterbalanced to control for order effects. The data appear next. As in Chapter 9, they are measured on an interval-ratio scale and are normally distributed; he believes that studying under quiet conditions will lead to better performance.

Music	No Music
7	7
6	8
5	7
6	7
8	9
8	8

a. What statistical test should be used to analyze these data?
b. Identify H_0 and H_a for this study.
c. Conduct the appropriate analysis.
d. Should H_0 be rejected? What should the researcher conclude?
e. If significant, compute and interpret the effect size.
f. If significant, draw a graph representing the data.
g. Determine the 95% confidence interval.

6. Identify the statistical procedure that should be used to analyze the data from each of the following studies:
   a. A study that investigates whether men or women (age 16 to 20) spend more money on clothing. Assume the amount of money spent is normally distributed.
   b. A study that investigates whether students perform better in a class that uses group learning exercises versus a class that uses the traditional lecture method. Two classes that learn the same information are selected. Performance on a 50-item final exam at the end of the semester is measured.
   c. In the (b) study above, researchers instead decide to use the same participants in both conditions. Thus, group learning exercises are used for half of the semester and traditional lectures for the other half of the semester. These two procedures are counterbalanced across students to avoid design flaws. As in the (b) study above, performance on a 50-item final exam is measured.

CRITICAL THINKING CHECK ANSWERS

10.1

1. The researcher will need 60 subjects for a between-subjects design and 15 subjects for a within-subjects design.
2. This is a matched-subjects design. The researcher might consider measuring cognitive functioning before the study begins to ensure that there are no differences between the two groups of subjects before the treatment. Obviously, the researchers would also measure cognitive functioning at the end of the study.

10.2

1. Difference scores represent the difference in performance for each subjects between the two treatment conditions in the study. Thus, to calculate the difference scores, we subtract each subject's score in one condition from their score in the second condition—consistently subtracting scores in condition A from condition B for each subject (or vice versa).
2. We subtract zero from the mean of the difference scores in the numerator for the correlated-groups t test because the zero represents μ (what we expect the mean of the difference scores to be if the independent variable had no effect). In other words, if the independent variable did not affect subjects' performance, then we would expect the subjects to receive the same score in each condition. This would lead to difference scores of zero for each subject, and the mean difference score across all subjects would be zero. Thus, if in an experimental study the independent variable really had no effect, the numerator for the t test would be $(\overline{D} - \mu)$, and the t-score would be zero. However, if the independent variable had an effect, then the numerator will be greater than zero because we would have a number larger than zero ($\overline{D}$—the mean of the difference scores) minus 0 (μ—what we expect the difference scores to be when the independent variable has no effect).

WEB RESOURCES

The book-specific website at CengageBrain.com offers students a variety of study tools and useful resources such as glossaries and flashcards.

Chapter 10 ▪ Study Guide

CHAPTER 10 SUMMARY AND REVIEW: EXPERIMENTAL DESIGN AND ANALYSIS II

Correlated-groups designs and the parametric statistic appropriate for analyzing these designs were covered. This coverage included the difference between within-subjects and matched-subjects designs along with the advantages and disadvantages of each. In addition, this discussion included how to calculate a correlated-groups t test and the appropriate measures of effect size for this test.

CHAPTER 10 REVIEW EXERCISES

(Answers to exercises appear in Appendix C.)

FILL-IN SELF-TEST

Answer the following questions. If you have trouble answering any of the questions, restudy the relevant material before going on to the multiple-choice self-test.

1. If the order of conditions affects the results in a within-subjects design, there are ________.
2. A procedure used to combat order effect is known as ________.
3. A special type of counterbalancing technique for designs with many possible orderings is known as a ________.
4. A(n) ________ is a parametric inferential test used to compare the means of two related samples.
5. When using a correlated-groups t test, we calculate ________ scores representing the difference between subjects' performance in one condition and their performance in a second condition.
6. The standard deviation of the sampling distribution of mean differences between dependent samples in a two-group experiment is the ________.

MULTIPLE-CHOICE SELF-TEST

Select the single best answer for each of the following questions. If you have trouble answering any of the questions, restudy the relevant material.

1. Within-subjects design is to between-subjects design as ________ is to ________.
   a. using different subjects in each group; using the same subjects in each group
   b. using the same subjects in each group; using different subjects in each group
   c. matched-subjects design; correlated-groups design
   d. experimental group; control group
2. Which of the following represent correlated-groups designs?
   a. matched-subjects designs
   b. between-subjects designs
   c. within-subjects designs
   d. all of the above
3. A matched-subjects design uses:
   a. the same subjects in each condition.
   b. different subjects in each condition.
   c. some of the same subjects and some different subjects in each condition.
   d. different subjects in each condition, but they've been matched on a variable of importance to the study.
4. If a correlated-groups t test and an independent-groups t test both have $df = 10$, which experiment used fewer subjects?
   a. both used the same number of subjects ($n = 10$)
   b. both used the same number of participants ($n = 11$)
   c. the correlated-groups t test
   d. the independent-groups t test

5. If researchers reported that, for a within-subjects design, $t(15) = 2.57$, $p < .05$, you can conclude that:
   a. a total of 16 people participated in the study.
   b. a total of 17 people participated in the study.
   c. a total of 30 people participated in the study.
   d. there is no way to determine how many people participated in the study.
6. The value of the *t* test will ______ as sample variance decreases.
   a. increase
   b. decrease
   c. stay the same
   d. not be affected
7. Which of the following *t* test results has the greatest chance of statistical significance?
   a. $t(28) = 3.12$
   b. $t(14) = 3.12$
   c. $t(18) = 3.12$
   d. $t(10) = 3.12$
8. If the null hypothesis is false, then the *t* test should be:
   a. equal to 0.00.
   b. greater than 1.
   c. greater than .05.
   d. greater than .95.
9. $Ha: \mu_1 - \mu_2 > 0$ is the ______ hypothesis for a(n) ______-groups *t* test.
   a. null; independent
   b. alternative; independent
   c. null; correlated
   d. alternative; correlated
10. If a researcher reported for a correlated-groups *t* test that $t(26) = 2.90$, $p < .005$, how many subjects were there in the study?
    a. 13
    b. 26
    c. 27
    d. 28
11. $t_{cv} = \pm 2.15$ and $t_{obt} = -2.20$. Based on these results we:
    a. reject H_0.
    b. fail to reject H_0.
    c. accept H_0.
    d. reject H_a.

SELF-TEST PROBLEM

1. A researcher is interested in whether studying with music helps or hinders the learner. To control for differences in cognitive ability, the researcher decides to use a within-subjects design. He selects a random sample of participants and has them study different material of equal difficulty in both the music and no music conditions. Next, the students take a 20-item quiz on the material. The study is completely counter balanced to control for order effects. The data appear next. They are measured on an interval-ratio scale and are normally distributed.

Music	No Music
17	17
16	18
15	17
16	17
18	19
18	18

   a. What statistical test should be used to analyze these data?
   b. Identify H_0 and H_a for this study.
   c. Conduct the appropriate analysis.
   d. Should H_0 be rejected? What should the researcher conclude?
   e. If significant, compute and interpret the effect size.
   f. If significant, draw a graph representing the data.
   g. Calculate the 95% confidence interval.

Chapter 10 ▪ Statistical Software Resources

CORRELATED-GROUPS *T* TEST

Using Excel

To illustrate the use of the correlated-groups t test, let's use the study described earlier in the chapter in which participants are asked to learn two lists of words. One list is composed of 20 concrete words (for example, *desk*, *lamp*, and *bus*), whereas the other is composed of 20 abstract words (for example, *love*, *hate*, and *deity*). Each participant is tested twice, once in each condition. Because each participant provides one pair of scores, a correlated-groups t test is the appropriate way to compare the means of the two conditions. We expect to find that recall performance is better for the concrete words. Thus, the null hypothesis is H_0: $\mu_{\text{Concrete}} \leq \mu_{\text{Abstract}}$, and the alternative hypothesis is H_a: $\mu_{\text{Concrete}} > \mu_{\text{Abstract}}$, representing a one-tailed test of the null hypothesis.

Using Excel to calculate a correlated-groups t test is very similar to using it to calculate an independent-groups t test. We'll use the data from Table 10.2 presented earlier in the chapter to illustrate its use.

For this t test, we are comparing memory for concrete versus abstract words for a group of 8 participants. Each participant served in both conditions. First enter the data from Table 10.2 into an Excel spreadsheet (as seen next). The data for the concrete-word condition are entered into Column A and the data for the abstract-word condition into Column B.

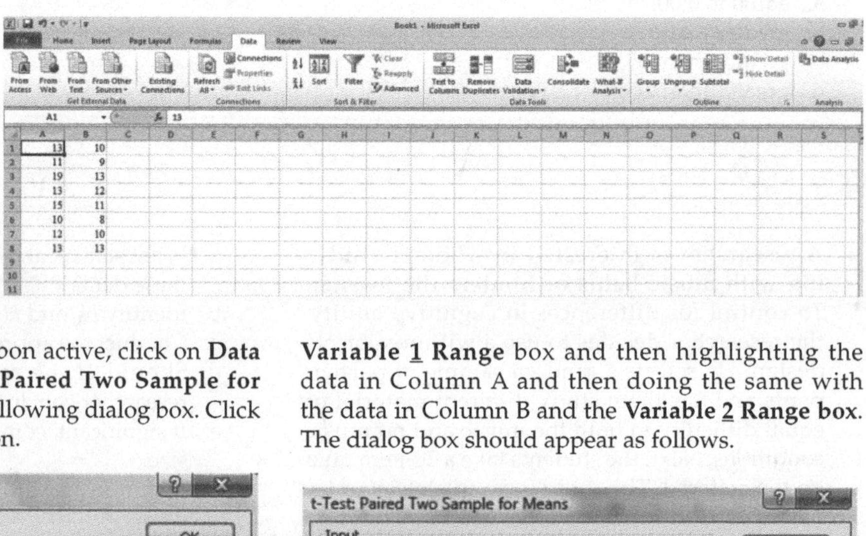

Then, with the **Data** ribbon active, click on **Data Analysis** and select **t-test: Paired Two Sample for Means** as indicated in the following dialog box. Click **OK** after doing this operation.

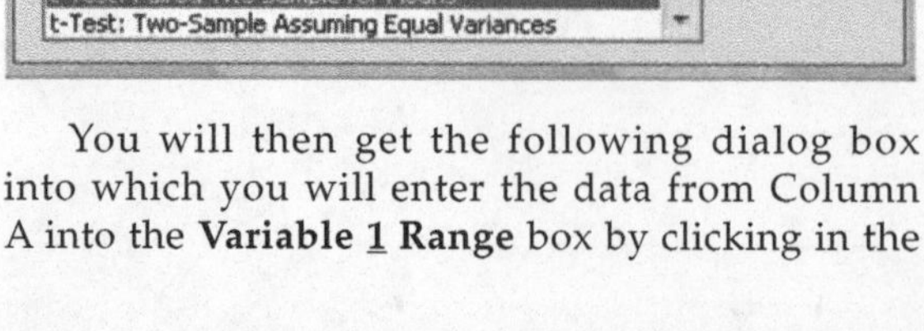

You will then get the following dialog box into which you will enter the data from Column A into the **Variable 1 Range** box by clicking in the **Variable 1 Range** box and then highlighting the data in Column A and then doing the same with the data in Column B and the **Variable 2 Range box.** The dialog box should appear as follows.

Click **OK**, and you will receive the output as it appears next.

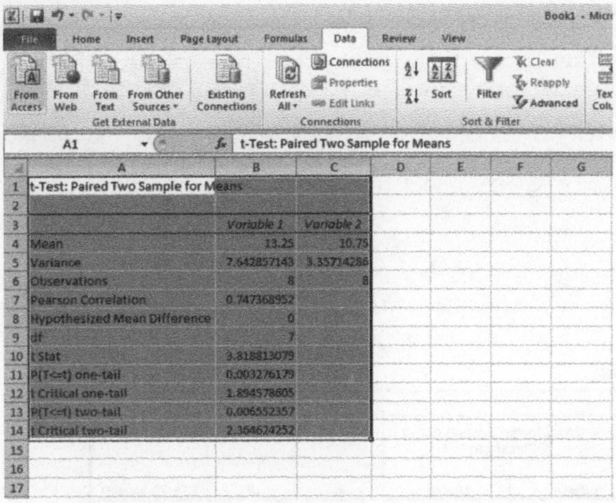

t-Test: Paired Two Sample for Means

	Variable 1	Variable 2
Mean	13.25	10.75
Variance	7.642857143	3.35714286
Observations	8	8
Pearson Correlation	0.747368952	
Hypothesized Mean Difference	0	
df	7	
t Stat	3.818813079	
P(T<=t) one-tail	0.003276179	
t Critical one-tail	1.894578605	
P(T<=t) two-tail	0.006552357	
t Critical two-tail	2.364624252	

We can see that $t(7) = 3.82$, $p = .0033$ (one-tailed).

Using SPSS

To illustrate using SPSS for the correlated-groups *t* test, we'll use the same problem described above in which a researcher has a group of participants study a list of 20 concrete words and 20 abstract words and then measures recall for the words within each condition. The researcher predicts that the participants will have better recall for the concrete words. The data from Table 10.2 are entered into SPSS as follows. We have 8 participants, and each serves in both conditions. Thus, the scores for each participant in both conditions appear in a single row.

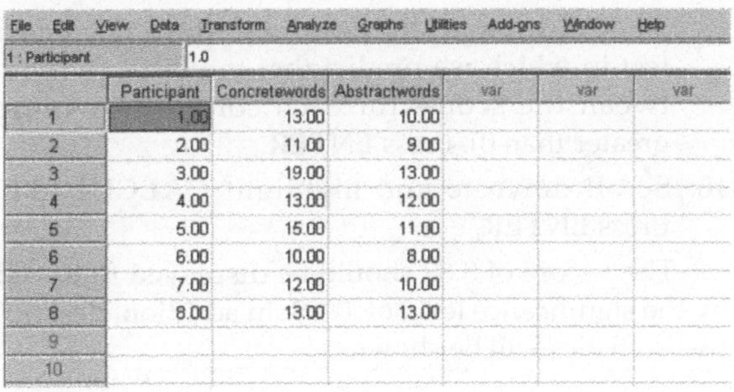

	Participant	Concretewords	Abstractwords
1	1.00	13.00	10.00
2	2.00	11.00	9.00
3	3.00	19.00	13.00
4	4.00	13.00	12.00
5	5.00	15.00	11.00
6	6.00	10.00	8.00
7	7.00	12.00	10.00
8	8.00	13.00	13.00

Next, we click on the **Analyze** tab followed by the **Compare Means** tab and then **Paired-Samples T Test** as follows.

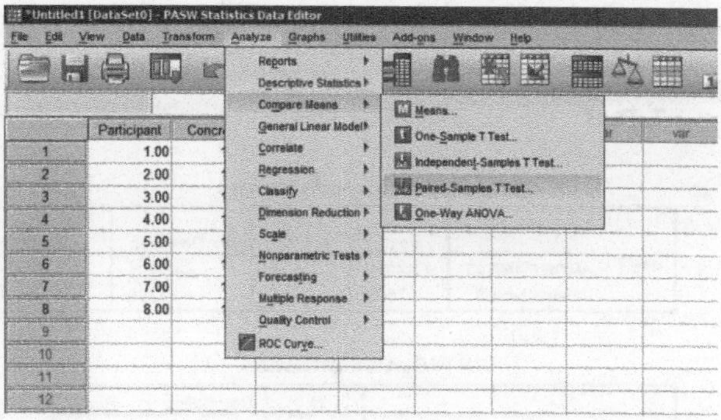

These actions will produce the following dialog box.

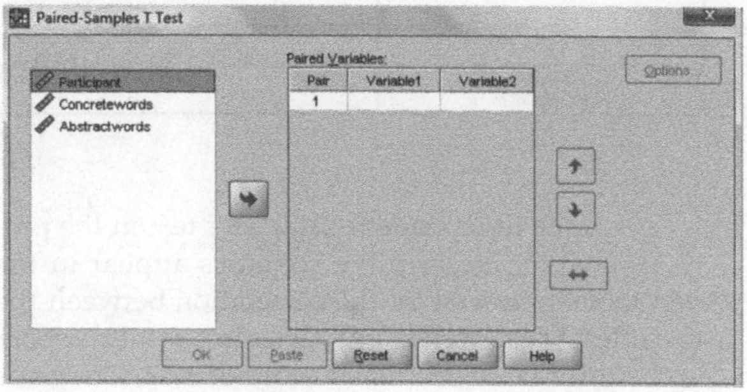

Highlight the **Concretewords** variable and then click the arrow button in the middle of the screen. The Concretewords variable should now appear under **Variable1** in the box to the right of the window. Do the same for the **Abstractwords** variable, and it should appear under **Variable2** in the box on the right. The dialog box should now appear as follows.

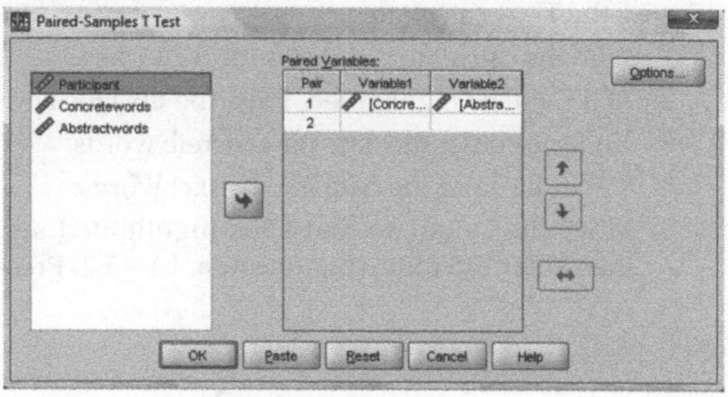

Click **OK**, and the output will appear in an output window as below.

T-Test

Paired Samples Statistics

		Mean	N	Std. Deviation	Std. Error Mean
Pair 1	Concretewords	13.2500	8	2.76457	.97742
	Abstractwords	10.7500	8	1.83225	.64780

Paired Samples Correlations

		N	Correlation	Sig.
Pair 1	Concretewords & Abstractwords	8	.747	.033

Paired Samples Test

		Paired Differences					t	df	Sig. (2-tailed)
					95% Confidence Interval of the Difference				
		Mean	Std. Deviation	Std. Error Mean	Lower	Upper			
Pair 1	Concretewords - Abstractwords	2.50000	1.85164	.65465	.95199	4.04801	3.819	7	.007

As in the independent-samples t test in the previous chapter, descriptive statistics appear in the first table, followed by the correlation between the variables. The correlated-groups t test results appear in the third table with the t score of 3.82, 7 degrees of freedom, and the two-tailed significance level. Because this was a one-tailed test, we can find the significance level for this one-tailed t test by dividing the two-tailed significant level in half. Thus, for this problem $t\ (7) = 3.82$, $p = .0035$ (one-tailed). As in the previous t test in Chapter 9, the 95% confidence interval is also reported.

Using the TI-84

Let's use the data from Table 10.2 to conduct the test using the TI-84 calculator:

1. With the calculator on, press the **STAT** key.
2. **EDIT** will be highlighted. Press the **ENTER** key.
3. Under **L1** enter the data for concrete words.
4. Under **L2** enter the data for abstract words.
5. Move the cursor so that **L3** is highlighted and then enter the following formula: L1 – L2. Press **ENTER** (to enter **L1** press the 2nd key followed by the **1** key and then to produce **L2**, press the 2nd key followed by the **2** key). This will produce a list of difference scores (the concrete-word scores minus the abstract-word scores) for each participant.
6. Press the **STAT** key once again and highlight **TESTS**.
7. Scroll down to **T-Test**. Press the **ENTER** key.
8. Highlight **DATA**. Enter 0 next to μ_0. Enter **L3** next to **List** (by pressing the 2nd key followed by the **3** key).
9. Scroll down to μ: and select $> \mu_0$ (for a one-tailed test in which we predict that the difference between the scores for each condition will be greater than 0). Press **ENTER**.
10. Scroll down to and highlight **CALCULATE**. Press **ENTER**.

The t score of 3.82 should be displayed followed by the significance level of .0033. In addition, descriptive statistics will be shown.

CHAPTER

11 Experimental Design and Analysis III: Designs with More Than Two Levels of an Independent Variable

Learning Objectives

- Explain the additional information that can be gained by using designs with more than two levels of an independent variable.
- Explain what a one-way randomized ANOVA is and what it does.
- Use the formulas provided to calculate a one-way randomized ANOVA.
- Interpret the results from a one-way randomized ANOVA.
- Calculate Tukey's post hoc test for a one-way randomized ANOVA.
- Identify what a one-way repeated measures ANOVA is and what it does.
- Use the formulas provided to calculate a one-way repeated measures ANOVA.
- Interpret the results from a one-way repeated measures ANOVA.
- Calculate Tukey's post hoc test for a one-way repeated measures ANOVA.

The experiments described in Chapter 9 involved manipulating one independent variable with only two levels—either a control group and an experimental group or two experimental groups. In this chapter, we will discuss experimental designs that involve one independent variable with more than two levels. Examining more levels of an independent variable allows us to address more complicated and interesting questions. Often experiments begin as two-group designs and then develop into more complex designs as the questions asked become more elaborate and sophisticated. The same design principles presented in Chapter 9 also apply to these more complex designs; that is, we still need to be concerned about control, internal validity, and external validity.

Using Designs with More Than Two Levels of an Independent Variable

Researchers may decide to use a design with more than two levels of an independent variable for three reasons. First, it allows them to compare multiple treatments. Second, it enables them to compare multiple treatments with no treatment (the control group). Third, more complex designs allow researchers to compare a placebo group with control and experimental groups (Mitchell & Jolley, 2004).

Comparing More Than Two Kinds of Treatment in One Study

To illustrate this advantage of more complex experimental designs, imagine that we want to compare the effects of various types of rehearsal on memory. We have subjects study a list of 10 words using either rote rehearsal (repetition) or some form of elaborative rehearsal. In addition, we specify the type of elaborative rehearsal to be used in the different experimental groups. Group 1 (the control group) uses rote rehearsal, group 2 uses an imagery mnemonic technique, and group 3 uses a story mnemonic device. You may be wondering why we don't simply conduct three studies or comparisons. Why don't we compare group 1 to group 2, group 2 to group 3, and group 1 to group 3 in three different experiments? There are several reasons this is not recommended.

You may remember from Chapter 10 that a *t* test is used to compare performance between two groups. If we do three experiments, we need to use three *t* tests to determine these differences. The problem is that using multiple tests inflates the Type I error rate. Remember, a Type I error means that we reject the null hypothesis when we should have failed to reject it; that is, we claim that the independent variable has an effect when it does not. For most statistical tests, we use the .05 alpha (α) level, meaning that we are willing to accept a 5% risk of making a Type I error. Although the chance of making a Type I error on one *t* test is .05, the overall chance of making a Type I error increases as more tests are conducted.

Imagine that we conducted three *t* tests or comparisons among the three groups in the memory experiment. The probability of a Type I error on any single comparison is .05. The probability of a Type I error on at least one of the three tests, however, is considerably higher. To determine the chance of a Type I error when making multiple comparisons, we use the formula $1 - (1 - \alpha)^c$, where α refers to the acceptable probability of a Type I error (.05) and *c* equals the number of comparisons performed. Using this formula for the present example, we get the following:

$$1 - (1 - .05)^3 = 1 - (.95)^3 = 1 - .86 = .14$$

Thus, the probability of a Type I error on at least one of the three tests is .14, or 14%.

Bonferroni adjustment Setting a more stringent alpha level for multiple tests to minimize Type I errors.

One way of counteracting the increased chance of a Type I error is to use a more stringent alpha level. The **Bonferroni adjustment**, in which the desired alpha level is divided by the number of tests or comparisons, is typically used to accomplish this. For example, if we were using the *t* test to make the three comparisons described previously, we would divide .05 by 3 and get .017. By not accepting the result as significant unless the alpha level is .017 or less, we minimize the chance of a Type I error when making multiple comparisons. We know from discussions in previous chapters, however, that although using a more stringent alpha level decreases the chance of a Type I error, it increases the chance of a Type II error (failing to reject the null hypothesis when it should have been rejected—missing an effect of an independent variable). Thus, the Bonferroni adjustment is not the best method of handling the problem. A better method is to use a single statistical test that compares all groups rather than using multiple comparisons and statistical tests. Luckily for us, there is a statistical technique that will do this—the analysis of variance (ANOVA), which will be discussed shortly.

Another advantage of comparing more than two kinds of treatment in one experiment is that it reduces both the number of experiments conducted and the number of participants needed. Once again, refer to the three-group memory experiment. If we do one comparison with three groups, we can conduct only one experiment, and we need subjects for only three groups. If, however, we conduct three comparisons, each with two groups, then we need to perform three experiments, and we need subjects for six groups or conditions.

Comparing Two or More Kinds of Treatment with the Control Group (No Treatment)

Using more than two groups in an experiment also allows researchers to determine whether each treatment is more or less effective than no treatment (the control group). To illustrate this, imagine that we are interested in the effects of aerobic exercise on anxiety. We hypothesize that the more aerobic activity one engages in, the more anxiety will be reduced. We use a control group that does not engage in any aerobic activity and a high aerobic activity group that engages in 50 minutes per day of aerobic activity—a simple two-group design. Assume, however, that when using this design, we find that both those in the control group and those in the experimental group have high levels of anxiety at the end of the study—not what we expected to find. How could a design with more than two groups provide more information? Suppose we add another group to this study—a moderate aerobic activity group (25 minutes per day)—and get the following results:

Control group	High anxiety
Moderate aerobic activity	Low anxiety
High aerobic activity	High anxiety

Based on these data, we have a V-shaped function. Up to a certain point, aerobic activity reduces anxiety. However, when the aerobic activity exceeds a certain level, anxiety increases again. If we had conducted the original study with only two groups, we would have missed this relationship and erroneously concluded that there was no relationship between aerobic activity and anxiety. Using a design with multiple groups allows us to see more of the relationship between the variables.

Figure 11.1 illustrates the difference between the results obtained with the three-group and the two-group design in this hypothetical study. It also shows the other two-group comparisons—control compared to moderate aerobic activity and moderate aerobic activity compared to high aerobic activity. This set of graphs illustrates how two-group designs limit our ability to see the complete relationship between variables.

Figure 11.1a shows clearly how the three-group design allows us to assess more fully the relationship between the variables. If we had conducted only a two-group study, such as those illustrated in Figure 11.1b, c, or d, we would have drawn a much different conclusion than that drawn from the

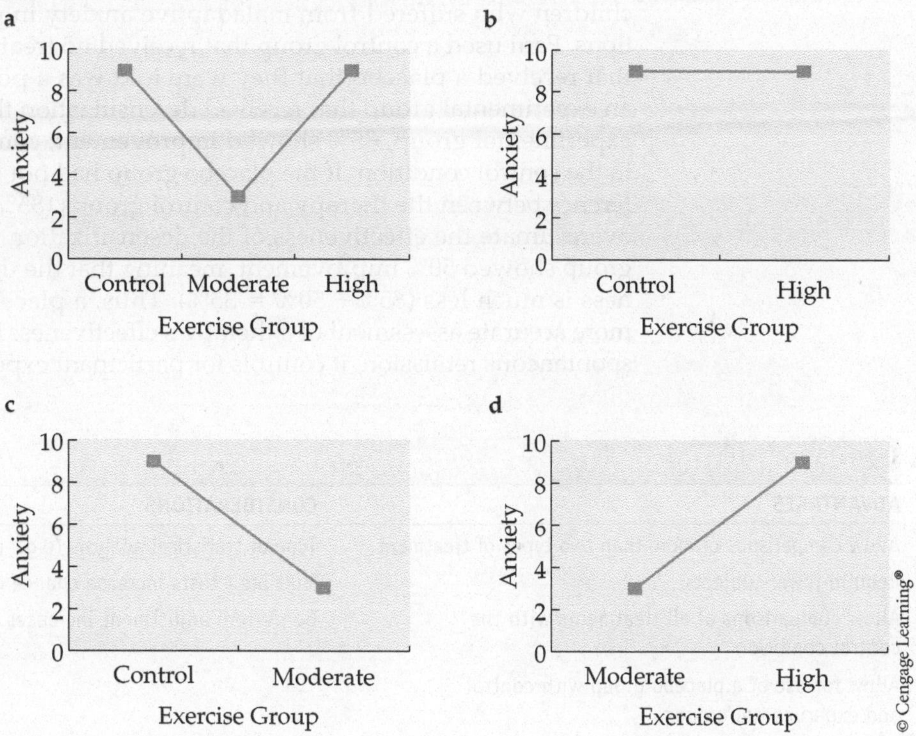

FIGURE 11.1 Determining relationships with three-group versus two-group designs: (a) three-group design; (b) two-group comparison of control to high aerobic activity; (c) two-group comparison of control to moderate aerobic activity; (d) two-group comparison of moderate aerobic activity to high aerobic activity

three-group design. Comparing only the control to the high aerobic activity group (Figure 11.1b) would have led us to conclude that aerobic activity does not affect anxiety. Comparing only the control and the moderate aerobic activity group (Figure 11.1c) would have led to the conclusion that increasing aerobic activity reduces anxiety. Comparing only the moderate aerobic activity group and the high aerobic activity group (Figure 11.1d) would have led to the conclusion that increasing aerobic activity increases anxiety.

Being able to assess the relationship between the variables means that we can determine the type of relationship that exists. In the preceding example, the variables produced a V-shaped function. Other variables may be related in a straight linear manner or in an alternative curvilinear manner (for example, a J-shaped or S-shaped function). In summary, adding levels to the independent variable allows us to determine more accurately the type of relationship that exists between the variables.

Comparing a Placebo Group with the Control and Experimental Groups

A final advantage of designs with more than two groups is that they allow for the use of a *placebo group*. How can adding a placebo group improve an experiment? Consider an often-cited study by Paul (1966, 1967) involving children who suffered from maladaptive anxiety in public speaking situations. Paul used a control group that received no treatment; a placebo group that received a placebo that they were told was a potent tranquilizer; and an experimental group that received desensitization therapy. Of those in the experimental group, 85% showed improvement, compared with only 22% in the control condition. If the placebo group had not been included, the difference between the therapy and control groups (85% − 22% = 63%) would overestimate the effectiveness of the desensitization program. The placebo group showed 50% improvement, meaning that the therapy's true effectiveness is much less (85% − 50% = 35%). Thus, a placebo group allows for a more accurate assessment of a therapy's effectiveness because, in addition to spontaneous remission, it controls for participant expectation effects.

Designs with More Than Two Levels of an Independent Variable — IN REVIEW

ADVANTAGES	CONSIDERATIONS
Allow comparisons of more than two types of treatment	Type of statistical analysis (e.g., multiple *t* tests or ANOVA)
Require fewer subjects	Multiple *t* tests increase chance of Type I error
Allow comparisons of all treatments with the control condition	Bonferroni adjustment increases chance of Type II error
Allow for use of a placebo group with control and experimental groups	

CRITICAL THINKING CHECK 11.1

1. Imagine that a researcher wants to compare four different types of treatment. The researcher decides to conduct six individual studies to make these comparisons. What is the probability of a Type I error, with alpha = .05, across these six comparisons? Use the Bonferroni adjustment to determine the suggested alpha level for these six tests.

Analyzing the Multiple-Group Experiment Using Parametric Statistics

ANOVA (analysis of variance) An inferential statistical test for comparing the means of three or more groups.

As noted previously, *t* tests are not recommended for comparing performance across groups in a multiple-group design because of the increased probability of a Type I error. For multiple-group designs in which interval-ratio data are collected, the recommended statistical analysis is the **ANOVA (analysis of variance)**—an inferential parametric statistical test for comparing the means of three or more groups. As its name indicates, this procedure allows us to analyze the variance in a study. You should be familiar with variance from Chapter 5 on descriptive statistics. Nonparametric analyses are also available for designs in which ordinal data are collected (the Kruskal–Wallis analysis of variance) and for designs in which nominal data are collected (the chi-square test).

Between-Subjects Designs: One-Way Randomized ANOVA

We will begin our coverage of statistics appropriate for multiple-group designs by discussing those used with data collected from a between-subjects design. Recall that a between-subjects design is one in which different participants serve in each condition. Imagine that we conducted the experiment mentioned at the beginning of the chapter in which subjects are asked to study a list of 10 words using rote rehearsal or one of two forms of elaborative rehearsal. A total of 24 subjects are randomly assigned, 8 to each condition. Table 11.1 lists the number of words correctly recalled by each participant.

one-way randomized ANOVA An inferential statistical test for comparing the means of three or more groups using a between-subjects design and one independent variable.

Because these data represent an interval-ratio scale of measurement and because there are more than two groups, an ANOVA is the appropriate statistical test to analyze the data. In addition, because this is a between-subjects design, we use a **one-way randomized ANOVA.** The term *randomized* indicates that participants are randomly assigned to conditions in a between-subjects design. The term *one-way* indicates that the design uses only one independent variable—in this case, type of rehearsal. We will discuss statistical tests appropriate for correlated-groups designs later in this chapter and tests appropriate for designs with more than one independent variable in Chapter 12. Note that although all of the studies used to illustrate the ANOVA procedure in this chapter have an equal number of subjects in each condition, this is not necessary to the procedure.

TABLE 11.1 Numbers of Words Recalled Correctly in Rote Rehearsal, Imagery, and Story Conditions

ROTE REHEARSAL	IMAGERY	STORY	
2	4	6	
4	5	5	
3	7	9	
5	6	10	
2	5	8	
7	4	7	
6	8	10	
3	5	9	
$\bar{X} = 4$	$\bar{X} = 5.5$	$\bar{X} = 8$	Grand mean = 5.833

One-Way Randomized ANOVA: What It Is and What It Does. The ANOVA is a parametric inferential statistical test for comparing the means of three or more groups. In addition to helping maintain an acceptable Type I error rate, the ANOVA has the advantage over using multiple *t* tests of being more powerful and thus less susceptible to a Type II error. In this section, we will discuss the simplest use of ANOVA—a design with one independent variable with three levels.

Let's continue to use the experiment and data presented in Table 11.1. Remember that we are interested in the effects of rehearsal type on memory. The null hypothesis (H_0) for an ANOVA is that the sample means represent the same population (H_0: $\mu_1 = \mu_2 = \mu_3$). The alternative hypothesis (H_a) is that they represent different populations (H_a: at least one $\mu \neq$ another μ). When a researcher rejects H_0 using an ANOVA, it means that the independent variable affected the dependent variable to the extent that at least one group mean differs from the others by more than would be expected based on chance. Failing to reject H_0 indicates that the means do not differ from each other more than would be expected based on chance. In other words, there is not enough evidence to suggest that the sample means represent at least two different populations.

In our example, the mean number of words recalled in the rote rehearsal condition is 4, for the imagery condition it is 5.5, and in the story condition it is 8. If you look at the data from each condition, you will notice that most participants in each condition did not score exactly at the mean for that condition. In other words, there is variability within each condition. The **grand mean**—the mean performance across all subjects in all conditions—is 5.833. Because none of the participants in any condition recalled exactly 5.833 words, there is also variability between conditions. We are interested in whether this variability is due primarily to the independent variable (differences in rehearsal type) or to **error variance**—the amount of variability among the scores caused by chance or uncontrolled variables (such as individual differences between subjects).

grand mean The mean performance across all participants in a study.

error variance The amount of variability among the scores caused by chance or uncontrolled variables.

The error variance can be estimated by looking at the amount of variability *within* each condition. How will this give us an estimate of error variance? Each participant in each condition was treated similarly; each was instructed to rehearse the words in the same manner. Because the participants in each condition were treated in the same manner, any differences observed in the number of words recalled are attributable only to error variance. In other words, some subjects may have been more motivated, or more distracted, or better at memory tasks—all factors that would contribute to error variance in this case. Therefore, the **within-groups variance** (the variance within each condition or group) is an estimate of the population error variance.

within-groups variance The variance within each condition; an estimate of the population error variance.

Now we can compare the means between the groups. If the independent variable (rehearsal type) had an effect, we would expect some of the group means to differ from the grand mean. If the independent variable had no effect on the number of words recalled, we would only expect the group means to vary from the grand mean slightly, as a result of error variance attributable to individual differences. In other words, all subjects in a study will not score exactly the same. Therefore, even when the independent variable has no effect, we do not expect that the group means will exactly equal the grand mean, but they should be very close to the grand mean. If there were no effect of the independent variable, then any variance between groups would be due to error.

Between-groups variance may be attributed to several sources. There could be systematic differences between the groups, referred to as *systematic variance*. The systematic variance between the groups could be due to the effects of the independent variable (variance due to the experimental manipulation). However, it could also be due to the influence of uncontrolled confounding variables (variance due to extraneous variables). In addition, there is always some error variance in any between-groups variance estimate. In sum, **between-groups variance** is an estimate of systematic variance (the effect of the independent variable and any confounds) *and* error variance.

between-groups variance An estimate of the effect of the independent variable and error variance.

***F*-ratio** The ratio of between-groups variance to within-groups variance.

By looking at the ratio of between-groups variance to within-groups variance, known as the ***F*-ratio**, we can determine whether most of the variability is attributable to systematic variance (hopefully due to the independent variable and not to confounds) or to chance and random factors (error variance):

$$F = \frac{\text{Between-groups variance}}{\text{Within-groups variance}} = \frac{\text{Systematic variance} + \text{Error variance}}{\text{Error variance}}$$

Looking at the *F*-ratio, we can see that if the systematic variance (which we assume is due to the effect of the independent variable) is substantially greater than the error variance, the ratio will be substantially greater than 1. If there is no systematic variance, then the ratio will be approximately 1 (error variance divided by error variance). There are two points to remember regarding *F*-ratios. First, for an *F*-ratio to be significant (show a statistically meaningful effect of an independent variable), it must be substantially greater than 1 (we will discuss exactly how much greater than 1 later in the chapter). Second, if an *F*-ratio is approximately 1, then the between-groups variance equals the within-groups variance and there is no effect of the independent variable.

Refer to Table 11.1, and think about the within-groups versus between-groups variance in this study. Notice that the amount of variance within the groups is small—the scores within each group vary from each individual group mean, but not by very much. The between-groups variance, on the other hand, is large—the scores across the three conditions vary to a greater extent. With these data, then, it appears that we have a relatively large between-groups variance and a smaller within-groups variance. Our *F*-ratio will therefore be greater than 1. To assess how large it is, we will need to conduct the appropriate calculations (described in the next section). At this point, however, you should have a general understanding of how an

ANOVA analyzes variance to determine whether the independent variable has an effect.

CRITICAL THINKING CHECK 11.2

1. Imagine that the following data are from the study just described (the effect of types of rehearsal on number of words recalled). Do you think that the between-groups and within-groups variances are large, moderate, or small? Will the corresponding *F*-ratio be greater than, equal to, or less than 1?

Rote Rehearsal	*Imagery*	*Story*	
2	4	5	
4	2	2	
3	5	4	
5	3	2	
2	2	3	
7	7	6	
6	6	3	
3	2	7	
$\overline{X} = 4$	$\overline{X} = 3.88$	$\overline{X} = 4$	Grand mean = 3.96

Calculations for the One-Way Randomized ANOVA. To see exactly how ANOVA works, we begin by calculating the sums of squares (*SS*). This should sound somewhat familiar to you because we calculated sums of squares as part of the calculation for standard deviation in Chapter 5. The sums of squares in that formula represented the sum of the squared deviations of each score from the overall mean. Determining the sums of squares is the first step in calculating the various types or sources of variance in an ANOVA.

Several types of sums of squares are used in the calculation of an ANOVA. This section includes *definitional formulas* for each. The definitional formula follows the definition for each sum of squares and should give you the basic idea of how each *SS* is calculated. When we are dealing with very large data sets, however, the definitional formulas can become somewhat cumbersome. Thus, statisticians have transformed the definitional formulas into *computational formulas*. A computational formula is easier to use in terms of the number of steps required. However, computational formulas do not follow the definition of the *SS* and thus do not necessarily make sense in terms of the definition of each *SS*. If your instructor prefers that you use the computational formulas, they are provided in Appendix B.

total sum of squares The sum of the squared deviations of each score from the grand mean.

The first sum of squares that we need to describe is the **total sum of squares** (SS_{Total})—the sum of the squared deviations of each score from the grand mean. In a definitional formula, this is represented as $\Sigma(X - \overline{X}_G)^2$, where X represents each individual score and $\overline{X}_G$ is the grand mean. In other words, we determine how much each individual participant varies from the grand mean, square that deviation score, and sum all of the squared deviation scores. For our study on the effects of rehearsal type on memory, the total sum of squares (SS_{Total}) = 127.32. To see where this number comes from, see Table 11.2. (For the computational formula, see Appendix B.) After we have calculated the sum of squares within and between groups, they should equal the total sum of squares when added together. In this way, we can check our calculations for accuracy. If the sums of squares within and between do not equal the sum of squares total, then you know that there is an error in at least one of the calculations.

within-groups sum of squares The sum of the squared deviations of each score from its group mean.

Because an ANOVA analyzes the variances between groups and within groups, we need to use different formulas to determine the variance attributable to these two factors. The **within-groups sum of squares** is the sum of the squared deviations of each score from its group or condition mean and is a reflection of the amount of error variance. In the definitional formula, it is $\Sigma(X - \overline{X}_g)^2$, where X refers to each individual score, and $\overline{X}_g$ is the mean for each group or condition. To determine this, we find the difference between each score and its group mean, square these deviation scores, and then sum all of the squared deviation scores. The use of this definitional formula to calculate SS_{Within} is illustrated in Table 11.3. The computational formula appears in Appendix B. Thus, rather than comparing every score in the entire study to the grand mean of the study (as is done for SS_{Total}), we compare each score in each condition to the mean of that condition.

TABLE 11.2 Calculation of SS_{Total} Using the Definitional Formula

ROTE REHEARSAL		IMAGERY		STORY	
X	$(X - \bar{X}_G)^2$	X	$(X - \bar{X}_G)^2$	X	$(X - \bar{X}_G)^2$
2	14.69	4	3.36	6	0.03
4	3.36	5	0.69	5	0.69
3	8.03	7	1.36	9	10.03
5	0.69	6	0.03	10	17.36
2	14.69	5	0.69	8	4.70
7	1.36	4	3.36	7	1.36
6	0.03	8	4.70	10	17.36
3	8.03	5	0.69	9	10.03
	$\Sigma = 50.88$		$\Sigma = 14.88$		$\Sigma = 61.56$

$SS_{Total} = 50.88 + 14.88 + 61.56 = 127.32$

NOTE: All numbers have been rounded to two decimal places.

Thus, SS_{Within} is a reflection of the amount of variability within each condition. Because the participants within each condition were treated in a similar manner, we would expect little variation among the scores within each group. This means that the within-groups sum of squares (SS_{Within}) should be small, indicating a small amount of error variance in the study. For our memory study, the within-groups sum of squares (SS_{Within}) is 62.

TABLE 11.3 Calculation of SS_{Within} Using the Definitional Formula

ROTE REHEARSAL		IMAGERY		STORY	
X	$(X - \bar{X}_g)^2$	X	$(X - \bar{X}_g)^2$	X	$(X - \bar{X}_g)^2$
2	4	4	2.25	6	4
4	0	5	0.25	5	9
3	1	7	2.25	9	1
5	1	6	0.25	10	4
2	4	5	0.25	8	0
7	9	4	2.25	7	1
6	4	8	6.25	10	4
3	1	5	0.25	9	1
	$\Sigma = 24$		$\Sigma = 14$		$\Sigma = 24$

$SS_{Within} = 24 + 14 + 24 = 62$

NOTE: All numbers have been rounded to two decimal places.

TABLE 11.4 Calculation of $SS_{Between}$ Using the Definitional Formula

Rote Rehearsal
$(\bar{X}_g - \bar{X}_G)^2 n = (4 - 5.833)^2 8 = (-1.833)^2 8 = (3.36)8 = 26.88$
Imagery
$(\bar{X}_g - \bar{X}_G)^2 n = (5.5 - 5.833)^2 8 = (-0.333)^2 8 = (0.11)8 = 0.88$
Story
$(\bar{X}_g - \bar{X}_G)^2 n = (8 - 5.833)^2 8 = (-2.167)^2 8 = (4.696)8 = 37.57$
$SS_{Between} = 26.88 + 0.88 + 37.57 = 65.33$

between-groups sum of squares The sum of the squared deviations of each group's mean from the grand mean, multiplied by the number of subjects in each group.

The **between-groups sum of squares** is the sum of the squared deviations of each group's mean from the grand mean, multiplied by the number of participants in each group. In the definitional formula, this is $\Sigma[(\bar{X}_g - \bar{X}_G)^2 n]$, where $\bar{X}_g$ is the mean for each group, $\bar{X}_G$ is the grand mean, and n is the number of subjects in each group. The use of the definitional formula to calculate $SS_{Between}$ is illustrated in Table 11.4. The computational formula appears in Appendix B. The between-groups variance is an indication of the systematic variance across the groups (the variance due to the independent variable and any confounds) and error. The basic idea behind the between-groups sum of squares is that if the independent variable had no effect (if there were no differences between the groups), then we would expect all the group means to be about the same. If all the group means were similar, they would also be approximately equal to the grand mean, and there would be little variance across conditions. If, however, the independent variable caused changes in the means of some conditions (caused them to be larger or smaller than other conditions), then the condition means would not only differ from each other but would also differ from the grand mean, indicating variance across conditions. In our memory study, $SS_{Between} = 65.33$.

We can check the accuracy of our calculations by adding SS_{Within} and $SS_{Between}$. When summed, these numbers should equal SS_{Total}. Thus, SS_{Within} (62) + $SS_{Between}$ (65.33) = 127.33. The SS_{Total} that we calculated earlier was 127.32 and is essentially equal to $SS_{Within} + SS_{Between}$, taking into account rounding decimals to two places.

mean square An estimate of either variance between groups or variance within groups.

Calculating the sums of squares is an important step in the ANOVA. It is not, however, the end. Now that we have determined SS_{Total}, SS_{Within}, and $SS_{Between}$, we must transform these scores into the mean squares. The term **mean square** (*MS*) is an abbreviation of mean squared deviation scores. The *MS* scores are estimates of variance between and within the groups. To calculate the *MS* for each group (MS_{Within} and $MS_{Between}$), we divide each *SS* by the appropriate *df* (degrees of freedom). The reason for this is that the *MS* scores are variance estimates. You may remember from Chapter 5 that when calculating standard deviation and variance, we divide the sum of squares by *N* (or *N* – 1 for the unbiased estimator) to get the average deviation from the mean. In this same manner, we must divide the *SS* scores by their degrees of freedom (the number of scores that contributed to each *SS* minus 1).

In the present example, we first need to determine the degrees of freedom for each type of variance. Let's begin with df_{Total}, which we will use to check our accuracy when calculating df_{Within} and df_{Between}. In other words, df_{Within} and df_{Between} should sum to df_{Total}. We determined SS_{Total} by calculating the deviations around the grand mean. We therefore had one restriction on our data—the grand mean. This leaves us with $N - 1$ total degrees of freedom (the total number of subjects in the study minus the one restriction). For our study on the effects of rehearsal type on memory,

$$df_{\text{Total}} = 24 - 1 = 23$$

If we use a similar logic, the degrees of freedom within each group would then be $n - 1$ (the number of participants in each condition minus 1). However, we have more than one group: We have *k* groups, where *k* refers to the number of groups or conditions in the study. The degrees of freedom within groups is therefore $k(n - 1)$ or $(N - k)$. For our example,

$$df_{\text{Within}} = 24 - 3 = 21$$

Last, the degrees of freedom between groups is the variability of *k* means around the grand mean. Therefore, df_{Between} equals the number of groups (*k*) minus 1 ($k - 1$). For our study, this is

$$df_{\text{Between}} = 3 - 1 = 2$$

Notice that the sum of df_{Within} and df_{Between} is df_{Total}: $21 + 2 = 23$. This allows us to check our calculations for accuracy. If the degrees of freedom between and within do not sum to the degrees of freedom total, we know there is a mistake somewhere.

Now that we have calculated the sums of squares and their degrees of freedom, we can use these numbers to calculate estimates of the variance between and within groups. As stated previously, the variance estimates are called mean squares and are determined by dividing each *SS* by its corresponding *df*. In our example,

$$MS_{\text{Between}} = \frac{SS_{\text{Between}}}{df_{\text{Between}}} = \frac{65.33}{2} = 32.67$$

$$MS_{\text{Within}} = \frac{SS_{\text{Within}}}{df_{\text{Within}}} = \frac{62}{21} = 2.95$$

We can now use the estimates of between-groups and within-groups variances to determine the *F*-ratio:

$$F = \frac{MS_{\text{Between}}}{MS_{\text{Within}}} = \frac{32.67}{2.95} = 11.07$$

The definitional formulas for the sums of squares along with the formulas for the degrees of freedom, mean squares, and the final *F*-ratio are

TABLE 11.5 ANOVA Summary Table: Definitional Formulas

SOURCE	*df*	*SS*	*MS*	*F*
Between groups	$k - 1$	$\Sigma[(\bar{X}_g - \bar{X}_G)^2 n]$	$\frac{SS_{Between}}{df_{Between}}$	$\frac{MS_{Between}}{MS_{Within}}$
Within groups	$N - k$	$\Sigma(X - \bar{X}_g)^2$	$\frac{SS_{Within}}{df_{Within}}$	
Total	$N - 1$	$\Sigma(X - \bar{X}_G)^2$		

summarized in Table 11.5. The ANOVA summary table for the *F*-ratio just calculated is presented in Table 11.6. This is a common format for summarizing ANOVA findings. You may see ANOVA summary tables in journal articles because they are a concise way of presenting the results from an analysis of variance.

Interpreting the One-Way Randomized ANOVA. Our obtained *F*-ratio of 11.07 is obviously greater than 1.00. However, we do not know whether it is large enough to let us reject the null hypothesis. To make this decision, we need to compare the obtained F (F_{obt}) of 11.07 with the F_{cv}—the critical value that determines the cutoff for statistical significance. The underlying *F* distribution is actually a family of distributions, each based on the degrees of freedom between and within each group. Remember that the alternative hypothesis is that the population means represented by the sample means are not from the same population. Table A.5 in Appendix A provides the critical values for the family of *F* distributions when $\alpha = .05$ and when $\alpha = .01$. To use the table, look at the df_{Within} running down the left-hand side of the table and the $df_{Between}$ running across the top of the table. F_{cv} is found where the row and column of these two numbers intersect. For our example, $df_{Within} = 21$ and $df_{Between} = 2$. Because there is no 21 in the df_{Within} column, we use the next lower number, 20. According to Table A.5, F_{cv} for the .05 level is 3.49. Because our F_{obt} exceeds this, it is statistically significant at the .05 level. Let's check the .01 level also. The critical value for the .01 level is 5.85. Our F_{obt} is greater than this critical value also. We can therefore conclude that F_{obt} is significant at the .01 level. In APA publication format, this is written as $F(2, 21) = 11.07, p < .01$. This means that we reject H_0 and support H_a. In other words, at least one group mean differs significantly from the others. The calculation

TABLE 11.6 ANOVA Summary Table for the Memory Study

SOURCE	*df*	*SS*	*MS*	*F*
Between groups	2	65.33	32.67	11.07
Within groups	21	62	2.95	
Total	23	127.33		

of this ANOVA using Excel, SPSS, and the TI-84 calculator is presented in the Statistical Software Resources section at the end of the chapter.

Let's consider what factors might affect the size of the final F_{obt}. Because F_{obt} is derived using the between-groups variance as the numerator and the within-groups variance as the denominator, anything that increases the numerator or decreases the denominator will increase F_{obt}. What might increase the numerator? Using stronger controls in the experiment could have this effect because it would make any differences between the groups more noticeable or larger. This means that $MS_{Between}$ (the numerator in the *F*-ratio) would be larger and therefore lead to a larger final *F*-ratio.

What would decrease the denominator? Once again, using better control to reduce the overall error variance would have this effect and so would increasing the sample size, which increases df_{Within} and ultimately decreases MS_{Within}. Why would each of these affect the *F*-ratio in this manner? Each would decrease the size of MS_{Within}, which is the denominator in the *F*-ratio. Dividing by a smaller number would lead to a larger final *F*-ratio and, therefore, a greater chance that it would be significant.

Graphing the Means and Effect Size. As noted in Chapter 10, we usually graph the means when we find a significant difference between them. As in our previous graphs, the independent variable is placed on the *x*-axis and the dependent variable on the *y*-axis. A bar graph representing the mean performance of each group is shown in Figure 11.2. In this experiment, those in the rote rehearsal condition remembered an average of 4 words, those in the imagery condition remembered an average of 5.5 words, and those in the story condition remembered an average of 8 words.

In addition to graphing the data, we should assess effect size. Based on F_{obt}, we know that there was more variability between groups than within groups. In other words, the between-groups variance (the numerator in the *F*-ratio) was larger than the within-groups variance (the denominator in the *F*-ratio). However, it would be useful to know how much of the variability in the dependent variable can be attributed to the independent variable.

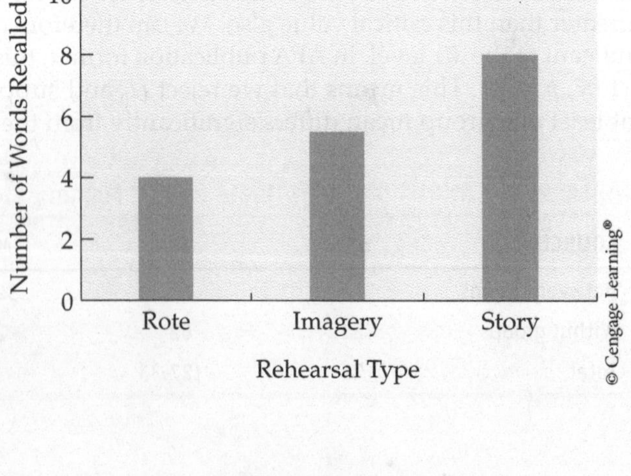

FIGURE 11.2 Number of words recalled as a function of rehearsal type

eta-squared (η^2) An inferential statistic for measuring effect size with an ANOVA.

In other words, it would be useful to have a measure of effect size. For an ANOVA, effect size can be estimated using **eta-squared** (η^2), which is calculated as follows:

$$\eta^2 = \frac{SS_{\text{Between}}}{SS_{\text{Total}}}$$

Because SS_{Between} reflects the differences between the means from the various levels of an independent variable and SS_{Total} reflects the total differences between all scores in the experiment, η^2 reflects the proportion of the total differences in the scores that is associated with differences between sample means, or how much of the variability in the dependent variable (memory) is attributable to the manipulation of the independent variable (rehearsal type).

Referring to the summary for our example in Table 11.6, we see that η^2 is calculated as follows:

$$\eta^2 = \frac{65.33}{127.33} = .51$$

In other words, approximately 51% of the variance among the scores can be attributed to the rehearsal condition to which the participant was assigned. In this example, the independent variable of rehearsal type is fairly important in determining the number of words recalled by subjects because the η^2 of 51% represents a considerable effect.

Assumptions of the One-Way Randomized ANOVA. As with most statistical tests, certain conditions must be met to ensure that the statistic is being used properly. The assumptions for the one-way randomized ANOVA are similar to those for the *t* test for independent groups:

- The data are on an interval-ratio scale.
- The underlying distribution is normally distributed.
- The variances among the populations being compared are homogeneous.
- The observations are all independent of one another.

Because the ANOVA is a robust statistical test, violations of some of these assumptions do not necessarily affect the results. Specifically, if the distributions are slightly skewed rather than normally distributed, this skewed data will not affect the results of the ANOVA. In addition, if the sample sizes are equal, the assumption of homogeneity of variances can be violated. However, it is not acceptable to violate the assumption of interval-ratio data. If the data collected in a study are ordinal or nominal in scale, other nonparametric statistical procedures must be used. These procedures will be discussed in Chapter 14.

Tukey's Post Hoc Test. Because the results from our ANOVA indicate that at least one of the sample means differs significantly from the others

post hoc test When used with an ANOVA, a means of comparing all possible pairs of groups to determine which ones differ significantly from each other.

Tukey's honestly significant difference (HSD) A post hoc test used with ANOVA for making all pairwise comparisons when conditions have equal n's.

(represents a different population from the others), we must now compute a post hoc test (a test conducted after the fact—in this case, after the ANOVA). A **post hoc test** involves comparing each of the groups in the study with each of the other groups to determine which ones differ significantly from each other. This may sound familiar to you. In fact, you may be thinking, isn't that what a t test does? In a sense, you are correct. However, remember that a series of multiple t tests inflates the probability of a Type I error. A post hoc test is designed to permit multiple comparisons and still maintain alpha (the probability of a Type I error) at .05.

The post hoc test presented here is **Tukey's honestly significant difference (HSD)**, which allows a researcher to make all pairwise comparisons among the sample means in a study while maintaining an acceptable alpha (usually .05, but possibly .01) when the conditions have equal n's. If there is not an equal number of participants in each condition, then another post hoc test, such as Fisher's protected t test, which can be used with equal or unequal n's, is appropriate. Because the coverage of statistics in this text is necessarily selective, you will need to consult a more comprehensive statistics text regarding alternative post hoc tests if you need such a test.

Tukey's test identifies the smallest difference between any two means that is significant with alpha = .05 or alpha = .01. The formula for Tukey's HSD is

$$HSD_{.05} = Q(k, df_{\text{Within}})\sqrt{\frac{MS_{\text{Within}}}{n}}$$

Using this formula, we can determine the HSD for the .05 alpha level. This involves using Table A.6 in Appendix A to look up the value for Q. To look up Q, we need k (the number of means being compared—in our study on memory, this is 3) and df_{Within} (found in the ANOVA summary table, Table 11.6). Referring to Table A.6 for $k = 3$ and $df_{\text{Within}} = 21$ (because there is no 21 in the table, we use 20), we find that at the .05 level, $Q = 3.58$. In addition, we need MS_{Within} from Table 11.6 and n (the number of participants in each group). Using these numbers, we calculate HSD as follows:

$$HSD_{.05} = (3.58)\sqrt{\frac{2.95}{8}} = (3.58)\sqrt{0.369} = (3.58)(0.607) = 2.17$$

This tells us that a difference of 2.17 or greater for any pair of means is significant at the .05 level. In other words, the difference between the means is greater than what would be expected based on chance.

Table 11.7 summarizes the differences between the means for each pairwise comparison. In other words, the numbers represented in Table 11.7 represent the differences between the mean performance in each condition compared to every other condition. Can you identify which comparisons are significant using Tukey's HSD?

TABLE 11.7 Differences Between Each Pair of Means in the Memory Study

	ROTE REHEARSAL	IMAGERY	STORY
Rote Rehearsal	—	1.5	4.0
Imagery		—	2.5
Story			—

If you identify the differences between the story condition and the rote rehearsal condition and between the story condition and the imagery condition as the two honestly significant differences, you are correct because the difference between the means is greater than 2.17. Because these differences are significant at alpha = .05, we should also check $HSD_{.01}$. To do this, we use the same formula, but we use Q for the .01 alpha level from Table A.6. The calculations are as follows:

$$HSD_{.01} = (4.64)\sqrt{\frac{2.95}{8}} = (4.64)\sqrt{0.607} = 2.82$$

The only difference significant at this level is between the rote rehearsal and the story conditions. Thus, based on these data, those in the story condition recalled significantly more words than those in the imagery condition ($p < .05$) and those in the rote rehearsal condition ($p < .01$).

One-Way Randomized ANOVA — IN REVIEW

CONCEPT	DESCRIPTION
Null hypothesis (H_0)	The independent variable had no effect—the samples all represent the same population.
Alternative hypothesis (H_a)	The independent variable had an effect—at least one of the samples represents a different population than the others.
F-ratio	The ratio formed when the between-groups variance is divided by the within-groups variance.
Between-groups variance	An estimate of the variance of the group means about the grand mean; includes both systematic variance and error variance.
Within-groups variance	An estimate of the variance within each condition in the experiment; also known as error variance, or variance due to chance.
Eta-squared (η^2)	A measure of effect size—the variability in the dependent variable attributable to the independent variable.
Tukey's post hoc test	A test conducted to determine which conditions in a study with more than two groups differ significantly from each other.

CRITICAL THINKING CHECK 11.3

1. Of the following four *F*-ratios, which appears to indicate that the independent variable had an effect on the dependent variable?

   1.25/1.11 0.91/1.25 1.95/0.26 0.52/1.01

2. The following ANOVA summary table represents the results from a study of the effects of exercise on stress. There were three conditions in the study: a control group, a moderate exercise group, and a high exercise group. Each group had 10 subjects, and the mean stress levels for each group were control = 75.0, moderate exercise = 44.7, and high exercise = 63.7. Stress was measured using a 100-item stress scale, with 100 representing the highest level of stress. Complete the ANOVA summary table, and determine whether the *F*-ratio is significant. In addition, calculate eta-squared and Tukey's HSD if necessary.

ANOVA Summary Table

Source	*df*	*SS*	*MS*	*F*
Between		4,689.27		
Within		82,604.20		
Total				

Correlated-Groups Designs: One-Way Repeated Measures ANOVA

Like between-subjects designs, correlated-groups designs may use more than two levels of an independent variable. You should remember from Chapter 10 that there are two types of correlated-groups designs: a within-subjects design and a matched-subjects design. The same statistical analyses are used for both designs. We will use a within-subjects design to illustrate the statistical analysis appropriate for a correlated-groups design with more than two levels of an independent variable.

Imagine now that we want to conduct the same study as before, on the effects of rehearsal type on memory, but using a within-subjects rather than a between-subjects design. Why might we want to do this? As noted in Chapter 9, within-subjects designs—in fact, all correlated-groups designs—are more powerful than between-subjects designs. Therefore, one reason for this choice is to increase statistical power. In addition, the within-subjects design uses fewer participants and provides almost perfect control across conditions. Because the same people participate in each condition, we know that the individuals in each condition are equivalent and that the only difference between conditions is the type of rehearsal used.

In this study, the same three conditions will be used—rote rehearsal, rehearsal with imagery, and rehearsal with a story. The only difference is that

TABLE 11.8 Numbers of Words Recalled in a Within-Subjects Study of the Effects of Rehearsal Type on Memory

ROTE REHEARSAL	IMAGERY	STORY	
2	4	5	
3	2	3	
3	5	6	
3	7	6	
2	5	8	
5	4	7	
6	8	10	
4	5	9	
$\bar{X} = 3.5$	$\bar{X} = 5$	$\bar{X} = 6.75$	Grand mean = 5.083

the same eight subjects serve in every condition. Obviously, we cannot use the same list of words across conditions because there could be a large practice effect. We therefore have to use three lists of words that are equivalent in difficulty and that are counterbalanced across conditions. In other words, not all participants in each condition will receive the same list of words. Let's assume that we have taken the design problems into account and that the data in Table 11.8 represent the performance of the participants in this study. The number of words recalled in each condition is out of 10 words.

You can see that the data are similar to those from the between-subjects design described earlier in the chapter. Because of the similarity in the data, we can see how the statistics used with a within-subjects design are more powerful than those used with a between-subjects design. Because we have interval-ratio data, we will once again use an ANOVA to analyze these data. The only difference will be that the ANOVA used in this case is a **one-way repeated measures ANOVA**. The phrase *repeated measures* refers to the fact that measures are taken repeatedly on the same individuals; that is, the same participants serve in all conditions. The difference between this ANOVA and the one-way randomized ANOVA is that the conditions are correlated (related); therefore, the ANOVA procedure must be modified to take this relationship into account.

one-way repeated measures ANOVA An inferential statistical test for comparing the means of three or more groups using a correlated-groups design and one independent variable.

One-Way Repeated Measures ANOVA: What It Is and What It Does. With a one-way repeated measures ANOVA, participants in different conditions are equated prior to the experimental manipulation because the same subjects are used in each condition. This means that the single largest factor contributing to error variance (individual differences across subjects) has been removed. This also means that the error variance will be smaller. What part of the *F*-ratio is the error variance? Remember that the denominator in the *F*-ratio is the error variance. Thus, if the error variance (the denominator) is smaller, the resulting *F*-ratio will be larger. The end result is that a repeated measures ANOVA is more sensitive to small differences between groups.

The null and alternative hypotheses for the repeated measures ANOVA are the same as those for the randomized ANOVA. The null hypothesis is that the means from the conditions tested are similar or the same, and the alternative hypothesis is that the mean from at least one condition differs from the means of the other conditions:

$$H_0 : \mu_1 = \mu_2 = \mu_3$$

$$H_a : \text{At least one } \mu \neq \text{another } \mu$$

A repeated measures ANOVA is calculated in a manner similar to that for a randomized ANOVA. We first determine the sums of squares (*SS*), then the degrees of freedom (*df*) and mean squares (*MS*), and finally the *F*-ratio. The main difference lies in the calculation of the sums of squares. As with the randomized ANOVA, I will describe what the different sums of squares are, provide the definitional formulas, and show how to use these formulas with the data from Table 11.8. The computational formulas for the sums of squares for a repeated measures ANOVA are presented in Appendix B. If your instructor prefers that you use them (rather than the definitional formulas) with the experimental data from Table 11.8, refer to this appendix.

Calculations for the One-Way Repeated Measures ANOVA. The total sum of squares is calculated for a repeated measures ANOVA in the same manner as it is for a randomized ANOVA. The total sum of squares (SS_{Total}) is the total amount of variability in the entire data set (across all the conditions). It is calculated by summing the squared deviations of each score from the grand mean, or $\Sigma(X - \overline{X}_G)^2$, where X refers to each individual score, and $\overline{X}_G$ is the grand mean. The total sum of squares for the present example is 115.82. The calculations for this are shown in Table 11.9.

Because there is only one group of subjects, what was referred to as the between-groups sum of squares in a randomized ANOVA is now called a between-treatments, or simply a between, sum of squares. The between sum of squares is the sum of the differences between each condition or treatment mean and the grand mean, squared and multiplied by the number of scores in each treatment. It is calculated in the same manner as in the randomized ANOVA: $\Sigma[(\overline{X}_t - \overline{X}_G)^2 n]$, where $\overline{X}_t$ represents the mean for each treatment, $\overline{X}_G$ is the grand mean, and n is the number of scores in each treatment. The between sum of squares in the present example is 42.34 and is calculated in Table 11.10.

Finally, what was the within-groups sum of squares in the randomized ANOVA is split into two sources of variance in the repeated measures ANOVA: subject variance and error (residual) variance. To calculate these sums of squares, we begin by calculating the within-groups sum of squares just as we did in the randomized ANOVA. In other words, we calculate the sum of the squared difference scores for each score and its treatment mean, or $\Sigma(X - \overline{X}_t)^2$, where X represents each score, and $\overline{X}_t$ represents each

TABLE 11.9 Calculation of SS_{Total} Using the Definitional Formula

ROTE REHEARSAL		IMAGERY		STORY	
X	$(X - \overline{X}_G)^2$	X	$(X - \overline{X}_G)^2$	X	$(X - \overline{X}_G)^2$
2	9.50	4	1.17	5	0.01
3	4.34	2	9.50	3	4.34
3	4.34	5	0.01	6	0.84
3	4.34	7	3.67	6	0.84
2	9.50	5	0.01	8	8.51
5	0.01	4	1.17	7	3.67
6	0.84	8	8.51	10	24.18
4	1.17	5	0.01	9	15.34
	$\Sigma = 34.04$		$\Sigma = 24.05$		$\Sigma = 57.73$
$SS_{Total} = 34.04 + 24.05 + 57.73 = 115.82$					

NOTE: All numbers have been rounded to two decimal places.

TABLE 11.10 Calculation of $SS_{Between}$ Using the Definitional Formula

Rote Rehearsal

$(\overline{X}_t - \overline{X}_G)^2 n = (3.5 - 5.083)^2 8 = (-1.583)^2 8 = (2.51)8 = 20.05$

Imagery

$(\overline{X}_t - \overline{X}_G)^2 n = (5 - 5.083)^2 8 = (-0.083)^2 8 = (0.007)8 = 0.06$

Story

$(\overline{X}_t - \overline{X}_G)^2 n = (6.75 - 5.083)^2 8 = (1.667)^2 8 = (2.779)8 = 22.23$

$SS_{Between} = 20.05 + 0.06 + 22.23 = 42.34$

treatment mean. The within-groups sum of squares is 73.48. The calculation for this is shown in Table 11.11.

After we have calculated the within-groups sum of squares, we can determine the subject sum of squares, which is a reflection of the amount of within-groups variance due to individual differences. It is the sum of the squared difference scores for the mean of each subject across conditions and the grand mean, multiplied by the number of conditions. In a definitional formula, it is $\Sigma[(\overline{X}_s - \overline{X}_G)^2 k]$, where $\overline{X}_s$ represents the mean across treatments for each subject, $\overline{X}_G$ is the grand mean, and k is the number of treatments. The participant sum of squares is 52.40. The calculation for this is shown in Table 11.12.

After the variability due to individual differences ($SS_{Subjects}$) has been removed from the within-groups sum of squares, the error sum of squares

TABLE 11.11 Calculation of SS_{Within} Using the Definitional Formula

ROTE REHEARSAL		IMAGERY		STORY	
X	$(X - \overline{X}_t)^2$	X	$(X - \overline{X}_t)^2$	X	$(X - \overline{X}_t)^2$
2	2.25	4	1	5	3.06
3	0.25	2	9	3	14.06
3	0.25	5	0	6	0.56
3	0.25	7	4	6	0.56
2	2.25	5	0	8	1.56
5	2.25	4	1	7	0.06
6	6.25	8	9	10	10.56
4	0.25	5	0	9	5.06
	$\Sigma = 14$		$\Sigma = 24$		$\Sigma = 35.48$

$SS_{Within} = 14 + 24 + 35.48 = 73.48$

NOTE: All numbers have been rounded to two decimal places.

TABLE 11.12 Calculation of $SS_{Subjects}$ Using the Definitional Formula

ROTE REHEARSAL	IMAGERY	STORY		
X	X	X	$\overline{X}_S$	$(\overline{X}_S - \overline{X}_G)^2 3$
2	4	5	3.67	5.99
3	2	3	2.67	17.47
3	5	6	4.67	0.51
3	7	6	5.33	0.18
2	5	8	5.00	0.02
5	4	7	5.33	0.18
6	8	10	8.00	25.53
4	5	9	6.00	2.52
				$SS_{Subject} = 52.40$

NOTE: All numbers have been rounded to two decimal places.

is left. In definitional form, this is $SS_{Within} - SS_{Subjects}$, or, in our example, 73.48 − 52.40 = 21.08. We will soon see that the final *F*-ratio is computed by dividing $MS_{Between}$ by MS_{Error}. The main difference, then, between the repeated measures ANOVA and the randomized ANOVA is that the within-groups variance is divided into two sources of variance (that attributable to individual differences and that attributable to error variance), and only the variance attributable to error is used in the calculation of MS_{Error}.

TABLE 11.13 Repeated Measures ANOVA Summary Table: Definitional formulas

SOURCE	*df*	*SS*	*MS*	*F*
Subjects	$n-1$	$\Sigma[(\bar{X}_s - \bar{X}_G)^2 k]$	$\frac{SS_{Subjects}}{df_{Subjects}}$	
Between	$k-1$	$\Sigma[(\bar{X}_t - \bar{X}_G)^2 n]$	$\frac{SS_{Between}}{df_{Between}}$	$\frac{MS_{Between}}{MS_{Error}}$
Error	$(k-1)(n-1)$	$[\Sigma(X - \bar{X}_t)^2] - SS_{subject}$	$\frac{SS_{Error}}{df_{Error}}$	
Total	$N-1$	$\Sigma(X - \bar{X}_G)^2$		

TABLE 11.14 Repeated Measures ANOVA Summary Table for the Memory Study

SOURCE	*df*	*SS*	*MS*	*F*
Subjects	7	52.40	7.49	
Between	2	42.34	21.17	14.02
Error	14	21.08	1.51	
Total	23	115.82		

The next step is to calculate the *MS*, or mean square, for each term. You may remember that the *MS* for each term is calculated by dividing the *SS* by the *df*. Therefore, to calculate the *MS* for each term, we need to know the degrees of freedom for each term. Table 11.13 provides the definitional formulas for the sums of squares and the formulas for the degrees of freedom, the mean squares, and the *F*-ratio. The df_{Total} is calculated the same way that it was for the randomized ANOVA, $N - 1$. In this case, large *N* is the total number of scores in the study, not the total number of participants. Thus, the df_{Total} is $24 - 1 = 23$. The $df_{Subjects}$ is calculated by subtracting 1 from the number of subjects $(n - 1)$ and is $8 - 1 = 7$. The $df_{Between}$ is once again calculated by subtracting 1 from the number of conditions $(k - 1)$, or $3 - 1 = 2$. Last, the df_{Error} is calculated by multiplying $df_{Between}$ by $df_{Subjects}$: $(k - 1)(n - 1) = 2 \times 7 = 14$. After the *MS* for each term is determined (see Tables 11.13 and 11.14), we can calculate the *F*-ratio. In the repeated measures ANOVA, we divide $MS_{Between}$ by MS_{Error}. The degrees of freedom, sums of squares, mean squares, and F_{obt} calculated for these data are shown in Table 11.14.

Interpreting the One-Way Repeated Measures ANOVA. The repeated measures ANOVA is interpreted in the same way as the randomized ANOVA.

We use Table A.5 in Appendix A to determine the critical value for the F-ratio. Using the $df_{Between}$ of 2 and the df_{Error} of 14 with Table A.5, we find that F_{cv} for the .05 level is 3.74. Because our F_{obt} is much larger than this, we know that it is significant at the .05 level. Let's also look at F_{cv} for the .01 level, which is 6.51. Once again, our F_{obt} is larger than this. In APA publication format, this is reported as $F(2, 14) = 14.02, p < .01$. The calculation of this ANOVA using Excel is presented in the Statistical Software Resources section at the end of the chapter.

If you look back to Table 11.6—the ANOVA summary table for the one-way randomized ANOVA, with very similar data to the repeated measures ANOVA—you can see how much more powerful the repeated measures ANOVA is than the randomized ANOVA. Notice that although the total sums of squares are very similar, the resulting F-ratio for the repeated measures ANOVA is much larger (14.02 versus 11.07). If the F_{obt} is larger, then there is a higher probability that it will be statistically significant. Notice also that although the data used to calculate the two ANOVAs are similar, the group means in the repeated measures ANOVA are more similar (closer together) than those from the randomized ANOVA, yet the F_{obt} from the repeated measures ANOVA is larger. Thus, with somewhat similar data, the resulting F-ratio for the repeated measures ANOVA is larger and thus affords more statistical power.

Graphing the Means and Effect Size. As with the one-way randomized ANOVA discussed earlier in the chapter, we should graph the results of this ANOVA because of the significant difference between the means. The resulting graph appears in Figure 11.3. In addition, we should compute effect size using eta-squared. Eta-squared is calculated by dividing $SS_{Between}$ by SS_{Total}, or 42.34/115.82 = .366. This tells us that 36.6% of the variability among the scores can be attributed to the different rehearsal conditions. Notice that even though a fairly large amount of the variability in the dependent variable is accounted for by knowing the condition to which a participant was

FIGURE 11.3 Number of words recalled as a function of rehearsal type

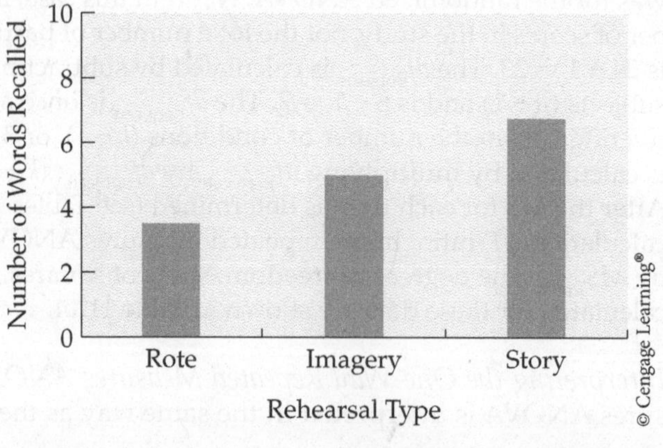

assigned, the effect size is not as large as that from the randomized ANOVA we calculated earlier in the chapter. This shows the importance of determining effect size. Although the repeated measures ANOVA may lead to a larger final F-ratio and greater statistical significance, it does not necessarily mean that the independent variable explains more of the variability in the dependent variable.

Assumptions of the One-Way Repeated Measures ANOVA. As with the randomized ANOVA, certain conditions must be met to ensure that the statistic is being used properly. The first three assumptions for the one-way repeated measures ANOVA are the same as the first three listed for the one-way randomized ANOVA:

- The data are on an interval-ratio scale.
- The underlying distribution is normally distributed.
- The variances among the populations being compared are homogeneous.
- The groups are correlated (within-subjects or matched-subjects).

Tukey's Post Hoc Test. As with the randomized ANOVA, we can perform post hoc tests when the resulting F-ratio is significant. Once again, we will use Tukey's HSD post hoc test:

$$\text{HSD} = Q(k, df_{\text{Error}})\sqrt{\frac{MS_{\text{Error}}}{n}}$$

Remember that we determine Q by using Table A.6 in Appendix A. For our example, the honestly significant difference for the .05 level is

$$\text{HSD}_{.05} = 3.70\sqrt{\frac{1.51}{8}} = 3.70\sqrt{0.1887} = 3.70(0.434) = 1.61$$

To calculate HSD for the .01 level, we refer to Table A.6 once again and find that

$$\text{HSD}_{.01} = 4.89(0.434) = 2.12$$

Table 11.15 compares the means from the three conditions in the present study. We can see that the difference in means between the rote rehearsal and the story conditions is significant at the .01 level, and the difference

TABLE 11.15 Differences Between Each Pair of means in the Within-Subjects Study

	ROTE REHEARSAL	IMAGERY	STORY
Rote Rehearsal	—	1.5	3.25
Imagery		—	1.75
Story			—

between the imagery and the story conditions is significant at the .05 level. Thus, based on these data, those in the story condition recalled significantly more words than those in the imagery condition ($p < .05$) and those in the rote rehearsal condition ($p < .01$).

One-Way Repeated Measures ANOVA — IN REVIEW

CONCEPT	DESCRIPTION
Null hypothesis (H_0)	The independent variable had no effect; the samples all represent the same population.
Alternative hypothesis (H_a)	The independent variable had an effect; at least one of the samples represents a different population than the others.
F-ratio	The ratio formed when the between variance is divided by the error variance.
Between variance	An estimate of the variance of the treatment means about the grand mean; includes both systematic variance and error variance.
Subject variance	The variance due to individual differences; removed from the error variance.
Error variance	An estimate of the variance within each condition in the experiment after variance due to individual differences has been removed.
Eta-squared (η^2)	A measure of effect size; the variability in the dependent variable attributable to the independent variable.
Tukey's post hoc test	A test conducted to determine which conditions in a study with more than two groups differ significantly from each other.

CRITICAL THINKING CHECK 11.4

1. Explain why a repeated measures ANOVA is statistically more powerful than a simple randomized one-way ANOVA.
2. Identify other advantage(s) associated with using a within-subjects design.

Summary

In this chapter, we discussed designs that use more than two levels of an independent variable. Advantages to such designs include being able to compare more than two kinds of treatment, to use fewer participants, to compare all treatments with a control group, and to use placebo groups. In addition, we discussed the statistical analyses most appropriate for use with these designs—most commonly, with interval-ratio data, an ANOVA. A randomized one-way ANOVA is used for between-subjects designs, and a repeated measures one-way ANOVA is used for correlated-groups designs. Also discussed were appropriate post hoc tests (Tukey's HSD) and measures of effect size (eta-squared). After completing this chapter, you should appreciate the advantages of using more complicated designs and understand the basic statistics used to analyze such designs.

KEY TERMS

Bonferroni adjustment
ANOVA (analysis of variance)
one-way randomized ANOVA
grand mean
error variance
within-groups variance
between-groups variance
F-ratio
total sum of squares
within-groups sum of squares
between-groups sum of squares
mean square
eta-squared (η^2)
post hoc test
Tukey's honestly significant difference (HSD)
one-way repeated measures ANOVA

CHAPTER EXERCISES

(Answers to odd-numbered exercises appear in Appendix C.)

1. What is/are the advantage(s) of conducting a study with three or more levels of the independent variable?
2. What is the difference between a randomized ANOVA and a repeated measures ANOVA? What does the term *one-way* mean with respect to an ANOVA?
3. Explain between-groups variance and within-groups variance.
4. If a researcher decides to use multiple comparisons in a study with three conditions, what is the probability of a Type I error across these comparisons? Use the Bonferroni adjustment to determine the suggested alpha level.
5. If H_0 is true, what should the *F*-ratio equal or be close to? If H_a is supported, should the *F*-ratio be greater than, less than, or equal to 1?
6. When should post hoc comparisons be performed?
7. What information does eta-squared (η^2) provide?
8. Why is a repeated measures ANOVA statistically more powerful than a randomized ANOVA?
9. A researcher conducts a study of the effects of amount of sleep on creativity. The creativity scores for four levels of sleep (2 hours, 4 hours, 6 hours, and 8 hours) for $N = 20$ subjects are presented here.

Amount of Sleep (in hours)

2	4	6	8
3	4	10	10
5	7	11	13
6	8	13	10
4	3	9	9
2	2	10	10

a. Complete the following ANOVA summary table. (If your instructor wants you to calculate the sums of squares, use the preceding data to do so.)

Source	*df*	*SS*	*MS*	*F*
Between groups		187.75		
Within groups		55.20		
Total		242.95		

b. Is F_{obt} significant at $\alpha = .05$; at $\alpha = .01$?
c. Perform post hoc comparisons if necessary.
d. What conclusions can be drawn from the *F*-ratio and the post hoc comparisons?
e. What is the effect size, and what does this mean?
f. Graph the means.

10. In a study of the effects of stress on illness, a researcher tallied the number of colds people contracted during a 6-month period as a function of the amount of stress they reported during that same time period. There were three stress levels: minimal, moderate, and high stress. The sums of squares appear in the following ANOVA summary table. The mean for each condition and the number of subjects per condition are also noted.

Source	*df*	*SS*	*MS*	*F*
Between groups		22.167		
Within groups		14.750		
Total		36.917		

Stress Level	*Mean*	*n*
Minimal	3	4
Moderate	4	4
High	6	4

a. Complete the ANOVA summary table.
b. Is F_{obt} significant at $\alpha = .05$? at $\alpha = .01$?
c. Perform post hoc comparisons if necessary.

d. What conclusions can be drawn from the F-ratio and the post hoc comparisons?
e. What is the effect size, and what does this mean?
f. Graph the means.

11. A researcher interested in the effects of exercise on stress had participants exercise for 30, 60, or 90 minutes per day. The mean stress level on a 100-point stress scale (with 100 indicating high stress) for each condition appears next, along with the ANOVA summary table with the sums of squares indicated.

Source	*df*	*SS*	*MS*	F
Between groups		4,689.27		
Within groups		82,604.20		
Total		87,293.47		

Exercise Level	*Mean*	*n*
30 minutes	75.0	10
60 minutes	44.7	10
90 minutes	63.7	10

a. Complete the ANOVA summary table.
b. Is F_{obt} significant at $\alpha = .05$; at $\alpha = .01$?
c. Perform post hoc comparisons if necessary.
d. What conclusions can be drawn from the F-ratio and the post hoc comparisons?
e. What is the effect size, and what does this mean?
f. Graph the means.

12. A researcher conducted an experiment on the effects of a new drug on depression. The researcher had a control group that received nothing, a placebo group, and an experimental group that received the drug. A depression inventory that provided a measure of depression on a 50-point scale was used (50 indicates that an individual is very high on the depression variable). The ANOVA summary table appears next, along with the mean depression score for each condition.

Source	*df*	*SS*	*MS*	F
Between groups		1,202.313		
Within groups		2,118.00		
Total		3,320.313		

Drug Condition	*Mean*	*n*
Control	36.26	15
Placebo	33.33	15
Drug	24.13	15

a. Complete the ANOVA summary table.
b. Is F_{obt} significant at $\alpha = .05$; at $\alpha = .01$?
c. Perform post hoc comparisons if necessary.
d. What conclusions can be drawn from the F-ratio and the post hoc comparisons?
e. What is the effect size, and what does this mean?
f. Graph the means.

13. A researcher is interested in the effects of practice on accuracy in a signal-detection task. Subjects are tested with no practice, after 1 hour of practice, and after 2 hours of practice. Each person participates in all three conditions. The following data indicate how many signals each participant detected accurately at each level of practice.

	Amount of Practice		
Subject	*No Practice*	*1 Hour*	*2 Hours*
1	3	4	6
2	4	5	5
3	2	3	4
4	1	3	5
5	3	6	7
6	3	4	6
7	2	3	4

Source	*df*	*SS*	*MS*	*F*
Subject		16.27		
Between		25.81		
Error		4.87		
Total		46.95		

a. Complete the ANOVA summary table. (If your instructor wants you to calculate the sums of squares, use the preceding data to do so.)
b. Is F_{obt} significant at $\alpha = .05$? at $\alpha = .01$?
c. Perform post hoc comparisons if necessary.
d. What conclusions can be drawn from the F-ratio and the post hoc comparisons?
e. What is the effect size, and what does this mean?
f. Graph the means.

14. A researcher has been hired by a pizzeria to determine which type of crust customers prefer. The restaurant offers three types of crust: hand-tossed, thick, and thin. Following are the mean number of 1-inch pieces of pizza eaten for each condition from 10 subjects who had the opportunity to eat as many pieces with each type of crust as they desired. The ANOVA summary table also follows.

Source	*df*	*SS*	*MS*	*F*
Subject		2.75		
Between		180.05		
Error		21.65		
Total		204.45		

Crust Type	*Mean*	*n*
Hand-tossed	2.73	10
Thick	4.20	10
Thin	8.50	10

a. Complete the ANOVA summary table.
b. Is F_{obt} significant at $\alpha = .05$? at $\alpha = .01$?
c. Perform post hoc comparisons if necessary.
d. What conclusions can be drawn from the F-ratio and the post hoc comparisons?
e. What is the effect size, and what does this mean?
f. Graph the means.

15. A researcher is interested in whether massed or spaced studying has a greater impact on grades in a course. The researcher has her class study for 6 hours all in one day for one exam (massed study condition). She has them study for 2 hours each day for 3 days for another exam (3-day spaced condition). Last, she has them study for 1 hour a day for 6 days for a third exam (6-day spaced condition). The mean exam score (out of a possible 100 points) for each condition appears next, along with the ANOVA summary table.

Source	*df*	*SS*	*MS*	*F*
Subject		136.96		
Between		3,350.96		
Error		499.03		
Total		3,986.95		

Study Condition	*Mean*	*n*
Massed	69.13	15
3-day spaced	79.33	15
6-day spaced	90.27	15

a. Complete the ANOVA summary table.
b. Is F_{obt} significant at $\alpha = .05$; at $\alpha = .01$?
c. Perform post hoc comparisons if necessary.
d. What conclusions can be drawn from the F-ratio and the post hoc comparisons?
e. What is the effect size, and what does this mean?
f. Graph the means.

CRITICAL THINKING CHECK ANSWERS

11.1

1. The probability of a Type I error is 26.5%: $[1 - (1 - .05)^6] = [1 - (.95)^6] = [1 - .735] = 26.5\%$. With the Bonferroni adjustment, the alpha level is .008 for each comparison.

11.2

1. Both the within-groups and between-groups variances are moderate to small. This should lead to an F-ratio of approximately 1.

11.3

1. The F-ratio $1.95/0.26 = 7.5$ suggests that the independent variable had an effect on the dependent variable.
2.

ANOVA Summary Table

Source	*df*	*SS*	*MS*	*F*
Between	2	4,689.27	2,344.64	0.766
Within	27	82,604.20	3,059.41	
Total	29	87,293.47		

The resulting F-ratio is less than 1 and thus not significant. Although stress levels differ across some of the groups, the difference is not large enough to be significant.

11.4

1. A repeated measures ANOVA is statistically more powerful because the within-groups variance is divided into two sources of variance: that due to individual differences (subject) and that left over (error). Only the error variance is used to calculate the F-ratio. We therefore divide by a smaller number, thus resulting in a larger F-ratio and a greater chance that it will be significant.
2. The within-subjects design also has the advantages of requiring fewer participants, assuring equivalency of groups, and usually requiring less time to conduct the study. See Chapter 9 for a review of this information.

WEB RESOURCES

The book-specific website at CengageBrain.com offers students a variety of study tools and useful resources such as glossaries and flashcards.

Chapter 11 ■ Study Guide

CHAPTER 11 SUMMARY AND REVIEW: EXPERIMENTAL DESIGN AND ANALYSIS III: DESIGNS WITH MORE THAN TWO LEVELS OF AN INDEPENDENT VARIABLE

In this chapter, designs using more than two levels of an independent variable were discussed. Advantages to such designs include being able to compare more than two kinds of treatment, using fewer subjects, comparing all treatments to a control group, and using placebo groups. In addition, the chapter discussed statistical analyses most appropriate for use with these designs—most commonly with interval-ratio data, an ANOVA. A randomized one-way ANOVA would be used for between-subjects designs, and a repeated-measures one-way ANOVA for correlated-groups designs. Also discussed were appropriate post hoc tests (Tukey's HSD) and measures of effect size (eta-squared). After completing this chapter, you should appreciate the advantages of using more complicated designs and possess an understanding of the basic statistics used to analyze such designs.

CHAPTER 11 REVIEW EXERCISES

(Answers to exercises appear in Appendix C.)

FILL-IN SELF-TEST

Answer the following questions. If you have trouble answering any of the questions, restudy the relevant material before going on to the multiple-choice self test.

1. The ________ provides a means of setting a more stringent alpha level for multiple tests to minimize Type I errors.
2. A ________ is an inert substance that subjects believe is a treatment.
3. A(n) ________ is an inferential statistical test for comparing the means of three or more groups.
4. The mean performance across all participants is represented by the ________.
5. The ________ variance is an estimate of the effect of the independent variable, confounds, and error variance.
6. The sum of squared deviations of each score from the grand mean is the ________.
7. When we divide an *SS* score by its degrees of freedom, we have calculated a ________.
8. ________ is an inferential statistic for measuring effect size with an ANOVA.
9. For an ANOVA, we use ________ to compare all possible pairs of groups to determine which ones differ significantly from each other.
10. The ANOVA for use with one independent variable and a correlated-groups design is the ________.

MULTIPLE-CHOICE SELF-TEST

Select the single best answer for each of the following questions. If you have trouble answering any of the questions, restudy the relevant material.

1. The *F*-ratio is determined by dividing ________ by ________.
   a. error variance; systematic variance
   b. between-groups variance; within-groups variance
   c. within-groups variance; between-groups variance
   d. systematic variance; error variance

2. If the between-groups variance is large, then we have observed:
   a. experimenter effects.
   b. large systematic variance.
   c. an effect of the independent variable.
   d. possibly both b and c.
3. The larger the *F*-ratio, the greater the chance that:
   a. a mistake has been made in the computation.
   b. there are large systematic effects present.
   c. the experimental manipulation probably did not have the predicted effects.
   d. the between-groups variation is no larger than would be expected by chance alone and no larger than the within-groups variance.
4. One reason to use an ANOVA over a *t* test is to reduce the risk of:
   a. a Type II error.
   b. a Type I error.
   c. confounds.
   d. error variance.
5. If the null hypothesis for an ANOVA is false, then the *F*-ratio should be:
   a. greater than 1.00.
   b. a negative number.
   c. 0.00.
   d. 1.00.
6. In a randomized ANOVA, if there are four groups with 15 subjects in each group, then the *df* for the *F*-ratio is equal to:
   a. 60.
   b. 59.
   c. 3, 56.
   d. 3, 57.
7. For an *F*-ratio with $df = (3, 20)$, the F_{cv} for $\alpha = .05$ would be:
   a. 3.10.
   b. 4.94.
   c. 8.66.
   d. 5.53.
8. If a researcher reported an *F*-ratio with $df = (2, 21)$ for a randomized one-way ANOVA, then there were ______ conditions in the experiment and ______ total subjects.
   a. 2; 21
   b. 3; 23
   c. 2; 24
   d. 3; 24
9. Systematic variance and error variance comprise the ______ variance.
   a. within-groups
   b. total
   c. between-groups
   d. participant
10. If a randomized one-way ANOVA produced $MS_{between} = 25$ and $MS_{within} = 5$, then the *F*-ratio would be:
    a. $25/5 = 5$.
    b. $5/25 = .20$.
    c. $25/30 = .83$.
    d. $30/5 = 6$.
11. One advantage of a correlated-groups design is that the effects of ______ have been removed.
    a. individual differences
    b. experimenter effects
    c. subject bias effects
    d. measurement error

SELF-TEST PROBLEMS

1. Calculate Tukey's HSD and eta-squared for the following ANOVA.

ANOVA Summary Table

Source	*df*	*SS*	*MS*	*F*
Subjects	9	25		
Between	2	150		
Error	18	100		
Total	29			

2. The following ANOVA table corresponds to an experiment on pain reliever effectiveness. Three types of pain reliever are used (aspirin, acetaminophen, and ibuprofen), and effectiveness is rated on a 0–10 scale. The scores for the six subjects in each group follow:

Aspirin: 4, 6, 4, 4, 3, 5
Acetaminophen: 6, 4, 6, 7, 3, 5
Ibuprofen: 7, 6, 5, 8, 6, 5

The sums of squares are provided in the following table. However, for practice, see if you can correctly calculate them by hand.

ANOVA Summary Table

Source	*df*	*SS*	*MS*	*F*
Subjects		9.12		
Between		10.19		
Error		13.90		
Total				

a. Complete the ANOVA Summary Table presented here.

b. Is F_{obt} significant at $\alpha = .05$?

c. Perform post hoc comparisons if necessary.

d. What conclusions can be drawn from the *F*-ratio and the post hoc comparisons?

e. What is the effect size and what does this mean?

f. Graph the means.

Chapter 11 ▪ Statistical Software Resources

If you need help getting started with Excel or SPSS, please see Appendix D: Getting Started with Excel and SPSS.

ONE-WAY RANDOMIZED ANOVA

Using Excel

We'll use the data from Table 11.1 to illustrate the use of Excel to compute a one-way randomized ANOVA. In this study, we had participants use one of three different types of rehearsal (rote, imagery, or story) and then had them perform a recall task. Thus we manipulated rehearsal and measured memory for the 10 words participants studied. Because there were different participants in each condition, we use a randomized ANOVA. We begin by entering the data into Excel, with the data from each condition appearing in a different column. This can be seen next.

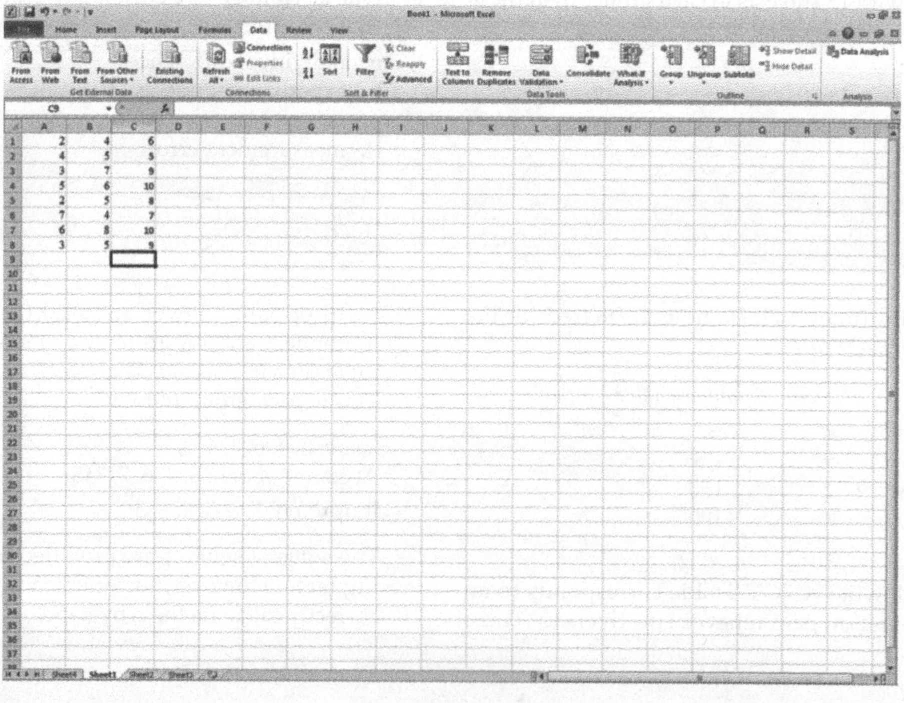

Next, with the **Data** ribbon highlighted, click on the **Data Analysis** tab in the top right corner. You should receive the following dialog box.

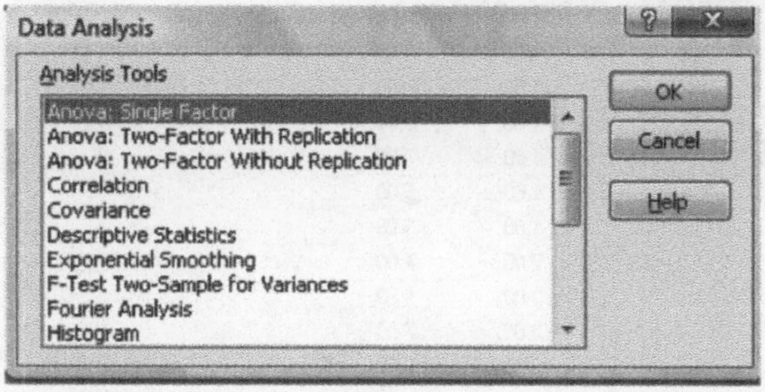

Select **Anova: Single Factor**, as in the preceding box, and click **OK**. The following dialog box will appear.

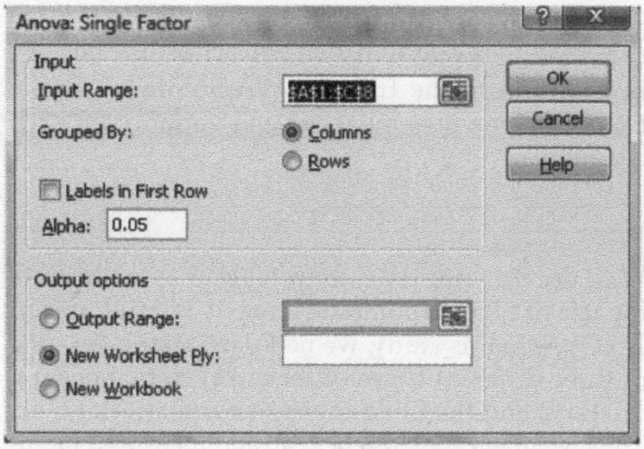

With the cursor in **the Input Range** box, highlight the three columns of data so that they are entered into the Input Range box as they are in the preceding box. Then click **OK**. The output from the ANOVA will appear on a new Worksheet, as seen next.

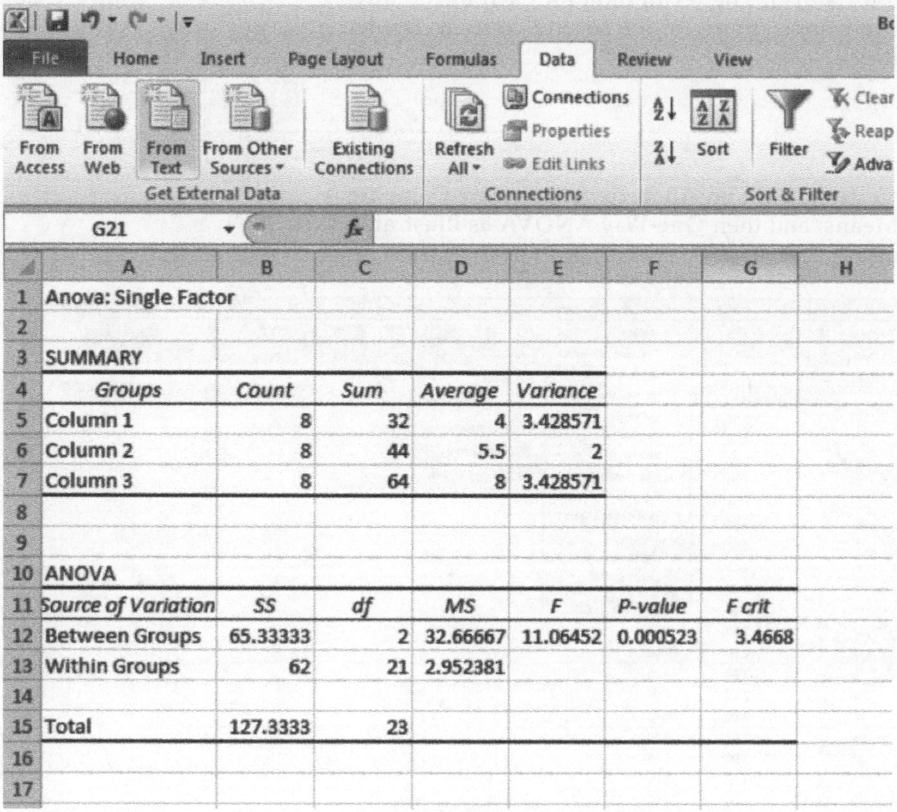

Anova: Single Factor						
SUMMARY						
Groups	*Count*	*Sum*	*Average*	*Variance*		
Column 1	8	32	4	3.428571		
Column 2	8	44	5.5	2		
Column 3	8	64	8	3.428571		
ANOVA						
Source of Variation	*SS*	*df*	*MS*	*F*	*P-value*	*F crit*
Between Groups	65.33333	2	32.66667	11.06452	0.000523	3.4668
Within Groups	62	21	2.952381			
Total	127.3333	23				

You can see from the ANOVA Summary Table provided by Excel that $F\ (2,21)=11.06$, $p=.000523$. In addition to the full ANOVA Summary Table, Excel also provides the mean and variance for each condition.

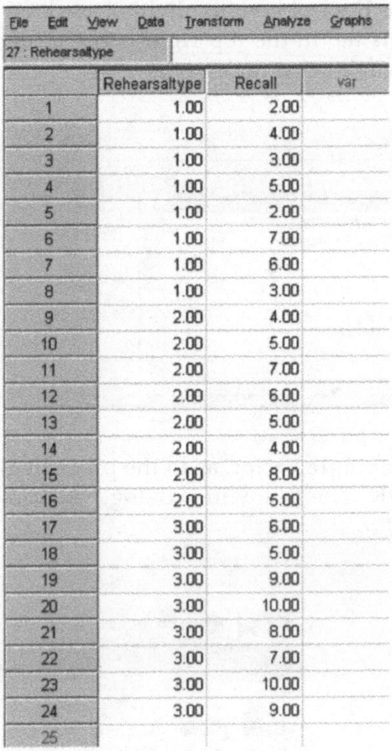

	Rehearsaltype	Recall	var
1	1.00	2.00	
2	1.00	4.00	
3	1.00	3.00	
4	1.00	5.00	
5	1.00	2.00	
6	1.00	7.00	
7	1.00	6.00	
8	1.00	3.00	
9	2.00	4.00	
10	2.00	5.00	
11	2.00	7.00	
12	2.00	6.00	
13	2.00	5.00	
14	2.00	4.00	
15	2.00	8.00	
16	2.00	5.00	
17	3.00	6.00	
18	3.00	5.00	
19	3.00	9.00	
20	3.00	10.00	
21	3.00	8.00	
22	3.00	7.00	
23	3.00	10.00	
24	3.00	9.00	
25			

Using SPSS

We'll use the same data (from Table 11.1) to illustrate the use of SPSS to compute a one-way randomized ANOVA. In this study, we had participants use one of three different types of rehearsal (rote, imagery, or story) and then had them perform a recall task. Thus we manipulated rehearsal and measured memory for the 10 words participants studied. Because there were different participants in each condition, we use a randomized ANOVA. We begin by entering the data into SPSS. The first column is labeled Rehearsaltype and indicates which type of rehearsal the participants used (1 for rote, 2 for imagery, and 3 for story). The recall data for each of the three conditions appear in the second column, labeled Recall.

Next, click on **Analyze**, followed by **Compare Means**, and then **One-Way ANOVA** as illustrated next.

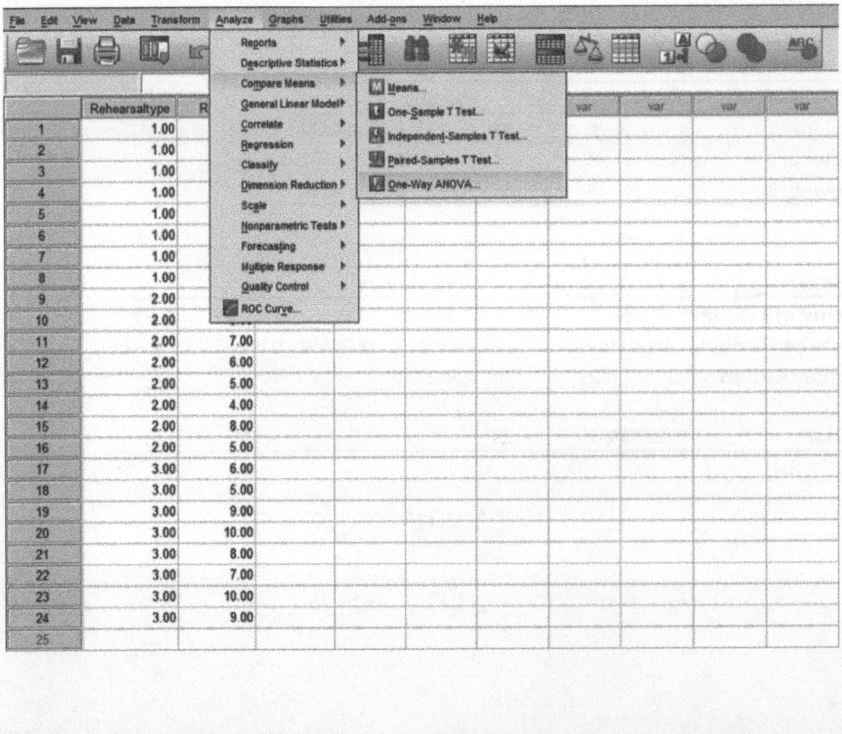

You should receive the following dialog box.

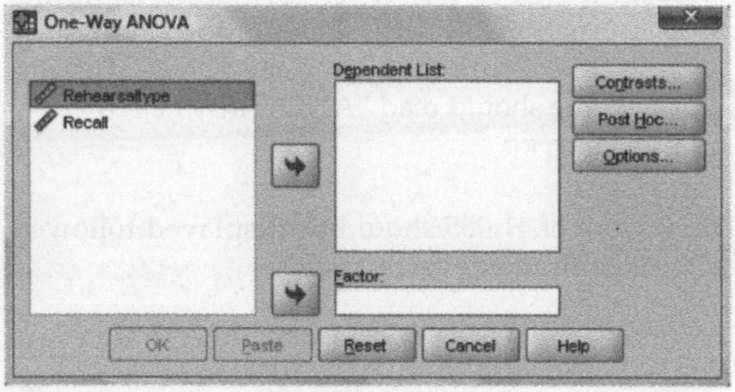

Enter Rehearsaltype into the **Factor** box by highlighting it and using the appropriate arrow. Do the same for Recall by entering it into the **Dependent List** box. After doing this, the dialog box should appear as follows.

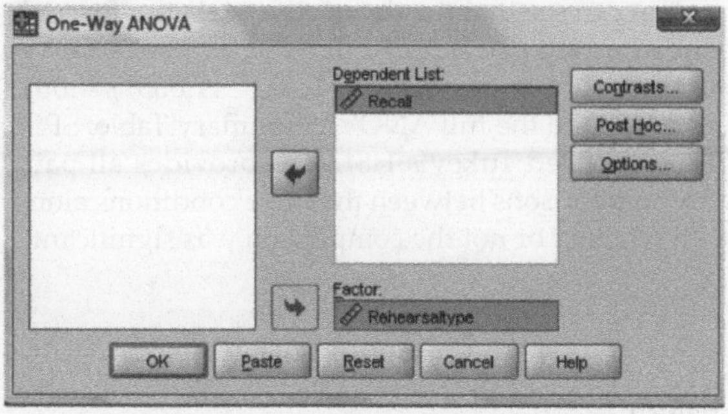

Next click on the **Options** button and select **Descriptive** and **Continue**. Then click on the **Post Hoc** button and select **Tukey** and then **Continue**. Then click on **OK**. The output from the ANOVA will appear in a new Output window as seen next.

Oneway

Descriptives

Recall

	N	Mean	Std. Deviation	Std. Error	95% Confidence Interval for Mean Lower Bound	95% Confidence Interval for Mean Upper Bound	Minimum	Maximum
1	8	4.0000	1.85164	.65465	2.4520	5.5480	2.00	7.00
2	8	5.5000	1.41421	.50000	4.3177	6.6823	4.00	8.00
3	8	8.0000	1.85164	.65465	6.4520	9.5480	5.00	10.00
Total	24	5.8333	2.35292	.48029	4.8398	6.8269	2.00	10.00

ANOVA

Recall

	Sum of Squares	df	Mean Square	F	Sig.
Between Groups	65.333	2	32.667	11.065	.001
Within Groups	62.000	21	2.952		
Total	127.333	23			

Post Hoc Tests

Multiple Comparisons

Recall
Tukey HSD

(I) Rehearsaltype	(J) Rehearsaltype	Mean Difference (I-J)	Std. Error	Sig.	95% Confidence Interval Lower Bound	95% Confidence Interval Upper Bound
1.00	2.00	-1.50000	.85912	.212	-3.6655	.6655
	3.00	-4.00000*	.85912	.000	-6.1655	-1.8345
2.00	1.00	1.50000	.85912	.212	-.6655	3.6655
	3.00	-2.50000*	.85912	.022	-4.6655	-.3345
3.00	1.00	4.00000*	.85912	.000	1.8345	6.1655
	2.00	2.50000*	.85912	.022	.3345	4.6655

*. The mean difference is significant at the 0.05 level.

You can see that the descriptive statistics for each condition are provided, followed by the ANOVA Summary Table in which F (2, 21)=11.065, p=.001. In addition to the full ANOVA Summary Table, SPSS also calculated Tukey's HSD and provides all pairwise comparisons between the three conditions along with whether or not the comparison was significant.

Using the TI-84

Let's use the data from Table 11.1 to conduct the analysis.

1. With the calculator on, press the STAT key.
2. EDIT will be highlighted. Press the ENTER key.
3. Under L1 enter the data from Table 9.1 for the rote group.
4. Under L2 enter the data from Table 9.1 for the imagery group.
5. Under L3 enter the data from Table 9.1 for the story group.
6. Press the STAT key once again and highlight TESTS.
7. Scroll down to ANOVA. Press the ENTER key.
8. Next to "ANOVA" enter (L1,L2,L3) using the 2nd function key with the appropriate number keys. Make sure that you use commas. The finished line should read "ANOVA(L1,L2,L3)".
9. Press ENTER.

The F score of 11.065 should be displayed followed by the significance level of .0005.

One-Way Repeated Measures ANOVA

Using Excel

We'll begin by entering the data from Table 11.8 into Excel, with the data from each condition appearing in a different column and the data for each participant appearing the in the same row. Remember that the data for each participant have to appear in a single row. To emphasize this, I've used the first column to indicate each participant in the study, followed by their data in the corresponding row. This can be seen in the following image.

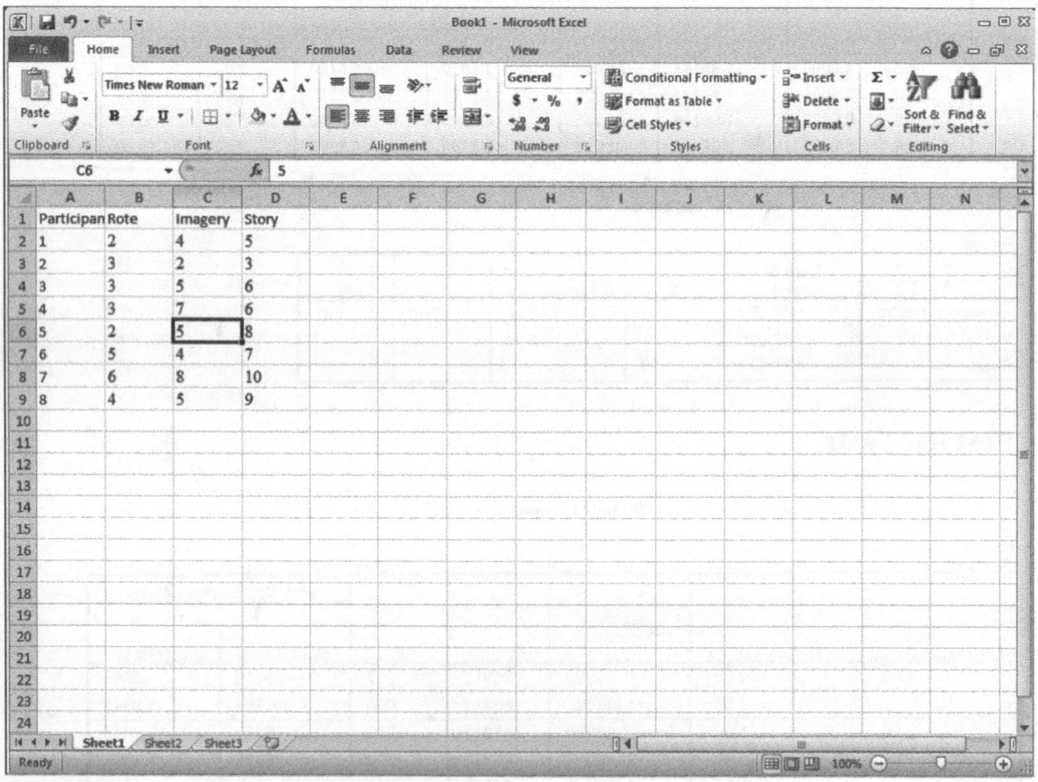

Next, with the **Data** ribbon highlighted, click on the **Data Analysis** tab in the top right corner. You will receive the following dialog box.

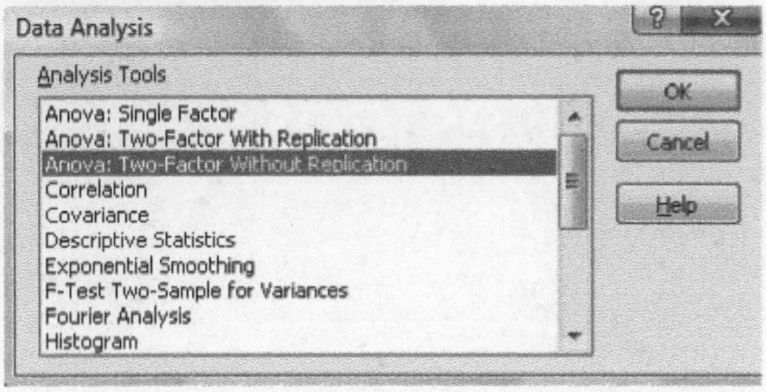

Select **Anova: Two-Factor Without Replication**, as in the preceding box, and click **OK**. The following dialog box will appear.

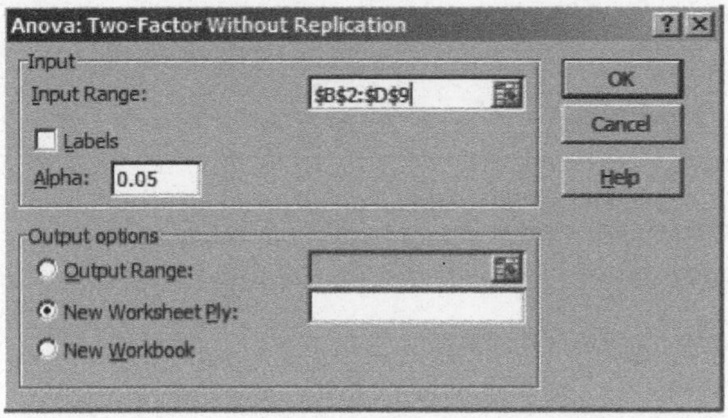

With the cursor in the **Input Range** box, highlight the three columns of data so that they are entered into the Input Range box as they are in the preceding window. Make sure you highlight only the data in columns B, C, and D. Then click **OK**. The output from the ANOVA will appear on a new Worksheet as seen next.

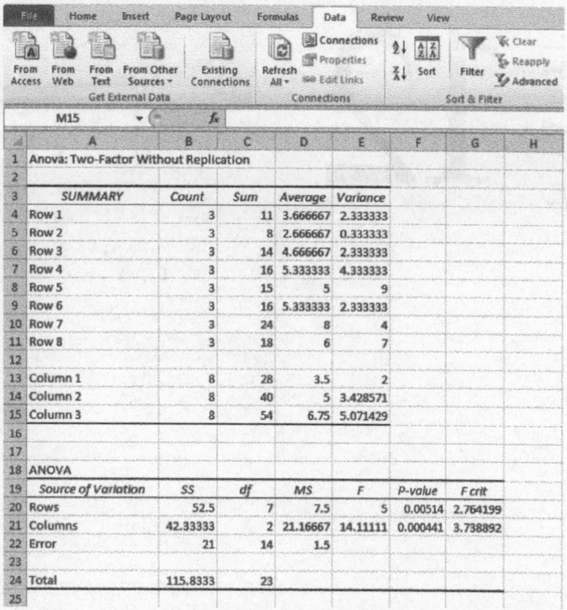

Anova: Two-Factor Without Replication

SUMMARY	Count	Sum	Average	Variance
Row 1	3	11	3.666667	2.333333
Row 2	3	8	2.666667	0.333333
Row 3	3	14	4.666667	2.333333
Row 4	3	16	5.333333	4.333333
Row 5	3	15	5	9
Row 6	3	16	5.333333	2.333333
Row 7	3	24	8	4
Row 8	3	18	6	7
Column 1	8	28	3.5	2
Column 2	8	40	5	3.428571
Column 3	8	54	6.75	5.071429

ANOVA

Source of Variation	SS	df	MS	F	P-value	F crit
Rows	52.5	7	7.5	5	0.00514	2.764199
Columns	42.33333	2	21.16667	14.11111	0.000441	3.738892
Error	21	14	1.5			
Total	115.8333	23				

You can see from the ANOVA Summary Table provided by Excel that $F(2,14) = 14.11$, $p = .000441$. In addition to the full ANOVA Summary Table, Excel also provides the mean and variance for each row (participant) and each condition. Moreover, there is also an F score reported for the Rows term (the participants). We report only the F score for the Columns (this represents between-groups variance/within-groups variance)—the F score for the Rows term can be ignored.

Using SPSS

The advanced SPSS package is necessary to conduct this analysis. Thus, this analysis is not illustrated here.

Using the TI-84

The TI-84 does not compute a one-way repeated measures ANOVA.

CHAPTER

12 Experimental Design and Analysis IV: Complex Experimental Designs

Learning Objectives

- Explain factorial notation and the advantages of factorial designs.
- Identify main effects and interaction effects based on looking at graphs.
- Draw graphs for factorial designs based on matrices of means.
- Explain what a two-way randomized ANOVA is and what it does.
- Calculate a two-way randomized ANOVA.
- Interpret a two-way randomized ANOVA.
- Explain what a two-way repeated measures ANOVA is.

In Chapter 11, we discussed designs with more than two levels of an independent variable. In this chapter, we will look at more complex designs—those with more than one independent variable. These are usually referred to as **factorial designs**, indicating that more than one factor or variable is being manipulated in the study. We will discuss the advantages of such designs over simpler designs. In addition, we will explain how to interpret the findings (called main effects and interaction effects) from such designs. Last, we will consider the statistical analysis of such designs.

factorial design A design with more than one independent variable.

Using Designs with More Than One Independent Variable

Remember the study discussed in Chapter 11 on the effects of rehearsal on memory. The subjects used one of three types of rehearsal (rote, imagery, or story) to determine their effects on the number of words recalled. Imagine that upon further analysis of the data, we discovered that subjects recalled concrete words (for example, *desk, bike, tree*) better than abstract words (for example, *love, truth, honesty*) in one rehearsal condition but not in another. Such a result is called an *interaction* between variables; this concept will be discussed in more detail later in the chapter. One advantage of using factorial designs is that they allow us to assess how variables interact. In the real world, it would be unusual to find that a certain behavior is produced by only one variable; behavior is usually contingent upon many variables operating together in an interactive way. Designing experiments with more than one independent variable allows researchers to assess how multiple variables may affect behavior.

Factorial Notation and Factorial Designs

A factorial design, then, is one with more than one factor or independent variable. A *complete factorial design* is one in which all levels of each independent variable are paired with all levels of every other independent variable. An *incomplete factorial design* also has more than one independent variable, but all levels of each variable are not paired with all levels of every other variable. The design illustrated in this chapter is a complete factorial design.

Remember that an independent variable must have at least two levels; if it does not vary, it is not a variable. Thus, the simplest complete factorial design is one with two independent variables, each with two levels. Let's consider an example. Suppose we manipulate two independent variables: word type (concrete versus abstract words) and rehearsal type (rote versus imagery). The independent variable Word Type has two levels: abstract and concrete; the independent variable Rehearsal Type also has two levels: rote and imagery. This is known as a 2 × 2 factorial design.

The factorial notation for a factorial design is determined as follows:

(number of levels of independent variable 1) × (number of levels of independent variable 2) × (number of levels of independent variable 3) . . .

factorial notation The notation that indicates how many independent variables are used in a study and how many levels are used for each variable.

Thus, the **factorial notation** indicates how many independent variables are used in the study and how many levels are used for each independent variable. This is often confusing for students who frequently think that, in the factorial notation 2 × 2, the first number (2) indicates that there are two independent variables, and the second number (2) indicates that each has two levels. This is *not* how to interpret factorial notation. Rather, each number in the notation specifies the number of levels of a single independent variable. Thus, a 3 × 6 factorial design is one with two independent variables; each of the two numbers in the factorial notation represents a single independent variable. In a 3 × 6 factorial design, one independent variable has three levels and the other has six levels.

Referring to our 2 × 2 factorial design, we see that there are two independent variables, each with two levels. This factorial design has four conditions (2 × 2 = 4): abstract words with rote rehearsal, abstract words with imagery rehearsal, concrete words with rote rehearsal, and concrete words with imagery rehearsal. How many conditions would there be in a 3 × 6 factorial design? If you answer 18, you are correct. Is it possible to have a 1 × 3 factorial design? If you answer no, you are correct. It is not possible to have a factor (variable) with one level because then it does not vary.

Main Effects and Interaction Effects

main effect An effect of a single independent variable.

interaction effect The effect of each independent variable across the levels of the other independent variables.

Two kinds of information can be gleaned from a factorial design. The first piece of information is whether there are any main effects. A **main effect** is an effect of a single independent variable. In our design with two independent variables, two main effects are possible: an effect of word type and an effect of rehearsal type. In other words, there can be as many main effects as there are independent variables. The second piece of information is whether there is an interaction effect. As the name implies, this is information regarding how the variables or factors interact. Specifically, an **interaction effect** is the effect

TABLE 12.1 Results of the 2 × 2 Factorial Design: Effects of Word Type and Rehearsal Type on Memory

REHEARSAL TYPE (INDEPENDENT VARIABLE B)	WORD TYPE (INDEPENDENT VARIABLE A)		ROW MEANS (MAIN EFFECT OF B)
	CONCRETE	ABSTRACT	
Rote rehearsal	5	5	5
Imagery rehearsal	10	5	7.5
Column means (Main effect of A)	7.5	5	

of each independent variable across the levels of the other independent variable. When there is an interaction between two independent variables, the effect of one independent variable depends on the level of the other independent variable. If this makes no sense at this point, don't worry; it will become clearer as we work through our example.

Let's look at the data from our study of the effects of word type and rehearsal type on memory. Table 12.1 presents the mean performance for participants in each condition. This was a completely between-subjects design—different subjects served in each of the four conditions. There were 8 subjects in each condition, for a total of 32 subjects in the study. Each participant in each condition was given a list of 10 words (either abstract or concrete) to learn using the specified rehearsal technique (rote or imagery).

Typically, researchers begin by assessing whether there is an interaction effect because having an interaction effect indicates that the effect of one independent variable depends on the level of the other independent variable. However, when first beginning to interpret two-way designs, students usually find it easier to begin with the main effects and then move on to the interaction effect. What we need to keep in mind is that if we later find an interaction effect, then any main effects will have to be qualified. Remember, because we have two independent variables, there is the possibility for two main effects: one for word type (variable A in the table) and one for rehearsal type (variable B in the table). The main effect of each independent variable tells us about the relationship between that single independent variable and the dependent variable. In other words, do different levels of one independent variable bring about changes in the dependent variable?

We can find the answer to this question by looking at the row and column means in Table 12.1. The column means tell us about the overall effect of variable A (word type). The column means indicate that there is a difference in the numbers of words recalled between the concrete and abstract word conditions. More concrete words were recalled (7.5) than abstract words (5). The column means represent the average performance for the concrete and abstract word conditions summarized across the rehearsal conditions. In other words, we obtained the column mean of 7.5 for the concrete word conditions by averaging the number of words recalled in the concrete word/rote rehearsal condition and the concrete word/imagery rehearsal condition [(5 + 10)/2 = 7.5]. Similarly, the column mean for the abstract word conditions (5) was obtained by averaging the data from the two abstract word conditions [(5 + 5)/2 = 5]. (Please note that determining the row and column means in this manner is possible only when the numbers of participants in each of the conditions are equal. If the numbers of participants in the conditions are unequal, then all individual scores in the single row or column must be used in the calculation of the row or column mean.)

The main effect for variable B (rehearsal type) can be assessed by looking at the row means. The row means indicate that there is a difference in the number of words recalled between the rote rehearsal and the imagery rehearsal conditions. More words were recalled when subjects used the imagery rehearsal technique (7.5) than when they used the rote rehearsal technique (5). As with the column means, the row means represent the average performance in the rote and imagery rehearsal conditions summarized across the word type conditions.

At face value, the main effects tell us that, overall, subjects recall more words when they are concrete and when imagery rehearsal is used. However, we now need to assess whether there is an interaction between the variables. If so, the main effects noted previously will have to be qualified, because an interaction indicates that the effect of one independent variable depends on the level of the other independent variable. In other words, an interaction effect indicates that the effect of one independent variable is different at different levels of the other independent variable.

Look again at the data in Table 12.1. There appears to be an interaction in these results because when rote rehearsal is used, word type makes no difference (the means are the same—5 words recalled). However, when imagery rehearsal is used, word type makes a big difference. Specifically, when imagery is used with concrete words, subjects do very well (recall an average of 10 words); yet when imagery is used with abstract words, subjects perform the same as they did in both of the rote rehearsal conditions (recall an average of only 5 words). Think about what this means. When there is an interaction between the two variables, the effect of one independent variable differs at different levels of the other independent variable; there is a contrast or a difference in the way participants perform across the levels of the independent variables.

Another way to assess whether there is an interaction effect in a study is to graph the means. Figure 12.1 shows a line graph of the data presented in Table 12.1. The interaction may be easier for you to see here. First, when there is an interaction between variables, the lines are not parallel; they have markedly different slopes. You can see in the figure that one line is flat (representing the data from the rote rehearsal conditions), whereas the other line has a positive slope (representing the data from the imagery

FIGURE 12.1 Line graph representing interaction between rehearsal type and word type

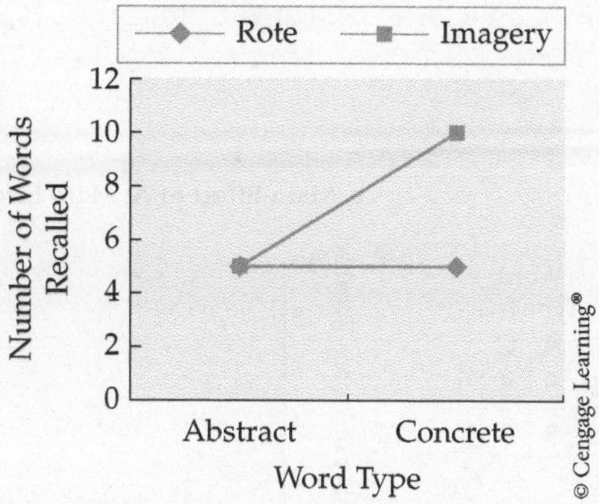

rehearsal conditions). Look at the figure, and think about the interaction. The flat line indicates that when rote rehearsal was used, word type had no effect (the line is flat because the means are the same). The line with the positive slope indicates that when imagery rehearsal was used, word type had a big effect—subjects remembered more concrete words than abstract words.

You are probably familiar with the concept of interaction in your own life. When we say "It depends," we are indicating that what we do in one situation depends on some other variable—there is an interaction. For example, whether you go to a party depends on whether you have to work and who is going to be at the party. If you have to work, you will not go to the party under any circumstance. However, if you do not have to work, you might go if a "certain person" is going to be there. If that person is not going to be there, you will not go. See if you can graph this interaction. The dependent variable, which always goes on the y-axis, is the likelihood of going to the party. One independent variable is placed on the x-axis (whether or not you have to work), and the levels of the other independent variable are captioned in the graph (whether the certain person is or is not present at the party).

To determine whether main effects or an interaction effect are significant, we need to conduct statistical analyses. We will discuss the appropriate analysis later in this chapter.

Possible Outcomes of a 2 × 2 Factorial Design

A 2 × 2 factorial design has several possible outcomes. Because there are two independent variables, there may or may not be a significant effect of each. In addition, there may or may not be a significant interaction effect. Thus, there are eight possible outcomes in all (possible combinations of significant and nonsignificant effects). Figure 12.2 illustrates these eight possible outcomes for a 2 × 2 factorial design, using the same study we have been discussing as an example. Obviously, only one of these outcomes is possible

FIGURE 12.2 Possible outcomes of a 2 × 2 factorial design with rehearsal type and word type as independent variables

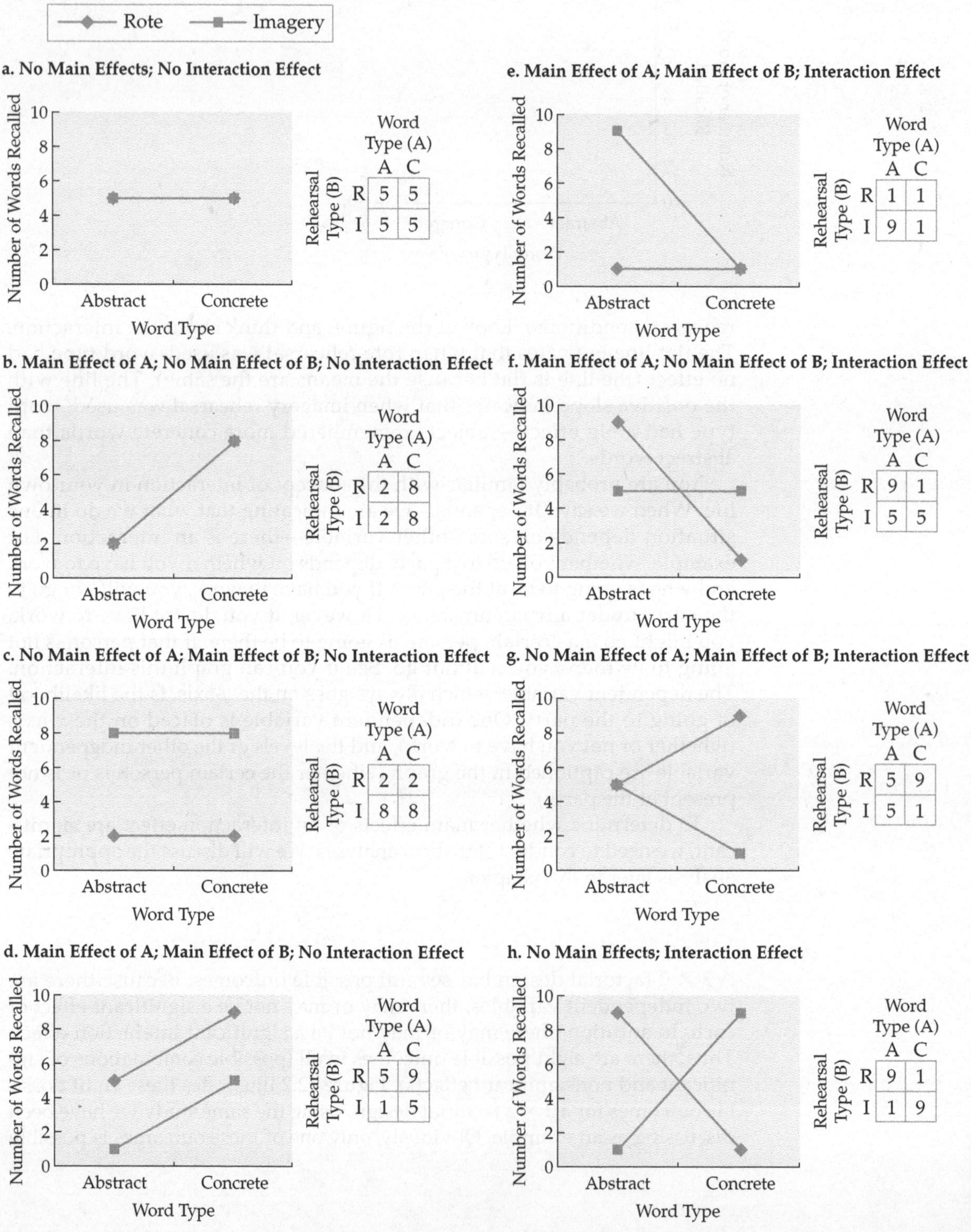

in a single study. All eight are graphed here to give you a concrete illustration of each possibility.

For each graph, the dependent variable (number of words recalled) is placed on the *y*-axis, and independent variable A (word type) is placed on the *x*-axis. The two means for one level of independent variable B (rehearsal type) are plotted, and a line is drawn to represent this level of independent variable B. In the same fashion, the means for the second level of independent variable B are plotted, and a second line is drawn to represent this level of independent variable B. Next to each graph is a matrix showing the means from the four conditions in the study. The graphs were derived by plotting the four means from each matrix. In addition, whether mains effects and an interaction effect are present has been indicated.

Can you tell from looking at the graphs which ones represent interaction effects? If you identify graphs a, b, c, and d as not having interaction effects and graphs e, f, g, and h as having interaction effects, you are correct. You should have a greater appreciation for interaction after looking at these graphs. Notice that in graphs a through d, there is no interaction because each level of independent variable A (word type) affects the levels of independent variable B (rehearsal type) in the same way. For example, look at graphs c and d. In graph c, the lines are parallel with no slope. This indicates that for both rote and imagery rehearsal, word type makes no difference. In graph d, the lines are parallel and sloped. This indicates that for both rote and imagery rehearsal, word type has the same effect: Performance is poorer for abstract words and then increases by the same amount for concrete words.

Now look at graphs e through h, which represent interaction effects. Sometimes there is an interaction because there is no relationship between the independent variable and the dependent variable at one level of the second independent variable, but a strong relationship at the other level of the second independent variable. Graphs e and f show this. In graph e, when rote rehearsal is used, word type makes no difference, whereas when imagery rehearsal is used, word type makes a big difference. In graph f, the interaction is due to a similar result. Sometimes, however, an interaction may indicate that an independent variable has an opposite effect on the dependent variable at different levels of the second independent variable. Graphs g and h illustrate this. In graph g, when rote rehearsal is used, performance improves for concrete words versus abstract words (a positive relationship). However, when imagery rehearsal is used, performance decreases for concrete words versus abstract words (a negative relationship). Finally, graph h shows similar but more dramatic results. There is a complete crossover interaction, where exactly the opposite result is occurring for independent variable B at the levels of independent variable A. Notice also in this graph that although there is a large crossover interaction, there are no main effects.

To make sure you completely understand interpreting main effects and interaction effects, cover the titles in each part of Figure 12.2 and quiz yourself on whether there are main effects and/or an interaction effect in each graph.

Complex Designs — IN REVIEW

	DESCRIPTION	ADVANTAGE OR EXAMPLE
Factorial Design	Any design with more than one independent variable.	In the example in this chapter, word type and rehearsal type were both manipulated to assess main effects and an interaction effect. The advantage is that it more closely resembles the real world because the results are due to more than one factor (variable).
Factorial Notation	The numerical notation corresponding to a factorial design. It indicates, in brief form, the number of independent variables and the number of levels of each variable.	A 3×4 design has two independent variables, one with three levels and one with four levels.
Main Effect	An effect of a single independent variable. A main effect describes the effect of a single variable as if there were no other variables in the study.	In a study with two independent variables, two main effects are possible—one for each variable.
Interaction Effect	The effect of each independent variable at the levels of the other independent variable.	Interaction effects allow us to assess whether the effect of one variable depends on the level of the other variable. In this way, we can more closely simulate the real world, where multiple variables often interact.

CRITICAL THINKING CHECK 12.1

1. What is the factorial notation for the following design? A pizza parlor owner is interested in what type of pizza is most preferred by his customers. He manipulates the type of crust for the pizzas by using thin, thick, and hand-tossed crusts. In addition, he manipulates the topping for the pizzas by offering cheese, pepperoni, sausage, veggie, and everything. He then has his customers sample the various pizzas and rate them. After you have determined the factorial notation, indicate how many conditions are in this study.
2. How many main effect(s) and interaction effect(s) are possible in a 4×6 factorial design?
3. Draw a graph representing the following data from a study using the same independent variables as in the chapter example. Determine whether there are any main effects or an interaction effect.

   Rote rehearsal/Concrete words: $\overline{X} = 10$
   Rote rehearsal/Abstract words: $\overline{X} = 1$
   Imagery rehearsal/Concrete words: $\overline{X} = 9$
   Imagery rehearsal/Abstract words: $\overline{X} = 9$

Statistical Analysis of Complex Designs

As discussed in Chapter 11, an ANOVA is the type of statistical analysis most commonly used when interval-ratio data have been collected. For the factorial designs discussed in this chapter, a two-way ANOVA would be used. The term *two-way* indicates that there are two independent variables in the study. If a design has three independent variables, then we would use a three-way ANOVA; if there were four independent variables, a four-way ANOVA; and so on. With a between-subjects design, a two-way randomized ANOVA is used. With a correlated-groups factorial design, a two-way repeated measures ANOVA is used. If the data in a study are not interval-ratio and the design is complex (more than one independent variable), then nonparametric statistics are appropriate. These will not be discussed in this chapter but can be found in more advanced statistics texts.

Two-Way Randomized ANOVA: What It Is and What It Does

A two-way ANOVA is similar to a one-way ANOVA in that it analyzes the variance between groups and within groups. The logic is the same: If either of the variables has an effect, the variance between the groups should be greater than the variance within the groups. As with the one-way ANOVA, an *F*-ratio is formed by dividing the between-groups variance by the within-groups variance. The difference is that in the two-way ANOVA, between-groups variance may be attributable to factor A (one of the independent variables in the study), to factor B (the second independent variable in the study), and to the interaction of factors A and B. With two independent variables, there is a possibility of a main effect for each variable, and an *F*-ratio is calculated to represent each of these effects. In addition, there is the possibility of an interaction effect, and an *F*-ratio is also needed to represent this effect. Thus, with a two-way ANOVA, there are three *F*-ratios to calculate and ultimately to interpret.

In a 2×2 factorial design, such as the one we have been looking at in this chapter, there are three null and alternative hypotheses. The null hypothesis for factor A states that there is no main effect for factor A, and the alternative hypothesis states that there is an effect of factor A (the differences observed between the groups are greater than what would be expected based on chance). In other words, the null hypothesis states that the population means represented by the sample means are from the same population, and the alternative hypothesis states that the population means represented by the sample means are not from the same population. A second null hypothesis states that there is no main effect for factor B, and the alternative hypothesis states that there is an effect of factor B. The third null hypothesis states that there is no interaction of factors A and B, and the alternative hypothesis states that there is an interaction effect.

TABLE 12.2 Number of Words Recalled as a Function of Word Type and Rehearsal Type

REHEARSAL TYPE (INDEPENDENT VARIABLE B)	WORD TYPE (INDEPENDENT VARIABLE A)		ROW MEANS (MAIN EFFECT OF B)
	CONCRETE	ABSTRACT	
Rote rehearsal	4	5	
	5	4	
	3	5	
	6	6	4.5 (across all rote rehearsal conditions)
	2	4	
	2	5	
	6	6	
Cell mean = 4	4	5	Cell mean = 5
Imagery rehearsal	10	6	
	12	5	
	11	6	
	9	7	8 (across all imagery rehearsal conditions)
	8	6	
	10	6	
	10	7	
Cell mean = 10	10	5	Cell mean = 6
Column Means (Main effect of A)	7 (across all concrete word conditions)	5.5 (across all abstract word conditions)	Grand mean = 6.25

Table 12.2 presents the number of words recalled by the 32 participants in the memory study with 8 participants in each condition. We will use these data to illustrate the use of a two-way randomized ANOVA. As in Chapter 11, the definitional formulas for the various sums of squares (SS) will be provided and used to calculate each SS. The computational formulas are provided in Appendix B if your instructor prefers that you use them.

Calculations for the Two-Way Randomized ANOVA. In a two-way ANOVA, there are several sources of variance; therefore, several sums of squares must be calculated. Let's begin with the total sum of squares (SS_{Total}), which represents the sum of the squared deviation scores for all subjects in the study. This is calculated in the same manner as it was in Chapter 11. The definitional formula is $SS_{\text{Total}} = \Sigma(X - \overline{X}_G)^2$, where X refers to each individual's score,

TABLE 12.3 Calculation of SS_{Total} Using the Definitional Formula

ROTE/CONCRETE		ROTE/ABSTRACT		IMAGERY/CONCRETE		IMAGERY/ABSTRACT	
X	$(X - \overline{X}_G)^2$	X	$(X - \overline{X}_G)^2$	X	$(X - \overline{X}_G)^2$	X	$(X - \overline{X}_G)^2$
4	5.0625	5	1.5625	10	14.0625	6	0.0625
5	1.5625	4	5.0625	12	33.0625	5	1.5625
3	10.5625	5	1.5625	11	22.5625	6	0.0625
6	0.0625	6	0.0625	9	7.5625	7	0.5625
2	18.0625	4	5.0625	8	3.0625	6	0.0625
2	18.0625	5	1.5625	10	14.0625	6	0.0625
6	0.0625	6	0.0625	10	14.0625	7	0.5625
4	5.0625	5	1.5625	10	14.0625	5	1.5625
	$\Sigma = 58.50$		16.50		122.50		4.50

$SS_{Total} = 58.50 + 16.50 + 122.50 + 4.50 = 202$

and $\overline{X}_G$ is the grand mean for the study. The use of this formula is illustrated in Table 12.3, where we see that $SS_{Total} = 202$. As in the one-way ANOVA, we can use SS_{Total} as a check on the accuracy of our calculations. In other words, when we finish calculating all of the other sums of squares, they should sum to equal the total sum of squares. The df_{Total} is determined in the same manner as in the ANOVA examples in Chapter 11, $N - 1$. In this case, $df_{Total} = 31$.

In addition to total variance, there is variance due to factor A (word type). This will tell us whether the main effect of factor A is significant. Similarly, there is variance due to factor B (rehearsal type), which will tell us whether the main effect of factor B is significant. Both of these sources of variance are determined by first calculating the appropriate sums of squares for each term and then dividing by the corresponding degrees of freedom for each term to obtain the mean square for each factor. The **sum of squares factor A** (SS_A) represents the sum of the squared deviation scores of each group mean for factor A minus the grand mean times the number of scores in each factor A condition (column). The definitional formula is $SS_A = \Sigma[(\overline{X}_A - \overline{X}_G)^2 n_A]$, where $\overline{X}_A$ is the mean for each condition of factor A, $\overline{X}_G$ is the grand mean, and n_A is the number of people in each of the factor A conditions. The use of this formula is illustrated in Table 12.4. Notice that $n_A = 16$. We use 16 because the column means for factor A are derived based on the 16 scores that make up the concrete word conditions (8 subjects in the concrete/rote condition and 8 subjects in the concrete/imagery condition) and the 16 scores that make up the abstract word conditions (8 subjects in the abstract/rote condition and 8 subjects in the abstract/imagery condition). As can be seen in Table 12.4, $SS_A = 18$. The df_A are equal to the number of levels of factor A minus 1. Because factor A has two levels, there is 1 degree of freedom. The mean square for factor A can now be calculated by dividing SS_A by df_A. Thus, the mean square for factor A (MS_A) is $18/1 = 18$.

sum of squares factor A The sum of the squared deviation scores of each group mean for factor A minus the grand mean times the number of scores in each factor A condition.

TABLE 12.4 Calculation of SS_A Using the Definitional Formula

$$
\begin{aligned}
SS_A &= \Sigma[(\bar{X}_A - \bar{X}_G)^2 n_A] \\
&= [(7 - 6.25)^2 16] + [(5.5 - 6.25)^2 16] \\
&= [(0.75)^2 16] + [(-0.75)^2 16] \\
&= [(0.5625)16] + [(0.5625)16] \\
&= 9 + 9 \\
&= 18
\end{aligned}
$$

sum of squares factor B The sum of the squared deviation scores of each group mean for factor B minus the grand mean times the number of scores in each factor B condition.

The **sum of squares factor B** (SS_B) is calculated in a similar manner. In other words, SS_B is the sum of the squared deviation scores of each group mean for factor B minus the grand mean times the number of scores in each factor B condition. The definitional formula is $SS_B = \Sigma[(\bar{X}_B - \bar{X}_G)^2 n_B]$, where $\bar{X}_B$ is the mean for each condition of factor B, $\bar{X}_G$ is the grand mean, and n_B is the number of people in each of the factor B conditions. The SS_B calculated in Table 12.5 is 98. Notice that, as with factor A, n_B is 16—the total number of scores that contribute to the row means. In addition, as with factor A, the mean square for factor B is calculated by dividing SS_B by df_B. The df_B is derived by taking the number of levels of factor B minus 1. This is $2 - 1 = 1$, and MS_B is therefore $98/1 = 98$.

sum of squares interaction The sum of the squared difference of each condition mean minus the grand mean times the number of scores in each condition. SS_A and SS_B are then subtracted from this sum.

We also have to consider the variance due to the interaction of factors A and B, which will tell us whether or not there is a significant interaction effect. The **sum of squares interaction** ($SS_{A \times B}$) is the sum of the squared difference of each condition mean minus the grand mean times the number of scores in each condition. Because this gives us an estimate of the amount of variance in the scores about their respective condition means, it includes the amount of variance due to factor A, factor B, and the interaction. Thus, after this sum is calculated, we must subtract the variance due solely to factor A and the variance due solely to factor B. The definitional formula is thus $SS_{A \times B} = \Sigma[(\bar{X}_C - \bar{X}_G)^2 n_C] - SS_A - SS_B$, where $\bar{X}_C$ is the mean for each condition (cell), $\bar{X}_G$ is the grand mean, and n_C is the number of scores in each condition or cell. The calculation of $SS_{A \times B}$ is illustrated in Table 12.6. As can be seen, the sum of squares for the interaction term is 50. We must

TABLE 12.5 Calculation of SS_B Using the Definitional Formula

$$
\begin{aligned}
SS_B &= \Sigma[(\bar{X}_B - \bar{X}_G)^2 n_B] \\
&= [(4.5 - 6.25)^2 16] + [(8 - 6.25)^2 16] \\
&= [(-1.75)^2 16] + [(1.75)^2 16] \\
&= [(3.0625)16] + [(3.0625)16] \\
&= 49 + 49 \\
&= 98
\end{aligned}
$$

TABLE 12.6 Calculation of $SS_{A \times B}$ Using the Definitional Formula

$$SS_{A\times B} = \Sigma[(\bar{X}_C - \bar{X}_G)^2 n_C] - SS_A - SS_B$$
$$= [(4 - 6.25)^2 8] + [(5 - 6.25)^2 8] + [(10 - 6.25)^2 8] + [(6 - 6.25)^2 8] - 18 - 98$$
$$= [(-2.25)^2 8] + [(-1.25)^2 8] + [(3.75)^2 8] + [(-0.25)^2 8] - 18 - 98$$
$$= [(5.625)8] + [(1.5625)8] + [(14.0625)8] + [(0.0625)8] - 18 - 98$$
$$= 40.50 + 12.50 + 112.50 + 0.50 - 18 - 98$$
$$= 50$$

divide this number by its corresponding degrees of freedom. The degrees of freedom for the interaction are based on the number of conditions in the study. In the present study, there are four conditions. To determine the degrees of freedom across the conditions, we multiply the degrees of freedom for the factors involved in the interaction. In the present case, factor A has 1 degree of freedom, and factor B also has 1 degree of freedom. Thus, $df_{A\times B} = (A - 1)(B - 1)$. Using this to determine $MS_{A\times B}$, we find that $50/1 = 50$.

Last, we have to determine the amount of variance due to error—the within-groups variance. As in a one-way ANOVA, the within-groups variance is an indication of the amount of variance of the scores within a cell or condition about that cell mean. The **sum of squares error** (SS_{Error}) is the sum of the squared deviations of each score from its condition (cell) mean. The definitional formula is $SS_{Error} = \Sigma(X - \bar{X}_C)^2$. The calculation of SS_{Error} is illustrated in Table 12.7. In the present study, SS_{Error} is 36. We can now check

sum of squares error The sum of the squared deviations of each score from its group (cell) mean; the within-groups sum of squares in a factorial design.

TABLE 12.7 Calculation of SS_{Error} Using the Definitional Formula

ROTE/CONCRETE		ROTE/ABSTRACT		IMAGERY/CONCRETE		IMAGERY/ABSTRACT	
X	$(X - \bar{X}_C)^2$	X	$(X - \bar{X}_C)^2$	X	$(X - \bar{X}_C)^2$	X	$(X - \bar{X}_C)^2$
4	0	5	0	10	0	6	0
5	1	4	1	12	4	5	1
3	1	5	0	11	1	6	0
6	4	6	1	9	1	7	1
2	4	4	1	8	4	6	0
2	4	5	0	10	0	6	0
6	4	6	1	10	0	7	1
4	0	5	0	10	0	5	1
$\Sigma =$	18		4		10		4

$SS_{Error} = 18 + 4 + 10 + 4 = 36$

all of our calculations by summing SS_A, SS_B, $SS_{A\times B}$, and SS_{Error}: 18 + 98 + 50 + 36 = 202. We previously found that SS_{Total} = 202, so we know that our calculations are correct.

The df_{Error} is determined by assessing the degrees of freedom within each of the design's conditions. In other words, the number of conditions in the study is multiplied by the number of participants in each condition minus the one score not free to vary, or $AB(n - 1)$. In the present example, this is 4(8 − 1), or 28. As a check, when we total the degrees of freedom for A, B, A × B, and error, they should equal df_{Total}. In this case, $df_A = 1$, $df_B = 1$, $df_{A\times B} = 1$, and $df_{Error} = 28$. They sum to 31, which is the df_{Total} we calculated previously. To determine MS_{Error}, we divide SS_{Error} by its degrees of freedom: 36/28 = 1.29.

Now that we have calculated the sum of squares, degrees of freedom, and mean squares for each term, we can determine the corresponding *F*-ratios. In a two-way ANOVA, there are three *F*-ratios: one for factor A, one for factor B, and one for the interaction of factors A and B. Each of the *F*-ratios is determined by dividing the *MS* for the appropriate term by the MS_{Error}. Thus, for factor A (word type), the *F*-ratio is 18/1.29 = 13.95. For factor B (rehearsal type), the *F*-ratio is determined in the same manner: 98/1.29 = 75.97. Last, for the interaction, the *F*-ratio is 50/1.29 = 38.76. The definitional formulas for the sums of squares and the formulas for the degrees of freedom, mean squares, and *F*-ratios are summarized in Table 12.8. Table 12.9 shows the ANOVA summary table for the data from the present study.

Interpreting the Two-Way Randomized ANOVA. Our obtained *F*-ratios are all greater than 1.00. To determine whether they are large enough to let us reject the null hypotheses, however, we need to compare our obtained *F*-ratios with F_{cv}. As we learned in Chapter 11, the underlying *F* distribution

TABLE 12.8 ANOVA Summary Table: Definitional Formulas

SOURCE	*df*	*SS*	*MS*	*F*
Factor A (word type)	$A - 1$	$\Sigma[(\bar{X}_A - \bar{X}_G)^2 n_A]$	$\frac{SS_A}{df_A}$	$\frac{MS_A}{MS_{Error}}$
Factor B (rehearsal type)	$B - 1$	$\Sigma[(\bar{X}_B - \bar{X}_G)^2 n_B]$	$\frac{SS_B}{df_B}$	$\frac{MS_B}{MS_{Error}}$
A × B	$(A - 1)(B - 1)$	$\Sigma[(\bar{X}_C - \bar{X}_G)^2 n_C] - SS_A - SS_B$	$\frac{SS_{A\times B}}{df_{A\times B}}$	$\frac{MS_{A\times B}}{MS_{Error}}$
Error	$AB(n - 1)$	$\Sigma(X - \bar{X}_C)^2$	$\frac{SS_{Error}}{df_{Error}}$	
Total	$N - 1$	$\Sigma(X - \bar{X}_G)^2$		

TABLE 12.9 Two-Way ANOVA Summary Table

SOURCE	*df*	*SS*	*MS*	*F*
Factor A (word type)	1	18	18	13.95
Factor B (rehearsal type)	1	98	98	75.97
A × B	1	50	50	38.76
Error	28	36	1.29	
Total	31	202		

is actually a family of distributions, each based on the degrees of freedom between and within each group. Remember that the alternative hypotheses are that the population means represented by the sample means are not from the same population. Table A.5 in Appendix A provides the critical values for the family of F distributions when $\alpha = .05$ and when $\alpha = .01$. We use this table exactly as we did in Chapter 11. That is, we use the df_{Error} (remember, df_{Error} is the degrees of freedom within groups, or the degrees of freedom for error variance) running down the left-hand side of the table and the $df_{Between}$ running across the top of the table. F_{cv} is found where the row and column corresponding to these two numbers intersect. You might be wondering what $df_{Between}$ is in the present example. It always represents the degrees of freedom between groups. However, in a two-way ANOVA, we have three values of $df_{Between}$: one for factor A, one for factor B, and one for the interaction term. Therefore, we need to determine three values of F_{cv}, one for each of the three terms in the study.

To determine F_{cv} for factor A (word type), we look at the degrees of freedom for factor A ($df_A = 1$). This represents the degrees of freedom between groups for variable A, or the number running across the top of Table A.5. We move down the left-hand column to the df_{Error} (df_{Within}), which is 28. Where 1 and 28 intersect, we find that F_{cv} for the .05 level is 4.20, and F_{cv} for the .01 level is 7.64. This means that for our F_{obt} to be significant at either of these levels, it has to exceed the F_{cv} for that alpha level. Because our F_{obt} for factor A exceeds both of these values of F_{cv}, it is significant at the .01 level. In APA publication format, this is written as $F(1, 28) = 13.95, p < .01$. This means that there was a significant main effect of factor A (word type). If we look at the column means from Table 12.2 for word type, we see that participants did better (remembered more words) when concrete words were used than when abstract words were used. I have initially interpreted the main effect of factor A at face value, but we will see when we interpret the interaction that subjects did not remember concrete words better in both of the rehearsal type conditions.

We also need to determine F_{cv} for variable B and for the interaction term. Because the degrees of freedom are the same for all of the terms in this study (1, 28), we use the same values of F_{cv}. In addition, because the values of F_{obt} also exceed the F_{cv} of 7.64 for the .01 level, we know that the F_{obt} for factor B

FIGURE 12.3 Number of words recalled as a function of word type and rehearsal type

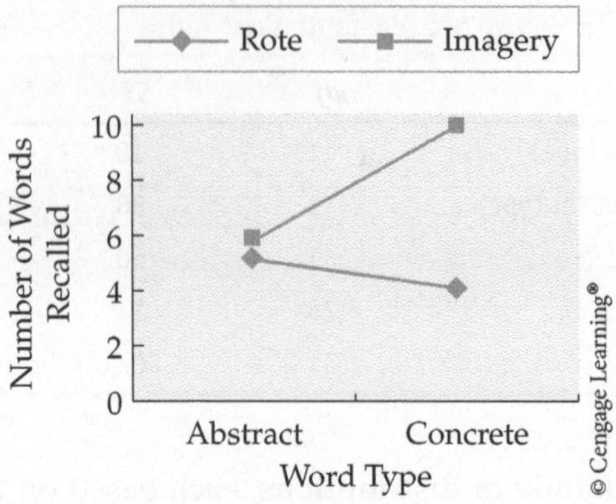

and for the interaction term are also significant at the .01 level. Thus, for factor B (rehearsal type), $F(1, 28) = 75.97$, $p < .01$, indicating a significant main effect of rehearsal type. Referring to the row means from Table 12.2, we see that subjects remembered substantially more words when imagery rehearsal was used than when rote rehearsal was used. Once again, I have interpreted the main effect of factor B at face value, but we will see that the interaction qualifies this interpretation. In other words, imagery rehearsal led to better performance overall, but not when we break it down by word type. Last, the interaction term, $F(1, 28) = 38.76$, $p < .01$, indicates that there was a significant interaction effect. When rote rehearsal was used, word type made little difference; however, when imagery rehearsal was used,the performance for the two word types varied. With imagery rehearsal, participants remembered significantly more concrete words than abstract words. As discussed earlier in the chapter, it is sometimes easier to interpret the interaction effect when looking at a figure. Thus, the condition means from Table 12.2 are graphed in Figure 12.3. You can see how to use either Excel or SPSS to complete these calculations in the statistical software resources section at the end of the chapter.

Assumptions of the Two-Way Randomized ANOVA. The two-way randomized ANOVA is used when you have a factorial design. The remaining assumptions are as follows:

- All conditions (cells) contain independent samples of subjects (in other words, there are different subjects in each condition).
- Interval or ratio data are collected.
- The populations represented by the data are roughly normally distributed.
- The populations represented by the data all have homogeneous variances.

Post Hoc Tests and Effect Size. As with a one-way ANOVA, post hoc tests, such as Tukey's HSD (honestly significant difference) test, are recommended.

For the present example, a 2 × 2 design, post hoc tests are not necessary, because any significant main effect indicates a significant difference between the two groups that make up that variable. In other words, because each independent variable in the present study has only two values, a significant main effect of that variable indicates significant differences between the two groups. If one or both of the independent variables in a factorial design have more than two levels and the main effect(s) is (are) significant, then Tukey's HSD test should be conducted to determine exactly which groups differ significantly from each other. In addition, it is also possible to use a variation of the Tukey HSD test to compare the means from a significant interaction effect. These calculations are beyond the scope of this book but can be found in a more advanced statistics text.

"I THINK YOU SHOULD BE MORE EXPLICIT HERE IN STEP TWO."

As noted in previous chapters, when a significant relationship is observed, we should also calculate the effect size—the proportion of variance in the dependent variable that is accounted for by the manipulation of the independent variable(s). In Chapter 11, we used eta-squared (η^2) as a measure of effect size with ANOVAs. You may remember that $\eta^2 = SS_{Between}/SS_{Total}$. When using a two-way ANOVA, we have three values of $SS_{Between}$: one for variable A, one for variable B, and one for the interaction term. Referring to Table 12.9, we can obtain the *SS* scores needed for these calculations. For factor A (word type), η^2 is calculated as

$$\eta^2 = \frac{18}{202} = .089$$

This means that factor A (word type) can account for 8.9% of the total variance in the number of words recalled. We can also calculate the effect sizes for factor B (rehearsal type) and the interaction term using the same formula. For factor B, η^2 is 98/202 = .485. In other words, factor B (rehearsal type) can account for 48.5% of the total variance in the number of words recalled. Clearly, rehearsal type is very important in determining the number of words recalled; according to Cohen (1988), this effect size is meaningful. Last, for the interaction effect, η^2 = 50/202 = .25. Thus, the interaction of factors A and B can account for 25% of the variance in the number of words recalled. This means that knowing the individual cell or condition (in other words, the factor A by factor B condition) that the subjects were in can account for 25% of the variance in the dependent variable. This is also a meaningful effect size.

Two-Way Randomized ANOVA — IN REVIEW

CONCEPT	DESCRIPTION
Null hypothesis (H_0)	The independent variable had no effect; the samples all represent the same population. In a two-way ANOVA, there are three null hypotheses: one for factor A, one for factor B, and one for the interaction of factors A and B.
Alternative hypothesis (H_a)	The independent variable had an effect; at least one of the samples represents a different population than the others. In a two-way ANOVA, there are three alternative hypotheses: one for factor A, one for factor B, and one for the interaction of factors A and B.
F-ratio	The ratio formed when the between-groups variance is divided by the within-groups variance. In a two-way ANOVA, there are three *F*-ratios: one for factor A, one for factor B, and one for the interaction of factors A and B.
Between-groups variance	An estimate of the variance of the group means from the grand mean. In a two-way ANOVA, there are three types of between-groups variance: that attributable to factor A, that attributable to factor B, and that attributable to the interaction of factors A and B.
Within-groups variance	An estimate of the variance within each condition in the experiment; also known as error variance, or variance due to chance.
Eta-squared (η^2)	A measure of effect size—the variability in the dependent variable attributable to the independent variable. In a two-way ANOVA, eta-squared is calculated for factor A, for factor B, and for the interaction of factors A and B.
Tukey's post hoc test	A test conducted to determine which conditions from a variable with more than two conditions differ significantly from each other.

CRITICAL THINKING CHECK 12.2

1. Assuming there were two significant main effects in a hypothetical 2 × 4 design, would Tukey's HSD need to be calculated for these main effects? Why or why not?
2. A researcher is attempting to determine the effects of practice and gender on a timed task. Participants in the experiment are given a computerized search task. They search a computer screen of various characters and attempt to find a particular character on each trial. When they find the designated character, they press a button to stop a timer. Their reaction time (in milliseconds) on each trial is recorded. Subjects practice for 1, 2, or 3 hours and are either female or male. The ANOVA summary table appears next, along with the means for each condition and the number of subjects in each condition.

Two-Way ANOVA Summary Table

Source	*df*	*SS*	*MS*	*F*
Factor A (gender)		684,264		
Factor B (practice)		989,504		
A × B		489,104		
Error		2,967,768		
Total		5,130,640		

Condition	*Mean*	*n*
Female/1 hour	1,778.125	8
Female/2 hours	1,512.375	8
Female/3 hours	1,182.75	8
Male/1 hour	1,763.375	8
Male/2 hours	1,764.25	8
Male/3 hours	1,662	8

a. Identify the factorial notation for the design.
b. Complete the ANOVA summary table.
c. Determine significance levels for any main or interaction effect(s).
d. Explain any significant main or interaction effect(s).
e. Calculate eta-squared for any significant effects.
f. Draw a graph representing the data.

Two-Way Repeated Measures ANOVA and Mixed ANOVAs

When a complex within-subjects (the same subjects are used in all conditions) or matched-subjects (subjects are matched across conditions) design is used, and the data collected are interval-ratio in scale, then the appropriate statistic is a two-way repeated measures ANOVA. This ANOVA is similar to the two-way randomized ANOVA in that it indicates whether there is a significant main effect of either independent variable in the study and whether the interaction effect is significant. However, a correlated-groups design requires slight modifications in the formulas applied. If you find yourself in a situation where it is necessary to use a two-way repeated measures ANOVA, you can find the calculations in a more advanced statistics text. In addition, some complex designs are *mixed*—one variable is manipulated between-subjects and one within-subjects. Calculations for such designs can be found in a more advanced statistics text.

Beyond the Two-Way ANOVA

In this and the previous chapter, we have discussed one- and two-way ANOVAs. It is possible to add more factors (independent variables) to a study and to analyze the data with an ANOVA. For example, if a study used three independent variables, then a three-way ANOVA would be used. In this situation, there would be three main effects, three two-way interactions, and one three-way interaction to interpret. This means that there would be seven *F*-ratios to calculate. Obviously, this complicates the interpretation of the data considerably. Because three-way interactions are so difficult to interpret, most researchers try to design studies that are not quite so complex.

All of the studies discussed so far have had only one dependent variable. Besides adding independent variables, it is also possible to add dependent variables to a study. With one dependent variable, we use *univariate* statistics to analyze the data. Thus, all of the statistics discussed thus far in this text have been univariate statistics. When we have more than one dependent variable, we must use *multivariate* statistics to analyze the data. Many types of multivariate statistics are available, including the multivariate *t* test and the multivariate ANOVA, referred to as a MANOVA. These advanced statistics are beyond the scope of this book. If you encounter them in the literature, however, you can interpret them in a similar fashion to those statistics we have covered. In other words, the larger the *t*-score or *F*-ratio, the more likely it is that samples represent different populations and that the test statistic is significant.

Finally, a *meta-analysis* is a statistical procedure (also beyond the scope of this book) that combines, tests, and describes the results from many different studies. Before this technique was developed, researchers had to rely on more subjective reviews of the literature to summarize the general findings from many studies. By allowing researchers to assess the results from a large number of studies through one statistical procedure, a meta-analysis enables us to draw more objective conclusions about the generalizability of research findings.

Summary

In this chapter, we described experimental designs that use more than one independent variable. We discussed several advantages of using such designs and introduced the concepts of factorial notation, main effects, and interaction effects. After reading the section on main and interaction effects, you should be able to graph data from a factorial design and interpret what the graph means. We then discussed the statistical analysis of such designs by using a two-way randomized ANOVA. We presented the various calculations necessary to compute a two-way randomized ANOVA, along with the assumptions of the test and a description of how to interpret the results.

KEY TERMS

factorial design
factorial notation
main effect
interaction effect
sum of squares factor A
sum of squares factor B
sum of squares interaction
sum of squares error

CHAPTER EXERCISES

(Answers to odd-numbered exercises appear in Appendix C.)

1. What is the advantage of manipulating more than one independent variable in an experiment?
2. How many independent variables are in a 4 × 6 factorial design? How many conditions (cells) are in this design?
3. In a study, a researcher manipulated the number of hours that participants studied (either 4, 6, or 8), the type of study technique they used (shallow processing versus deep processing), and whether subjects studied individually or in groups. What is the factorial notation for this design?
4. What is the difference between a cell (condition) mean and the means used to interpret a main effect?
5. How many main effects and interaction effects are possible in a 2 × 6 factorial design?
6. What is the difference between a complete factorial design and an incomplete factorial design?
7. The cell means for two experiments appear next. Determine whether there are any effects of factor A, factor B, and A × B for each experiment. In addition, draw a graph representing the data from each experiment.

Experiment 1

	A_1	A_2
B_1	3	5
B_2	5	8

Experiment 2

	A_1	A_2
B_1	12	4
B_2	4	12

8. Explain the difference between a two-way ANOVA and a three-way ANOVA.
9. If you find two significant main effects in a 2 × 6 factorial design, should you compute Tukey's post hoc comparisons for both main effects?
10. Complete each of the following ANOVA summary tables. In addition, answer the following questions for each of the ANOVA summary tables:
    a. What is the factorial notation?
    b. How many conditions were in the study?

c. How many subjects were in the study?
d. Identify significant main effects and interaction effects.

Source	df	SS	MS	F
A	1	60		
B	2	40		
A × B	2	90		
Error	30			
Total	35	390		

Source	df	SS	MS	F
A	2	40		
B	3	60		
A × B	6	150		
Error	72			
Total	83	400		

Source	df	SS	MS	F
A	1	10		
B	1	60		
A × B	1	20		
Error	36			
Total	39	150		

11. In a study, a researcher measures the preference of men and women for two brands of frozen pizza (one low-fat and one regular) based on the number of 1-inch pieces of each type of pizza eaten when both types are available to the participants. The following table shows the number of pieces of each type of pizza eaten for each of the 24 subjects in the study.

	Women	Men
Brand 1	3	9
(low-fat)	4	7
	2	6
	2	8
	5	9
	3	7

	Women	Men
Brand 2	8	4
(regular)	9	2
	7	5
	10	6
	9	2
	10	5

Source	df	SS	MS	F
Gender		0.167		
Pizza brand		6.00		
Gender × Pizza		130.67		
Error		35.00		
Total		171.83		

a. Complete the ANOVA summary table. (If your instructor wants you to calculate the sums of squares, use the preceding data to do so.)
b. Are the values of F_{obt} significant at $\alpha = .05$? At $\alpha = .01$?
c. What conclusions can be drawn from the F-ratios?
d. What is the effect size, and what does this mean?
e. Graph the means.

12. A researcher is attempting to determine the effects of practice and gender on a timed task. Participants in an experiment are given a computerized search task. They search a computer screen of various characters and attempt to find a particular character on each trial. When they find the designated character, they press a button to stop a timer. Their reaction time (in seconds) on each trial is recorded. Subjects practice for 2, 4, or 6 hours and are either female or male. The reaction time data for the 30 subjects appear here.

	Women	Men
2 Hours	12	11
	13	12
	12	13
	11	12
	11	11
4 Hours	10	8
	10	8
	10	10
	8	10
	7	9
6 Hours	7	5
	5	6
	7	8
	6	6
	7	8

Source	df	SS	MS	F
Gender		0.027		
Practice		140.60		
Gender × Practice		0.073		
Error		28.00		
Total		168.70		

a. Complete the ANOVA summary table. (If your instructor wants you to calculate the sums of squares, use the preceding data to do so.)
b. Are the values of F_{obt} significant at $\alpha = .05$? At $\alpha = .01$?
c. What conclusions can be drawn from the F-ratios?
d. What is the effect size, and what does this mean?
e. Graph the means.

CRITICAL THINKING CHECK ANSWERS

12.1

1. This would be a 3 × 5 design. There are three types of crust and five types of toppings, so there are 15 conditions in this study.
2. A 4 × 6 factorial design has two independent variables. Thus, there is the possibility of two main effects (one for each independent variable) and one interaction effect (the interaction between the two independent variables).
3. There appears to be a main effect of word type, with concrete words recalled better than abstract words. There also appears to be a main effect of rehearsal type, with those who used imagery rehearsal remembering more words than those who used rote rehearsal. In addition, there appears to be an interaction effect. When imagery rehearsal is used, word type makes no difference; recall is very high for both types of words. When rote rehearsal is used, word type makes a large difference; concrete words are recalled very well and abstract words very poorly.

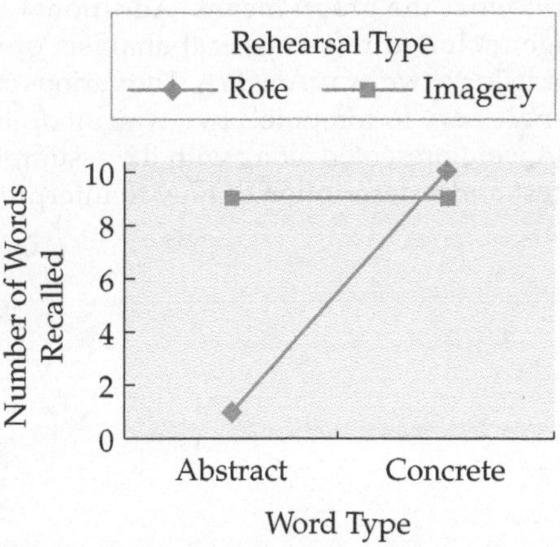

12.2

1. Tukey's HSD would not need to be calculated for the main effect of the variable with two levels because if there is a significant main effect for a variable with two levels, then we know that the difference between those two levels is significant. We would need to calculate Tukey's HSD for the variable with four levels to determine exactly which groups among the four differed significantly from each other.
2. a. This is a 2 × 3 design.

Practice	*Gender* *Female*	*Male*	*Row Means (Practice)*
1 hour	1,778.125	1,763.375	1,770.75
2 hours	1,512.375	1,764.25	1,638.31
3 hours	1,182.75	1,662	1,422.38
Column means (gender)	1,491.08	1,729.88	

b. *Two-Way ANOVA Summary Table*

Source	*df*	*SS*	*MS*	*F*
Factor A (gender)	1	684,264	684,264	9.68
Factor B (practice)	2	989,504	494,752	7.00
A × B	2	489,104	244,552	3.46
Error	42	2,967,768	70,661.143	
Total	47	5,130,640		

c. Gender: $F(1, 42) = 9.68, p < .01$
Practice: $F(2, 42) = 7.00, p < .01$
Interaction: $F(2, 42) = 3.46, p < .05$

d. The significant main effect of gender indicates that females performed more quickly than males. The significant main effect of practice indicates that as the amount of time spent practicing increased, reaction time decreased. The significant interaction effect indicates that practice affected only females; the more females practiced, the more quickly they responded. However, practice did not affect males; reaction times for males were consistent across the various practice conditions.

e. Eta-squared was .13 for gender, .19 for practice, and .095 for the interaction. Thus, overall, the proportion of variance in the dependent variable accounted for by the independent variables is .415, or 41.5%.

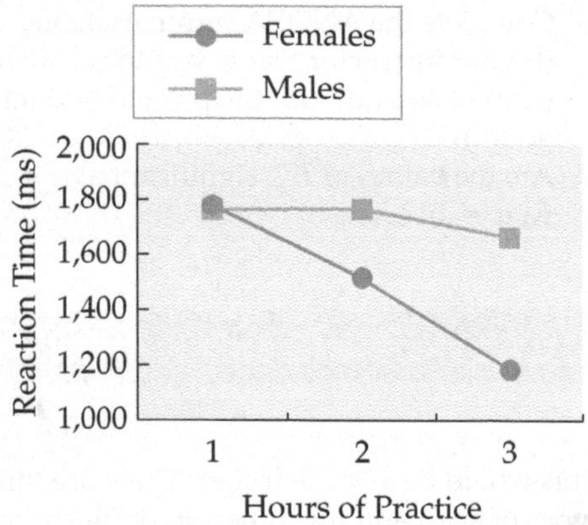

WEB RESOURCES

The book-specific website at CengageBrain.com offers students a variety of study tools and useful resources such as glossaries and flashcards.

Chapter 12 ■ Study Guide

CHAPTER 12 SUMMARY AND REVIEW: EXPERIMENTAL DESIGN AND ANALYSIS IV: COMPLEX EXPERIMENTAL DESIGNS

In this chapter, designs using more than one independent variable were described. The chapter discussed several advantages of using such designs and introduced the concepts of factorial notation, main effects, and interaction effects. After reading the section on main and interaction effects, you should be able to graph data from a factorial design and interpret what the graph means. Additional topic coverage included the statistical analysis of such designs, using a two-way ANOVA. The various calculations necessary to compute a two-way randomized ANOVA were presented along with the assumptions of the test and a description of how to interpret the results.

CHAPTER 12 STUDY GUIDE REVIEW EXERCISES

(Answers to exercises appear in Appendix C.)

FILL-IN SELF-TEST

Answer the following questions. If you have trouble answering any of the questions, restudy the relevant material before going on to the multiple-choice self test.

1. The notation that indicates how many independent variables were used in a study and how many levels there were for each variable is called ________.
2. An effect of a single independent variable is a ________.
3. In a 4 × 6 factorial design, there are ________ independent variables, one with ________ levels and one with ________ levels.
4. In a two-way randomized ANOVA, there is the possibility for ________ main effect(s) and ________ interaction effects.
5. In a two-way ANOVA, the sum of the squared deviations of each score minus its cell mean is the ________.
6. In an ANOVA, we use ________ to measure effect size.

MULTIPLE-CHOICE SELF-TEST

Select the single best answer for each of the following questions. If you have trouble answering any of the questions, restudy the relevant material.

1. When we manipulate more than one independent variable in a study, we:
   a. will have significant main effects.
   b. will have at least one significant interaction effect.
   c. are using a factorial design.
   d. All of the above
2. In a study examining the effects of time of day (morning, afternoon, or evening) and teaching style (lecture only versus lecture with small-group discussion) on student attentiveness, how many main effects are possible?
   a. 3
   b. 6
   c. 5
   d. 2
3. In a study examining the effects of time of day (morning, afternoon, or evening) and teaching style (lecture only versus lecture with small-group discussion) on student attentiveness, how many interaction effects are possible?
   a. 1
   b. 2
   c. 6
   d. 5
4. In a study examining the effects of time of day (morning, afternoon, or evening) and teaching style (lecture only versus lecture with small-group discussion) on student attentiveness, the factorial notation would be:
   a. 2 × 2.
   b. 2 × 3.
   c. 2 × 5.
   d. 3 × 3.
5. A 2 × 4 × 5 × 6 factorial design has ________ potential main effects.
   a. 2
   b. 3
   c. 4
   d. 24
6. An experiment with three independent variables, each with three levels, is a ________ design.
   a. 2 × 3
   b. 3 × 3
   c. 2 × 2 × 2
   d. 3 × 3 × 3
7. If the lines in a graph are not parallel, then there is most likely a(n):
   a. main effect of variable A.
   b. main effect of variable B.
   c. interaction effect.
   d. All of the above
8. A two-way randomized ANOVA is to ________ and a two-way repeated measures ANOVA is to ________.
   a. two independent variables manipulated between-subjects; two dependent variables manipulated within-subjects
   b. two dependent variables manipulated between-subjects; two independent variables manipulated within-subjects
   c. two independent variables manipulated between-subjects; two independent variables manipulated within-subjects
   d. two dependent variables manipulated between-subjects; two dependent variables manipulated within-subjects
9. When the effect of one independent variable depends on the level of the other independent variable we have observed a(n):
   a. main effect of one variable.
   b. main effect of a level of an independent variable.
   c. interaction effect.
   d. All of the above

10. How many conditions would there be in a factorial design with three levels of factor A and three levels of factor B?
    a. 6
    b. 3
    c. 9
    d. Unable to determine
11. In a study with two levels of factor A, four levels of factor B, and 5 participants in each condition, the *df* error would be:
    a. 39.
    b. 32.
    c. 8.
    d. 40.
12. In a study with two levels of factor A, four levels of factor B, and 5 participants in each condition, the *dfs* for factors A and B, respectively, would be ______ and ______.
    a. 2; 4
    b. 4; 4
    c. 1; 4
    d. 1; 3

SELF-TEST PROBLEMS

1. The following ANOVA table corresponds to an experiment with two factors: 1) Time of Day (morning, afternoon, or evening) and 2) Type of Teaching Method (lecture only or lecture with small-group activities). The attention level (on a 0 to 10 scale) of college students during the morning, afternoon, or evening is measured in each of the teaching method conditions. This is a completely between-subjects design. The scores for the five subjects in each group follow.

   Lecture Only/Morning: 8, 9, 9, 9, 10
   Lecture Only/Afternoon: 5, 6, 7, 8, 9
   Lecture Only/Evening: 5, 5, 6, 7, 7
   Lecture-Small-Group/Morning: 3, 4, 5, 6, 7
   Lecture-Small-Group/Afternoon: 5, 6, 6, 6, 7
   Lecture-Small-Group/Evening: 7, 7, 8, 9, 9

   The sums of squares are provided in the following table. However, for practice, see if you can correctly calculate them by hand.

   ANOVA Summary Table

Source	*df*	*SS*	*MS*	*F*
A (Time)		1.67		
B (Teaching Method)		7.50		
A × B		45.02		
Within		32.00		
Total				

   a. Construct the matrix showing the means in each cell and provide the factorial notation.
   b. Complete the ANOVA Summary Table.
   c. Are the F_{obt} significant at $\alpha = .05$? At $\alpha = .01$?
   d. What conclusions can be drawn from the *F*-ratio?
   e. What is the effect size, and what does this mean?
   f. Graph the means.

Chapter 12 ▪ Statistical Software Resources

TWO-WAY RANDOMIZED ANOVA

Let's use the memory study from this chapter to illustrate the calculation of a two-way randomized ANOVA. In this study, Factor A is word type (concrete versus abstract), Factor B is rehearsal type (rote versus imagery), and the dependent variable is the number of words recalled. Thus, there are two independent variables (word type and rehearsal type), each with two levels. Table 12.2 earlier in the chapter presents the number of words recalled by the 32 participants in the memory study with 8 participants in each condition.

Using Excel

We begin by entering the data from Table 12.2 into Excel with the column headings for word type and the row headings for rehearsal type included. See the example that follows.

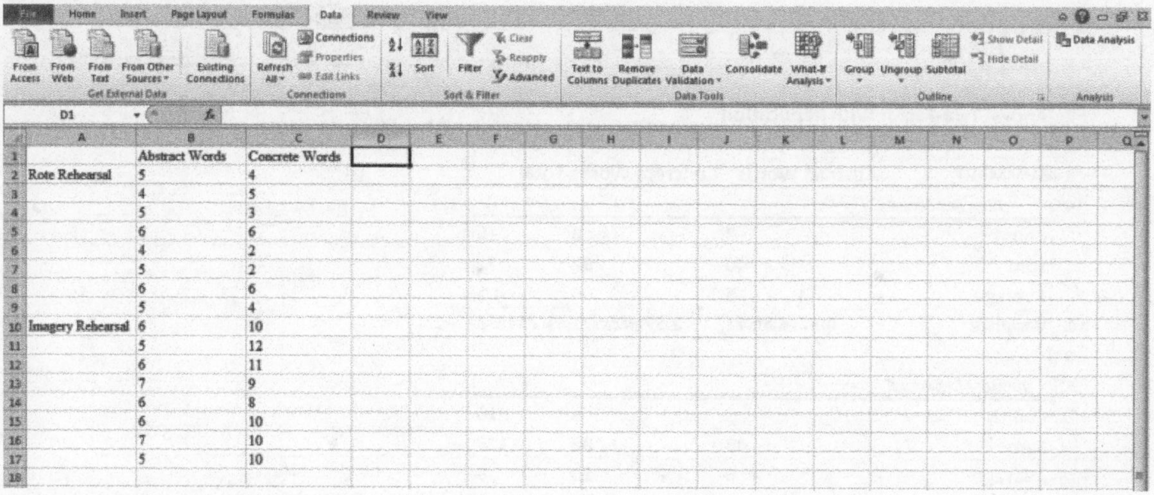

Next, with the **Data** ribbon highlighted, click on the **Data Analysis** tab at the top right corner. You will receive the following dialog box.

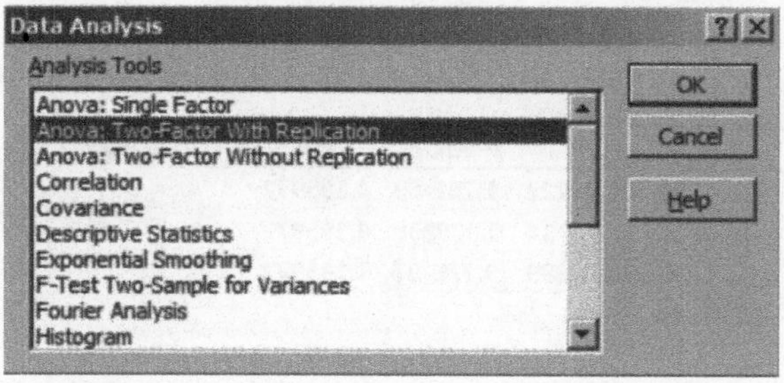

Select **Anova: Two-Factor With Replication** and click **OK**. The following dialog box will appear.

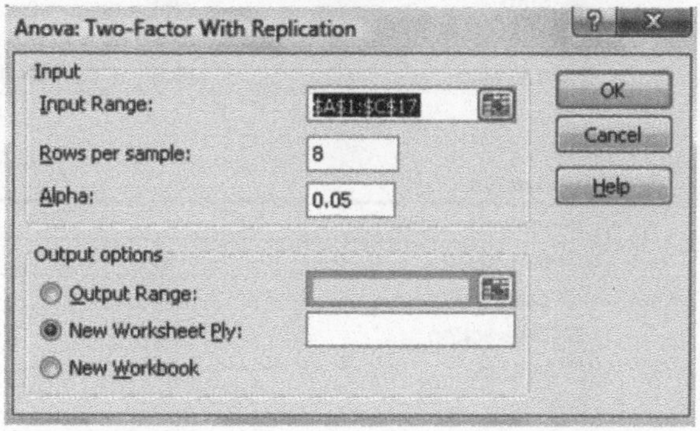

With the cursor in the **Input Range** box, highlight the three columns of labels and data so that the column and row specifications for the data are entered into the **Input Range** box as in the preceding window. Next enter the number of **Rows per sample, which in this case is** 8. Then click **OK**. The output from the ANOVA will appear on a new worksheet as seen in the following.

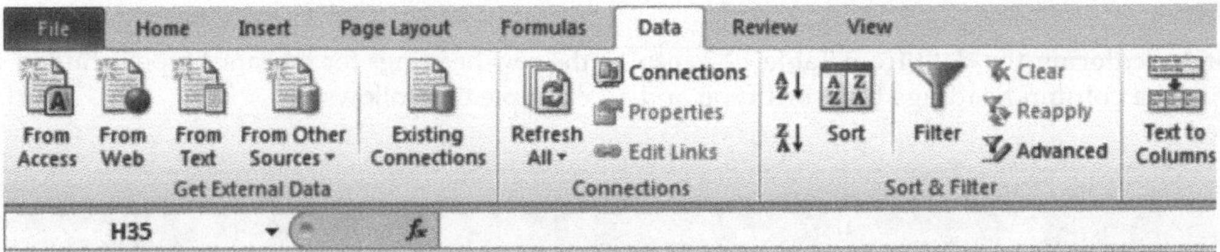

	A	B	C	D	E	F	G	H
1	Anova: Two-Factor With Replication							
2								
3	SUMMARY	Abstract Words	Concrete Words	Total				
4	*Rote Rehearsal*							
5	Count	8	8	16				
6	Sum	40	32	72				
7	Average	5	4	4.5				
8	Variance	0.571428571	2.571428571	1.733333				
9								
10	*Imagery Rehearsal*							
11	Count	8	8	16				
12	Sum	48	80	128				
13	Average	6	10	8				
14	Variance	0.571428571	1.428571429	5.2				
15								
16	*Total*							
17	Count	16	16					
18	Sum	88	112					
19	Average	5.5	7					
20	Variance	0.8	11.46666667					
21								
22								
23	ANOVA							
24	*Source of Variation*	*SS*	*df*	*MS*	*F*	*P-value*	*F crit*	
25	Sample	98	1	98	76.22222	1.76E-09	4.195972	
26	Columns	18	1	18	14	0.000836	4.195972	
27	Interaction	50	1	50	38.88889	9.72E-07	4.195972	
28	Within	36	28	1.285714				
29								
30	Total	202	31					
31								

In the preceding **ANOVA** table what is called "Sample" is the independent variable of rehearsal type, what is called "Columns" is the independent variable of word type, and the interaction is labeled as such. We see that the three *F* scores are all significant. In addition, the means and variances for each condition, and summarized across conditions, are reported. Thus, there is an effect of rehearsal type, $F\ (1, 28) = 76.22$, $p = .000000002$, with participants recalling more words in the imagery rehearsal condition. There is also an effect of word type, $F\ (1, 28) = 14$, $p = .0008$, with participants recalling significantly more concrete words than abstract words. Lastly, there is an interaction effect, $F\ (1, 28) = 38.89$, $p = .00000097$, showing that participants recalled abstract words somewhat similarly across the two rehearsal type conditions but that they recalled concrete words much better in the imagery rehearsal condition in comparison to the rote rehearsal condition.

Using SPSS

We'll use the data from Table 12.2 to illustrate the use of SPSS to compute a two-way randomized ANOVA. We begin by entering the data into SPSS as indicated in the Data Sheet below. The first two columns indicate the condition in which the participants served with 1,1 indicating the abstract word, rote rehearsal condition; 1,2 the abstract word, imagery rehearsal condition; 2,1 the concrete word, rote rehearsal condition; and 2,2 the concrete word, imagery rehearsal condition. The recall data for each of the participants in these four conditions are entered into the third column.

File Edit View Data Transform Analyze Graphs Utilities Add-ons Window Help

	Wordtype	Rehearsaltype	Wordsrecalled	var	var	var	var	var	var	var
1	1.00	1.00	5.00							
2	1.00	1.00	4.00							
3	1.00	1.00	5.00							
4	1.00	1.00	6.00							
5	1.00	1.00	4.00							
6	1.00	1.00	5.00							
7	1.00	1.00	6.00							
8	1.00	1.00	5.00							
9	1.00	2.00	6.00							
10	1.00	2.00	5.00							
11	1.00	2.00	6.00							
12	1.00	2.00	7.00							
13	1.00	2.00	6.00							
14	1.00	2.00	6.00							
15	1.00	2.00	7.00							
16	1.00	2.00	5.00							
17	2.00	1.00	4.00							
18	2.00	1.00	5.00							
19	2.00	1.00	3.00							
20	2.00	1.00	6.00							
21	2.00	1.00	2.00							
22	2.00	1.00	2.00							
23	2.00	1.00	6.00							
24	2.00	1.00	4.00							
25	2.00	2.00	10.00							
26	2.00	2.00	12.00							
27	2.00	2.00	11.00							
28	2.00	2.00	9.00							
29	2.00	2.00	8.00							
30	2.00	2.00	10.00							
31	2.00	2.00	10.00							
32	2.00	2.00	10.00							
33										
34										
35										

Data View | Variable View

Next, click on **Analyze**, followed by **General Linear Model**, and **Univariate** as indicated below.

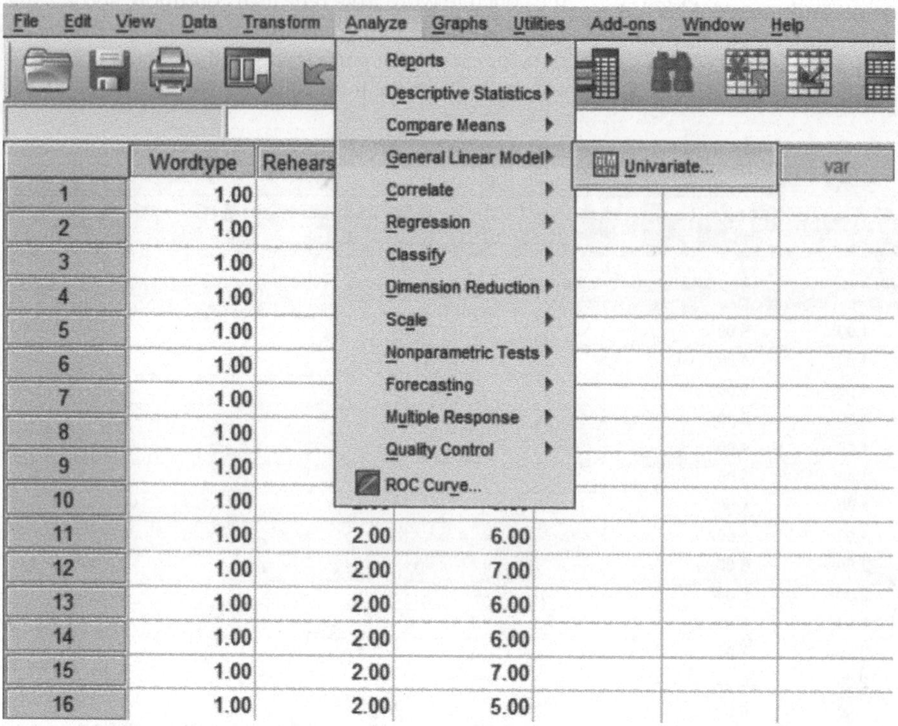

The following dialog box will be produced.

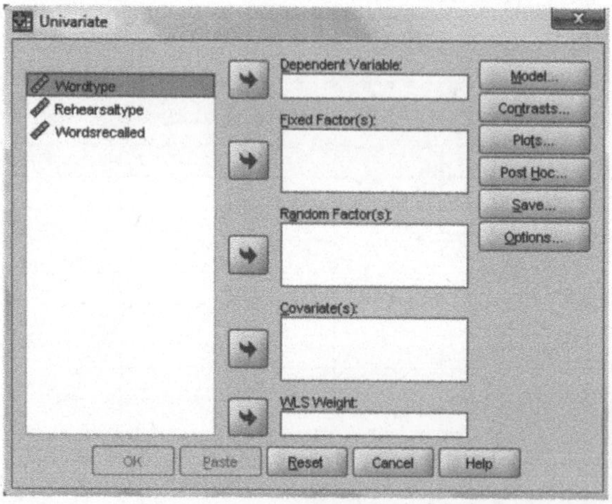

Enter the dependent variable (Wordsrecalled) into the **Dependent Variable** box and the two independent variables (Wordtype and Rehearsaltype) into the **Fixed Factors** box by highlighting each variable and utilizing the appropriate arrow keys.

Next select **Options**, which will produce the following dialog box.

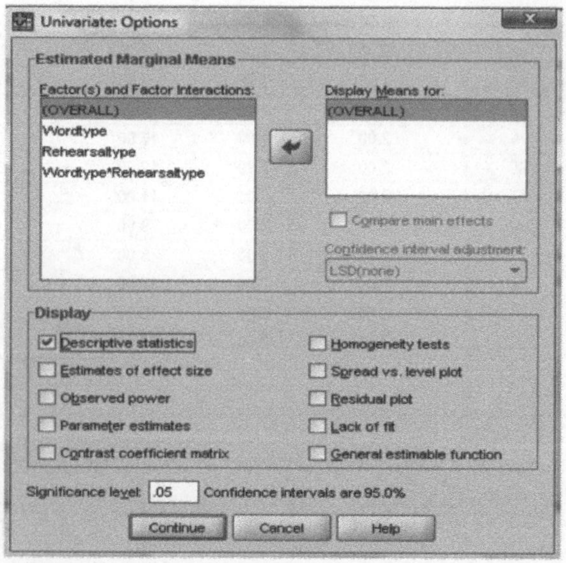

Select **Descriptive statistics** and then tell SPSS that you want descriptive statistics on all factors by moving OVERALL into the **Display Means for** box. Click **Continue** and then **OK**. The output will be displayed in an output window as seen in the following.

Univariate Analysis of Variance

Between-Subjects Factors

		N
Wordtype	1.00	16
	2.00	16
Rehearsaltype	1.00	16
	2.00	16

Descriptive Statistics

Dependent Variable:Wordsrecalled

Wordtype	Rehearsaltype	Mean	Std. Deviation	N
1.00	1.00	4.0000	1.60357	8
	2.00	10.0000	1.19523	8
	Total	7.0000	3.38625	16
2.00	1.00	5.0000	.75593	8
	2.00	6.0000	.75593	8
	Total	5.5000	.89443	16
Total	1.00	4.5000	1.31656	16
	2.00	8.0000	2.28035	16
	Total	6.2500	2.55267	32

Tests of Between-Subjects Effects

Dependent Variable:Wordsrecalled

Source	Type III Sum of Squares	df	Mean Square	F	Sig.
Corrected Model	166.000[a]	3	55.333	43.037	.000
Intercept	1250.000	1	1250.000	972.222	.000
Wordtype	18.000	1	18.000	14.000	.001
Rehearsaltype	98.000	1	98.000	76.222	.000
Wordtype * Rehearsaltype	50.000	1	50.000	38.889	.000
Error	36.000	28	1.286		
Total	1452.000	32			
Corrected Total	202.000	31			

a. R Squared = .822 (Adjusted R Squared = .803)

The output begins with a legend for the variables and then is followed by descriptive statistics. The ANOVA summary table follows. The rows that correspond to the standard two-way ANOVA are those labeled **Wordtype** through **Total**. We can see that the three *F*-ratios reported in these rows correspond to those from the Excel example and that they can be interpreted in the same manner as they were earlier. There is an effect of rehearsal type, $F(1, 28) = 76.22$, $p = .000$, with participants recalling more words in the imagery rehearsal condition. There is also an effect of word type, $F(1, 28) = 14$, $p = .001$ with participants recalling significantly more concrete words than abstract words. Finally, there is an interaction effect (Wordtype * Rehearsaltype), $F(1, 28) = 38.89$, $p = .000$, showing that participants recalled abstract words somewhat similarly across the two rehearsal type conditions but that they recalled concrete words much better in the imagery rehearsal condition in comparison to the rote rehearsal condition.

CHAPTER

13 Quasi-Experimental and Single-Case Designs

Learning objectives

- Describe how quasi-experimental designs differ from correlational and experimental designs.
- Explain what a subject variable is.
- Differentiate single group designs and nonequivalent control group designs.
- Describe advantages and disadvantages of posttest-only designs and pretest/posttest designs.
- Explain a time-series design.
- Describe the differences among cross-sectional, longitudinal, and sequential developmental designs.
- Describe advantages and disadvantages of ABA versus ABAB reversal designs.
- Differentiate multiple-baseline designs (i.e., across subjects, across behaviors, and across situations).

Quasi-experimental research can be thought of as an intermediate point between correlational and true experimental research. As such, it allows us to draw slightly stronger conclusions than we might with correlational research. We can say there is more than a simple relationship between variables, but we cannot draw as strong a conclusion as we can with true experimental research. We cannot say that we have observed a causal relationship between variables. Quasi-experimental research frequently fits into the category of field research; that is, it often involves conducting research in more naturalistic settings. In this chapter, we will begin with a brief discussion of what quasi-experimental research is and how it differs from correlational and experimental research. We will then describe various types of quasi-experimental research designs and discuss how the quasi-experimental method limits internal validity in a study. Next, we will discuss three types of quasi-experimental designs used by developmental psychologists—cross-sectional designs, longitudinal designs, and sequential designs—which all use age as a nonmanipulated independent variable. Finally, we will discuss another type of field research, single-case research. As with quasi-experimental designs, we will discuss the value of single-case research and describe various types of single-case designs.

Conducting Quasi-Experimental Research

The term *quasi* (meaning "having some but not all of the features") preceding the term *experimental* indicates that we are dealing with a design that resembles an experiment but is not exactly an experiment. How does a quasi-experimental design differ from an experimental design? Sometimes the difference is the lack of any control group or comparison group. In other words, only one group is given a treatment and then assessed. At other times, the independent variable is not a true manipulated independent variable; instead, it is a participant variable or a nonmanipulated independent variable. Finally, there may be designs considered quasi-experimental because participants are not randomly assigned to conditions. In other words, they are already part of a group, and the researcher attempts to manipulate a variable between preexisting groups.

Nonmanipulated Independent Variables

In some quasi-experiments, the researcher is interested in comparing groups of individuals (as is done in an experiment), but the groups occur naturally. In other words, subjects are not assigned randomly to the groups. Notice the difference between this and correlational research. We are not simply looking for relationships between variables—such as between smoking and cancer. In quasi-experimental research, we are testing a hypothesis; for example: Individuals who have smoked for 20 years have a higher incidence of respiratory illness than nonsmokers. We would then randomly select a group of individuals who had smoked for 20 years and a group of individuals who had never smoked to serve as a control. Thus, rather than simply looking for a relationship between smoking and cancer/illness, we are comparing two groups to test a hypothesis.

nonmanipulated independent variable The independent variable in a quasi-experimental design in which subjects are not randomly assigned to conditions but rather come to the study as members of each condition.

The independent variable is referred to as a **nonmanipulated independent variable** because subjects are not randomly assigned to the two groups. We are not truly manipulating smoking by assigning subjects to either smoke or not smoke. Instead, subjects come to the study as either smokers or nonsmokers. However, we do make comparisons between the groups. Thus, the study has the intent and "flavor" of an experiment without being a true experiment. Nonmanipulated independent variables are also known as *subject variables*. A subject variable, you may recall from Chapter 1, is a characteristic of the participant that cannot be changed, such as ethnicity, gender, age, or political affiliation. If a study is designed to assess differences in individuals on some subject variable, by default it is a quasi-experiment and not a true experiment because it uses a nonmanipulated independent variable; that is, subjects are not randomly assigned to conditions.

An Example: Snow and Cholera

In the 1850s in London, England, there were frequent outbreaks of cholera, an infection of the small intestine. The cause at the time was unknown, but the common theory was that cholera was somehow spread as people came in contact with cholera victims and shared or breathed the same air. This was known as the effluvia theory. John Snow, in his quest for the cause of cholera, had an alternative hypothesis (Goldstein & Goldstein, 1978). Snow thought that people contracted cholera by drinking contaminated water. He based his hypothesis on the observation that, of the several different water companies serving London, some provided water from upstream (it had not yet passed through the city where it might have become contaminated), whereas others used water from downstream (after it had passed through the city where it might have become contaminated).

To test this hypothesis, Snow used a quasi-experimental design. Obviously, it was not feasible to use a true experimental design because it would have been impossible to randomly assign different houses to contract with a specific water company. Snow therefore had to look at houses that already received their water from a downstream company versus houses that received water from upstream. You should begin to see some of the problems inherent in quasi-experimental research. If people chose their water company, then there was most likely a reason for the choice. In most cases, the reason was socioeconomic: The wealthier neighborhoods used upstream (more costly) companies, whereas the poorer neighborhoods used downstream (less costly) companies. This obviously presented a problem for Snow because he had no way of knowing whether differences in cholera incidence were due to the different water companies or to something else related to socioeconomic level, such as diet, living conditions, or medical care.

Luckily for Snow, he was able to find one neighborhood in which socioeconomic status was stable but different houses received water from two different companies in an unsystematic manner. In other words, the choice of water companies in this neighborhood appeared to be random. It was so random that, in some cases, the choice of water company varied from house to house on a single street. Here was a naturally occurring situation in which socioeconomic level was controlled and water company varied. It was important, however, to ensure that not only the water company but also the contamination level of the water varied. Snow was lucky in this respect, too, because one company had moved upstream after a previous cholera epidemic, whereas the other company had stayed downstream. Snow calculated the number of deaths by cholera for individuals receiving water from upstream versus those receiving water from downstream. He found that there were 37 deaths per 10,000 households for the upstream company and 315 deaths per 10,000 households for the downstream company. Therefore, it appeared that water contamination was responsible for the spread of cholera.

As a review, the nonmanipulated independent variable in Snow's study was water company. This was a subject variable because individuals came to the study with their choice of water company already established. The dependent variable was the number of deaths by cholera. Snow observed a difference in death rates between the two companies and concluded that the type of water (more contaminated versus less contaminated) appeared to be the cause. Snow was particularly lucky because of the naturally occurring situation in which socioeconomic level was controlled but water company varied. This type of control is often lacking in quasi-experimental research. However, even with such control, there is still not as much control as in an experiment because subjects are not randomly assigned to conditions. Therefore, it is still possible for uncontrolled differences between the groups to affect the outcome of the study.

Quasi-Experimental Versus Correlational Methods **IN REVIEW**

METHOD	VARIABLES	CONCLUSIONS	CAUTIONS
Correlational method	Two measured variables	The variables may berelated in some way.	We cannot conclude that the relationship is causal.
Quasi-experimental method	Typically one nonmanipulated independent variable and one measured dependent variable	Systematic differences have been observed between two or more groups, but we cannot say that the nonmanipulated independent variable definitely caused the differences.	Due to confounds inherent in the use of nonmanipulated independent variables, there may be alternative explanations for the results.

CRITICAL THINKING CHECK 13.1

1. Which of the following variables are always subject variables (nonmanipulated independent variables)?

Gender	Ethnicity
religious affiliation	visual acuity
amount of time spent studying	amount of alcohol consumed

2. How does the quasi-experimental method allow us to draw slightly stronger conclusions than the correlational method? Why is it that the conclusions drawn from quasi-experimental studies cannot be stated in as strong a manner as those from a true experiment?

Types of Quasi-Experimental Designs

The quasi-experimental design has several possible variations (Campbell & Stanley, 1963). One distinction is whether there are one or two groups of participants. A second distinction has to do with how often measurements are taken. We will begin by discussing quasi-experimental designs in which only one group of participants is observed. These designs include the single-group posttest-only design, the single-group pretest/posttest design, and the single-group time-series design. We will then consider designs that use two groups and are referred to as *nonequivalent control group designs.* These include the nonequivalent control group posttest-only design, the nonequivalent control group pretest/posttest design, and the multiple-group time-series design.

Single-Group Posttest-Only Design

single-group posttest-only design A design in which a single group of participants is given a treatment and then tested.

The **single-group posttest-only design** is the simplest quasi-experimental design. As the name implies, it involves the use of a single group of subjects to whom some treatment is given. The subjects are then assessed on the dependent variable. Research in education is frequently of this type. For example, some new educational technique—such as interactive learning, outcomes learning, or computer-assisted learning—is proposed, and school systems begin to adopt this new method. Posttest measures are then taken to determine the amount learned by students. However, there is neither a comparison group nor a comparison of the results to any previous measurements (usually because what is learned via the new method is so "different" from the old method that the claim is made that comparisons are not valid). You should see the problem with this type of design. How can we claim a method is better when we cannot compare the results for the group who participated with the results for any other group or standard? This design is open to so many criticisms and potential flaws that results based on this type of study should always be interpreted with caution.

Most frequently, you will see single-group posttest-only designs reported in popular literature, where they are frequently misinterpreted by those who read them. How many times have you read about people who lived through a certain experience or joined a particular group claiming that the experience or the group had an effect on their lives? These are examples of single-group posttest-only designs. Single-group posttest-only designs cannot be used to draw conclusions about how an experience has affected the individuals involved. The change in their lives could be due to any number of variables other than the experience they lived through or the program they went through.

Single-Group Pretest/Posttest Design

single-group pretest/posttest design A design in which a single group of subjects takes a pretest, receives some treatment, and then takes a posttest measure.

The **single-group pretest/posttest design** is an improvement over the posttest-only design in that measures are taken twice—before the treatment and after the treatment. The two measures can then be compared, and any differences in the measures are assumed to be the result of the treatment. For example, if we had a single group of depressed individuals who wanted to receive treatment (counseling) for their depression, we would measure their level of depression before the treatment, have them then participate in the counseling, and then measure their level of depression after the treatment. Can you think of possible problems with this design? The greatest problem is the lack of a comparison group. With no comparison group, we do not know whether any observed change in depression is due to the treatment or to something else that may have happened during the time of the study. For example, maybe the pretest depression measure was taken right after the holidays when depression is higher for many people. Therefore, the participants might have scored lower on the posttest depression measure regardless of whether they received counseling or not.

Single-Group Time-Series Design

single-group time-series design A design in which a single group of subjects is measured repeatedly before and after a treatment.

The **single-group time-series design** involves using a single group of subjects, taking multiple measures over a period of time before introducing the treatment, and then continuing to take several measures after the treatment. The advantage of this design is that the multiple measures allow us to see whether the behavior is stable before treatment and how, or if, it changes at the multiple points in time when measures are taken after treatment.

An often cited good example of a time-series design, discussed by Campbell (1969), was used to evaluate the 1955 crackdown on speeding in Connecticut. The state found it necessary to institute the crackdown after a record-high number of traffic fatalities occurred in 1955. A pretest/posttest design would simply compare the number of fatalities before the crackdown with the number after the crackdown. The number of deaths fell from 324 in 1955 to 284 in 1956. However, alternative hypotheses, other than the crackdown, could be offered to explain this drop. For example, perhaps the number of deaths in 1955 was unusually high based on chance; in other words, it was just a "fluke." Campbell recommended a time-series design, examining traffic fatalities over an extended period of time. Figure 13.1 illustrates the results of this design; it includes traffic fatalities for the years 1951 through 1959. As can be seen in the figure, 1955 was a record-high year; after the crackdown, the number of fatalities declined not only in 1956 but also in the 3 following years. Using the time-series design, then, allowed for a clearer interpretation than was possible with data from only 1955 and 1956.

However, Campbell still saw a problem with attributing the decline to the crackdown. The problem is statistical regression, or regression to the mean, discussed in Chapter 9. To briefly review this concept, with the very high death rate in 1955, we would expect a drop in the death rate for several years, whether there was a speeding crackdown or not. Why? Because then the average death rate (calculated over several years) would remain the same. We will discuss Campbell's recommendation for an improved design when we cover the multiple-group time-series design.

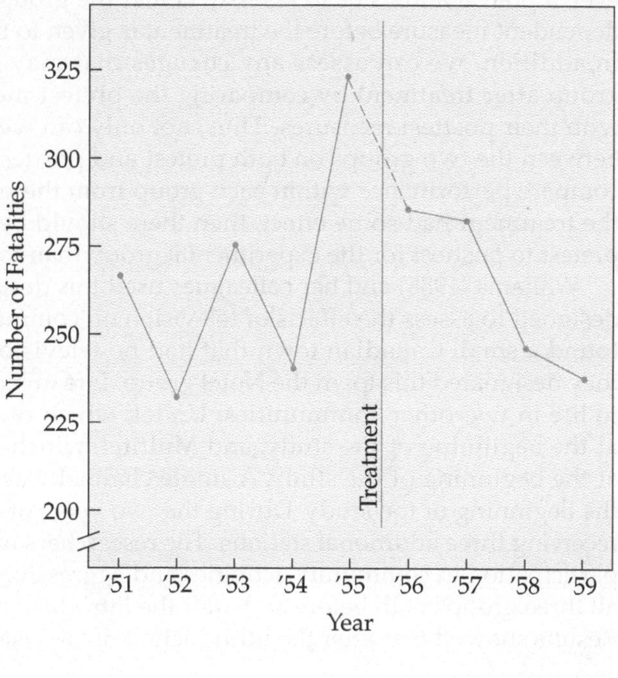

FIGURE 13.1 Connecticut traffic fatalities: 1951–1959

SOURCE: Campbell, D. T. (1969). Reforms as experiments. *American Psychologist, 24,* 409–429.

Nonequivalent Control Group Posttest-Only Design

nonequivalent control group posttest-only design A design in which at least two nonequivalent groups are given a treatment and then a posttest measure.

The **nonequivalent control group posttest-only design** is similar to the single-group posttest-only design; however, a nonequivalent control group is added as a comparison group. Notice that the control group is nonequivalent, meaning that participants are not assigned to either the experimental or the control group in a random manner. Instead, they are members of each group because of something they chose or did—they come to the study already a member of one of the groups. This design is similar to the quasi-experimental study conducted by Snow on cholera, discussed earlier in this chapter. Subjects selected either the upstream or the downstream water company, and Snow took posttest measures on death rates by cholera. As noted earlier, Snow had some evidence that the two groups were somewhat equivalent on income level because they all lived in the same neighborhood. In many situations, however, there is no assurance that the two groups are at all equivalent on any variable prior to the study. For this reason, we cannot say definitively that the treatment is responsible for any observed changes in the groups. It could be that the groups were not equivalent at the beginning of the study; hence, the differences observed between the two groups on the dependent variable may be due to the nonequivalence of the groups and not to the treatment.

Nonequivalent Control Group Pretest/Posttest Design

nonequivalent control group pretest/posttest design A design in which at least two nonequivalent groups are given a pretest, then a treatment, and then a posttest measure.

An improvement over the previous design involves the addition of a pretest measure, making it a **nonequivalent control group pretest/posttest design**. This is still not a true experimental design, because, as with the previous designs, subjects are not randomly assigned to the two conditions. However, a pretest allows us to assess whether the groups are equivalent on the dependent measure before the treatment is given to the experimental group. In addition, we can assess any changes that may have occurred in each group after treatment by comparing the pretest measures for each group with their posttest measures. Thus, not only can we compare performance between the two groups on both pretest and posttest measures, but we can compare performance within each group from the pretest to the posttest. If the treatment had some effect, then there should be a greater change from pretest to posttest for the experimental group than for the control group.

Williams (1986) and her colleagues used this design in a series of studies designed to assess the effects of television on communities. The researchers found a small Canadian town that had no television reception until 1973; they designated this town the Notel group. Life in Notel was then compared to life in two other communities: Unitel, which received only one station at the beginning of the study, and Multitel, which received four channels at the beginning of the study. A single channel was introduced to Notel at the beginning of the study. During the two years of the study, Unitel began receiving three additional stations. The researchers measured such factors as participation in community activities and aggressive behavior in children in all three groups both before and after the introduction of television in Notel. Results showed that after the introduction of television in Notel, there was a

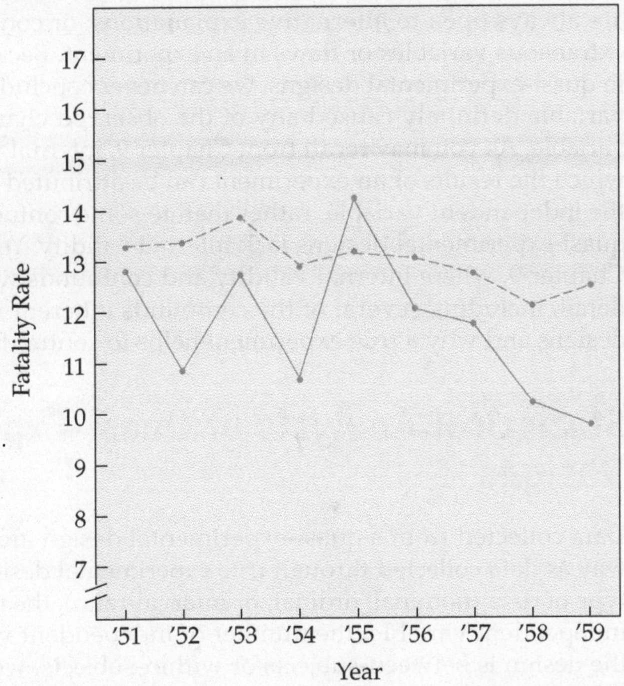

FIGURE 13.2 Multiple-group time-series design comparing Connecticut fatality rates (solid line) with the fatality rates of four other states (dashed line) used as a control group

SOURCE: Campbell, D. T. (1969). Reforms as experiments. *American Psychologist, 24,* 409–429.

significant decline in participation in community activities and a significant increase in aggressive behavior in children.

Multiple-Group Time-Series Design

multiple-group time-series design A design in which a series of measures are taken on two or more groups both before and after a treatment.

The logical extension of the previous design is to take more than one pretest and posttest. In a **multiple-group time-series design**, several measures are taken on nonequivalent groups before and after treatment. Refer to the study of the crackdown on speeding in Connecticut following a high number of traffic fatalities in 1955. Converting that single-group time-series design to a multiple-group time-series design would involve finding a comparison group—a state that did not crack down on speeding—during the same time period. Campbell (1969) found four other states that did not crack down on speeding at the same time as Connecticut. Figure 13.2 presents the data from this design. As can be seen, the fatality rates in the states used as the control group remained fairly stable, while the fatality rates in Connecticut decreased. Based on these data, Campbell concluded that the crackdown had the desired effect on fatality rates.

Internal Validity and Confounds in Quasi-Experimental Designs

As we have pointed out several times in our discussion of quasi-experimental research, the results need to be interpreted with caution because the design includes only one group or a nonequivalent control group. These results are always open to alternative explanations, or confounds—uncontrolled extraneous variables or flaws in an experiment. Because of the weaknesses in quasi-experimental designs, we can never conclude that the independent variable definitely caused any of the observed changes in the dependent variable. As you may recall from Chapter 9, internal validity is the extent to which the results of an experiment can be attributed to the manipulation of the independent variable, rather than to some confounding variable. Thus, quasi-experimental designs lack internal validity. You may want to review Chapter 9, where internal validity and confounds were discussed in some detail, including several of the confounds inherent in quasi- experimental designs and why a true experiment helps to control for these confounds.

Statistical Analysis of Quasi-Experimental Designs

Data collected from a quasi-experimental design are analyzed in the same way as data collected through true experimental designs. Depending on the type of data (nominal, ordinal, or interval-ratio), the number of levels of the independent variable, the number of independent variables, and whether the design is between-subjects or within-subjects, we choose the appropriate statistic as we did for the experimental designs discussed in Chapters 9 through 12. Even though we use the same statistics, however, we are limited in the conclusions we can draw. Our conclusions must be tempered because of the confounds inherent in quasi-experimental designs.

Quasi-Experimental Designs — IN REVIEW

	SINGLE-GROUP DESIGNS	NONEQUIVALENT CONTROL GROUP DESIGNS
Posttest-only	Open to many confounds. No comparison group. No equivalent control group.	Control group is nonequivalent. No pretest measures to establish equivalence of groups. Can compare groups on posttest measures, but differences may be due to treatment or confounds.
Pretest/Posttest	Compare scores on pretest to those on posttest. No equivalent control group for comparison. If change is observed, it may be due to treatment or confounds.	Can compare between groups on pretest and posttest. Can compare within groups from pretest to posttest. Because subjects are not randomly assigned to groups, we cannot say that they are equivalent. If change is observed, it may be due to treatment or confounds.
Time-series	Because many measures are taken, can see effect of treatment over time. No control group for comparison. If change is observed, it may be due to treatment or confounds.	Because many measures are taken, we can see effect of treatment over time. Nonequivalent control group available for comparison. Because subjects are not randomly assigned to groups, we cannot say they are equivalent. If change is observed, may be due to treatment or confounds.

CRITICAL THINKING CHECK 13.2

1. Imagine I randomly select a group of smokers and a group of nonsmokers. I then measure lung disease in each group. What type of design is this? If I observe a difference between the groups in rate of lung disease, why can't I conclude that this difference is caused by smoking?
2. How are pretest/posttest designs an improvement over posttest-only designs?

Developmental Designs

Developmental psychologists typically use a special group of designs known as *developmental designs*. These designs are a type of quasi-experimental design in which age is used as a nonmanipulated independent variable. There are two basic developmental designs: the cross-sectional design and the longitudinal design. The cross-sectional design shares some characteristics with between-subjects designs in that individuals of different ages are studied. The longitudinal design shares some characteristics with within-subjects designs in that the same individuals are studied over time as they mature through different ages.

Cross-Sectional Designs

cross-sectional design A type of developmental design in which subjects of different ages are studied at the same time.

When using the **cross-sectional design**, researchers study individuals of different ages at the same time. Thus, a researcher interested in differences across ages in cognitive abilities might study groups of 5-year-olds, 8-year-olds, 11-year-olds, and so on. The advantage of this design is that a wide variety of ages can be studied in a short period of time. In fact, in some studies it is possible to collect all of the data in a single day. Even though ease of data collection is a great advantage for the cross-sectional method, this method does have disadvantages. The main issue is that the researcher is typically attempting to determine whether or not there are differences across different ages; however, the reality of the design is such that the researcher tests not only individuals of different ages but also individuals who were born at different times and raised in different generations or cohorts. A **cohort** is a group of individuals born at about the same time. Thus, in a cross-sectional study, the researcher wants to be able to conclude that any difference observed in the dependent variable (for example, cognitive abilities) is due to age; however, because these individuals were also raised at different times, some or all of the observed differences in cognitive ability could be due to a **cohort effect**—a generational effect. How might a cohort effect affect cognitive abilities in a cross-sectional study? Individuals born in different generations went through different educational systems and also had varying opportunities for education; those born earlier had less access to education.

cohort A group of individuals born at about the same time.

cohort effect A generational effect in a study that occurs when the era in which individuals are born affects how they respond in the study.

Longitudinal Designs

longitudinal design A type of developmental design in which the same subjects are studied repeatedly over time as they age.

An alternative to a cross-sectional design is a longitudinal design. With a **longitudinal design**, the same participants are studied repeatedly over a period of time. Depending on the age range the researcher wants to study, a longitudinal design may span from a few years or months to decades. If the study described previously were conducted longitudinally, the same participants would periodically (for example, every 3 years) be tested on cognitive abilities. This type of study eliminates any cohort effects because the same subjects are studied over a period of time. Thus, we do not have the confound of using subjects of different ages who were born in different generations. However, longitudinal designs introduce their own unique problems into a research study. First, they are more expensive and time-consuming than cross-sectional studies. In addition, researchers using longitudinal studies need to be particularly cognizant of attrition problems over time because those who drop out of the study likely differ in some possibly meaningful way from those who remain in the study. For example, they may be healthier, wealthier, or more conscientious and, in general, have more stable lives.

Sequential Designs

sequential design A developmental design that is a combination of the cross-sectional and longitudinal designs.

One way to overcome many of the problems with both cross-sectional and longitudinal designs is to use a design that is a combination of the two. The **sequential design** is a combined cross-sectional and longitudinal design in that a researcher begins with participants of different ages (a cross-sectional design) and tests or measures them. Then, either a number of months or years later, the researcher retests or measures the same individuals (a longitudinal design). Thus, a researcher could measure cognitive abilities in 5-, 8-, and 11-year-olds; then 3 years later, measure the same individuals when they are 8, 11, and 14 years old; and last measure them again when they are 11, 14, and 17 years old. Sequential designs are more expensive and time-consuming than the previous two types of designs, but they have the advantage of allowing researchers to examine cohort effects, usually without taking as much time as a longitudinal design alone.

Conducting Single-Case Research

single-case design A design in which only one participant is used.

Up to this point, the experiments we have discussed have all involved studying groups of people. In certain types of research, researchers use methods that minimize the number of subjects in a study. This may sound contrary to the basic principles of design that we have discussed so far. However, these methods, often referred to as **single-case designs**, are versions of a within-subjects experiment in which only one person is measured repeatedly. Often the research is replicated on one or two other subjects. Thus, we sometimes

small-*n* design A design in which only a few subjects are studied.

refer to these studies as **small-*n* designs**. Such studies can also be thought of as a variation of the pretest/posttest quasi-experimental design discussed earlier in the chapter. However, in this case, pretest and posttest measures are taken on the single participant in the study.

A researcher may choose a single-case design for several reasons. The researcher may want information on only the single participant being studied. The researcher may not be interested in trying to generalize the results to a population, but only in how this one participant reacts to the manipulation. Single-case research is frequently used in clinical settings. In clinical studies, many researchers believe that it is unethical to use traditional experimental methods in which one group of participants receives the treatment and the other group serves as a control. They believe it is unethical to withhold treatment from one group—particularly when the participants may really need the treatment. In such cases, single-case or small-*n* designs are more ethically appealing because they involve providing treatment to all who participate in the study.

Sidman (1960) argues that of the several reasons for conducting single-case studies, each is based on a flaw in designs that use many subjects (group designs). One problem with group designs, according to Sidman, is that they do not allow for adequate replication of results, whereas single-case designs do. Thus, single-case designs are better at demonstrating a reliable effect of an independent variable. Second, group designs contribute to error variance in a study. You may remember that error variance is the random differences in scores found within the conditions of an experiment. Using many people in a group design increases error variance resulting from individual differences. This increase in error variance may make it difficult to identify a relationship between the variables in the study. Third, Sidman notes that when using group designs, we typically look at the mean performance within each group. However, a mean score for a given condition may not accurately represent the performance of all of the participants in that condition. After we have drawn conclusions based on the mean performance within each group, we then attempt to generalize the results to individuals. Psychologists thus draw conclusions about individual behavior based on studying the average performance of a group of people.

Single-case and small-*n* designs address each of these problems. To determine the reliability of the effect, we can repeatedly manipulate the independent variable with the same participant or perform replications with a few other subjects. Error variance resulting from individual differences is eliminated because only one participant is used. Finally, rather than looking at group means and conducting the appropriate statistical analyses, we look at only the performance of the single participant in the study to determine the relationship between the independent and dependent variables. Most commonly, we graph the performance of the single participant and examine the resulting graph. The effect of the independent variable is determined by how much the participant's behavior changes from one condition to another.

Also, because the findings are based on individuals, it makes some sense to generalize the results to other individuals.

Types of Single-Case Designs

Single-case designs are of several types. The basic distinction is between a reversal design and a multiple-baseline design. The reversal design typically involves studying a single behavior in a single participant in a single situation, whereas the multiple-baseline design may involve studying multiple people, behaviors, or situations.

Reversal Designs

reversal design A single-case design in which the independent variable is introduced and removed one or more times.

A **reversal design** is a within-subjects design with only one participant in which the independent variable is introduced and removed one or more times. We typically begin the study by taking baseline measures—equivalent to a control condition in a group design. In other words, we need to assess how the participant performs before we introduce the independent variable. After baseline measures have been taken, we can introduce the independent variable. At this point, we have a simple AB design, with A representing baseline performance and B representing the introduction of the independent variable. The problem with this simple pretest/posttest design is that if a change in behavior is observed, we do not know whether it is due to the introduction of the independent variable or to some extraneous variable (confound) that happened to occur at the same time. Thus, to improve on this design, it is typically recommended that some type of reversal be introduced.

ABA reversal design A single-case design in which baseline measures are taken, the independent variable is introduced and behavior is measured, and the independent variable is then removed and baseline measures are taken again.

ABA Reversal Designs. An **ABA reversal design** involves taking baseline measures (A), introducing the independent variable (B) and measuring behavior again, and then removing the independent variable and retaking the baseline measures (A). In this manner, we can see whether the behavior changes with the introduction of the independent variable and then whether it changes back to baseline performance after the independent variable is removed. This combination of changes gives us a better indication of the effectiveness of the treatment. The problem with this design is an ethical one. If the treatment helped to improve the participant's life in some way, it is not ethical to end the experiment by removing the treatment and possibly return the participant to his or her original state. Thus, a further improvement over the ABA design is the ABAB design.

ABAB reversal design A design in which baseline and independent variable conditions are reversed twice.

ABAB Reversal Designs. The **ABAB reversal design** involves reintroducing the independent variable after the second baseline measurement. Thus, the experiment ends with the treatment, making it ethically more appealing. In addition, it allows us to further assess the effectiveness of the independent variable by introducing it a second time. A study by Hall et al.

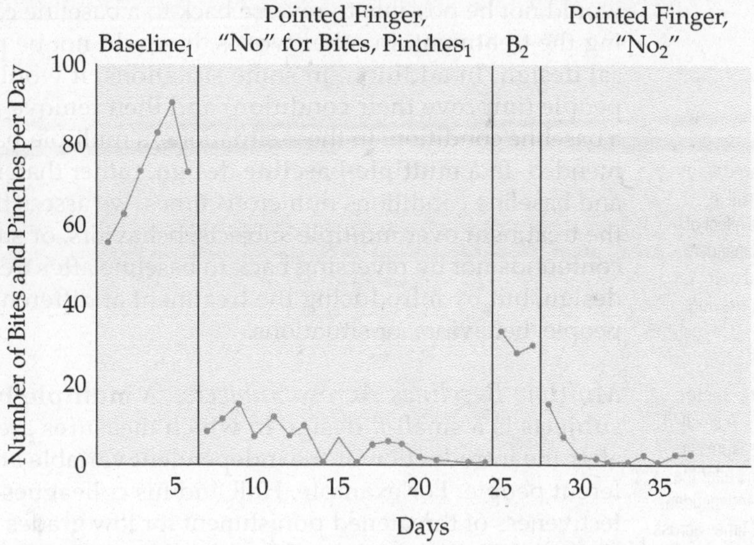

FIGURE 13.3 Number of bites and pinches during the school day
SOURCE: From "The Effective Use of Punishment to Modify Behavior in the Classroom" by R. V. Hall, S. Axelrod, M. Foundopoulos, J. Shellman, R. A. Campbell, and S. S. Cranston, in K. D. O'Leary & S. O'Leary (Eds.), *Classroom Management: The Successful Use of Behavior Modification*, p. 175. Copyright © 1972 by Allyn & Bacon. Reprinted with permission of Pearson Education.

(1971), assessing the effectiveness of punishment in reducing the aggressive behavior of a 7-year-old deaf girl, illustrates this design. The participant pinched and bit both herself and anyone else with whom she came in contact. The frequency of these behaviors averaged 72 occurrences per day, preventing normal classroom instruction. As can be seen in Figure 13.3, after a baseline measurement for 5 days, the experimenters introduced the treatment in which the teacher pointed at the participant and shouted "NO!" after each bite or pinch. The change in the subject's behavior with the introduction of the treatment was quite dramatic even on the first day of treatment. Even though the subject was deaf, the treatment was still very effective. The number of bites and pinches per day dropped to zero by the end of the first treatment period. The researchers then returned to baseline for a few days to eliminate the possibility of an alternative explanation for the behavior change. As can be seen in the figure, the number of bites and pinches increased during this time. The treatment was then reintroduced on day 26, and once again the number of bites and pinches per day declined dramatically. Thus, the ABAB reversal design has the advantage of being more ethical than the ABA design and of offering two baseline measures and two treatment measures to eliminate alternative explanations of behavior change. This design could be further extended to an ABABA design or an ABABAB design.

Multiple-Baseline Designs

Because single-case designs are a type of within-subjects design, carry-over effects from one condition to another are of concern. For example, if the treatment in a reversal design permanently changes the participant, then it would not be possible to reverse back to a baseline condition after introducing the treatment. In other words, it would not be possible to use a reversal design. In addition, in some situations, it would be unethical to treat people (improve their condition) and then remove the treatment to assess a baseline condition. In these situations, a multiple-baseline design is recommended. In a **multiple-baseline design**, rather than reversing the treatment and baseline conditions numerous times, we assess the effect of introducing the treatment over multiple subjects, behaviors, or situations. We control for confounds not by reversing back to baseline after treatment, as in a reversal design, but by introducing the treatment at different times across different people, behaviors, or situations.

multiple-baseline design A single-case or small-n design in which the effect of introducing the independent variable is assessed over multiple subjects, behaviors, or situations.

Multiple Baselines Across Subjects. A **multiple-baseline design across subjects** is a small-n design in which measures are taken at baseline and after the introduction of the independent variable at different times for different people. For example, Hall and his colleagues (1971) assessed the effectiveness of threatened punishment for low grades across three 10th-grade students. The three students were all failing their French class. The punishment was being kept after school for a half-hour of tutoring whenever they received a grade lower than C on their daily French quiz. Figure 13.4 shows the baseline and treatment results across the three students. Notice that the treatment was introduced at staggered times across the subjects to help

multiple-baseline design across subjects A small-n design in which measures are taken at baseline and after the introduction of the independent variable at different times across multiple subjects.

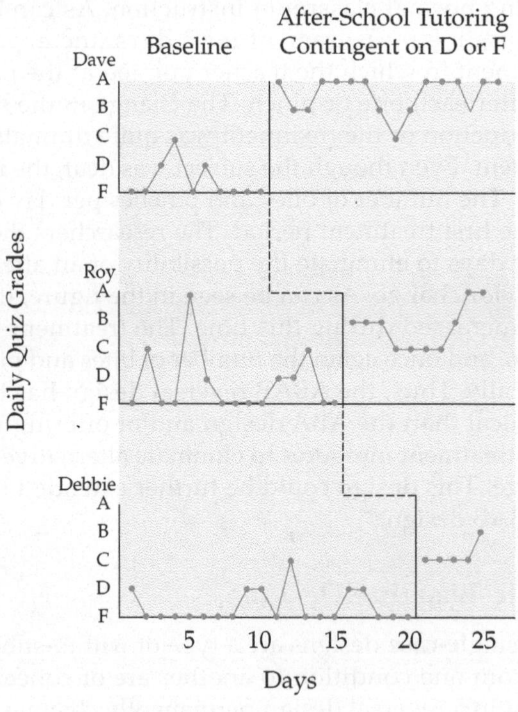

FIGURE 13.4
Quiz grades for three high school French students
SOURCE: From "The Effective Use of Punishment to Modify Behavior in the Classroom" by R. V. Hall, S. Axelrod, M. Foundopoulos, J. Shellman, R. A. Campbell, and S. S. Cranston, in K. D. O'Leary & S. O'Leary (Eds.), *Classroom Management: The Successful Use of Behavior Modification*, p. 177. Copyright © 1972 by Allyn & Bacon. Reprinted with permission of Pearson Education.

control for possible confounds. For the first participant, Dave, the threat of punishment was introduced on day 11, for Roy on day 16, and for Debbie on day 21. As shown in the graph, all participants immediately improved their quiz grades after the treatment was introduced. In fact, none of the three participants ever actually received extra tutoring because their grades improved immediately after the threat of punishment was introduced. By altering when the treatment is introduced to each participant, we minimize the possibility that some other extraneous variable produced the results. In other words, because behavior changed for each subject right after the treatment was introduced and because the treatment was introduced at different times to each subject, we can feel fairly confident that it was the treatment and not some extraneous variable that caused the behavior change.

multiple-baseline design across behaviors A single-case design in which measures are taken at baseline and after the introduction of the independent variable at different times across multiple behaviors.

Multiple Baselines Across Behaviors. An alternative multiple-baseline design uses only one subject and assesses the effects of introducing a treatment over several behaviors. This design is referred to as a **multiple-baseline design across behaviors**. For example, imagine that a teacher wanted to minimize the number of problem behaviors emitted by a student during the school day. The teacher might begin by taking baseline measures on all of the problem behaviors (for example, aggressive behaviors, talking out of turn, and temper tantrums). The treatment would be introduced first for only aggressive behaviors. Several days after introducing the treatment for aggressive behaviors, the teacher would introduce the treatment for talking out of turn, and then several days later for temper tantrums. By introducing the treatment for different behaviors at different times, we can eliminate potential confounds. In other words, if all of the treatments were introduced at the same time and behavior changed, we would not know whether the change was due to the treatment or to some extraneous variable that also changed at the same time. If we see a systematic improvement across behaviors when the treatment is introduced at different times, we can feel fairly certain that it was the treatment that brought about the change.

multiple-baseline design across situations A single-case design in which measures are taken at baseline and after the introduction of the independent variable at different times across multiple situations.

Multiple Baselines Across Situations. A third way to use the multiple-baseline design is to assess the introduction of treatment across different situations—a **multiple-baseline design across situations**. For example, Hall and his colleagues (1971) assessed the effectiveness of punishment on a young boy's crying, whining, and complaining behavior during school. The child emitted these behaviors only during reading and math classes each day. Hall devised a system in which the child was given five slips of colored paper bearing his name at the beginning of reading and math periods each day. One slip of paper was taken away each time he cried, whined, or complained. As can be seen in Figure 13.5, baseline performance was established for the number of cries, whines, and complaints in each class. Then the treatment was introduced on day 6 in the reading class and on day 11 in the math class. In both situations, the number of cries, whines, and complaints declined. Introducing the treatment at different times in the two classes minimizes the possibility that a confounding variable is responsible for the behavior change. You can also see that Hall then reversed the treatment and went back to baseline. Reversal was possible in this situation because the treatment did not have any carryover effects and because reversing the treatment had no ethical ramifications. The treatment was then reintroduced on day 21 in both classes. Thus, this design is really a multiple-baseline reversal design across situations.

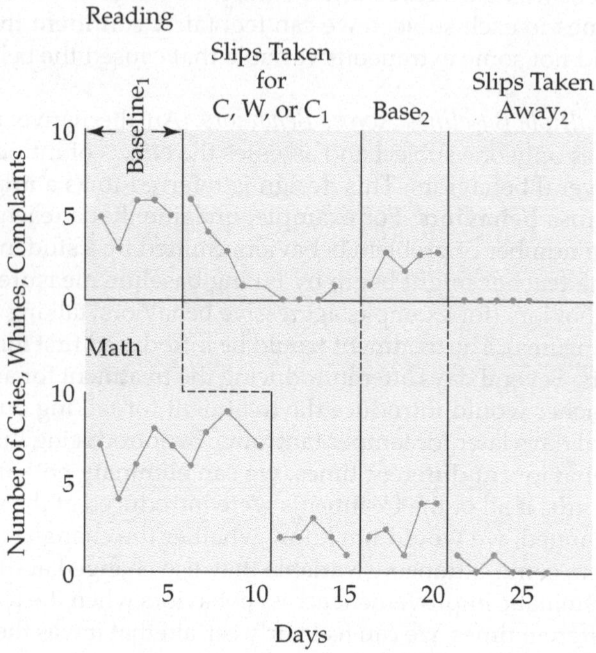

FIGURE 13.5 Frequency of cries (C), whines (W), and complaints (C_1) during reading and math classes
SOURCE: From "The Effective Use of Punishment to Modify Behavior in the Classroom" by R. V. Hall, S. Axelrod, M. Foundopoulos, J. Shellman, R. A. Campbell, and S. S. Cranston, in K. D. O'Leary & S. O'Leary (Eds.), *Classroom Management: The Successful Use of Behavior Modification*, p. 180. Copyright © 1972 by Allyn & Bacon. Reprinted with permission of Pearson Education.

Single-Case Designs — IN REVIEW

REVERSAL DESIGNS	MULTIPLE-BASELINE DESIGNS
ABA design: Measures taken at baseline, after introduction of independent variable, and at baseline again	Across subjects: Measures taken at baseline and after introduction of independent variable at different times across multiple subjects
ABAB design: Measures taken at baseline, after introduction of independent variable, at baseline again, and after introduction of independent variable again	Across behaviors: Measures taken at baseline and after introduction of independent variable at different times across multiple behaviors
	Across situations: Measures taken at baseline and after introduction of independent variable at different times across multiple situations

CRITICAL THINKING CHECK 13.3

1. Explain why single-case research is considered a variation of a within-subjects design. Why might it also be considered a variation of a quasi-experimental design?
2. Why is an ABAB design considered more ethical than an ABA design?
3. How do reversal designs attempt to control for confounds?
4. How do multiple-baseline designs attempt to control for confounds?

Summary

In this chapter, you were introduced to quasi-experimental designs—a type of design that falls somewhere between a correlational design and a true experimental design—and single-case designs. Important concepts related to quasi-experimental designs include nonmanipulated independent variables (subject variables), internal validity, and confounds. Quasi-experimental designs include both single-group designs and nonequivalent control group designs in addition to developmental designs. Single-case or small-*n* designs include reversal designs and multiple-baseline designs. In a reversal design, the independent variable is introduced and then removed (possibly several times) in order to assess its effect on the single participant in the study. In a multiple-baseline design, the independent variable is introduced at different times across a few subjects, behaviors, or situations.

KEY TERMS

nonmanipulated independent variable
single-group posttest-only design
single-group pretest/posttest design
single-group time-series design
nonequivalent control group posttest-only design
nonequivalent control group pretest/posttest design
multiple-group time-series design
cross-sectional design
cohort
cohort effect
longitudinal design
sequential design
single-case design
small-*n* design
reversal design
ABA reversal design
ABAB reversal design
multiple-baseline design
multiple-baseline design across subjects
multiple-baseline design across behaviors
multiple-baseline design across situations

CHAPTER EXERCISES

(Answers to odd-numbered exercises appear in Appendix C.)

1. What is the difference between a true experimental design and a quasi-experimental design?
2. A psychology professor is interested in whether implementing weekly quizzes improves student learning. She decides to use the weekly quizzes in one section of her introductory psychology class and not to use them in another section of the same course. Which type of quasi-experimental design do you recommend for this study?
3. If the psychology professor in exercise 2 had access to only one section of introductory psychology, describe how she might use a single-group design to assess the effectiveness of weekly quizzes. Which of the three single-group designs would you recommend?
4. Identify some possible confounds in each of the studies you outlined in your answers to exercises 2 and 3.
5. What are the similarities and differences between cross-sectional, longitudinal, and sequential designs?
6. Give three reasons a researcher might choose to use a single-case design.
7. Explain what a reversal design is. Identify advantages and disadvantages to using reversal designs.
8. How does a multiple-baseline design differ from a reversal design?
9. When conducting single-case research, why do we look at graphs of data rather than statistically analyze the data as with other designs?

CRITICAL THINKING CHECK ANSWERS

13.1

1. Gender, religious affiliation, ethnicity, and visual acuity would all be participant variables.
2. We have slightly more control in a quasi-experimental study than in a correlational study because we typically introduce some sort of treatment. However, because subjects come to us as members of either the control or the "experimental" group, we cannot conclude that the independent variable definitely caused changes in the dependent variable, as we can when using a true experimental design.

13.2

1. This is a nonequivalent control group posttest-only design. The participants came to the study as either smokers or nonsmokers. We then took posttest measures on them. We cannot conclude that any observed differences in lung disease are due to smoking because variables other than smoking may differ between the two groups.
2. Pretest/posttest designs are an improvement because they allow us to assess whether the groups are similar or different before we introduce the treatment and how much they change after the treatment is introduced. By this means, we can determine whether the groups are in fact equivalent before the treatment.

13.3

1. Single-case research is considered a variation of a within-subjects design because it involves studying one or a few participants in both the control and experimental conditions. It is also similar to the single-group pretest/posttest quasi-experimental design in that it involves taking pretest and posttest measures on a single participant rather than on a group of subjects.
2. An ABAB design is considered more ethical than an ABA design because the final condition involves administering the treatment to the participant, rather than leaving the participant with no treatment (baseline).
3. Reversal designs attempt to control for confounds by reversing the baseline and treatment conditions one or more times to assess the impact on behavior.
4. Multiple-baseline designs attempt to control for confounds by introducing the treatment at differing time intervals to a few different people, to the same person in different situations, or to the same person across different behaviors.

WEB RESOURCES

The book-specific website at CengageBrain.com offers students a variety of study tools and useful resources such as glossaries and flashcards.

Chapter 13 ▪ Study Guide

CHAPTER 13 SUMMARY AND REVIEW: QUASI-EXPERIMENTAL AND SINGLE-CASE DESIGNS

In this chapter, you have been introduced to quasi-experimental designs—a type of design that falls somewhere between a correlational design and a true experimental design—and single-case designs. Important concepts related to quasi-experimental designs include nonmanipulated independent variables (subject variables), internal validity, and confounds. Quasi-experimental designs include both single-group designs and non-equivalent control group designs, in addition to the special designs used by developmental psychologists: cross-sectional, longitudinal, and sequential designs. Single-case or small-*n* designs include reversal designs and multiple-baseline designs. In a reversal design, the independent variable is introduced and then removed (possibly several times) in order to assess its effect on the single participant in the study. In a multiple-baseline design, the independent variable is introduced at different times across a few subjects, behaviors, or situations.

CHAPTER 13 STUDY GUIDE REVIEW EXERCISES

(Answers to exercises appear in Appendix C.)

FILL-IN SELF-TEST

Answer the following questions. If you have trouble answering any of the questions, restudy the relevant material before going on to the multiple-choice self-test.

1. A ________ variable is a characteristic inherent in the subjects that cannot be changed.
2. The ________ design involves giving a treatment to a single group of participants and then testing them.
3. A design in which a single group of subjects is measured repeatedly before and after a treatment is a ________ design.
4. A design in which at least two nonequivalent groups are given a pretest, then a treatment, and then a posttest measure is a ________ design.
5. When participants from different age groups all serve together in the same experiment, then a ________ developmental design is being used.
6. A design in which only one participant is used is called a ________ design.
7. A design in which a few subjects are studied is called a ________ design.
8. A single-case design in which baseline measures are taken, the independent variable is introduced and behavior is measured, and the independent variable is then removed and baseline measures taken again is a(n) ________ design.
9. A small-*n* design in which measures are taken at baseline and after the introduction of the independent variable at different times across multiple subjects is a ________ design.

MULTIPLE-CHOICE SELF-TEST

Select the single best answer for each of the following questions. If you have trouble answering any of the questions, restudy the relevant material.

1. When using a _______ variable, subjects are _______ assigned to groups.
   a. nonmanipulated independent; randomly
   b. nonmanipulated independent; not randomly
   c. subject not randomly
   d. both b and c
2. Which of the following is a subject variable?
   a. ethnicity
   b. gender
   c. age
   d. all of the above
3. Correlational research differs from quasi-experimental research in that:
   a. with correlational research we measure two variables.
   b. with quasi-experimental research there is one nonmanipulated independent variable and one measured variable.
   c. with quasi-experimental research there is one manipulated independent variable and one measured variable.
   d. both a and b
4. Students in one of Mr. Kirk's classes participate in new interactive history learning modules. Students in another class learn history using the traditional lecture method. After three months, all students take a test to assess their knowledge of history. What kind of design did Mr. Kirk use?
   a. nonequivalent control group posttest-only design
   b. nonequivalent control group pretest-posttest design
   c. multiple-group time-series design
   d. single-group time-series design
5. A problem with nonequivalent control group designs is that:
   a. they are open to many confounds.
   b. there is no comparison group.
   c. there is no equivalent control group.
   d. both a and c
6. The difference between pretest/posttest designs and time-series designs is that time-series designs take _______ measures.
   a. fewer
   b. more
   c. the same number of
   d. more reliable
7. In terms of developmental designs, a _______ design is being used when the researcher tests the same subjects at difference ages over many years.
   a. matched-subjects
   b. sequential
   c. cross-sectional
   d. longitudinal
8. Which of the following is a type of single-case design?
   a. ABA reversal designs
   b. multiple baseline across subjects
   c. time-series design
   d. single-group posttest only design
9. The ABA design is generally considered _______ than the ABAB design because participants _______.
   a. more desirable; are left with the effects of the treatment
   b. less desirable; are not left with the effects of the treatment
   c. more desirable; are not left with the effects of the treatment
   d. less desirable; are left with the effects of the treatment

CHAPTER 14

Nonparametric Inferential Statistics

Learning Objectives

- Explain when nonparametric tests should be used.
- Explain what the chi-square goodness-of-fit test is and what it does.
- Calculate a chi-square goodness-of-fit test.
- List the assumptions of the chi-square goodness-of-fit test.
- Calculate the χ^2 test for independence.
- Interpret the χ^2 test for independence.
- Explain the assumptions of the χ^2 test for independence.
- Calculate Wilcoxon's rank-sum test.
- Interpret Wilcoxon's rank-sum test.
- Explain the assumptions of Wilcoxon's rank-sum test.
- Calculate Wilcoxon's matched-pairs signed-ranks *T* test.
- Interpret Wilcoxon's matched-pairs signed-ranks *T* test.
- Explain the assumptions of Wilcoxon's matched-pairs signed-ranks *T* test.
- Calculate the Kruskal-Wallis test.
- Interpret the Kruskal-Wallis test.
- Explain the assumptions of the the Kruskal-Wallis test.
- Calculate the Friedman test.
- Interpret the Friedman test.
- Explain the assumptions of the Friedman test.

Statistics used to analyze nominal and ordinal data are referred to as nonparametric tests. Nonparametric tests do not involve the use of any population parameters. In other words, μ and σ are not needed, and the underlying distribution does not have to be normal. In addition, most nonparametric tests are based on fewer assumptions than parametric tests. Nonparametric tests are usually easier to compute than parametric tests. They are, however, less powerful than parametric tests, meaning that it is more difficult to reject the null hypothesis. In this chapter, we'll learn when to use and how to calculate two nonparametric tests for nominal data: the χ^2 goodness-of-fit test and the χ^2 test of independence. We will also discuss four tests for ordinal data: the Wilcoxon rank-sum test, used with between-subjects designs with two groups; the Wilcoxon matched-pairs signed-ranks *T* test, used with correlated-groups two condition designs; the Kruskal-Wallis test, used with between-subjects designs with more than two groups; and the Friedman test, used with correlated-groups designs with more than two conditions.

chi-square (χ^2) goodness-of-fit test A nonparametric inferential procedure that determines how well an observed frequency distribution fits an expected distribution.

observed frequency The frequency with which participants fall into a category.

The Chi-Square (χ^2) Goodness-of-Fit Test: What It Is and What It Does

The **chi-square (χ2) goodness-of-fit test** is a nonparametric statistical test used for comparing categorical information against what we would expect based on previous knowledge. As such, it tests the **observed frequency**

expected frequency The frequency expected in a category if the sample data represent the population.

(the frequency with which participants fall into a category) against the **expected frequency** (the frequency expected in a category if the sample data represent the population). It is a nondirectional test, meaning that the alternative hypothesis is neither one-tailed nor two-tailed. The alternative hypothesis for a χ^2 goodness-of-fit test is that the observed data do not fit the expected frequencies for the population, and the null hypothesis is that they do fit the expected frequencies for the population. There is no conventional way to write these hypotheses in symbols, as we have done with the previous statistical tests. To illustrate the χ^2 goodness-of-fit test, let's look at a situation in which its use is appropriate.

Calculations for the χ^2 Goodness-of-Fit Test

Suppose that a researcher is interested in determining whether the teenage pregnancy rate at a particular high school is different from the rate statewide. Assume that the rate statewide is 17%. A random sample of 80 female students is selected from the target high school. Seven of the students are either pregnant now or have been pregnant previously. The χ^2 goodness-of-fit test measures the observed frequencies against the expected frequencies. The observed and expected frequencies are presented in Table 14.1.

As shown in the table, the observed frequencies represent the number of high school female students in the sample of 80 who were pregnant versus not pregnant. The expected frequencies represent what we would expect based on chance, given what is known about the population. In this case, we would expect 17% of the female students to be pregnant because this is the rate statewide. If we take 17% of 80 ($.17 \times 80 = 14$), we would expect 14 of the students to be pregnant. By the same token, we would expect 83% of the students ($.83 \times 80 = 66$) to be not pregnant. If the calculated expected frequencies are correct, when summed they should equal the sample size ($14 + 66 = 80$).

After the observed and expected frequencies have been determined, we can calculate χ^2 as follows:

$$\chi^2 = \Sigma \frac{(O - E)^2}{E}$$

where O is the observed frequency, E is the expected frequency, and Σ indicates that we must sum the indicated fractions for each category in the study

TABLE 14.1 Observed and Expected Frequencies for the χ^2 Goodness-of-Fit Example

FREQUENCIES	PREGNANT	NOT PREGNANT
Observed	7	73
Expected	14	66

(in this case, for the pregnant and not pregnant groups). Using this formula with the present example, we have

$$\chi^2 = \frac{(7-14)^2}{14} + \frac{(73-66)^2}{66} = \frac{(7)^2}{14} + \frac{(7)^2}{66} = \frac{49}{14} + \frac{49}{66} = 3.5 + 0.74 = 4.24$$

Interpreting the χ^2 Goodness-of-Fit Test

The null hypothesis is rejected if χ^2_{obt} is greater than χ^2_{cv}. The χ^2_{cv} is found in Table A.7 in Appendix A. To use the table, you need to know the degrees of freedom for the χ^2 test. This is the number of categories minus 1. In our example, we have two categories (pregnant and not pregnant); thus, we have 1 degree of freedom. At alpha = .05, then $\chi^2_{cv} = 3.84$. Our χ^2_{obt} of 4.24 is larger than the critical value, so we can reject the null hypothesis and conclude that the observed frequency of pregnancy is significantly lower than expected by chance. In other words, the female teens at the target high school have a significantly lower pregnancy rate than would be expected based on the statewide rate. In APA style, the result is reported as

$$\chi^2(1, N = 80) = 4.24, p < .05$$

Assumptions and Appropriate Use of the χ^2 Goodness-of-Fit Test

Although the χ^2 goodness-of-fit test is a nonparametric test and therefore less restrictive than a parametric test, it does have its own assumptions. First, the test is appropriate for nominal (categorical) data. If data are measured on a higher scale of measurement, they can be transformed to a nominal scale. Second, the frequencies in each expected frequency cell should not be too small. If the frequency in any expected frequency cell is too small (< 5), then the χ^2 test should not be conducted. Last, to be generalizable to the population, the sample should be randomly selected and the observations must be independent. In other words, each observation must be based on the score of a different participant. Instructions on using SPSS and the TI-84 calculator to conduct this χ^2 goodness-of-fit test appear in the Statistical Software Resource section at the end of the chapter.

Chi-Square (χ^2) Test of Independence: What It Is and What It Does

chi-square (χ^2) test A nonparametric inferential test used when frequency data have been collected to determine how well an observed breakdown of people over various categories fits some expected breakdown.

The logic of the **chi-square (χ^2) test** of independence is the same as for any χ^2 statistic; we are comparing how well an observed breakdown of people over various categories fits some expected breakdown (such as an equal breakdown). In other words, a χ^2 test compares an observed frequency distribution to an expected frequency distribution. If we find a difference, we determine whether the difference is greater than what would be expected based on chance. The difference between the χ^2 test of independence and the χ^2 goodness-of-fit test is that the goodness-of-fit test compares how well an observed frequency distribution of one nominal variable fits some expected pattern of frequencies, whereas the test of independence compares how well an observed frequency distribution of two nominal variables fits some expected pattern of frequencies. The formula we use is the same as for the χ^2 goodness-of-fit test:

$$\chi^2 = \Sigma \frac{(O - E)^2}{E}$$

The null hypothesis and the alternative hypothesis are similar to those used with the *t* tests. The null hypothesis is that there are no observed differences in frequency between the groups we are comparing; the alternative hypothesis is that there are differences in frequency between the groups and that the differences are greater than we would expect based on chance.

Calculations for the χ^2 Test of Independence

As a means of illustrating the χ^2 test of independence, imagine that a sample of randomly chosen teenagers is categorized as having been employed as babysitters or never having been employed in this capacity. The teenagers are then asked whether they have ever taken a first-aid course. In this case, we would like to determine whether babysitters are more likely to have taken first aid than those who have never worked as babysitters. Because we are examining the observed frequency distribution of two nominal variables (babysitting and taking a first-aid class), the χ^2 test of independence is appropriate. We find that 65 of the 100 babysitters have had a first-aid course, and 35 of the babysitters have not. In the nonbabysitter group, 43 out of 90 have had a first-aid course, and the remaining 47 have not. Table 14.2 is a contingency table showing the observed and expected frequencies.

TABLE 14.2 Observed and Expected frequencies for Babysitters and Nonbabysitters Having Taken a First-Aid Course

	TAKEN FIRST-AID COURSE		
	YES	NO	ROW TOTALS
Babysitters	65 (57)	35 (43)	100
Nonbabysitters	43 (51)	47 (39)	90
Column Totals	**108**	**82**	**190**

To determine the expected frequency for each cell, we use this formula:

$$E = \frac{(RT)(CT)}{N}$$

where RT is the row total, CT is the column total, and N is the total number of observations. Thus, the expected frequency for the upper-left cell is

$$E = \frac{(100)(108)}{190} = \frac{10{,}800}{190} = 56.8$$

The expected frequencies appear in parentheses in Table 14.2. Notice that the expected frequencies when summed equal 190, the N in the study. After we have the observed and expected frequencies, we can calculate χ^2:

$$\chi^2 = \Sigma \frac{(O - E)^2}{E}$$

$$= \frac{(65 - 57)^2}{57} + \frac{(35 - 43)^2}{43} + \frac{(43 - 51)^2}{51} + \frac{(47 - 39)^2}{39}$$

$$= 1.123 + 1.488 + 1.255 + 1.641 = 5.507$$

Interpreting the χ^2 Test of Independence

The degrees of freedom for this χ^2 test are equal to $(r - 1)(c - 1)$, where r is the number of rows and c is the number of columns. In our example, we have $(2 - 1)(2 - 1) = 1$. We now refer to Table A.7 in Appendix A to identify χ^2_{cv} for $df = 1$. At the .05 level, $\chi^2_{cv} = 3.841$. Our χ^2_{obt} of 5.507 exceeds the critical value, and we reject the null hypothesis. In other words, there is a significant difference between babysitters and nonbabysitters in terms of their having taken a first-aid class—significantly more babysitters have taken a first-aid class. In APA style, this result is reported as $\chi^2(1, N = 190) = 5.507, p < .05$. Instructions on using SPSS and the TI-84 calculator to conduct this χ^2 test of independence appear in the Statistical Software Resource section at the end of the chapter.

Effect Size: Phi Coefficient

As with the t tests discussed in Chapters 9 and 10, we can also compute the effect size for a χ^2 test of independence. For a 2×2 contingency table, we use the **phi coefficient** (ϕ), where

phi coefficient An inferential test used to determine effect size for a chi-square test.

$$\phi = \sqrt{\frac{\chi^2}{N}}$$

In our example, this is

$$\phi = \sqrt{\frac{5.507}{190}} = \sqrt{0.02898} = 0.17$$

Cohen's (1988) specifications for the phi coefficient indicate that a phi coefficient of .10 is a small effect, .30 is a medium effect, and .50 is a large effect. Our effect size is small. Hence, even though the χ^2 is significant, the effect size is not large. In other words, the difference observed in whether a teenager had taken a first-aid class is not strongly accounted for by being a babysitter. Why do you think the χ^2 was significant even though the effect size was small? If you attribute this to the large sample size, you are correct.

Assumptions of the χ^2 Test of Independence

The assumptions underlying the χ^2 test of independence are the same as those noted previously for the χ^2 goodness-of-fit test:

- The sample is random.
- The observations are independent.
- The data are nominal.

The χ^2 Tests — **IN REVIEW**

	χ^2 GOODNESS-OF-FIT TEST	χ^2 TEST OF INDEPENDENCE
What It Is	A nonparametric test comparing observed frequencies on one nominal variable to expected frequencies based on population data	A nonparametric test comparing observed to expected frequencies for a two-group between-subjects design
What It Does	Will identify how well an observed frequency distribution of one nominal variable fits some expected pattern of frequencies	Will identify differences in frequency on two variables between groups
Assumptions	• Random sample • Independent observations • Nominal data	• Random sample • Independent observations • Nominal data

CRITICAL THINKING CHECK 14.1

1. How does the χ^2 goodness-of-fit test differ in use from the previously described *z* test and *t* test? In other words, when should it be used?
2. Why are the χ^2 tests nonparametric tests, and what does this mean?

Wilcoxon Rank-Sum Test: What It Is and What It Does

Wilcoxon rank-sum test A nonparametric inferential test for comparing sample medians of two independent groups of scores.

The **Wilcoxon rank-sum test** is similar to the independent-groups *t* test (discussed in Chapter 9); however, it uses ordinal data rather than interval-ratio data and compares medians rather than means. Imagine that a teacher of fifth-grade students wants to compare the number of books read per term by female versus male students in her class. Rather than reporting the data as the actual number of books read (interval-ratio data), she ranks the female and male students, giving the student who read the fewest books a rank of 1 and the student who read the most books the highest rank. She does this because the distribution representing numbers of books read is skewed (not normal). She predicts that the girls will read more books than the boys. Thus, H_0 is that the median number of books read by girls is equal to or less than the median number of books read by boys ($Md_{girls} \leq Md_{boys}$), and H_a is that the median number of books read by girls is greater than the number of books read by boys ($Md_{girls} > Md_{boys}$). The number of books read by each group and the corresponding rankings are presented in Table 14.3. In our example, none of the students read the same number of books, thus each student receives a different rank. However, if two students had read the same number of books (for example, if two students each read 10 books), these scores would take positions 1 and 2 in the ranking, each would be given a rank of 1.5 (halfway between the ranks of 1 and 2), and the next rank assigned would be 3.

Calculations for the Wilcoxon Rank-Sum Test

As a check to confirm that the ranking has been done correctly, the highest rank should be equal to $n_1 + n_2$; in our example, $n_1 + n_2 = 12$, and the highest rank is also 12. In addition, the sum of the ranks should equal $N(N + 1)/2$, where N is the total number of people in the study. In our example, $12(12 + 1)/2 = 78$. If we add the ranks $(1 + 2 + 3 + 4 + 5 + 6 + 7 + 8 + 9 + 10 + 11 + 12)$, they also sum to 78. Thus, the ranking was done correctly.

The Wilcoxon test is completed by first summing the ranks for the group expected to have the smaller total. Because the teacher expects the boys to read less, she sums their ranks. This sum, as seen in Table 14.3, is 24.

TABLE 14.3 Number of Books Read and the Corresponding Ranks for Female and Male Students

GIRLS		BOYS	
X	RANK	X	RANK
20	4	10	1
24	8	17	2
29	9	23	7
33	10	19	3
57	12	22	6
35	11	21	5
			$\Sigma = 24$

Interpreting the Wilcoxon Rank-Sum Test

Using Table A.8 in Appendix A, we see that for a one-tailed test at the .05 level, if $n_1 = 6$ and $n_2 = 6$, the maximum sum of the ranks in the group expected to be lower is 28. If the sum of the ranks of the group expected to be lower (the boys in this situation) exceeds 28, then the result is not significant. Note that this is the only test statistic that we have discussed so far, where the obtained value needs to be *equal to or less than* the critical value to be statistically significant. When we use this table, n_1 is always the smaller of the two groups; if the values of n are equal, it does not matter which is n_1 and which is n_2. Moreover, Table A.8 presents the critical values for one-tailed tests only. If a two-tailed test is used, the table can be adapted by dividing the alpha level in half. In other words, we would use the critical values for the .025 level from the table to determine the critical value at the .05 level for a two-tailed test. We find that the sum of the ranks of the group predicted to have lower scores (24) is less than the cutoff for significance. Our conclusion is to reject the null hypothesis. In other words, we observed that the ranks in the two groups differed, there were not an equal number of high and low ranks in each group, and one group (the girls in this case) read significantly more books than the other. If we report this finding in APA style, it appears as $W_s(n_1 = 6, n_2 = 6) = 24, p < .05$ (one-tailed).

Assumptions of the Wilcoxon Rank-Sum Test

The Wilcoxon rank-sum test is a nonparametric procedure that is analogous to the independent-groups t test. The assumptions of the test are as follows:

- The data are ratio, interval, or ordinal in scale, all of which must be converted to ranked (ordinal) data before conducting the test.
- The underlying distribution is not normal.
- The observations are independent.

If the observations are not independent (a correlated-groups design), then the Wilcoxon matched-pairs signed-ranks T test should be used.

Wilcoxon Matched-Pairs Signed-Ranks *T* Test: What It Is and What It Does

Wilcoxon matched-pairs signed-ranks *T* test A nonparametric inferential test for comparing sample medians of two dependent or related groups of scores.

The **Wilcoxon matched-pairs signed-ranks *T* test** is similar to the correlated-groups t test, except that it is nonparametric and compares medians rather than means. Imagine that the same teacher in the previous problem wants to compare the number of books read by all students (female and male) over two terms. During the first term, the teacher keeps track of how many books each student reads. During the second term, the teacher institutes a reading reinforcement program through which students can earn prizes based on the number of books they read. The number of books read by students is once again measured. As before, the distribution representing the number of books read is skewed (not normal). Thus, a nonparametric statistic is necessary. However, in this case, the design is within-subjects—two measures are taken on each student: one before the reading reinforcement program is instituted and one after the program is instituted.

Table 14.4 shows the number of books read by the students across the two terms. Notice that the number of books read during the first term represents the data used in the previous Wilcoxon rank-sum test. The teacher uses a one-tailed test and predicts that students will read more books after the reinforcement program is instituted. Thus, H_0 is that the median number of books read in the first term is equal to or greater

TABLE 14.4 Number of Books Read in Each Term

TERM 1 (NO REINFORCEMENT)	TERM 2 (REINFORCEMENT IMPLEMENTED)	DIFFERENCE SCORE (D) (TERM 1 − TERM 2)	RANK	SIGNED RANK
X	X			
10	15	−5	4.5	−4.5
17	23	−6	6	−5
19	20	−1	1.5	−1.5
20	20	0	—	—
21	28	−7	8	−8
22	26	−4	3	−3
23	24	−1	1.5	−1.5
24	29	−5	4.5	−4.5
29	37	−8	10	−10
33	40	−7	8	−8
57	50	7	8	8
35	55	−20	11	−11
				$+\Sigma = 8$
				$-\Sigma = 58$

than the median number of books read in the second term (after the reinforcement is introduced) ($Md_{before} \geq Md_{after}$), and H_a is that the median number of books read is greater after the reinforcement program is instituted ($Md_{before} < Md_{after}$).

Calculations for the Wilcoxon Matched-Pairs Signed-Ranks *T* Test

The first step in completing the Wilcoxon signed-ranks test is to compute a difference score for each individual. In this case, we have subtracted the number of books read in term 2 from the number of books read in term 1 for each student. Keep in mind the logic of a matched-pairs test. If the reinforcement program had no effect, we would expect all of the difference scores to be 0 or very close to 0. Columns 1 to 3 in Table 14.4 give the number of books read in each term and the difference scores. Next, we rank the absolute values of the difference scores. This is shown in column 4 of Table 14.4. Notice that the difference score of 0 is not ranked. Also note what happens when ranks are tied; for example, there are two difference scores of −1. These difference scores take positions 1 and 2 in the ranking; each is given a rank of 1.5 (halfway between the ranks of 1 and 2), and the next rank assigned is 3. As a check, the highest rank should equal the number of ranked scores. In our problem, we ranked 11 difference scores; thus, the highest rank should be 11, and it is.

After the ranks have been determined, we attach to each rank the sign of the previously calculated difference score. This is represented in the last column of Table 14.4. The final step necessary to complete the Wilcoxon signed-ranks test is to sum the positive ranks and then sum the negative ranks. Once again, if there is no difference in the number of books read across the two terms, we would expect the sum of the positive ranks to equal or be very close to the sum of the negative ranks. The sums of the positive and negative ranks are shown at the bottom of the last column in Table 14.4.

For a two-tailed test, T_{obt} is equal to the smaller of the summed ranks. Thus, if we were computing a two-tailed test, our T_{obt} would equal 8. However, our test is one-tailed; the teacher predicted that the number of books read would increase during the reinforcement program. For a one-tailed test, we predict whether we expect more positive or more negative difference scores. Because we subtracted term 2 (the term in which students were reinforced for reading) from term 1, we would expect more negative differences. The T_{obt} for a one-tailed test is the sum of the signed ranks *predicted* to be smaller. In this case, we would predict the summed ranks for the positive differences to be smaller than that for negative differences. Thus, T_{obt} for a one-tailed test is also 8.

Interpreting the Wilcoxon Matched-Pairs Signed-Ranks *T* Test

Using Table A.9 in Appendix A, we see that for a one-tailed test at the .05 alpha level with $N = 11$ (we use $N = 11$ and not 12 because we ranked only 11 of the 12 difference scores), the maximum sum of the ranks in the group expected to be lower is 13. If the sum of the ranks for the group expected to be lower exceeds 13, then the result is not significant. Note that, as with the Wilcoxon rank-sum test, the obtained value needs to be *equal to or less than* the critical value to be statistically significant. Our conclusion is to reject the null hypothesis. In other words, we observed that the sum of the positive versus the negative ranks differed, or the number of books read in the two conditions differed; significantly more books were read in the reinforcement condition than in the no reinforcement condition. If we report this in APA style, it appears as $T(N = 11) = 8$, $p < .05$ (one-tailed).

Assumptions of the Wilcoxon Matched-Pairs Signed-Ranks *T* Test

The Wilcoxon matched-pairs signed-ranks *T* test is a nonparametric procedure that is analogous to the correlated-groups *t* test. The assumptions of the test are as follows:

- The data are ratio, interval, or ordinal in scale, all of which must be converted to ranked (ordinal) data before conducting the test.
- The underlying distribution is not normal.
- The observations are dependent or related (a correlated-groups design).

Wilcoxon Tests — **IN REVIEW**

	TYPE OF TEST	
	WILCOXON RANK-SUM TEST	**WILCOXON MATCHED-PAIRS SIGNED-RANKS *T* TEST**
What It Is	A nonparametric test for a two-group between-subjects design.	A nonparametric test for a two-group correlated-groups (within- or matched-subjects) design.
What It Does	Will identify differences in ranks on a variable between groups.	Will identify differences in signed ranks on a variable for correlated groups.
Assumptions	• Ordinal data • Distribution not normal • Independent observations	• Ordinal data • Distribution not normal • Dependent or related observations

CRITICAL THINKING CHECK 14.2

1. I have recently conducted a study in which I ranked my participants (college students) on height and weight. I am interested in whether there are any differences in height and weight depending on whether the participant is an athlete (defined as being a member of a sports team) or not an athlete. Which statistic would you recommend using to analyze these data? If the actual height (in inches) and weight (in pounds) data were available, what statistic would be appropriate?
2. Determine the difference scores and ranks for the following set of matched-pairs data. Finally, calculate T for these data, and determine whether the T-score is significant for a two-tailed test.

Participant	Score 1	Score 2
1	12	15
2	10	9
3	15	14
4	17	23
5	17	16
6	22	19
7	20	30
8	22	25

The Kruskal-Wallis Test: What It Is and What It Does

Kruskal-Wallis test An inferential nonparametric test used to determine differences between three or more groups on a ranked variable for a between-subjects design.

Just as the ANOVA is an extension of a t test, the Wilcoxon tests have an analogous extension. For a between-subjects design with more than two groups, the **Kruskal-Wallis test** is appropriate. As with a one-way randomized ANOVA, the Kruskal-Wallis test is used in situations where there is one independent variable with three or more levels and the design is between-subjects. However, unlike the ANOVA, the Kruskal-Wallis test is used either when the data are ordinal or when the assumptions of population normality or homogeneity of variance have been violated. The data used to calculate the Kruskal-Wallis test are always ordinal (ranked).

Let's use a similar study to that from Chapter 11 in which a researcher is studying the difference in recall performance between three different types of rehearsal (rote, imagery, and story). Subjects are given a list of 15 words to learn utilizing one of three rehearsal types. Because the data are interval-ratio in scale, when we studied this problem in Chapter 11 we used the one-way randomized ANOVA to analyze the data. In this situation, however, the researcher

TABLE 14.5 Number of Words Recalled Correctly in Rote, Imagery, and Story Rehearsal Conditions

ROTE	IMAGERY	STORY
2	6	10
4	8	9
3	9	12
2	7	8
8	6	4
4	11	13

is worried that the data are somewhat skewed thus affecting the normality and homogeneity of variances assumptions associated with the ANOVA test. The researcher therefore decides to use the Kruskal-Wallis test. The number of words recalled by the subjects in each condition appears in Table 14.5.

Calculations for the Kruskal-Wallis Test

In order to use the Kruskal-Wallis test, the number of words recalled must be converted to an ordinal ranking scale. Thus, each of the subjects' recall scores is converted to a rank with the lowest score receiving a rank of 1, the second lowest a rank of 2, and so on. When two subjects recall the same number of words, for example, the two subjects who both recalled 2 words in the Rote condition, they take positions 1 and 2 in the ranking and are each given a rank of 1.5. This is illustrated in Table 14.6.

As a check to confirm that the ranking has been completed correctly, the highest rank should be equal to $n_1 + n_2 + n_3$; in our example $n_1 + n_2 + n_3 =$ 18, and the highest rank is also 18. In addition, the sum of the ranks should equal $N(N + 1)/2$, where N is the total number of people in the study. In our example, $18(18 + 1)/2 = 171$, and if we add the ranks ($1.5 + 1.5 + 3 + 5 + 5 + 5 + 7.5 + 7.5 + 9 + 11 + 11 + 11 + 13.5 + 13.5 + 15 + 16 + 17 + 18$) they sum to 171 also. Thus the ranking was completed correctly. The null hypothesis for the Kruskal-Wallis test states that there are no systematic differences in the ranks between conditions whereas the alternative hypothesis states that we expect systematic differences in the ranks between conditions.

Once the ranks have been determined, the ranks within each condition are summed or totaled, as can be seen in Table 14.6 in which the symbol T has been used to indicate the sum of the ranks in each condition. The T values will be used in the calculation of the Kruskal-Wallis test. The formula used for the Kruskal-Wallis test produces a chi-square statistic and is calculated as follows:

$$\chi^2 = \frac{12}{N(N + 1)}\left(\sum \frac{T^2}{n}\right) - 3(N + 1)$$

TABLE 14.6 Number of Words Recalled Correctly and Corresponding Ranks in Rote, Imagery, and Story Rehearsal Conditions

ROTE	RANK	IMAGERY	RANK	STORY	RANK
2	1.5	6	7.5	10	15
4	5	8	11	9	13.5
3	3	9	13.5	12	17
2	1.5	7	9	8	11
8	11	6	7.5	4	5
4	5	11	16	13	18
	$T = 27$		$T = 64.5$		$T = 79.5$

We can now use the data from Table 14.6 to calculate the chi-square value.

$$\chi^2 = \frac{12}{18(18+1)}\left(\frac{27^2}{6} + \frac{64.5^2}{6} + \frac{79.5^2}{6}\right) - 3(18+1)$$

$$= \frac{12}{(18)(19)}\left(\frac{729}{6} + \frac{4{,}160.25}{6} + \frac{6{,}320.25}{6}\right) - 3(19)$$

$$= \frac{12}{342}(121.5 + 693.38 + 1{,}053.38) - 57$$

$$= .035(1{,}868.26) - 57$$

$$= 65.39 - 57$$
$$= 8.39$$

Interpreting the Kruskal-Wallis Test

The degrees of freedom for the Kruskal-Wallis test are calculated in a similar manner to the degrees of freedom for a chi-square test; in other words, the number of conditions minus one. In this example we have $df = 3 - 1 = 2$. In addition, the Kruskal-Wallis test is based on approximately the same distribution as the chi-square test so we can use the chi-square probability table to determine whether the obtained statistic is significant. Thus, referring to Table A.7 in Appendix A, we find that the χ^2_{cv} when $df = 2$ is 5.992. Because our $\chi^2_{obt} = 8.39$ and exceeds the critical value, we can reject H_0. Thus, there are significant differences in number of words recalled between the three rehearsal type conditions. In addition, because our χ^2_{obt} is so large we should check the critical values at the .01 and .005 levels provided in Table A.7. When we check these we find that $\chi^2 = 8.39$ $(2, N = 18)$, $p < .005$.

Assumptions of the Kruskal-Wallis Test

The assumptions of the Kruskal-Wallis test are that the data are ranked (ordinal), the distribution is not normal, there are at least five scores in each condition, and that the observations are independent (there are different subjects in each condition).

The Friedman Test: What It Is and What It Does

Friedman test An inferential nonparametric test used to determine differences between three or more conditions on a ranked variable for a correlated-groups design.

If the Kruskal-Wallis is the nonparametric version of the one-way randomized ANOVA, the **Friedman test** is analogous to the one-way repeated-measures ANOVA and is used in situations where there is one independent variable with three or more levels and the design is correlated groups. As with the Kruskal-Wallis test, the Friedman test is used either when the data are ordinal or when the assumptions of population normality or homogeneity of variance have been violated. The data used to calculate the Friedman test are always ordinal (ranked).

Let's use the same study and data as we did earlier with the Kruskal-Wallis test, except in this situation imagine that we used the same participants in each of the conditions—a within-subjects correlated-groups design. Thus, each subject serves in each of the three rehearsal conditions (rote, imagery, and story) and studies a list of equally difficult words in each condition. The null hypothesis for the Friedman test states that there are no systematic differences in the ranks between conditions whereas the alternative hypothesis states that we expect systematic differences in the ranks between conditions. The number of words recalled by the subjects in each condition appears in Table 14.7.

Calculations for the Friedman Test

In order to use the Friedman test, the number of words recalled across the three conditions for each participant must be converted to an ordinal ranking scale. Thus, each subject's recall scores across the three conditions is converted to a rank with the lowest score receiving a rank of 1, the second lowest a rank of 2, and the highest score a rank of 3. Therefore, in a study with three conditions, such as this one, the highest rank a single participant's score can

TABLE 14.7 Number of Words Recalled Correctly in Rote, Imagery, and Story Rehearsal Conditions

ROTE	IMAGERY	STORY
2	6	10
4	8	9
3	9	12
2	7	8
6	4	8
4	11	13

TABLE 14.8 Number of Words Recalled Correctly and Corresponding Ranks in Rote, Imagery, and Story Rehearsal Conditions for Each Subject

SUBJECT	ROTE	RANK	IMAGERY	RANK	STORY	RANK
1	2	1	6	2	10	3
2	4	1	8	2	9	3
3	3	1	9	2	12	3
4	2	1	7	2	8	3
5	6	2	4	1	8	3
6	4	1	11	2	13	3
		$R = 7$		$R = 11$		$R = 18$

receive is 3. If scores within a single subject's data are the same, they split the ranks. For example, if one participant recalled 2 words in both the Rote and Imagery conditions, they would receive a rank of 1.5 in each of those conditions. This situation has not occurred in our data. The ranks for each participant appear in Table 14.8.

Once the ranks have been determined, the ranks within each condition are summed or totaled, as can be seen in Table 14.8 in which the symbol R (for Rank) has been used to indicate the sum of the ranks in each condition. The R values will be used in the calculation of the Friedman test. The formula used for the Friedman test produces a chi-square statistic and is calculated as follows:

$$\chi^2 = \frac{12}{nk(k+1)}(\Sigma R^2) - 3n(k+1)$$

where n refers to the number of subjects and k refers to the number of conditions. We can now use the data from Table 14.8 to calculate the chi-square value.

$$\begin{aligned}
\chi^2 &= \frac{12}{6 \times 3(3+1)}(\Sigma R^2) - 3 \times 6(3+1) \\
&= \frac{12}{18(4)}(7^2 + 11^2 + 18^2) - 18(4) \\
&= \frac{12}{72}(49 + 121 + 324) - 72 \\
&= .167(494) - 72 \\
&= 82.5 - 72 \\
&= 10.5
\end{aligned}$$

Interpreting the Friedman Test

The degrees of freedom for the Friedman test are calculated in a similar manner to the degrees of freedom for any chi-square test; in other words, the number of conditions minus one. In this example we have $df = 3 - 1 = 2$. In addition, the Friedman test is based on approximately the same distribution as the chi-square test so we can use the chi-square probability table to determine whether the obtained statistic is significant. Thus, referring to Table A.7 in Appendix A we find that the χ^2_{cv} when $df = 2$ is 5.992. Because our $\chi^2_{obt} = 10.5$ and exceeds the critical value we can reject H_0. Thus, there are significant differences in number of words recalled between the three rehearsal type conditions. In addition, because our χ^2_{obt} is so large we should check the critical values at the .01 and .005 levels in Table A.7. When we check these we find that $\chi^2 = 10.50$ (2, $N = 6$), $p < .005$.

Assumptions of the Friedman Test

The assumptions of the Friedman test are that the data are ranked (ordinal), the distribution is not normal, there are at least five scores in each condition, and that the observations are not independent (a correlated-groups design was used).

Nonparametric Tests for More than Two Groups — IN REVIEW

	TYPE OF TEST	
	KRUSKAL-WALLIS TEST	**FRIEDMAN TEST**
What It Is	A nonparametric test for a between-subjects design with more than two groups.	A nonparametric test for a correlated-groups (within-or matched-subjects) design with more than two groups.
What It Does	Will identify differences in ranks on a variable between groups.	Will identify differences in ranks on a variable for correlated groups.
Assumptions	• Ordinal data • Distribution is not normal • Independent observations • More than five observations per condition	• Ordinal data • Distribution is not normal • Dependent or related observations • More than five observations per condition

CRITICAL THINKING CHECK 14.3

1. Explain when you would use the Kruskal-Wallis test versus the Friedman test.
2. Determine the ranks for the data below which represent subject preference for ketchups of differing colors. The preference scores are on a 1–5 scale with a score of 5 indicating the highest preference. In addition, there are five people in each condition for a total of 15 subjects in the experiment.

	Ketchup Color	
Red	Green	Blue
4	2	5
3	1	3
5	1	4
4	3	5
3	2	4

Summary

Nonparametric tests are those for which population parameters (μ and σ) are not needed. In addition, the underlying distribution of scores is not assumed to be normal, and the data are most commonly nominal (categorical) or ordinal in nature. We described and used the chi-square goodness-of-fit nonparametric test and the chi-square test of independence, both used with nominal data. In addition, we learned how to use four nonparametric tests for ordinal data, the Wilcoxon rank-sum test for two group between-subjects designs, the Wilcoxon matched-pairs signed-ranks *T* test for two group correlated-groups designs, the Kruskal-Wallis test for between-subjects designs with more than two conditions, and the Friedman test for correlated-groups designs with more than two conditions.

KEY TERMS

chi-square (χ^2) goodness-of-fit test
observed frequency
expected frequency
Wilcoxon rank-sum test
Wilcoxon matched-pairs signed ranks T test
chi-square (χ^2) test of independence
phi coefficient
Kruskal Wallis test
Friedman test

CHAPTER EXERCISES

1. When is it appropriate to use a χ^2 test?
2. A researcher believes that the percentage of people who exercise in California is greater than the national exercise rate. The national rate is 20%. The researcher gathers a random sample of 120 individuals who live in California and finds that the number who exercise regularly is 31 out of 120.
   a. What is χ^2_{obt}?
   b. What is *df* for this test?
   c. What is χ^2_{cv}?
   d. What conclusion should be drawn from these results?
3. A teacher believes that the percentage of students at her high school who go on to college is higher than the rate in the general population of high school students. The rate in the general population is 30%. In the most recent graduating class at her high school, the teacher found that 90 students graduated and that 40 of those went on to college.
   a. What is χ^2_{obt}?
   b. What is *df* for this test?
   c. What is χ^2_{cv}?
   d. What conclusion should be drawn from these results?
4. You notice in your introductory psychology class that more women tend to sit up front, and more men sit in the back. To determine whether this difference is significant, you collect data on the seating preferences for the students in your class. The data follow:

	Men	*Women*
Front of the Room	15	27
Back of the Room	32	19

   a. What is χ^2_{obt}?
   b. What is *df* for this test?
   c. What is χ^2_{cv}?
   d. What conclusion should be drawn from these results?
5. A researcher is interested in comparing the maturity level of students who volunteer for community service versus those who do not. The researcher assumes that those who perform community service will have higher maturity scores. Maturity scores tend to be skewed (not normally distributed). The maturity scores appear next. Higher scores indicate higher maturity levels.

No Community Service	Community Service
33	41
41	48
54	61
13	72
22	83
26	55

a. What statistical test should be used to analyze these data?
b. Identify H_0 and H_a for this study.
c. Conduct the appropriate analysis.
d. Should H_0 be rejected? What should the researcher conclude?

6. Researchers at a food company are interested in how a new spaghetti sauce made from green tomatoes (and green in color) will compare to their traditional red spaghetti sauce. They are worried that the green color will adversely affect the tastiness scores. They randomly assign subjects to either the green or red sauce condition. Participants indicate the tastiness of the sauce on a 10-point scale. Tastiness scores tend to be skewed. The scores follow:

Red Sauce	*Green Sauce*
7	4
6	5
9	6
10	8
6	7
7	6
8	9

a. What statistical test should be used to analyze these data?
b. Identify H_0 and H_a for this study.
c. Conduct the appropriate analysis.
d. Should H_0 be rejected? What should the researcher conclude?

7. Imagine that the researchers in exercise 6 want to conduct the same study as a within-subjects design. Participants rate both the green and red sauces by indicating the tastiness on a 10-point scale. As in exercise 6, researchers are concerned that the color of the green sauce will adversely affect tastiness scores. Tastiness scores tend to be skewed. The scores follow.
a. What statistical test should be used to analyze these data?
b. Identify H_0 and H_a for this study.
c. Conduct the appropriate analysis.
d. Should H_0 be rejected? What should the researcher conclude?

8. Explain when you would use the Kruskal-Wallis test versus the Wilcoxon rank-sum test.

9. Explain when you would use the Friedman test versus the Wilcoxon matched-pairs signed-ranks T test.

10. Imagine that marketing researchers working for a food company want to determine whether children would prefer ketchup of a different color. They develop red, green, and blue ketchups that all taste the same and have children ($N = 7$) taste each of the ketchups (a correlated-groups design) and rank them on a 5-point scale with 5 indicating the highest preference. The data from the 7 subjects appear below:

	Ketchup Color		
Subject	**Red**	**Green**	**Blue**
1	4	2	5
2	3	1	3
3	5	1	4
4	4	3	5
5	3	2	4
6	5	1	3
7	3	1	5

a. What statistical test should be used to analyze these data?
b. Identify H_0 and H_a for this study.
c. Conduct the appropriate analysis.
d. Should H_0 be rejected? What should the researcher conclude?

CRITICAL THINKING CHECK ANSWERS

14.1

1. The χ^2 test is a nonparametric test used with nominal (categorical) data. It examines how well an observed frequency distribution of a nominal variable fits some expected pattern of frequencies. The z and t tests are for use with interval and ratio data. They test how far a sample mean falls from a population mean.

2. A nonparametric test is one that does not involve the use of any population parameters, such as the mean and standard deviation. In addition, a nonparametric test does not assume a bell-shaped distribution. Thus, the χ^2 test is nonparametric because it fits these assumptions.

14.2

1. Because the subjects have been ranked (ordinal data) on height and weight, the Wilcoxon rank-sum test is appropriate. If the actual height (in inches) and weight (in pounds) were reported, the data would be interval-ratio. In this case, the independent-groups *t* test would be appropriate.

2.

Difference Score	*Rank*	*Signed Rank*
−3	5	−5
1	2	2
1	2	2
−6	7	−7
1	2	2
3	5	5
−10	8	−8
−3	5	−5
		$+\Sigma = 11$
		$-\Sigma = 25$

$T\ (N = 8) = 11$, not significant

14.3

1. Both tests are nonparametric tests that are used with ordinal data when the distribution is skewed. In addition, both tests are also used when there is one independent variable with more than two levels. The difference is that the Kruskal-Wallis test is used for between-subjects designs and the Friedman test is used for correlated-groups designs.

2.

Ketchup Color					
Red	**Rank**	**Green**	**Rank**	**Blue**	**Rank**
4	10.5	2	3.5	5	14
3	6.5	1	1.5	3	6.5
5	14	1	1.5	4	10.5
4	10.5	3	6.5	5	14
3	6.5	2	3.5	4	10.5

WEB RESOURCES

The book-specific website at Cengage.Brain.com offers students a variety of study tools and useful resources such as glossaries and flashcards.

Chapter 14 ▪ Study Guide

CHAPTER 14 SUMMARY AND REVIEW: NONPARAMETRIC INFERENTIAL STATISTICS

We discussed six nonparametric tests in this chapter. First, we learned when to use and how to calculated two nonparametric tests for nominal data—the chi-square goodness-of-fit test and the chi-square test of independence. In addition, we learned how to use four nonparametric tests for ordinal data, the Wilcoxon rank-sum test for two group between-subjects designs, the Wilcoxon matched-pairs signed-ranks *T* test for two group correlated-groups designs, the Kruskal-Wallis test for between-subjects designs with more than two conditions, and the Friedman test for correlated-groups designs with more than two conditions.

CHAPTER 14 REVIEW EXERCISES

1. ________ and ________ frequencies are used in the calculation of the χ^2 statistic.
2. When frequency data are collected, we use the ________ to determine how well an observed frequency distribution of two nominal variables fits some expected breakdown.
3. Effect size for a chi-square test is determined by using the ________.
4. The nonparametric inferential statistic for comparing two groups of different people when ordinal data are collected is the ________.

5. The Wilcoxon ________ test is used with within-subjects designs.
6. The Wilcoxon rank-sum test is used with ________ designs.
7. Chi-square tests use ________ data, whereas Wilcoxon tests use ________ data.
8. The extension of the Wilcoxon rank-sum test for use with more than two groups is the ________.

MULTIPLE-CHOICE SELF-TEST

1. Parametric is to nonparametric as ________ is to ________.
   a. *z* test; *t* test
   b. *t* test; *z* test
   c. χ^2 test; *z* test
   d. *t* test; χ^2 test
2. Which of the following is an assumption of χ^2 tests?
   a. It is a parametric test.
   b. It is appropriate only for ordinal data.
   c. The frequency in each expected frequency cell should be less than 5.
   d. The sample should be randomly selected.
3. The calculation of the *df* for the ________ is $(r - 1)(c - 1)$.
   a. independent-groups *t* test
   b. correlated-groups *t* test
   c. χ^2 test of independence
   d. Wilcoxon rank-sum test
4. The ________ is a measure of effect size for the ________.
   a. phi coefficient; χ^2 goodness-of-fit test
   b. eta-squared; χ^2 goodness-of-fit test
   c. phi coefficient; χ^2 test of independence
   d. eta-squared; Wilcoxon rank-sum test
5. The Wilcoxon rank-sum test is used with ________ data.
   a. interval
   b. ordinal
   c. nominal
   d. ratio
6. Wilcoxon rank-sum test is to ________ design as Wilcoxon matched-pairs signed-ranks *T* test is to ________ design.
   a. between-subjects; within-subjects
   b. correlated-groups; within-subjects
   c. correlated-groups; between-subjects
   d. within-subjects; matched-subjects

SELF-TEST PROBLEMS

1. A researcher believes that the percentage of people who smoke in the South is greater than the national rate. The national rate is 15%. The researcher gathers a random sample of 110 individuals who live in the South and finds that the number who smoke is 21 out of 110.
   a. What is χ^2_{obt}?
   b. What is *df* for this test?
   c. What is χ^2_{cv}?
   d. What conclusion should be drawn from these results?
2. You notice at the gym that it appears that more women tend to work out together, whereas more men tend to work out alone. To determine whether this difference is significant, you collect data on the workout preferences for a sample of men and women at your gym. The data follow.

	Males	Females
Together	12	24
Alone	22	10

   a. What is χ^2_{obt}?
   b. What is *df* for this test?
   c. What is χ^2_{cv}?
   d. What conclusion should be drawn from these results?
3. Researchers at a food company are interested in how a new ketchup made from green tomatoes (and green in color) will compare to their traditional red ketchup. They are worried that the green color will adversely affect the tastiness scores. They randomly assign subjects to either the green or red ketchup condition. Participants indicate the tastiness of the sauce on a 20-point scale. Tastiness scores tend to be skewed. The scores follow.

Green Ketchup	Red Ketchup
14	16
15	16
16	19
18	20
16	17
16	17
19	18

a. What statistical test should be used to analyze these data?
b. Identify H_0 and H_a for this study.
c. Conduct the appropriate analysis.
d. Should H_0 be rejected? What should the researcher conclude?

Chapter 14 ▪ Statistical Software Resources

CHI-SQUARE GOODNESS-OF-FIT TEST

Using SPSS

To begin using SPSS to calculate this chi-square test, we must enter the data into the Data Editor. We'll use the problem from this chapter to illustrate this test. The data appear in Table 14.1. We have 80 individuals in the sample, thus there will be 80 scores entered. A score of 1 indicates that the individual was pregnant (there are 7 scores of 1 entered), and a score of 2 indicates that the individual was not pregnant (there are 73 scores of 2 entered). A portion of the Data Editor with the data entered appears next. I've named the variable Observedpregnancy to indicate that we are interested in the pregnancy rate observed in the sample.

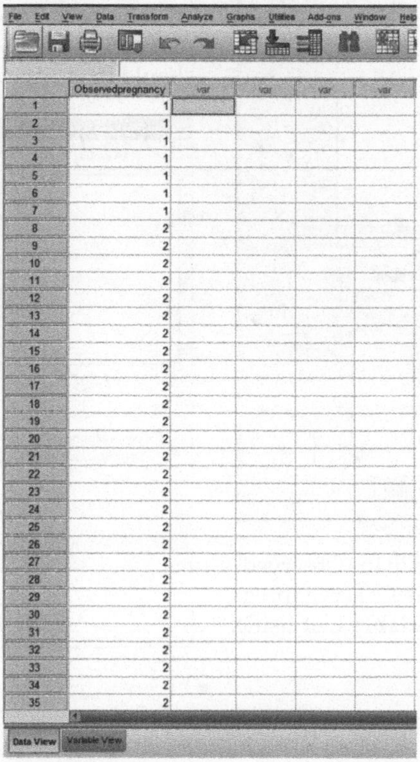

Next, we click on **Analyze**, then **Nonparametric Tests, Legacy Dialogs**, and finally **Chi-square**. This is illustrated in the following screen capture:

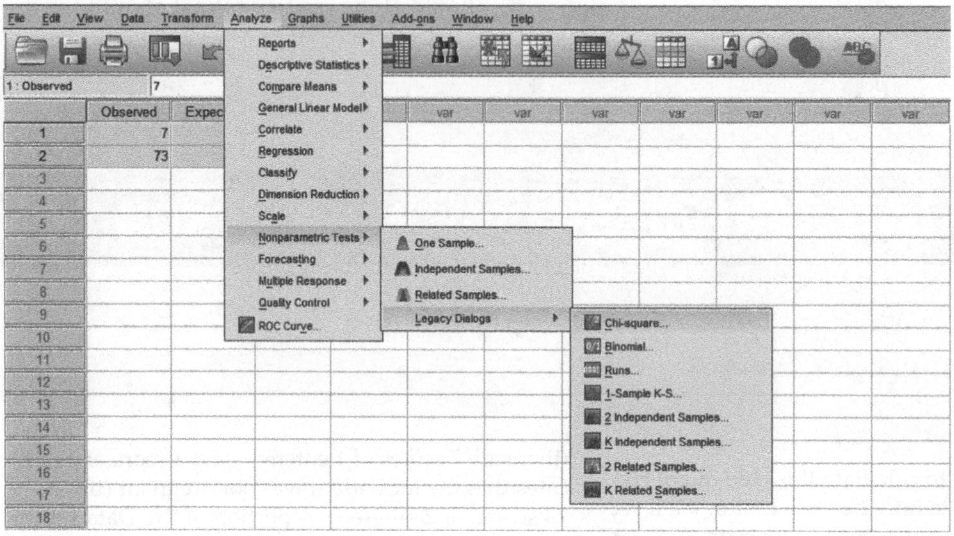

This will produce the following dialog box:

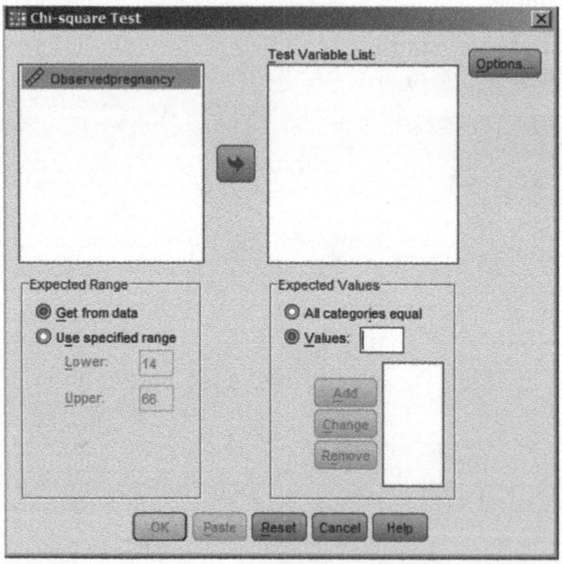

Our **Test Variable List** is the data in the Observedpregnancy variable. Thus, move the Observedpregnancy variable over to the **Test Variable List** using the arrow key. We also have to specify the expected values in the Expected Values box. Click on **Values** and then type the first value (14) into the box and click on **Add**. Next enter the second expected value (66) and enter it by clicking on **Add**. The dialog box should now appear as follows:

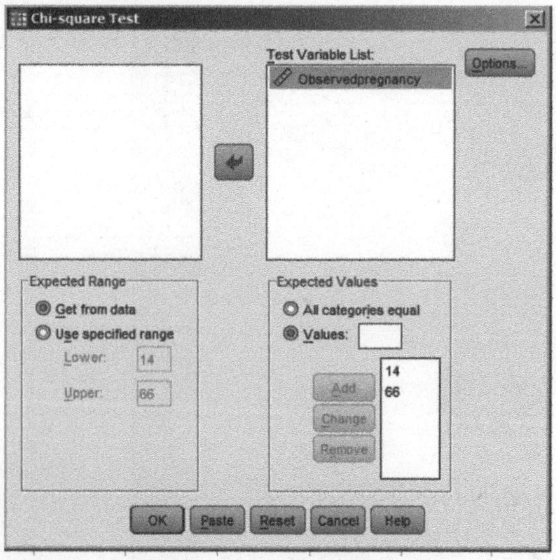

Click **OK** and you should receive the output that appears next.

NPar Tests

Chi-Square Test

Frequencies

Observedpregnancy

	Observed N	Expected N	Residual
1	7	14.0	-7.0
2	73	66.0	7.0
Total	80		

Test Statistics

	Observedpregnancy
Chi-square	4.242[a]
df	1
Asymp. Sig.	.039

a. 0 cells (.0%) have expected frequencies less than 5. The minimum expected cell frequency is 14.0.

We can reject the null hypothesis and conclude that the observed frequency of pregnancy is significantly lower than expected by chance. In other words, the female teens at the target high school have a significantly lower pregnancy rate than would be expected based on the statewide rate. In APA style, this would be reported as χ^2 (1, N = 80) = 4.24, p = .039.

Using the TI-84

Let's use the data from Table 14.1 to conduct the calculation using the TI-84 calculator.

1. With the calculator on, press the STAT key.
2. Highlight EDIT and press ENTER.
3. Enter the Observed Scores in L1 and the Expected Scores in L2.
4. Press the STAT key and highlight TESTS.
5. Scroll down to C: χ^2 GOF Test and press ENTER.
6. The calculator should show Observed: L1, Expected: L2, and df = 1.
7. Scroll down and highlight Calculate and press ENTER.

The χ^2 value of 4.24 should appear on the screen, along with the df = 1 and p = .039.

CHI-SQUARE TEST OF INDEPENDENCE

Using SPSS

We'll use the problem from this chapter to illustrate this test. The data can be found in Table 14.2. We begin by entering the data into SPSS. We enter the data by indicating whether the individual is a babysitter (1) or not a babysitter (2) and whether they have taken a first aid class (1) or not (2). Thus, a 1, 1 is a babysitter who has taken a first aid class whereas a 2, 1 is a nonbabysitter who has taken a first aid class. This coding system is illustrated in the following screen capture of the Data Editor:

File Edit View Data Transform Analyze Graphs Utilities Add-ons Wi

	BabysitterNonbabysitter	FirstAidNoFirst...	var	var
1	1	1		
2	1	1		
3	1	1		
4	1	1		
5	1	1		
6	1	1		
7	1	1		
8	1	1		
9	1	1		
10	1	1		
11	1	1		
12	1	1		
13	1	2		
14	1	2		
15	1	2		
16	1	2		
17	1	2		
18	1	2		
19	2	1		
20	2	1		
21	2	1		
22	2	1		
23	2	1		
24	2	2		
25	2	2		
26	2	2		
27	2	2		
28	2	2		
29	2	2		
30	2	2		
31	2	2		
32	2	2		
33	2	2		
34	2	2		

Please note that not all of the data are visible in the preceding screen capture so enter the data from Table 14.2 in which there is data for 36 individuals.

Next, click on **Analyze**, **Descriptive Statistics**, and then **Crosstabs** as indicated in the following screen capture:

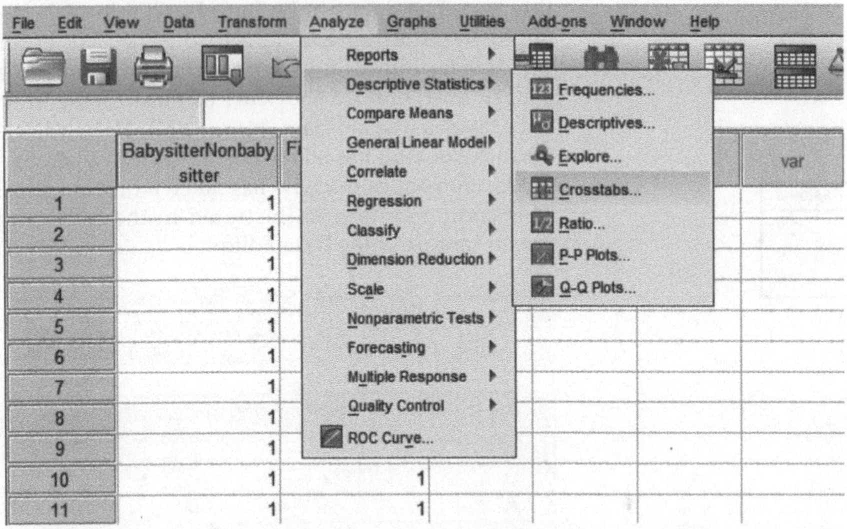

This will produce the dialog box seen next.

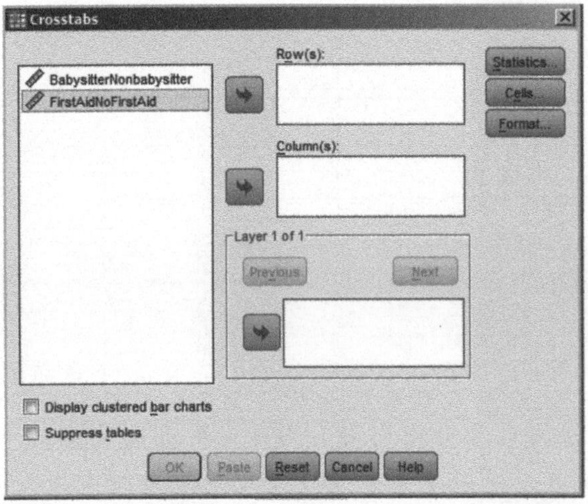

Next move one of the variables to the **Rows** box using the arrow keys and move the second variable to the **Columns** box (it does not matter which variable is entered into rows versus columns). The dialog box should now look as follows:

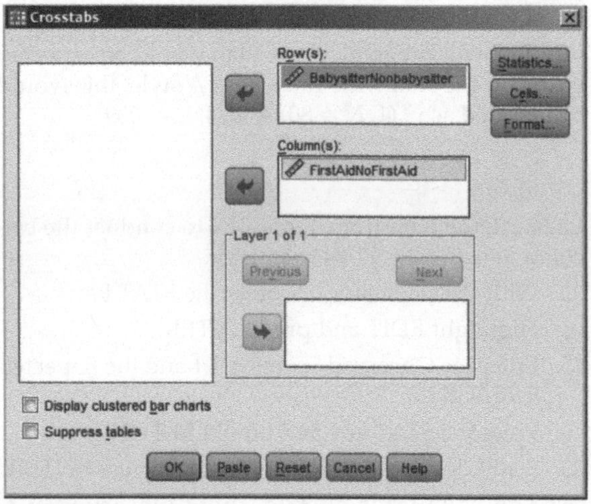

Click on **Statistics** and check the **Chi-square** box and click **Continue**.

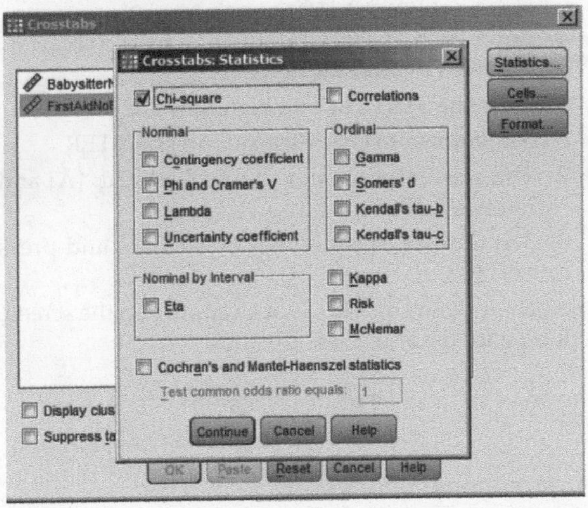

Next click on **Cells** and check the **Observed** and **Expected** boxes as seen next.

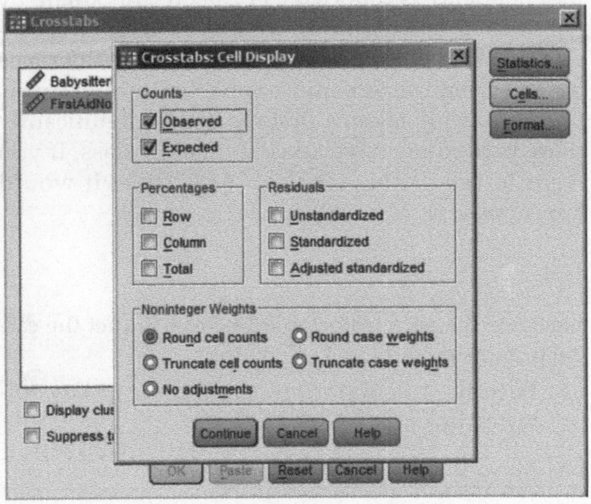

Click **Continue** and then **OK**. The output should appear as follows:

Crosstabs

Case Processing Summary

	Cases					
	Valid		Missing		Total	
	N	Percent	N	Percent	N	Percent
BabysitterNonbabysitter * FirstAidNoFirstAid	36	33.0%	73	67.0%	109	100.0%

BabysitterNonbabysitter * FirstAidNoFirstAid Crosstabulation

			FirstAidNoFirstAid		Total
			1	2	
BabysitterNonbabysitter	1	Count	12	6	18
		Expected Count	8.5	9.5	18.0
	2	Count	5	13	18
		Expected Count	8.5	9.5	18.0
Total		Count	17	19	36
		Expected Count	17.0	19.0	36.0

Chi-Square Tests

	Value	df	Asymp. Sig. (2-sided)	Exact Sig. (2-sided)	Exact Sig. (1-sided)
Pearson Chi-Square	5.461[a]	1	.019		
Continuity Correction[b]	4.012	1	.045		
Likelihood Ratio	5.611	1	.018		
Fisher's Exact Test				.044	.022
Linear-by-Linear Association	5.310	1	.021		
N of Valid Cases	36				

a. 0 cells (.0%) have expected count less than 5. The minimum expected count is 8.50.

b. Computed only for a 2x2 table

We are most interested in the data reported in the Chi-Square Tests box above. The chi-square test of independence is reported as Pearson Chi-Square by SPSS. Thus, based on this, we reject the null hypothesis. In other words, there is a significant difference between babysitters and nonbabysitters in terms of their having taken a first-aid class—significantly more babysitters have taken a first-aid class. If you were to report this result in APA style, it would appear as χ^2 (1, N = 190) = 5.461, p = .019.

Using the TI-84

Let's use the data from Table 14.2 to conduct the calculation using the TI-84 calculator.

1. With the calculator on, press the 2nd key followed by the MATRIX [X^{-1}] key.
2. Highlight EDIT and 1:[A] and press ENTER.
3. Enter the dimensions for the matrix. Our matrix is 2 × 2. Press ENTER.
4. Enter each observed frequency from Table 14.2 followed by ENTER.
5. Press the STAT key and highlight TESTS.
6. Scroll down to C: χ^2-Test and press ENTER.
7. The calculator should show Observed: [A] and Expected: [B].
8. Scroll down and highlight Calculate and press ENTER.

The χ^2 value of 5.461 should appear on the screen, along with the df = 1 and p = .019.

CHAPTER

15 APA Communication Guidelines

Learning Objectives

- Identify and briefly describe the basic components of an APA-format paper.
- Be familiar with the basic word processing skills necessary to create an APA-style paper.

In this chapter, we cover the guidelines set forth by the APA for writing style. APA has very specific writing style guidelines that can be found in the sixth edition of the *Publication Manual of the American Psychological Association* (APA, 2009). We will discuss the general writing style, including clarity and grammar, how to cite others' work properly and avoid plagiarism, and basic typing or word processing configurations for your document. In addition, we describe the basic organization of an APA-style paper and look at a sample paper. Last, we briefly explain guidelines for presenting your research at a conference.

Writing Clearly

The APA guidelines are intended to facilitate clear paper writing. First, the APA recommends an orderly and organized presentation of ideas. Toward this end, you should prepare an outline of the paper before you begin writing. Second, the APA guidelines stress smoothness of expression, or clear and logical communication. To meet this goal, provide transitions from paragraph to paragraph and from section to section, do not change topics suddenly, and make sure you have not omitted something that is necessary to understand the material being presented. Third, the APA recommends striving for economy of expression, avoiding wordiness and redundancy. Following are some examples of wordiness:

Wordy	*Better*
at the present time	now
based on the fact that	because
the present study	this study

In the following examples from the APA manual, the italicized words are redundant and can be omitted:

Six *different* groups saw
a total of 45 participants
in *close* proximity
just exactly
has been *previously* found

The APA manual provides several strategies to improve writing style and avoid potential problems, including writing from an outline; putting aside the first draft, then rereading it after a delay; and asking a colleague or peer to critique the draft for you.

Avoiding Grammatical Problems

Clarity and smoothness depend, among other things, on grammatical correctness. Be sure to check for subject and verb agreement. If the subject is singular, the verb in the sentence must be singular; if the subject is plural, the verb should be plural.

Incorrect: Participant apathy as well as performance on the task decrease with practice.
Correct: Participant apathy as well as performance on the task decreases with practice.

A pronoun must agree with its antecedent. Pronouns replace nouns (antecedents). If the antecedent is singular, the pronoun must be singular; if the antecedent is plural, the pronoun should be plural.

Incorrect: The participant first entered their four-digit code.
Correct: The participants first entered their four-digit code.
Or: The participant first entered his or her four-digit code.

In addition, pronouns must agree in gender (i.e., masculine, feminine, or neuter) with the nouns they replace. This rule also applies to relative pronouns—a pronoun that links subordinate clauses to nouns. The relative pronoun *who* should be used for human beings, whereas *that* or *which* should be used for nonhuman animals and for things.

Incorrect: The subjects that volunteered were asked to complete a survey.
Correct: The subjects who volunteered were asked to complete a survey.

Another common problem in student papers is the misuse of homophones. Homophones are words that sound the same or are pronounced the same but are spelled differently and have different meanings. For example, *to, too,* and *two* are homophones, as are *rite, write,* and *right* and *their, there,* and *they're*. Make sure you understand the proper use of each of these homophones.

Two other errors frequently made by students that resemble homophone errors are confusing *then* and *than* and *effect* and *affect*. The word *then* is an adverb meaning "at that time"; *than* is a conjunction meaning "in comparison with." The following examples illustrate correct usage:

Then: I was at work then.
I want to go to the gym first and then go to the store.
Than: She is a better dancer than I.
I would rather go to the game than study for my exam.

The word *effect* can be a noun or a verb. As a noun, it means "what is produced by a cause"; as a verb, it means "to bring about or accomplish."

Effect (noun): The amount of practice had a significant effect on reaction time.
Effect (verb): I effected a change in the grading policy.

The word *affect* can also be a noun or a verb. As a noun, it refers to emotion; as a verb, it means "to act on or to move."

Affect (noun): The participants in the placebo group maintained a flat affect.

Affect (verb): The amount of practice affected reaction time.

Other common problems include distinguishing between *that* and *which* and between *while* and *since*. *That* and *which* are relative pronouns used to introduce an element that is subordinate to the main clause of the sentence. *That* clauses are restrictive; that is, they are essential to the meaning of the sentence.

Example: The animals that performed well in the first experiment were used in the second experiment.

In other words, only those animals that performed well were used in the second experiment. *Which* clauses are nonrestrictive and merely add further information.

Example: The animals, which performed well in the first experiment, were not proficient in the second experiment.

In other words, the second experiment was more difficult for all of the animals.

While and *since* are subordinate conjunctions that also introduce an element that is subordinate to the main clause of the sentence. Although some style authorities accept the use of *while* and *since* when they do not refer strictly to time, the APA manual calls for the use of *while* and *since* primarily when referring to time. *While* should be used to refer to simultaneous events; *since* should be used to refer to a subsequent event.

While: The participants performed well while listening to music.
Since: Since this original study, many others have been published.

When the writer is not referring to temporal events, the APA manual suggests using *although, whereas, and,* or *but* rather than *while*, and *because* rather than *since*.

Beware of misusing nouns of foreign origin such as *data*, which is a Latin plural noun (the singular is *datum*).

Incorrect: The data is presented in Table 1.
Correct: The data are presented in Table 1.

Other nouns of foreign origin with plural forms that are frequently misused include the following:

Singular	*Plural*
phenomenon	phenomena
stimulus	stimuli
analysis	analyses
hypothesis	hypotheses

The APA prefers the use of active voice rather than passive voice because verbs are vigorous, direct communicators. Although the passive voice is acceptable in other forms of writing, in APA-style writing we are focusing on the actor. The following examples illustrate the use of active versus passive voice.

Nonpreferred: The data were analyzed using a two-way randomized ANOVA.

Preferred: We analyzed the data using a two-way randomized ANOVA.

Last, the APA recommends reducing bias in language. Wording that might imply bias on the basis of gender, sexual orientation, racial or ethnic background, disability, or age should be avoided. For example, the term *man* is not as precise as using the terms *women* and *men*. Use specific age ranges when referring to age groups. Be mindful that the term *gay* is used by some to refer to both men and women, whereas others use it only to refer to men. The terms *gay men* and *lesbians* are preferred.

Also remember that the term *sex* is biological whereas the term *gender* is cultural. Thus, *sex* is used when the biological distinction is predominant and *gender* is used when referring to women and men as social groups.

Reporting Numbers

You will most likely be reporting many numbers in your research paper, from the number of participants used to the statistics that you calculated. How should they be reported—as numbers or in words? The general rule for APA papers is to use words when expressing numbers below 10 that do not represent precise measurements and to use numerals for all numbers 10 and higher. This general rule has some exceptions, however:

- When starting a sentence with a number, use words.
  Example: Sixty students participated in the study.
- When reporting a percentage, use numerals followed by a percent sign.
  Example: The participants in the imagery practice condition improved by 40%, whereas those in the nonimagery practice condition improved by only 8%.
- When describing ages, use numerals.
  Example: The 10-year-olds performed better than the 8-year-olds.
- When reporting statistics, mathematical formulas, functions, or decimal quantities, use numerals.
  Example: The mean score for the women was 6.
- When referring to times, dates, or sums of money, use numerals.
  Example: Subjects had 2 hours to work on the task.
- When reporting fractions use words.
  Example: We found that one-fifth of the class performed quite poorly on this test.

TABLE 15.1 Statistical Abbreviations and Examples of Correct APA Format for Reporting Test Results

STATISTICAL ABBREVIATION	STATISTICAL TEST	EXAMPLE OF CORRECT APA REPORTING FORMAT
r	Pearson's product-moment correlation coefficient	$r(20) = .89, p = .001$
t	t test	$t(18) = 3.95, p = .001$
χ^2	χ^2 test	$\chi^2(1) = 4.13, p = .04$
F	ANOVA	$F(2, 24) = 5.92, p = .008$

One final consideration with respect to reporting numbers is how to report statistics. As noted, they are reported as numbers. However, each statistical term is represented by an italicized abbreviation. The abbreviations for some of the more commonly used descriptive statistics are given here:

M Mean
SD Standard deviation
df Degrees of freedom
N Total number of participants

When we report the results of a statistical significance test, APA style is to report the abbreviation for the test, with the degrees of freedom in parentheses, the calculated value of the test statistic, and the probability level.

Example: The participants in the imagery rehearsal condition remembered more words ($M = 7.9$) than the participants in the rote rehearsal condition ($M = 4.5$), $t(18) = 4.86$, $p = .01$ (one-tailed).

Table 15.1 provides examples of the correct APA format for reporting the results from several statistical significance tests.

Citing and Referencing

Another important element of an APA-style paper is citing and referencing properly. The most important general rule to keep in mind is that any information obtained from another source, whether quoted or simply reported, must be cited and referenced. The author's name and the publication date of the work are cited in the body of the paper. All sources cited in the paper must then appear in the references list, which in turn should contain entries only for those works cited in the text of the paper. This enables readers to identify the source of ideas and to locate the published sources.

Citation Style: One Author

APA journals use the author-date method of citation. This means that the surname of the author and the date of publication are inserted in the text at the appropriate point.

Jones (1999) found that …
A recent study of rehearsal type (Jones, 1999) suggests …
According to a recent study (Jones, 1999), imagery rehearsal …
Participants who used rote rehearsal remembered fewer words than those who used imagery rehearsal (Jones, 1999).

When the name of the author appears as part of the text, cite the year of publication in parentheses. When the name of the author is not part of the narrative, both the author and the date appear in parentheses, separated by a comma. This parenthetical citation may fall either within a sentence or at its end. Within a paragraph, do not include the year of publication in subsequent citations of the same study unless the entire citation is within parentheses.

Citation Style: Multiple Authors

When a work has two authors, cite both authors every time the reference occurs. When a work has three to five authors, cite all authors the first time the reference occurs. After that, cite only the first author's surname followed by the abbreviation "et al." (and others).

First citation: Burns, Menendez, Block, and Follows (2001) found …
Subsequent citation within the same paragraph: Burns et al. found …
Subsequent first citation per paragraph thereafter: Burns et al. (2001) found …

When a paper has six or more authors, cite only the surname of the first author followed by "et al." and the year of publication for the first and subsequent citations. When the paper appears in the references, however, include the names of all authors. When two or more authors are cited in parentheses, the word "and" is replaced by an ampersand (&).

Reference Style

APA reference style differs for journal articles, books, edited books, dissertations, magazines, newspaper articles, and information from the Web. When in doubt about referencing format, it is best to consult the APA *Publication Manual* (2009). References are presented in alphabetical order by the first author's last name. Each reference has several sections that are separated by periods—for example, author name(s), publication date, article title, and journal. The title of a journal (or book) and the volume number of the journal are italicized. The first line of each reference begins at the left margin, and all subsequent lines are indented—known as a hanging indent. The references, like the rest of the manuscript, are double-spaced. Following are the correct formats for some of the more commonly used types of references.

If you are referencing a source that is not covered here, consult the *Publication Manual.*

Journal Article

Karau, S. J., & Williams, K. D. (1993). Social loafing: A meta-analytic review and theoretical integration. *Journal of Personality and Social Psychology, 65,* 681–706.

Book: One Author, First Edition

Hunt, M. (1993). *The story of psychology.* New York: Doubleday.

Book: Multiple Authors, Second or Later Edition

Bordens, K. S., & Abbott, B. B. (1999). *Research design and methods: A process approach* (4th ed.). Mountain View, CA: Mayfield.

Edited Book

Sternberg, R. J., & Barnes, M. L. (Eds.). (1988). *The psychology of love.* New Haven, CT: Yale University Press.

Chapter or Article in an Edited Book

Massaro, D. (1992). Broadening the domain of the fuzzy logical model of perception. In H. L. Pick, Jr., P. van den Broek, & D. C. Knill (Eds.), *Cognition: Conceptual and methodological issues* (pp. 51–84). Washington, DC: American Psychological Association.

Magazine

King, P. (1991, March 18). Bawl players. *Sports Illustrated,* 14–17.

Diagnostic and Statistical Manual of Mental Disorders

American Psychiatric Association. (2013). *Diagnostic and statistical manual of mental disorders* (5th ed.). Washington, DC: Author.

Paper Presented at a Meeting

Roediger, H. L., III. (1991, August). *Remembering, knowing, and reconstructing the past.* Paper presented at the annual meeting of the American Psychological Association, San Francisco.

Poster Presented at a Meeting

Griggs, R. A., Jackson, S. L., Christopher, A. N., & Marek, P. (1999, January). *Introductory psychology textbooks: An objective analysis and update.* Poster session presented at the annual meeting of the National Institute on the Teaching of Psychology, St. Pete Beach, FL.

Internet Article Based on a Print Source (Digital Object Identifier, doi, should be included)
Jacobson, J. W., Mulick, J. A., & Schwartz, A. A. (1995). A history of facilitated communication: Science, pseudoscience, and antiscience. *American Psychologist, 50*, 750–765. doi: 10.1037/0003-066X.50.9.750

Article in an Internet-Only Journal
Fredrickson, B. L. (2000, March 7). Cultivating positive emotions to optimize health and well-being. *Prevention & Treatment, 3*, Article 0001a. Retrieved from http://journals.apa.org/prevention/volume3/pre0030001a.html

Typing and Word Processing

In APA style, the entire manuscript is double-spaced. This includes the title page, headings, footnotes, quotations, and references. Single or one-and-a-half spacing may be used in tables and figures. Use a 12-point font size in a serif style such as Times New Roman. Margins should be at least 1 inch at the top, bottom, left, and right of every page. Justify the left margin, but leave the right margin uneven, or ragged. Set your word processing program so that words are not divided at the end of a line, and hyphens are not used to break words at the ends of lines. Use one space after commas, colons, semicolons, periods in citations, and all periods in the reference section. The APA prefers two spaces after periods at the end of sentences. Begin numbering the manuscript on the title page and number all pages thereafter. The running head (the information at the top of each page) and page numbers should be about ½ inch from the top of the page. Paragraphs should be indented five to seven spaces.

Organizing the Paper

An APA-style manuscript has a specific organization. The proper order is title page, abstract, introduction, method, results, discussion, references, and any footnotes. Finally, tables, figures, and appendices appear at the very end of the manuscript. In the following sections, we discuss the basic content for each of these parts of the manuscript. Refer to the sample paper in Appendix E as you read through each of the following sections.

Title Page

The title page in an APA-style manuscript contains more information than simply the title of the paper. Refer to the title page in Appendix E. At the top of the page is the running head—an abbreviated title. It is preceded by the phrase "Running head:"; however, this phrase only appears on the title page. The actual running head (not the phrase "Running head:") should appear in all capital letters. In the sample paper, the running head is "WILLINGNESS TO DATE." The running head is left-justified and appears about ½ inch from the top of the page. Thus, it is actually printed in the top margin of the page. It should be a maximum of 50 characters, counting letters, punctuation, and spaces between words. Right-justified on the same line as the running head is the page number beginning with the title page as page 1. The running head and page number appear on every page of the manuscript (Remember: Although the running head appears on every page of the paper, it is preceded by the phrase "Running head" only on the title page.). Use the header/footer function from your word processing program to insert the running head and page number. Do not try to manually insert the running head on each page. APA style requires the running head so that those reviewing the manuscript have an easier time keeping the paper together and the pages in the correct order. In addition, if the paper is published in a journal, the running head will appear at the top of either odd or even numbered pages of the article. Thus, the running head should convey, in brief, what the paper is about.

The title is centered below the running head and page number in the top half of the page. A title should be no more than 12 words and should clearly and simply summarize the main idea of the paper. Notice that the title of the sample paper, "The Effects of Salary on Willingness to Date," states the effects of an independent variable on a dependent variable. Below the title of the paper is the author's name, and below that is his or her institutional affiliation. Last, author notes appear on the title page. Author notes include the heading "Author Note" followed by the departmental affiliation of each author and the sources of financial support. It can also provide background information about the study, such as that it was based on the author's master's thesis or dissertation. The author note also provides acknowledgments to colleagues who may have helped with the study. Last, the author note tells the reader whom to contact for further information concerning the article.

Abstract

Page 2 of the manuscript is the Abstract. See the Abstract in Appendix E. The word "Abstract" is centered at the top of the page, and this section is written as a block-style paragraph (no paragraph indent), and the running head and page number are in the top margin of the page. The Abstract is a brief, comprehensive summary of the contents of the manuscript. It should be between 150 and 250 words. Although the Abstract appears at the beginning of the manuscript, it is usually easier to write it after you have written the entire paper because it is a very brief description of the entire paper. When writing the Abstract, try to describe each section of the paper (Introduction, Method, Results, and Discussion) in one or two concise sentences. Describe the problem under investigation, the purpose of the study, the participants and general methodology, the findings with statistical significance levels and/or effects sizes, the confidence intervals, and the conclusions and implications or applications of the study. If your manuscript is published, the Abstract will appear in collections of abstracts such as those in the *Psychological Abstracts* described in Chapter 2.

Introduction

The Introduction begins on page 3. It is not labeled "Introduction"; instead, the title of the manuscript—exactly as it appears on the title page—is centered at the top of the page. The Introduction has three basic components. The first part introduces the problem under study. The second part contains previous relevant research to provide an appropriate history, citing works that are pertinent to the issue but not works of marginal or peripheral significance. When summarizing earlier works, emphasize pertinent findings, relevant methodological issues, and major conclusions. Do not include nonessential details. The third part of the Introduction states the purpose and rationale for the study. You should explain your approach to solving the problem, define the variables, and state your hypotheses, along with the rationale for each hypothesis.

Method

The Method section begins wherever the Introduction ends; it does not begin on a new page. The heading "**Method**" in boldfaced font is centered wherever the Method section begins. This section describes exactly how the study was conducted, in sufficient detail that it can be replicated by anyone who has read the Method section. The Method section is generally divided into subsections. Although the subsections vary across papers, the most common are Subjects (or Participants) and Procedure, although it is also possible to have a separate materials or apparatus section as in the sample paper in Appendix E. The Subjects subsection should include a description of the participants and how they were obtained. Major demographic characteristics, such as gender, age, and ethnicity, should be described where appropriate, and the total number of participants should be indicated. A Materials subsection, if used, usually describes testing materials used, such as a particular test or an inventory or a type of problem that subjects were asked to solve. An Apparatus subsection, if used, describes specific equipment used. The Procedure subsection summarizes each step in the execution of the research, including the groups used in the study, instructions given to the participants, the experimental manipulation, any counterbalancing or randomization used, and specific control features in the design. If the design is particularly complex, you may want to consider having a separate Design subsection preceding the Procedure.

Results

The Results section begins right after the Method section, with the heading "**Results**" in boldfaced print centered before the section begins. This section summarizes the data collected and the type of statistic(s) used to analyze the data. It should include a description of the results only, not an explanation of the results. In addition to using the APA format (as explained earlier in the chapter), it is also common to use tables and figures when presenting the results. Tables usually provide exact values and can be used to display complex data and analyses in an easy-to-read format. Figures provide a visual impression and can be used to illustrate complex relationships, but they are generally not as precise as tables. Remember that tables and figures are used to supplement the text. When using them, you must refer to them in the text, telling the reader what to look for. Although tables and figures are referred to in the Results section of the paper (and will be included here if the manuscript is published), the actual tables and figures appear at the end of the manuscript, after the references and footnotes.

Discussion

As with the previous two sections, the Discussion section begins immediately after the Results section with the heading "**Discussion**" centered at the beginning of the section. The Discussion section allows you to evaluate and interpret the results. Typically, this section begins with a restatement of the predictions of the study. You then discuss whether the predictions were supported. Next comes a discussion of the relationship between the results and past research and theories. Last, include any criticisms of the study (such as possible confounds) and implications for future research. If the Discussion is relatively brief, it can be combined with the Results section as a Results and Discussion section or Results and Conclusions section.

References

Use the correct format for references (as described earlier in the chapter). The references begin on a new page after the end of the discussion. Center the word "References" (no boldfaced print here) at the top of the page. Remember to double-space the references, use a hanging indent, and include the running head and page number in the top margin of each page. Also remember that any works cited in the text must appear in the references, but that only works cited in the text should be included.

Tables and Figures

Although tables and figures are typically used and referred to in the Results section to supplement the text, they appear at the end of the manuscript.

TABLE 15.2 Sample Table

Table 1
Means of Personality Variables by Major and Gender

	Science		Humanities	
	Helping First	**Mood First**	**Helping First**	**Mood First**
Men	22.22	23.00	45.40	61.11
Women	14.67	9.50	50.22	52.09

Tables always precede figures at the end of the manuscript, no matter what order they were referred to in the text. Each table appears on a separate page. There are no specific rules for formatting tables, other than that they should not appear cramped, that horizontal lines should be used to define areas of the table, and that vertical lines may not be used. The columns and rows of the table should be labeled clearly. The running head and page number continue to be used on the pages with tables. In addition, each table should be numbered and have a brief explanatory title. Because the sample paper in Appendix E has no tables, the example in Table 15.2 illustrates the basic table format.

Figures are always placed after the tables at the end of the manuscript. The running head and page number appear on the figure pages also. If there is more than one figure in the manuscript, each figure appears on a separate page. The figure caption appears at the bottom of the page and can be single-, one-and-a-half-, or double-spaced. It is preceded by the identifer "*Figure 1.*" or "*Figure 2.*" etc. in italics. A figure can consist of a graph, chart, photograph, map, or drawing. Several figures appear in Chapters 5, 6, 10, 11, and 12. You can use these or the figure that appears in the sample paper as guides. In graphs, the levels of the independent variable are plotted on the *x*-axis, and the values of the dependent variable are plotted on the *y*-axis. If a study has more than one independent variable, the levels of the second and successive independent variables are labeled within the figure.

Appendices

Appendices are used to provide information that might be distracting if presented in the text. Some examples of material that might be included in an appendix are a computer program specifically designed for the research study, an unpublished test, a mathematical proof, or a survey instrument.

The Use of Headings

APA-style papers use one to five levels of headings. Examples of the types of headings follow:

Level 1	**Centered, Boldface, Uppercase and Lowercase Heading** The heading is centered and boldfaced. The first letter of each word is capitalized. The text begins indented on a new line.
Level 2	**Flush Left, Boldface, Uppercase and Lowercase Heading** The heading is in boldface, flush on the left margin. The first letter of each word is capitalized, and the text begins indented on a new line.
Level 3	**Indented, boldface, lowercase paragraph heading ending with a period.** The heading is indented, boldfaced, and has a period at the end. The first letter of the first word is capitalized, and the text begins on the same line.
Level 4	***Indented, boldface, italicized, lowercase paragraph heading ending with a period.*** The heading is indented, boldfaced and italicized, and has a period at the end. The first letter of the first word is capitalized, and the text begins on the same line.
Level 5	*Indented, italicized, lowercase paragraph heading ending with a period.* The heading is indented, italicized, and has a period at the end. The first letter of the first word is capitalized, and the text begins on the same line.

Most papers will use Level 1 through Level 3 headings. It might be necessary to use Level 4 and 5 headings in more complex papers.

Level 1 headings are used for major sections such as the Method, Results, and Discussion. The heading is centered, and the first letter of each word is capitalized. (Please note that the labels Abstract, Title of the Paper in the Introduction, and References are not considered headings by the APA. Thus, although they are centered at the top of their respective sections, they are not boldfaced.) Level 2 headings are used to divide the major sections into subsections. Thus, in the sample paper, level 2 headings divide the Method section into subsections. These headings are in boldface, flush on the left margin, and the first letter of each word is capitalized. Level 3 headings may be used to organize material within a subsection. Thus, the Procedure subsection might be further subdivided into categories of instructions to participants, or the Materials subsection might be further divided into categories of tests. A level 3 heading begins on a new line, indented, and in boldface. Only the first letter in the first word is capitalized. The heading ends with a period, and the text begins on the same line.

APA Formatting Checklist

The checklist in Table 15.3 itemizes some of the most common errors found in student papers. Before finalizing a research paper, reread the manuscript and review this checklist for potential errors.

TABLE 15.3 APA Formatting Checklist

General Formatting and Typing

- There are at least 1-inch margins on all four sides of each page of the manuscript.
- The font is the correct size (12 point on a word processor) and the correct style (a serif font such as Times New Roman).
- The manuscript is double-spaced throughout, including title page, references, and appendices. Tables and figures can be single-, one-and-a-half-, or double-spaced.
- The page number appears on the same line with the running head with the running head left-justified and the page number right-justified.
- The running head and page number appear at the top of each page ½ inch from the top of the page (in the top margin).
- There is only one space after commas, colons, semicolons, periods in citations, and all periods in the reference section. Two spaces are preferred after periods at the ends of sentences.
- Arabic numerals are used correctly to express numbers that are 10 or greater; numbers that immediately precede a unit of measurement; numbers that represent fractions and percentages; numbers that represent times, dates, or ages.
- Words are used correctly to express numbers less than 10 and numbers at the beginning of a title, sentence, or heading.

Title Page

- The entire title page is double-spaced.
- The running head is aligned with the left margin, is less than 50 characters and spaces long, and appears in the top margin ½ inch from the top of the page. It is preceded by the phrase "Running head:" on the title page only. The running head itself is in capital letters, but not the phrase "Running head:".
- The page number appears on the same line as the running head and is right-justified.
- The title of the paper is centered in the top 1/3 of the page with the Author's names and affiliations centered below it.
- The author note appears on the title page at the bottom of the page with the header "Author Note" centered above it.

Abstract

- "Abstract" is centered at the top of the page—not in boldface.
- The first line of the abstract is even with the left margin (block style, not indented).
- The abstract is between 150 and 250 words.

Body of the Manuscript

- The title of the paper appears centered at the top of page 3 and is not in boldface.
- There are no one-sentence paragraphs.
- The word "while" is used primarily to indicate events that take place simultaneously (alternatives: "although," "whereas," "but").
- Abbreviated terms are written out completely the first time they are used and then they are always abbreviated thereafter.
- The word "and" is used in citations outside of parentheses.
- The ampersand (&) is used in citations within parentheses.
- Each and every citation used in the manuscript has a corresponding entry in the references section.
- The phrase "et al." is used only when there are three or more authors.
- In the Results section, all test statistics (F, t, χ^2, p) are italicized.
- The section headings Method, Results, and Discussion are in boldface.

(Continued)

TABLE 15.3 APA Formatting Checklist (*continued*)

References Section
• "References" is centered at the top of the first page—not in boldface.
• The first line of each reference is flush left; subsequent lines are indented (a hanging indent).
• All entries appear in alphabetical order.
• Authors' names are separated by commas.
• Authors' last names appear with first and (if provided) middle initials (first and middle names are not spelled out).
• The name of the journal and the volume number are italicized.
• Each and every entry is cited in the body of the manuscript.

Conference Presentations

Psychologists conducting research frequently attend research conferences where they present their findings. Their presentations typically take one of two forms: an oral presentation or a poster presentation.

Oral Presentations

Most oral presentations have one thing in common—you are limited in the amount of time you have to present. Typically you have 10 to 15 minutes to present your research and answer questions. Thus, the first dilemma is how to condense your entire paper to a 10- to 15-minute presentation. According to the *Publication Manual*, the material you deliver verbally should differ in the level of detail from your written work. It is appropriate to omit many of the details of the scientific procedures because someone listening to your presentation cannot process at the same level of detail as someone reading a written paper. Decide on a limited number of significant ideas you want the audience to process. In addition, use clear, simple language free of jargon to state what you studied, how you went about the research, what you discovered, and the implications of your results. It is appropriate to be redundant to emphasize important ideas. Also consider using transparencies, slides, or PowerPoint slides as part of your presentation. It is also recommended that you write your presentation out and practice delivering it out loud to learn it and to determine its length. You should also consider presenting your paper to a critical audience before delivering it at a conference. When you actually deliver the paper, do not read it. Instead, try to speak directly to the audience and refer, when necessary, to an outline of key points. In addition, make sure to leave time for questions. Last, have copies of your paper ready for distribution (APA, 2009).

Poster Presentations

Poster presentations differ from oral presentations in that they provide the opportunity for the presenter and the audience to talk with one another. Typically, posters are presented in an exhibit area with other posters, often on a similar topic, being presented at the same time. In this manner, those interested in the topic can visit the exhibit area, wander about, view the posters, and speak with the authors. Each presenter has a bulletin board, usually about 3½ feet high by 3 feet wide, to display a poster. Bring your own thumbtacks. In constructing the poster, use a few simple guidelines. As with paper presentations, minimize jargon and try to use clear and simple language to describe what you studied, how you went about the research, what you discovered, and the implications of your results. Pictures, tables, and figures work very well in poster presentations. Make sure you use an appropriate font size when preparing the poster. Viewers should be able to read it easily from a distance of 3 feet. As with oral presentations, have copies of your paper ready for distribution.

CRITICAL THINKING CHECK 15.1

1. Explain what a running head is and where it appears in the manuscript.
2. Identify and briefly explain what the subsections in a Method section should be.
3. Explain what information should and should not appear in a Results section.

Summary

After reading this chapter, you should have an understanding of the APA's writing standards. We presented basic APA formatting and writing guidelines. We discussed how to write clearly, avoid grammatical problems, report numbers, and properly cite and reference the works of others. In addition, we described the organization of an APA-style manuscript, with frequent references to the sample paper in Appendix E. Finally, we discussed presenting your research at conferences using either an oral presentation format or a poster presentation format.

CHAPTER EXERCISES

(Answers to odd-numbered exercises appear in Appendix C.)

1. What information is contained on the title page of a manuscript?
2. Briefly describe the type of information that should be in an introduction.
3. Identify the grammatical or formatting errors in each of the following statements:
   a. 50 students participated in the study.
   b. The *F*-score was 6.54 with a *p*-value of .05 and 1 and 12 degrees of freedom.
   c. The data is presented in Table 1.
   d. One group of participants took the medication while the other group did not.

CRITICAL THINKING CHECK ANSWERS

15.1

1. The running head that appears on the title page of the manuscript is preceded by the phrase "Running head:" whereas the running head that appears on the remainder of the manuscript pages is not preceded by the phrase "Running head:". The running head briefly (in 50 characters or less) conveys the nature of the paper. If the paper is ultimately published, the running head will appear at the top of either odd- or even-numbered pages of the journal article.
2. The Participants (Subjects) subsection should be first. It provides a description of the participants, which may include gender, age, and ethnicity. Next may appear a Materials or Apparatus subsection describing testing materials or equipment used. The final subsection is usually a Procedure (or a Design and Procedure) subsection. It should describe the variables in the study and the procedure used to collect the data in sufficient detail that another researcher can replicate the study after reading the section.
3. The Results section should identify the statistics used to analyze the data and the results of the analyses. It should not include any explanation or qualification of the results nor should it relate the results to the hypothesis being tested. These matters are covered in the Discussion section.

WEB RESOURCES

The book-specific website at CengageBrain.com offers students a variety of study tools and useful resources such as glossaries and flashcards.

Chapter 15 ■ Study Guide

CHAPTER 15 SUMMARY AND REVIEW: APA COMMUNICATION GUIDELINES

Basic APA formatting and writing guidelines were presented in this chapter. This included how to write clearly, avoid grammatical problems, report numbers, and properly cite and reference the works of others. Finally, the organization of an APA-style manuscript was described, with frequent references to the sample paper in Appendix E.

CHAPTER 15 REVIEW EXERCISES

(Answers to exercises appear in Appendix C.)

FILL-IN SELF-TEST

Answer the following questions. If you have trouble answering any of the questions, restudy the relevant material before going on to the multiple-choice self-test.

1. The subsections in a Method section of an APA-format paper include the ______.
2. Statistical findings are reported in the ______ section of an APA-format paper.
3. The page after the title page in an APA-format paper is always the ______.

MULTIPLE-CHOICE SELF-TEST

Select the single best answer for each of the following questions. If you have trouble answering any of the questions, restudy the relevant material.

1. A description of prior findings in the area of study is to the ________ as a report of statistical findings is to the ________.
   a. introduction; method section
   b. method section; introduction
   c. introduction; results section
   d. results section; method section
2. A summary of the entire research project is to the ________ as an interpretation of the findings is to the ________.
   a. abstract; results section
   b. method section; results section
   c. abstract; discussion section
   d. results; discussion section
3. Which list below represents the correct ordering of the sections of an APA paper?
   a. abstract, method, introduction, results
   b. introduction, abstract, method, results
   c. discussion, abstract, introduction, method
   d. title page, abstract, introduction, method
4. Based on APA style, what is wrong with the following reference?

   Karau, Steven. J., & Williams, Kenneth. D. (1993). Social loafing: A meta-analytic review and theoretical integration. *Journal of Personality and Social Psychology, 65,* 681–706.

   a. The name of the journal should be underlined.
   b. Only the initials for the authors' first and middle names should be used.
   c. The first letters of the words in the title of the paper should be capitalized.
   d. Nothing is wrong with the reference.

APPENDIX

A Statistical Tables

A.1 Random Numbers
A.2 Areas Under the Normal Curve (*z* Table)
A.3 Critical Values for the Student' *t* Distribution
A.4 Critical Values of the Pearson *r* (Pearson Product Moment Correlation Coefficient)
A.5 Critical Values for the *F* Distribution
A.6 Studentized Range Statistic
A.7 Critical Values for the Chi-Square Distribution
A.8 Critical Values for *W* (Wilcoxon Rank-Sum Test)
A.9 Critical Values for the Wilcoxon Matched-Pairs Signed-Ranks *T* Test

TABLE A.1 Random Numbers

	1	2	3	4	5	6	7	8	9	10
1	39614	74819	23303	87516	18981	42314	89531	07870	12536	41222
2	02541	85748	56140	72328	54780	21638	30219	04220	69476	45002
3	87434	15686	74598	54299	92089	30832	30118	18505	67564	75455
4	69937	72720	06396	45725	93951	14151	03069	64938	81282	92018
5	30217	90732	03477	69920	05899	64950	96540	41121	73559	47139
6	74643	92005	05388	42797	34732	31463	27872	58056	98703	85255
7	17723	79504	30484	09868	38245	29772	19579	09007	79314	71295
8	09395	39991	23279	51552	18198	47560	09070	06643	68828	87934
9	21973	26112	67133	39727	85483	49720	28341	64165	90276	26897
10	85933	70911	43491	53764	43614	54764	63356	47404	78254	60403
11	42238	49831	20973	03463	40351	16448	58791	13781	68649	30077
12	11679	22530	97439	79312	50730	50080	59519	66892	71575	68744
13	58854	35870	07032	91644	63494	00611	26018	45269	14037	81753
14	21489	69392	25387	52044	48854	21681	56769	56484	56748	46908
15	06469	62608	95975	95649	95550	22440	05049	16259	06264	42268
16	38751	02296	73270	13029	86045	75368	19512	56590	98819	22963
17	44689	16095	95770	86491	51064	24154	44686	91832	09545	65321
18	38733	27628	56475	64890	14744	30022	70836	08636	42319	36704
19	91265	37053	27298	16684	75518	86499	33758	63366	40964	31788
20	12341	31819	18943	69025	18575	55021	86764	30701	35862	30606
21	02772	52994	83438	66689	77898	57471	51105	25160	21380	98977
22	83632	79155	07501	94003	33840	64639	49638	20189	01406	37403
23	60273	69879	05014	66353	82444	04590	01591	52172	11244	48747
24	72043	56215	15075	80363	69817	95706	53583	68622	64000	71738
25	62198	76663	33956	06407	46018	65251	55897	86686	72765	49192
26	44391	91384	10573	61162	97936	58620	28613	33529	15322	99018
27	81137	70046	51476	70815	99604	35304	45699	35201	35014	99538
28	88919	01999	59446	45609	48651	31870	21733	66319	46468	90205
29	28016	75902	55462	20746	70013	21517	46756	12227	12172	63905
30	32688	50818	09219	69417	67210	92271	22840	40948	74473	27807
31	21085	99986	90579	05026	84208	29442	78843	47748	56599	82832
32	20428	52337	29526	05211	99377	10956	26259	16837	83248	02443
33	16377	63587	18741	77267	60596	36977	74605	20893	19462	61136
34	43752	18312	70650	78635	04359	35347	66054	42705	31321	25522
35	74595	21172	56672	02362	24411	66963	68042	65596	46193	86219
36	78700	35203	59012	87472	90460	29115	60164	99859	37950	29774
37	37686	43145	48745	45825	70982	38692	24111	18725	19787	52035
38	62836	37190	64406	55495	38545	79690	65020	85005	63094	73190
39	28237	43483	72763	35049	46008	73602	71899	41478	79980	13053
40	17896	78913	34611	45389	87031	59593	89049	74395	58014	81329
41	61395	89603	15298	68711	36087	35310	03766	12297	96362	96068
42	13860	41531	99262	75077	59394	34074	63052	56053	26579	60969
43	99201	77070	30502	89537	64812	49188	97991	97408	69927	83253
44	50815	81403	80027	73638	20195	60928	95619	98857	99743	06373
45	12553	07045	19554	66426	91173	37564	45736	98952	29124	50288

TABLE A.1 Random Numbers *(continued)*

	1	2	3	4	5	6	7	8	9	10
46	08202	76964	86354	04138	68315	45098	29731	00994	86391	76663
47	78681	49348	69232	49665	88576	31435	45445	45114	86855	30974
48	21523	02344	41744	91052	48033	55259	20070	35304	50175	39339
49	37052	10834	24631	22659	58300	96513	76076	72730	06103	58816
50	62268	63136	35899	35687	04210	75126	39473	89465	65075	29856
51	38277	46021	96399	69062	81152	13475	65337	93823	70135	15787
52	68620	46563	17963	40057	24590	22575	33124	45939	33238	11588
53	27711	75053	21842	41145	13065	40777	93404	51071	97728	13453
54	51423	93976	65864	79424	48966	20822	17848	11282	22393	46946
55	87111	40920	04568	85241	73261	17363	62151	11495	19426	04623
56	31457	69197	14273	52489	20250	04312	72765	55459	93634	08114
57	11275	57354	99108	67783	20867	57633	36529	79894	67442	78749
58	24738	81623	43339	62377	31994	36636	24127	79170	57644	43142
59	26063	90696	52743	10239	79951	29431	68850	06024	84278	17774
60	86890	70786	17291	39544	84737	26281	36076	26550	69395	56119
61	73325	46838	18946	92976	43299	66005	57006	80058	74934	49419
62	68557	22370	35913	30957	51765	10392	84551	00596	83520	71631
63	16866	67316	34663	48594	65436	75575	51737	33602	35529	58560
64	41298	17974	48171	13238	35468	58663	55432	25165	73844	52543
65	46178	44975	25344	31026	29358	49777	90658	80651	01983	02169
66	25930	87929	80510	15778	85107	58678	01983	97126	00564	61244
67	02526	32123	10916	34572	56443	43753	26536	33219	69122	74163
68	80622	16039	42225	14679	88050	62365	14983	27681	78312	31629
69	51091	87347	61458	08651	84822	64159	33320	59188	12526	42756
70	32032	13964	68743	50019	61049	87889	87827	71689	81379	45268
71	00484	82620	41074	13235	10252	13118	58967	39269	83221	40147
72	05746	52643	34139	09318	39429	54018	33098	85708	60355	75997
73	90147	64441	05184	41040	75236	14018	96502	70565	41085	18877
74	17112	86434	91901	81315	16663	75722	90165	38789	74615	19435
75	98138	35097	09900	58316	44812	25627	07634	94965	73637	12743
76	73340	00030	16175	79663	96139	09620	06533	85526	76017	92204
77	62739	84532	19307	38191	03080	73877	72350	80278	40811	35350
78	93650	63683	02908	80620	91836	45855	66053	31548	63180	17397
79	84818	18939	30581	59102	66185	28215	28117	62472	63920	82709
80	07087	27776	18856	08117	44135	72470	51614	23486	84133	95086
81	69759	29092	43043	52467	06441	85442	49094	77087	96653	59989
82	77457	31420	04997	97650	48963	93232	61394	76641	21065	07790
83	35642	68168	99463	53054	70143	98368	01507	24563	58748	93819
84	19616	74320	18093	14482	53798	80896	08118	48166	60022	97799
85	08824	87697	01286	55376	77956	27591	98054	17596	40841	21085
86	98876	87868	79050	76638	84380	17690	61811	70118	56245	09904
87	97436	44511	65629	71628	84806	07059	51058	67597	99117	52987
88	15029	29791	99460	26758	21267	84526	57465	85288	35734	69944
89	47481	35745	80478	97125	93401	18676	45882	28755	31805	78987
90	57727	63038	23891	60592	04956	00819	66778	54903	32145	21366

(continued)

TABLE A.1 Random Numbers *(continued)*

	1	2	3	4	5	6	7	8	9	10
91	59052	74855	74779	34359	62203	19150	94757	37866	08921	34590
92	31759	26526	36958	87795	56661	93495	40992	05477	12394	50493
93	13408	10419	47588	91004	71438	14162	15913	10582	53356	30935
94	40784	60942	35067	17352	35933	22404	54003	85497	91733	37114
95	25578	27194	01185	59301	22981	17753	80426	85534	52412	65731
96	67281	90510	24773	20692	45928	81741	07638	34250	00151	12611
97	75156	28476	85861	62232	06904	28497	98585	31225	88651	63209
98	00886	22699	53246	58311	95808	54463	04665	37063	72314	23986
99	93941	16409	78203	07727	10916	27584	29695	56751	80052	19454
100	37662	58023	67325	24651	18807	33435	88961	07716	09155	37966
101	87406	41154	03732	79059	60241	48157	77044	77070	28044	44254
102	42504	56673	03818	70240	54765	70672	95660	99951	46891	42404
103	75291	55474	38747	61321	65945	70604	28728	65794	87930	89340
104	36299	20993	99257	28539	04857	30763	53472	71252	95633	34483
105	84597	57437	16084	90543	44311	02420	92687	07700	52520	23447
106	01339	77912	98217	10354	13171	74500	90741	94559	86479	33587
107	84989	02220	32025	46312	60161	69590	67297	54002	77403	99503
108	49861	06783	45237	94178	50448	75576	53502	70408	03920	25679
109	20478	38323	96404	14624	43440	47789	62906	30155	82719	13838
110	25084	77112	46461	19607	88120	48998	39298	68961	94980	21665
111	99683	13728	46550	95970	42861	62645	64706	98971	15590	39086
112	88576	30968	62474	79066	35947	62261	91816	52373	85427	06401
113	87947	50767	13082	08535	50007	47251	79627	47161	90388	29648
114	97363	25452	91936	29043	54051	57839	66414	79440	04298	39566
115	07026	25551	62334	06898	68193	49025	04204	12642	86638	94295
116	94855	98806	94977	95905	05111	21859	99540	13116	34542	63316
117	54471	84019	78520	71743	15765	57428	22745	00065	61402	58077
118	95598	95449	30163	53934	15973	94787	29088	94468	92550	62199
119	79508	72698	93936	75445	67148	88316	72824	31091	70792	71189
120	69344	49406	45440	87520	55163	82209	00015	75305	94560	04186
121	40533	96074	72805	46226	06984	19928	36835	85262	80041	09725
122	32773	90316	22391	23971	42671	97667	10877	53548	16961	01869
123	84652	88429	89859	33272	94329	32874	78670	39467	34944	12929
124	06242	28165	30158	04448	08559	85133	12497	54417	57171	04664
125	31100	58358	56923	62643	47467	99735	20279	85524	59862	30169
126	19164	37522	32866	06495	10800	90370	45175	87631	52395	00920
127	62020	24007	98973	37366	94360	34991	70207	33776	44159	14853
128	99251	74203	71903	88835	73058	30061	54450	76256	36346	78890
129	04925	95455	94235	04948	21374	38608	00057	88482	04851	66123
130	16018	42290	56522	24473	70916	96268	70235	00728	74961	15370
131	77381	86478	27238	30733	53391	78252	43413	84165	12623	99856
132	16003	92042	66817	36298	03878	09742	05626	77638	11872	18914
133	79728	37849	45869	03904	68625	89163	96263	23888	25640	34053
134	62114	46023	17421	20212	27285	91385	15777	68808	88835	78987
135	54511	83298	99598	76251	88026	25910	89371	41611	86307	45995

TABLE A.1 Random Numbers *(continued)*

	1	2	3	4	5	6	7	8	9	10
136	39020	38705	44814	39677	97245	70233	82746	76238	58675	76171
137	00746	47633	33976	06011	63868	74571	85602	21805	73681	43811
138	96320	83130	41974	48664	59590	55024	12837	96231	10198	83482
139	03776	05966	21234	66527	83292	31998	74478	72815	46140	66065
140	53693	45801	35060	50247	04379	33108	83377	70812	69079	49249
141	04186	36371	25790	07918	89173	94202	81339	56386	97721	45273
142	52483	58626	93586	31781	50513	18920	43677	74414	42727	46413
143	49922	08374	68933	16398	69784	73560	57482	59586	21831	24220
144	88842	42747	41742	78893	31387	81376	21615	05030	20766	72671
145	24924	07377	73544	02921	13514	51621	99312	68729	08790	48673
146	38697	67357	41388	93283	56187	39093	60747	19652	24476	02488
147	65492	25507	31924	52593	40211	39907	54692	53553	68653	62542
148	46981	25733	51790	52181	99713	11791	22826	00439	37716	31124
149	92419	75268	32477	83407	67761	08239	38105	58212	27761	71403
150	78531	83192	50803	58800	02666	10611	33547	88029	59575	15901
151	87437	42161	88427	69610	62154	35744	63137	01001	52384	39931
152	35364	36300	28277	31799	25887	58083	62152	23623	23866	12418
153	78507	38711	04464	64415	44923	10182	26411	04577	79555	36987
154	74289	16564	00908	48107	81211	98003	14101	16451	86728	83127
155	19576	85966	99421	35398	66511	30070	46573	23475	69632	79835
156	83888	86715	53167	86628	98900	19323	01325	51333	77123	53643
157	52558	94886	04931	54523	00624	55637	34924	15361	87079	25507
158	30848	82175	66593	35466	37731	69025	23122	04826	20732	30385
159	34973	97296	74459	88391	10128	94123	06391	92267	75463	48468
160	27611	93970	06005	98616	28890	54076	11271	22845	90072	24261
161	92969	71154	26181	52033	39471	66386	98334	59917	68143	53807
162	65164	02318	89278	28928	25601	58202	31328	02889	00448	25801
163	13595	38529	16446	38407	22204	93038	48948	44041	51749	55322
164	45369	95706	53339	71707	58546	08168	45724	78256	79998	88561
165	87521	71220	75032	11141	39703	45972	18256	20494	94619	82744
166	57989	34739	98175	06613	75091	98872	48501	49961	95042	31934
167	52398	29427	23754	16681	51950	27962	40229	19272	92997	49047
168	17324	65519	92394	25938	62611	28707	58305	41235	98394	57274
169	11889	86230	95333	95371	64746	92052	69767	04007	81467	09769
170	63788	85653	25664	67469	39180	08755	05926	28259	54662	58646
171	92840	09580	15761	16788	98042	97741	38720	98341	36444	39095
172	82305	44880	93304	64691	56025	51409	14584	58225	49723	52991
173	49955	38728	69481	01323	17723	83157	11448	60597	51916	90819
174	58358	56847	19975	00370	58842	16104	83533	07008	56022	18152
175	92320	05584	63357	63593	76564	63939	69237	04346	09895	07589
176	62279	72652	44480	67863	09559	05803	17639	61096	47394	78575
177	11550	56073	14387	20361	95577	88556	30101	52452	57955	05884
178	12211	46742	79984	46120	65738	34460	54416	45960	02082	75050
179	89384	68977	51273	79285	80139	69109	43032	41572	99802	86265
180	29882	01181	29545	88598	46398	02495	28403	74115	13013	29574

(continued)

TABLE A.1 Random Numbers *(continued)*

	1	2	3	4	5	6	7	8	9	10
181	75420	24581	34180	02933	28180	84180	55863	55840	32788	33225
182	31330	21475	29404	04200	77341	95351	65166	19097	76598	92505
183	12884	57531	42825	13240	53387	41705	06960	84919	15835	41466
184	64343	40221	34644	67312	97550	60273	69171	51882	59601	68260
185	05635	72277	57640	05453	81853	02426	48333	07194	82639	24739
186	84420	19310	66969	33379	46081	83319	00109	94211	67572	47230
187	71780	77359	64536	23169	65061	93813	66523	46301	51425	66324
188	95712	12537	51767	32514	45629	52188	67692	26389	90531	32632
189	04069	86663	47975	84019	75108	57378	30548	37394	75405	76086
190	69785	86331	79153	87718	02453	14194	23406	95085	51354	72282
191	11077	13740	64078	36461	07998	74833	65394	56414	70730	61476
192	84178	34007	09641	14986	06694	64621	68345	42105	39839	87089
193	28128	74988	84266	07257	92892	14904	96410	70228	30322	14319
194	55526	47006	75447	94935	78536	25446	29456	16446	39872	06648
195	16145	81233	16323	37456	85440	35355	47389	37981	40452	07443
196	27166	27857	04848	33880	57246	38181	05127	77578	21639	47405
197	92173	59159	21696	01258	80090	93765	91472	67657	82374	17086
198	27633	14604	56124	18439	14520	26787	02600	56703	02522	99362
199	59354	46227	21428	66633	26728	22227	21993	15473	86893	04117
200	60591	87491	71349	47470	24207	61775	21366	58257	72358	49467

SOURCE: Lehman, R. S. (1995) *Statistics in the Behavioral Sciences: A Conceptual Introduction*. Pacific Grove, CA: Brooks/Cole. Reprinted by permission of the author.

TABLE A.2 Areas Under the Normal Curve (z Table)

z	Area Between Mean and z	Area Beyond z	z	Area Between Mean and z	Area Beyond z
0.00	0.00000	0.50000	0.43	0.16641	0.33359
0.01	0.00400	0.49600	0.44	0.17003	0.32997
0.02	0.00798	0.49202	0.45	0.17366	0.32634
0.03	0.01198	0.48802	0.46	0.17724	0.32276
0.04	0.01595	0.48405	0.47	0.18083	0.31917
0.05	0.01995	0.48005	0.48	0.18439	0.31561
0.06	0.02392	0.47608	0.49	0.18794	0.31206
0.07	0.02791	0.47209	0.50	0.19146	0.30854
0.08	0.03188	0.46812	0.51	0.19498	0.30502
0.09	0.03587	0.46413	0.52	0.19847	0.30153
0.10	0.03983	0.46017	0.53	0.20195	0.29805
0.11	0.04381	0.45619	0.54	0.20540	0.29460
0.12	0.04776	0.45224	0.55	0.20885	0.29115
0.13	0.05173	0.44827	0.56	0.21226	0.28774
0.14	0.05567	0.44433	0.57	0.21567	0.28433
0.15	0.05963	0.44037	0.58	0.21904	0.28096
0.16	0.06356	0.43644	0.59	0.22242	0.27758
0.17	0.06751	0.43249	0.60	0.22575	0.27425
0.18	0.07142	0.42858	0.61	0.22908	0.27092
0.19	0.07536	0.42464	0.62	0.23237	0.26763
0.20	0.07926	0.42074	0.63	0.23566	0.26434
0.21	0.08318	0.41682	0.64	0.23891	0.26109
0.22	0.08706	0.41294	0.65	0.24216	0.25784
0.23	0.09096	0.40904	0.66	0.24537	0.25463
0.24	0.09483	0.40517	0.67	0.24858	0.25142
0.25	0.09872	0.40128	0.68	0.25175	0.24825
0.26	0.10257	0.39743	0.69	0.25491	0.24509
0.27	0.10643	0.39357	0.70	0.25804	0.24196
0.28	0.11026	0.38974	0.71	0.26116	0.23884
0.29	0.11410	0.38590	0.72	0.26424	0.23576
0.30	0.11791	0.38209	0.73	0.26732	0.23268
0.31	0.12173	0.37827	0.74	0.27035	0.22965
0.32	0.12552	0.37448	0.75	0.27338	0.22662
0.33	0.12931	0.37069	0.76	0.27637	0.22363
0.34	0.13307	0.36693	0.77	0.27936	0.22064
0.35	0.13684	0.36316	0.78	0.28230	0.21770
0.36	0.14058	0.35942	0.79	0.28525	0.21475
0.37	0.14432	0.35568	0.80	0.28814	0.21186
0.38	0.14803	0.35197	0.81	0.29104	0.20896
0.39	0.15174	0.34826	0.82	0.29389	0.20611
0.40	0.15542	0.34458	0.83	0.29674	0.20326
0.41	0.15911	0.34089	0.84	0.29955	0.20045
0.42	0.16276	0.33724	0.85	0.30235	0.19765

(continued)

TABLE A.2 Areas Under the Normal Curve (*z* Table) (*continued*)

z	Area Between Mean and *z*	Area Beyond *z*	*z*	Area Between Mean and *z*	Area Beyond *z*
0.86	0.30511	0.19489	1.29	0.40149	0.09851
0.87	0.30786	0.19214	1.30	0.40320	0.09680
0.88	0.31057	0.18943	1.31	0.40491	0.09509
0.89	0.31328	0.18672	1.32	0.40658	0.09342
0.90	0.31594	0.18406	1.33	0.40825	0.09175
0.91	0.31860	0.18140	1.34	0.40988	0.09012
0.92	0.32121	0.17879	1.35	0.41150	0.08850
0.93	0.32383	0.17617	1.36	0.41309	0.08691
0.94	0.32639	0.17361	1.37	0.41467	0.08533
0.95	0.32895	0.17105	1.38	0.41621	0.08379
0.96	0.33147	0.16853	1.39	0.41775	0.08225
0.97	0.33399	0.16601	1.40	0.41924	0.08076
0.98	0.33646	0.16354	1.41	0.42074	0.07926
0.99	0.33892	0.16108	1.42	0.42220	0.07780
1.00	0.34134	0.15866	1.43	0.42365	0.07635
1.01	0.34376	0.15624	1.44	0.42507	0.07493
1.02	0.34614	0.15386	1.45	0.42648	0.07352
1.03	0.34851	0.15149	1.46	0.42785	0.07215
1.04	0.35083	0.14917	1.47	0.42923	0.07077
1.05	0.35315	0.14685	1.48	0.43056	0.06944
1.06	0.35543	0.14457	1.49	0.43190	0.06810
1.07	0.35770	0.14230	1.50	0.43319	0.06681
1.08	0.35993	0.14007	1.51	0.43449	0.06551
1.09	0.36215	0.13785	1.52	0.43574	0.06426
1.10	0.36433	0.13567	1.53	0.43700	0.06300
1.11	0.36651	0.13349	1.54	0.43822	0.06178
1.12	0.36864	0.13136	1.55	0.43944	0.06056
1.13	0.37077	0.12923	1.56	0.44062	0.05938
1.14	0.37286	0.12714	1.57	0.44180	0.05820
1.15	0.37494	0.12506	1.58	0.44295	0.05705
1.16	0.37698	0.12302	1.59	0.44409	0.05591
1.17	0.37901	0.12099	1.60	0.44520	0.05480
1.18	0.38100	0.11900	1.61	0.44631	0.05369
1.19	0.38299	0.11701	1.62	0.44738	0.05262
1.20	0.38493	0.11507	1.63	0.44846	0.05154
1.21	0.38687	0.11313	1.64	0.44950	0.05050
1.22	0.38877	0.11123	1.65	0.45054	0.04946
1.23	0.39066	0.10934	1.66	0.45154	0.04846
1.24	0.39251	0.10749	1.67	0.45255	0.04745
1.25	0.39436	0.10564	1.68	0.45352	0.04648
1.26	0.39617	0.10383	1.69	0.45450	0.04550
1.27	0.39797	0.10203	1.70	0.45543	0.04457
1.28	0.39973	0.10027	1.71	0.45638	0.04362

TABLE A.2 Areas Under the Normal Curve (*z* Table) (*continued*)

z	Area Between Mean and *z*	Area Beyond *z*	*z*	Area Between Mean and *z*	Area Beyond *z*
1.72	0.45728	0.04272	2.15	0.48423	0.01577
1.73	0.45820	0.04180	2.16	0.48461	0.01539
1.74	0.45907	0.04093	2.17	0.48501	0.01499
1.75	0.45995	0.04005	2.18	0.48537	0.01463
1.76	0.46080	0.03920	2.19	0.48575	0.01425
1.77	0.46165	0.03835	2.20	0.48610	0.01390
1.78	0.46246	0.03754	2.21	0.48646	0.01354
1.79	0.46328	0.03672	2.22	0.48679	0.01321
1.80	0.46407	0.03593	2.23	0.48714	0.01286
1.81	0.46486	0.03514	2.24	0.48745	0.01255
1.82	0.46562	0.03438	2.25	0.48779	0.01221
1.83	0.46639	0.03361	2.26	0.48809	0.01191
1.84	0.46712	0.03288	2.27	0.48841	0.01159
1.85	0.46785	0.03215	2.28	0.48870	0.01130
1.86	0.46856	0.03144	2.29	0.48900	0.01100
1.87	0.46927	0.03073	2.30	0.48928	0.01072
1.88	0.46995	0.03005	2.31	0.48957	0.01043
1.89	0.47063	0.02937	2.32	0.48983	0.01017
1.90	0.47128	0.02872	2.33	0.49011	0.00989
1.91	0.47194	0.02806	2.34	0.49036	0.00964
1.92	0.47257	0.02743	2.35	0.49062	0.00938
1.93	0.47321	0.02679	2.36	0.49086	0.00914
1.94	0.47381	0.02619	2.37	0.49112	0.00888
1.95	0.47442	0.02558	2.38	0.49134	0.00866
1.96	0.47500	0.02500	2.39	0.49159	0.00841
1.97	0.47559	0.02441	2.40	0.49180	0.00820
1.98	0.47615	0.02385	2.41	0.49203	0.00797
1.99	0.47672	0.02328	2.42	0.49224	0.00776
2.00	0.47725	0.02275	2.43	0.49246	0.00754
2.01	0.47780	0.02220	2.44	0.49266	0.00734
2.02	0.47831	0.02169	2.45	0.49287	0.00713
2.03	0.47883	0.02117	2.46	0.49305	0.00695
2.04	0.47932	0.02068	2.47	0.49325	0.00675
2.05	0.47983	0.02017	2.48	0.49343	0.00657
2.06	0.48030	0.01970	2.49	0.49362	0.00638
2.07	0.48078	0.01922	2.50	0.49379	0.00621
2.08	0.48124	0.01876	2.51	0.49397	0.00603
2.09	0.48170	0.01830	2.52	0.49413	0.00587
2.10	0.48214	0.01786	2.53	0.49431	0.00569
2.11	0.48258	0.01742	2.54	0.49446	0.00554
2.12	0.48300	0.01700	2.55	0.49462	0.00538
2.13	0.48342	0.01658	2.56	0.49477	0.00523
2.14	0.48382	0.01618	2.57	0.49493	0.00507

(*continued*)

TABLE A.2 Areas Under the Normal Curve (*z* Table) (*continued*)

z	Area Between Mean and *z*	Area Beyond *z*	*z*	Area Between Mean and *z*	Area Beyond *z*
2.58	0.49506	0.00494	2.90	0.49813	0.00187
2.59	0.49521	0.00479	2.91	0.49820	0.00180
2.60	0.49534	0.00466	2.92	0.49825	0.00175
2.61	0.49548	0.00452	2.93	0.49832	0.00168
2.62	0.49560	0.00440	2.94	0.49836	0.00164
2.63	0.49574	0.00426	2.95	0.49842	0.00158
2.64	0.49585	0.00415	2.96	0.49846	0.00154
2.65	0.49599	0.00401	2.97	0.49852	0.00148
2.66	0.49609	0.00391	2.98	0.49856	0.00144
2.67	0.49622	0.00378	2.99	0.49862	0.00138
2.68	0.49632	0.00368	3.00	0.49865	0.00135
2.69	0.49644	0.00356	3.02	0.49874	0.00126
2.70	0.49653	0.00347	3.04	0.49882	0.00118
2.71	0.49665	0.00335	3.06	0.49889	0.00111
2.72	0.49674	0.00326	3.08	0.49896	0.00104
2.73	0.49684	0.00316	3.10	0.49903	0.00097
2.74	0.49693	0.00307	3.12	0.49910	0.00090
2.75	0.49703	0.00297	3.14	0.49916	0.00084
2.76	0.49711	0.00289	3.16	0.49921	0.00079
2.77	0.49721	0.00279	3.18	0.49926	0.00074
2.78	0.49728	0.00272	3.20	0.49931	0.00069
2.79	0.49738	0.00262	3.25	0.49943	0.00057
2.80	0.49744	0.00256	3.30	0.49952	0.00048
2.81	0.49753	0.00247	3.35	0.49961	0.00039
2.82	0.49760	0.00240	3.40	0.49966	0.00034
2.83	0.49768	0.00232	3.45	0.49973	0.00027
2.84	0.49774	0.00226	3.50	0.49977	0.00023
2.85	0.49782	0.00218	3.60	0.49984	0.00016
2.86	0.49788	0.00212	3.70	0.49989	0.00011
2.87	0.49796	0.00204	3.80	0.49993	0.00007
2.88	0.49801	0.00199	3.90	0.49995	0.00005
2.89	0.49808	0.00192	4.00	0.49997	0.00003

SOURCE: Lehman, R. S. (1995) *Statistics in the Behavioral Sciences: A Conceptual Introduction*. Pacific Grove, CA: Brooks/Cole. Reprinted by permission of the author.

TABLE A.3 Critical Values for the Student's *t* Distribution

	Level of Significance for One-Tailed Test					
	.10	.05	.025	.01	.005	.0005
	Level of Significance for Two-Tailed Test					
df	.20	.10	.05	.02	.01	.001
1	3.078	6.314	12.706	31.821	63.657	636.619
2	1.886	2.920	4.303	6.965	9.925	31.598
3	1.638	2.353	3.182	4.541	5.841	12.941
4	1.533	2.132	2.776	3.747	4.604	8.610
5	1.476	2.015	2.571	3.365	4.032	6.859
6	1.440	1.943	2.447	3.143	3.707	5.959
7	1.415	1.895	2.365	2.998	3.499	5.405
8	1.397	1.860	2.306	2.896	3.355	5.041
9	1.383	1.833	2.262	2.821	3.250	4.781
10	1.372	1.812	2.228	2.764	3.169	4.587
11	1.363	1.796	2.201	2.718	3.106	4.437
12	1.356	1.782	2.179	2.681	3.055	4.318
13	1.350	1.771	2.160	2.650	3.012	4.221
14	1.345	1.761	2.145	2.624	2.977	4.140
15	1.341	1.753	2.131	2.602	2.947	4.073
16	1.337	1.746	2.120	2.583	2.921	4.015
17	1.333	1.740	2.110	2.567	2.898	3.965
18	1.330	1.734	2.101	2.552	2.878	3.922
19	1.328	1.729	2.093	2.539	2.861	3.883
20	1.325	1.725	2.086	2.528	2.845	3.850
21	1.323	1.721	2.080	2.518	2.831	3.819
22	1.321	1.717	2.074	2.508	2.819	3.792
23	1.319	1.714	2.069	2.500	2.807	3.767
24	1.318	1.711	2.064	2.492	2.797	3.745
25	1.316	1.708	2.060	2.485	2.787	3.725
26	1.315	1.706	2.056	2.479	2.779	3.707
27	1.314	1.703	2.052	2.473	2.771	3.690
28	1.313	1.701	2.048	2.467	2.763	3.674
29	1.311	1.699	2.045	2.462	2.756	3.659
30	1.310	1.697	2.042	2.457	2.750	3.646
40	1.303	1.684	2.021	2.423	2.704	3.551
60	1.296	1.671	2.000	2.390	2.660	3.460
120	1.289	1.658	1.980	2.358	2.617	3.373
∞	1.282	1.645	1.960	2.326	2.576	3.291

Source: Lehman, R. S. (1995) *Statistics in the Behavioral Sciences: A Conceptual Introduction*. Pacific Grove, CA: Brooks/Cole Publishing. Reprinted by permission of the author.

TABLE A.4 Critical Values of the Pearson *r* (Pearson Product-Moment Correlation Coefficient)

	Level of Significance for One-Tailed Test		
	.05	.025	.005
	Level of Significance for Two-Tailed Test		
df	.10	.05	.01
1	.98769	.99692	.999877
2	.90000	.95000	.990000
3	.8054	.8783	.95873
4	.7293	.8114	.91720
5	.6694	.7545	.8745
6	.6215	.7067	.8343
7	.5822	.6664	.7977
8	.5494	.6319	.7646
9	.5214	.6021	.7348
10	.4973	.5760	.7079
11	.4762	.5529	.6835
12	.4575	.5324	.6614
13	.4409	.5139	.6411
14	.4259	.4973	.6226
15	.4124	.4821	.6055
16	.4000	.4683	.5897
17	.3887	.4555	.5751
18	.3783	.4438	.5614
19	.3687	.4329	.5487
20	.3598	.4227	.5368
25	.3233	.3809	.4869
30	.2960	.3494	.4487
35	.2746	.3246	.4182
40	.2573	.3044	.3932
45	.2428	.2875	.3721
50	.2306	.2732	.3541
60	.2108	.2500	.3248
70	.1954	.2319	.3017
80	.1829	.2172	.2830
90	.1726	.2050	.2673
100	.1638	.1946	.2540

SOURCE: Abridged from Table VII in R. A. Fisher and F. Yates, *Statistical Tables for Biological, Agricultural, and Medical Research*, 6th ed., 1974, p. 63. © 1963 R. A. Fisher and F. Yates, reprinted by permission of Pearson Education Limited.

TABLE A.5 Critical Values for the *F* Distribution

df for Denominator (*df* within or error)	α	*df* for Numerator (*df* between) 1	2	3	4	5	6	7	8	9	10	11	12
1	.05	161	200	216	225	230	234	237	239	241	242	243	244
2	.05	18.5	19.0	19.2	19.2	19.3	19.3	19.4	19.4	19.4	19.4	19.4	19.4
	.01	98.5	99.0	99.2	99.2	99.3	99.3	99.4	99.4	99.4	99.4	99.4	99.4
3	.05	10.1	9.55	9.28	9.12	9.01	8.94	8.89	8.85	8.81	8.79	8.76	8.74
	.01	34.1	30.8	29.5	28.7	28.2	27.9	27.7	27.5	27.3	27.2	27.1	27.1
4	.05	7.71	6.94	6.59	6.39	6.26	6.16	6.09	6.04	6.00	5.96	5.94	5.91
	.01	21.2	18.0	16.7	16.0	15.5	15.2	15.0	14.8	14.7	14.5	14.4	14.4
5	.05	6.61	5.79	5.41	5.19	5.05	4.95	4.88	4.82	4.77	4.74	4.71	4.68
	.01	16.3	13.3	12.1	11.4	11.0	10.7	10.5	10.3	10.2	10.1	9.96	9.89
6	.05	5.99	5.14	4.76	4.53	4.39	4.28	4.21	4.15	4.10	4.06	4.03	4.00
	.01	13.7	10.9	9.78	9.15	8.75	8.47	8.26	8.10	7.98	7.87	7.79	7.72
7	.05	5.59	4.74	4.35	4.12	3.97	3.87	3.79	3.73	3.68	3.64	3.60	3.57
	.01	12.2	9.55	8.45	7.85	7.46	7.19	6.99	6.84	6.72	6.62	6.54	6.47
8	.05	5.32	4.46	4.07	3.84	3.69	3.58	3.50	3.44	3.39	3.35	3.31	3.28
	.01	11.3	8.65	7.59	7.01	6.63	6.37	6.18	6.03	5.91	5.81	5.73	5.67
9	.05	5.12	4.26	3.86	3.63	3.48	3.37	3.29	3.23	3.18	3.14	3.10	3.07
	.01	10.6	8.02	6.99	6.42	6.06	5.80	5.61	5.47	5.35	5.26	5.18	5.11
10	.05	4.96	4.10	3.71	3.48	3.33	3.22	3.14	3.07	3.02	2.98	2.94	2.91
	.01	10.0	7.56	6.55	5.99	5.64	5.39	5.20	5.06	4.94	4.85	4.77	4.71
11	.05	4.84	3.98	3.59	3.36	3.20	3.09	3.01	2.95	2.90	2.85	2.82	2.79
	.01	9.65	7.21	6.22	5.67	5.32	5.07	4.89	4.74	4.63	4.54	4.46	4.40
12	.05	4.75	3.89	3.49	3.26	3.11	3.00	2.91	2.85	2.80	2.75	2.72	2.69
	.01	9.33	6.93	5.95	5.41	5.06	4.82	4.64	4.50	439	4.30	4.22	4.16
13	.05	4.67	3.81	3.41	3.18	3.03	2.92	2.83	2.77	2.71	2.67	2.63	2.60
	.01	9.07	6.70	5.74	5.21	4.86	4.62	4.44	4.30	4.19	4.10	4.02	3.96
14	.05	4.60	3.74	3.34	3.11	2.96	2.85	2.76	2.70	2.65	2.60	2.57	2.53
	.01	8.86	6.51	5.56	5.04	4.69	4.46	4.28	4.14	4.03	3.94	3.86	3.80
15	.05	4.54	3.68	3.29	3.06	2.90	2.79	2.71	2.64	2.59	2.54	2.51	2.48
	.01	8.68	6.36	5.42	4.89	4.56	4.32	4.14	4.00	3.89	3.80	3.73	3.67
16	.05	4.49	3.63	3.24	3.01	2.85	2.74	2.66	2.59	2.54	2.49	2.46	2.42
	.01	8.53	6.23	5.29	4.77	4.44	4.20	4.03	3.89	3.78	3.69	3.62	3.55
17	.05	4.45	3.59	3.20	2.96	2.81	2.70	2.61	2.55	2.49	2.45	2.41	2.38
	.01	8.40	6.11	5.18	4.67	4.34	4.10	3.93	3.79	3.68	3.59	3.52	3.46
18	.05	4.41	3.55	3.16	2.93	2.77	2.66	2.58	2.51	2.46	2.41	2.37	2.34
	.01	8.29	6.01	5.09	4.58	4.25	4.01	3.84	3.71	3.60	3.51	3.43	3.37
19	.05	4.38	3.52	3.13	2.90	2.74	2.63	2.54	2.48	2.42	2.38	2.34	2.31
	.01	8.18	5.93	5.01	4.50	4.17	3.94	3.77	3.63	3.52	3.43	3.36	3.30

(continued)

TABLE A.5 Critical Values for the *F* Distribution *(continued)*

df for Numerator (*df* between)													
15	20	24	30	40	50	60	100	120	200	500	∞	α	*df* for Denominator (*df* within or error)
246	248	249	250	251	252	252	253	253	254	254	254	.05	1
19.4	19.4	19.5	19.5	19.5	19.5	19.5	19.5	19.5	19.5	19.5	19.5	.05	2
99.4	99.4	99.5	99.5	99.5	99.5	99.5	99.5	99.5	99.5	99.5	99.5	.01	
8.70	8.66	8.64	8.62	8.59	8.58	8.57	8.55	8.55	8.54	8.53	8.53	.05	3
26.9	26.7	26.6	26.5	26.4	26.4	26.3	26.2	26.2	26.2	26.1	26.1	.01	
5.86	5.80	5.77	5.75	5.72	5.70	5.69	5.66	5.66	5.65	5.64	5.63	.05	4
14.2	14.0	13.9	13.8	13.7	13.7	13.7	13.6	13.6	13.5	13.5	13.5	.01	
4.62	4.56	4.53	4.50	4.46	4.44	4.43	4.41	4.40	4.39	4.37	4.36	.05	5
9.72	9.55	9.47	9.38	9.29	9.24	9.20	9.13	9.11	9.08	9.04	9.02	.01	
3.94	3.87	3.84	3.81	3.77	3.75	3.74	3.71	3.70	3.69	3.68	3.67	.05	6
7.56	7.40	7.31	7.23	7.14	7.09	7.06	6.99	6.97	6.93	6.90	6.88	.01	
3.51	3.44	3.41	3.38	3.34	3.32	3.30	3.27	3.27	3.25	3.24	3.23	.05	7
6.31	6.16	6.07	5.99	5.91	5.86	5.82	5.75	5.74	5.70	5.67	5.65	.01	
3.22	3.15	3.12	3.08	3.04	3.02	3.01	2.97	2.97	2.95	2.94	2.93	.05	8
5.52	5.36	5.28	5.20	5.12	5.07	5.03	4.96	4.95	4.91	4.88	4.86	.01	
3.01	2.94	2.90	2.86	2.83	2.80	2.79	2.76	2.75	2.73	2.72	2.71	.05	9
4.96	4.81	4.73	4.65	4.57	4.52	4.48	4.42	4.40	4.36	4.33	4.31	.01	
2.85	2.77	2.74	2.70	2.66	2.64	2.62	2.59	2.58	2.56	2.55	2.54	.05	10
4.56	4.41	4.33	4.25	4.17	4.12	4.08	4.01	4.00	3.96	3.93	3.91	.01	
2.72	2.65	2.61	2.57	2.53	2.51	2.49	2.46	2.45	2.43	2.42	2.40	.05	11
4.25	4.10	4.02	3.94	3.86	3.81	3.78	3.71	3.69	3.66	3.62	3.60	.01	
2.62	2.54	2.51	2.47	2.43	2.40	2.38	2.35	2.34	2.32	2.31	2.30	.05	12
4.01	3.86	3.78	3.70	3.62	3.57	3.54	3.47	3.45	3.41	3.38	3.36	.01	
2.53	2.46	2.42	2.38	2.34	2.31	2.30	2.26	2.25	2.23	2.22	2.21	.05	13
3.82	3.66	3.59	3.51	3.43	3.38	3.34	3.27	3.25	3.22	3.19	3.17	.01	
2.46	2.39	2.35	2.31	2.27	2.24	2.22	2.19	2.18	2.16	2.14	2.13	.05	14
3.66	3.51	3.43	3.35	3.27	3.22	3.18	3.11	3.09	3.06	3.03	3.00	.01	
2.40	2.33	2.29	2.25	2.20	2.18	2.16	2.12	2.11	2.10	2.08	2.07	.05	15
3.52	3.37	3.29	3.21	3.13	3.08	3.05	2.98	2.96	2.92	2.89	2.87	.01	
2.35	2.28	2.24	2.19	2.15	2.12	2.11	2.07	2.06	2.04	2.02	2.01	.05	16
3.41	3.26	3.18	3.10	3.02	2.97	2.93	2.86	2.84	2.81	2.78	2.75	.01	
2.31	2.23	2.19	2.15	2.10	2.08	2.06	2.02	2.01	1.99	1.97	1.96	.05	17
3.31	3.16	3.08	3.00	2.92	2.87	2.83	2.76	2.75	2.71	2.68	2.65	.01	
2.27	2.19	2.15	2.11	2.06	2.04	2.02	1.98	1.97	1.95	1.93	1.92	.05	18
3.23	3.08	3.00	2.92	2.84	2.78	2.75	2.68	2.66	2.62	2.59	2.57	.01	
2.23	2.16	2.11	2.07	2.03	2.00	1.98	1.94	1.93	1.91	1.89	1.88	.05	19
3.15	3.00	2.92	2.84	2.76	2.71	2.67	2.60	2.58	2.55	2.51	2.49	.01	

TABLE A.5 Critical Values for the *F* Distribution *(continued)*

df for Denominator (*df* within or error)	α	*df* for Numerator (*df* between) 1	2	3	4	5	6	7	8	9	10	11	12
20	.05	4.35	3.49	3.10	2.87	2.71	2.60	2.51	2.45	2.39	2.35	2.31	2.28
	.01	8.10	5.85	4.94	4.43	4.10	3.87	3.70	3.56	3.46	3.37	3.29	3.23
22	.05	4.30	3.44	3.05	2.82	2.66	2.55	2.46	2.40	2.34	2.30	2.26	2.23
	.01	7.95	5.72	4.82	4.31	3.99	3.76	3.59	3.45	3.35	3.26	3.18	3.12
24	.05	4.26	3.40	3.01	2.78	2.62	2.51	2.42	2.36	2.30	2.25	2.21	2.18
	.01	7.82	5.61	4.72	4.22	3.90	3.67	3.50	3.36	3.26	3.17	3.09	3.03
26	.05	4.23	3.37	2.98	2.74	2.59	2.47	2.39	2.32	2.27	2.22	2.18	2.15
	.01	7.72	5.53	4.64	4.14	3.82	3.59	3.42	3.29	3.18	3.09	3.02	2.96
28	.05	4.20	3.34	2.95	2.71	2.56	2.45	2.36	2.29	2.24	2.19	2.15	2.12
	.01	7.64	5.45	4.57	4.07	3.75	3.53	3.36	3.23	3.12	3.03	2.96	2.90
30	.05	4.17	3.32	2.92	2.69	2.53	2.42	2.33	2.27	2.21	2.16	2.13	2.09
	.01	7.56	5.39	4.51	4.02	3.70	3.47	3.30	3.17	3.07	2.98	2.91	2.84
40	.05	4.08	3.23	2.84	2.61	2.45	2.34	2.25	2.18	2.12	2.08	2.04	2.00
	.01	7.31	5.18	4.31	3.83	3.51	3.29	3.12	2.99	2.89	2.80	2.73	2.66
60	.05	4.00	3.15	2.76	2.53	2.37	2.25	2.17	2.10	2.04	1.99	1.95	1.92
	.01	7.08	4.98	4.13	3.65	3.34	3.12	2.95	2.82	2.72	2.63	2.56	2.50
120	.05	3.92	3.07	2.68	2.45	2.29	2.17	2.09	2.02	1.96	1.91	1.87	1.83
	.01	6.85	4.79	3.95	3.48	3.17	2.96	2.79	2.66	2.56	2.47	2.40	2.34
200	.05	3.89	3.04	2.65	2.42	2.26	2.14	2.06	1.98	1.93	1.88	1.84	1.80
	.01	6.76	4.71	3.88	3.41	3.11	2.89	2.73	2.60	2.50	2.41	2.34	2.27
∞	.05	3.84	3.00	2.60	2.37	2.21	2.10	2.01	1.94	1.88	1.83	1.79	1.75
	.01	6.63	4.61	3.78	3.32	3.02	2.80	2.64	2.51	2.41	2.32	2.25	2.18

(continued)

TABLE A.5 Critical Values for the *F* Distribution *(continued)*

df for Numerator (*df* between)													
15	20	24	30	40	50	60	100	120	200	500	∞	α	*df* for Denominator (*df* within or error)
2.20	2.12	2.08	2.04	1.99	1.97	1.95	1.91	1.90	1.88	1.86	1.84	.05	20
3.09	2.94	2.86	2.78	2.69	2.64	2.61	2.54	2.52	2.48	2.44	2.42	.01	
2.15	2.07	2.03	1.98	1.94	1.91	1.89	1.85	1.84	1.82	1.80	1.78	.05	22
2.98	2.83	2.75	2.67	2.58	2.53	2.50	2.42	2.40	2.36	2.33	2.31	.01	
2.11	2.03	1.98	1.94	1.89	1.86	1.84	1.80	1.79	1.77	1.75	1.73	.05	24
2.89	2.74	2.66	2.58	2.49	2.44	2.40	2.33	2.31	2.27	2.24	2.21	.01	
2.07	1.99	1.95	1.90	1.85	1.82	1.80	1.76	1.75	1.73	1.71	1.69	.05	26
2.81	2.66	2.58	2.50	2.42	2.36	2.33	2.25	2.23	2.19	2.16	2.13	.01	
2.04	1.96	1.91	1.87	1.82	1.79	1.77	1.73	1.71	1.69	1.67	1.65	.05	28
2.75	2.60	2.52	2.44	2.35	2.30	2.26	2.19	2.17	2.13	2.09	2.06	.01	
2.01	1.93	1.89	1.84	1.79	1.76	1.74	1.70	1.68	1.66	1.64	1.62	.05	30
2.70	2.55	2.47	2.39	2.30	2.25	2.21	2.13	2.11	2.07	2.03	2.01	.01	
1.92	1.84	1.79	1.74	1.69	1.66	1.64	1.59	1.58	1.55	1.53	1.51	.05	40
2.52	2.37	2.29	2.20	2.11	2.06	2.02	1.94	1.92	1.87	1.83	1.80	.01	
1.84	1.75	1.70	1.65	1.59	1.56	1.53	1.48	1.47	1.44	1.41	1.39	.05	60
2.35	2.20	2.12	2.03	1.94	1.88	1.84	1.75	1.73	1.68	1.63	1.60	.01	
1.75	1.66	1.61	1.55	1.50	1.46	1.43	1.37	1.35	1.32	1.28	1.25	.05	120
2.19	2.03	1.95	1.86	1.76	1.70	1.66	1.56	1.53	1.48	1.42	1.38	.01	
1.72	1.62	1.57	1.52	1.46	1.41	1.39	1.32	1.29	1.26	1.22	1.19	.05	200
2.13	1.97	1.89	1.79	1.69	1.63	1.58	1.48	1.44	1.39	1.33	1.28	.01	
1.67	1.57	1.52	1.46	1.39	1.35	1.32	1.24	1.22	1.17	1.11	1.00	.05	∞
2.04	1.88	1.79	1.70	1.59	1.52	1.47	1.36	1.32	1.25	1.15	1.00	.01	

SOURCE: Lehman, R. S. (1995) *Statistics in the Behavioral Sciences: A Conceptual Introduction*. Pacific Grove, CA: Brooks/Cole Publishing.

TABLE A.6 Studentized Range Statistic (Q)

Error *df* (*df* within)	α	*k* = Number of Means or Number of Steps Between Ordered Means									
		2	3	4	5	6	7	8	9	10	11
5	.05	3.64	4.60	5.22	5.67	6.03	6.33	6.58	6.80	6.99	7.17
	.01	5.70	6.98	7.80	8.42	8.91	9.32	9.67	9.97	10.24	10.48
6	.05	3.46	4.34	4.90	5.30	5.63	5.90	6.12	6.32	6.49	6.65
	.01	5.24	6.33	7.03	7.56	7.97	8.32	8.61	8.87	9.10	9.30
7	.05	3.34	4.16	4.68	5.06	5.36	5.61	5.82	6.00	6.16	6.30
	.01	4.95	5.92	6.54	7.01	7.37	7.68	7.94	8.17	8.37	8.55
8	.05	3.26	4.04	4.53	4.89	5.17	5.40	5.60	5.77	5.92	6.05
	.01	4.75	5.64	6.20	6.62	6.96	7.24	7.47	7.68	7.86	8.03
9	.05	3.20	3.95	4.41	4.76	5.02	5.24	5.43	5.59	5.74	5.87
	.01	4.60	5.43	5.96	6.35	6.66	6.91	7.13	7.33	7.49	7.65
10	.05	3.15	3.88	4.33	4.65	4.91	5.12	5.30	5.46	5.60	5.72
	.01	4.48	5.27	5.77	6.14	6.43	6.67	6.87	7.05	7.21	7.36
11	.05	3.11	3.82	4.26	4.57	4.82	5.03	5.20	5.35	5.49	5.61
	.01	4.39	5.15	5.62	5.97	6.25	6.48	6.67	6.84	6.99	7.13
12	.05	3.08	3.77	4.20	4.51	4.75	4.95	5.12	5.27	5.39	5.51
	.01	4.32	5.05	5.50	5.84	6.10	6.32	6.51	6.67	6.81	6.94
13	.05	3.06	3.73	4.15	4.45	4.69	4.88	5.05	5.19	5.32	5.43
	.01	4.26	4.96	5.40	5.73	5.98	6.19	6.37	6.53	6.67	6.79
14	.05	3.03	3.70	4.11	4.41	4.64	4.83	4.99	5.13	5.25	5.36
	.01	4.21	4.89	5.32	5.63	5.88	6.08	6.26	6.41	6.54	6.66
15	.05	3.01	3.67	4.08	4.37	4.59	4.78	4.94	5.08	5.20	5.31
	.01	4.17	4.84	5.25	5.56	5.80	5.99	6.16	6.31	6.44	6.55
16	.05	3.00	3.65	4.05	4.33	4.56	4.74	4.90	5.03	5.15	5.26
	.01	4.13	4.79	5.19	5.49	5.72	5.92	6.08	6.22	6.35	6.46
17	.05	2.98	3.63	4.02	4.30	4.52	4.70	4.86	4.99	5.11	5.21
	.01	4.10	4.74	5.14	5.43	5.66	5.85	6.01	6.15	6.27	6.38
18	.05	2.97	3.61	4.00	4.28	4.49	4.67	4.82	4.96	5.07	5.17
	.01	4.07	4.70	5.09	5.38	5.60	5.79	5.94	6.08	6.20	6.31
19	.05	2.96	3.59	3.98	4.25	4.47	4.65	4.79	4.92	5.04	5.14
	.01	4.05	4.67	5.05	5.33	5.55	5.73	5.89	6.02	6.14	6.25
20	.05	2.95	3.58	3.96	4.23	4.45	4.62	4.77	4.90	5.01	5.11
	.01	4.02	4.64	5.02	5.29	5.51	5.69	5.84	5.97	6.09	6.19
24	.05	2.92	3.53	3.90	4.17	4.37	4.54	4.68	4.81	4.92	5.01
	.01	3.96	4.55	4.91	5.17	5.37	5.54	5.69	5.81	5.92	6.02
30	.05	2.89	3.49	3.85	4.10	4.30	4.46	4.60	4.72	4.82	4.92
	.01	3.89	4.45	4.80	5.05	5.24	5.40	5.54	5.65	5.76	5.85
40	.05	2.86	3.44	3.79	4.04	4.23	4.39	4.52	4.63	4.73	4.82
	.01	3.82	4.37	4.70	4.93	5.11	5.26	5.39	5.50	5.60	5.69
60	.05	2.83	3.40	3.74	3.98	4.16	4.31	4.44	4.55	4.65	4.73
	.01	3.76	4.28	4.59	4.82	4.99	5.13	5.25	5.36	5.45	5.53
120	.05	2.80	3.36	3.68	3.92	4.10	4.24	4.36	4.47	4.56	4.64
	.01	3.70	4.20	4.50	4.71	4.87	5.01	5.12	5.21	5.30	5.37
∞	.05	2.77	3.31	3.63	3.86	4.03	4.17	4.29	4.39	4.47	4.55
	.01	3.64	4.12	4.40	4.60	4.76	4.88	4.99	5.08	5.16	5.23

(continued)

TABLE A.6 Studentized Range Statistic (*Q*) *(continued)*

k = Number of Means or Number of Steps Between Ordered Means										
12	**13**	**14**	**15**	**16**	**17**	**18**	**19**	**20**	**α**	**Error *df* (*df* within)**
7.32	7.47	7.60	7.72	7.83	7.93	8.03	8.12	8.21	.05	5
10.70	10.89	11.08	11.24	11.40	11.55	11.68	11.81	11.93	.01	
6.79	6.92	7.03	7.14	7.24	7.34	7.43	7.51	7.59	.05	6
9.48	9.65	9.81	9.95	10.08	10.21	10.32	10.43	10.54	.01	
6.43	6.55	6.66	6.76	6.85	6.94	7.02	7.10	7.17	.05	7
8.71	8.86	9.00	9.12	9.24	9.35	9.46	9.55	9.65	.01	
6.18	6.29	6.39	6.48	6.57	6.65	6.73	6.80	6.87	.05	8
8.18	8.31	8.44	8.55	8.66	8.76	8.85	8.94	9.03	.01	
5.98	6.09	6.19	6.28	6.36	6.44	6.51	6.58	6.64	.05	9
7.78	7.91	8.03	8.13	8.23	8.33	8.41	8.49	8.57	.01	
5.83	5.93	6.03	6.11	6.19	6.27	6.34	6.40	6.47	.05	10
7.49	7.60	7.71	7.81	7.91	7.99	8.08	8.15	8.23	.01	
5.71	5.81	5.90	5.98	6.06	6.13	6.20	6.27	6.33	.05	11
7.25	7.36	7.46	7.56	7.65	7.73	7.81	7.88	7.95	.01	
5.61	5.71	5.80	5.88	5.95	6.02	6.09	6.15	6.21	.05	12
7.06	7.17	7.26	7.36	7.44	7.52	7.59	7.66	7.73	.01	
5.53	5.63	5.71	5.79	5.86	5.93	5.99	6.05	6.11	.05	13
6.90	7.01	7.10	7.19	7.27	7.35	7.42	7.48	7.55	.01	
5.46	5.55	5.64	5.71	5.79	5.85	5.91	5.97	6.03	.05	14
6.77	6.87	6.96	7.05	7.13	7.20	7.27	7.33	7.39	.01	
5.40	5.49	5.57	5.65	5.72	5.78	5.85	5.90	5.96	.05	15
6.66	6.76	6.84	6.93	7.00	7.07	7.14	7.20	7.26	.01	
5.35	5.44	5.52	5.59	5.66	5.73	5.79	5.84	5.90	.05	16
6.56	6.66	6.74	6.82	6.90	6.97	7.03	7.09	7.15	.01	
5.31	5.39	5.47	5.54	5.61	5.67	5.73	5.79	5.84	.05	17
6.48	6.57	6.66	6.73	6.81	6.87	6.94	7.00	7.05	.01	
5.27	5.35	5.43	5.50	5.57	5.63	5.69	5.74	5.79	.05	18
6.41	6.50	6.58	6.65	6.73	6.79	6.85	6.91	6.97	.01	
5.23	5.31	5.39	5.46	5.53	5.59	5.65	5.70	5.75	.05	19
6.34	6.43	6.51	6.58	6.65	6.72	6.78	6.84	6.89	.01	
5.20	5.28	5.36	5.43	5.49	5.55	5.61	5.66	5.71	.05	20
6.28	6.37	6.45	6.52	6.59	6.65	6.71	6.77	6.82	.01	
5.10	5.18	5.25	5.32	5.38	5.44	5.49	5.55	5.59	.05	24
6.11	6.19	6.26	6.33	6.39	6.45	6.51	6.56	6.61	.01	
5.00	5.08	5.15	5.21	5.27	5.33	5.38	5.43	5.47	.05	30
5.93	6.01	6.08	6.14	6.20	6.26	6.31	6.36	6.41	.01	
4.90	4.98	5.04	5.11	5.16	5.22	5.27	5.31	5.36	.05	40
5.76	5.83	5.90	5.96	6.02	6.07	6.12	6.16	6.21	.01	
4.81	4.88	4.94	5.00	5.06	5.11	5.15	5.20	5.24	.05	60
5.60	5.67	5.73	5.78	5.84	5.89	5.93	5.97	6.01	.01	
4.71	4.78	4.84	4.90	4.95	5.00	5.04	5.09	5.13	.05	120
5.44	5.50	5.56	5.61	5.66	5.71	5.75	5.79	5.83	.01	
4.62	4.68	4.74	4.80	4.85	4.89	4.93	4.97	5.01	.05	∞
5.29	5.35	5.40	5.45	5.49	5.54	5.57	5.61	5.65	.01	

SOURCE: Abridged from Table 29 in E. S. Pearson and H. O. Hartley, eds. *Biometrika Tables for Statisticians*, 3rd ed., 1966, Vol. 1, pp. 176–177. Reprinted by permission of Oxford University Press.

Table A.7 Critical Values for the χ^2 Distribution

df	.10	.05	.025	.01	.005
1	2.706	3.841	5.024	6.635	7.879
2	4.605	5.992	7.378	9.210	10.597
3	6.251	7.815	9.348	11.345	12.838
4	7.779	9.488	11.143	13.277	14.860
5	9.236	11.071	12.833	15.086	16.750
6	10.645	12.592	14.449	16.812	18.548
7	12.017	14.067	16.013	18.475	20.278
8	13.362	15.507	17.535	20.090	21.955
9	14.684	16.919	19.023	21.666	23.589
10	15.987	18.307	20.483	23.209	25.188
11	17.275	19.675	21.920	24.725	26.757
12	18.549	21.026	23.337	26.217	28.300
13	19.812	22.362	24.736	27.688	29.819
14	21.064	23.685	26.119	29.141	31.319
15	22.307	24.996	27.488	30.578	32.801
16	23.542	26.296	28.845	32.000	34.267
17	24.769	27.587	30.191	33.409	35.718
18	25.989	28.869	31.526	34.805	37.156
19	27.204	30.144	32.852	36.191	38.582
20	28.412	31.410	34.170	37.566	39.997
21	29.615	32.671	35.479	38.932	41.401
22	30.813	33.925	36.781	40.290	42.796
23	32.007	35.172	38.076	41.638	44.181
24	33.196	36.415	39.364	42.980	45.559
25	34.382	37.653	40.647	44.314	46.929
26	35.563	38.885	41.923	45.642	48.290
27	36.741	40.113	43.195	46.963	49.645
28	37.916	41.337	44.461	48.278	50.994
29	39.087	42.557	45.722	49.588	52.336
30	40.256	43.773	46.979	50.892	53.672
40	51.805	55.759	59.342	63.691	66.767
50	63.167	67.505	71.420	76.154	79.490
60	74.397	79.082	83.298	88.381	91.955
70	85.527	90.531	95.023	100.424	104.213

Source: Lehman, R. S. (1995) *Statistics in the Behavioral Sciences: A Conceptual Introduction*. Pacific Grove, CA: Brooks/Cole Publishing. Reprinted by permission of the author.

TABLE A.8 Critical Values for W (Wilcoxon Rank-Sum Test)

	$N_1 = 1$							$N_1 = 2$							
N_2	0.001	0.005	0.010	0.025	0.05	0.10	$2\overline{W}$	0.001	0.005	0.010	0.025	0.05	0.10	$2\overline{W}$	N_2
2							4						—	10	2
3							5						3	12	3
4							6					—	3	14	4
5							7					3	4	16	5
6							8					3	4	18	6
7							9				—	3	4	20	7
8						—	10				3	4	5	22	8
9						1	11				3	4	5	24	9
10						1	12				3	4	6	26	10
11						1	13				3	4	6	28	11
12						1	14			—	4	5	7	30	12
13						1	15			3	4	5	7	32	13
14						1	16			3	4	6	8	34	14
15						1	17			3	4	6	8	36	15
16						1	18			3	4	6	8	38	16
17						1	19			3	5	6	9	40	17
18					—	1	20		—	3	5	7	9	42	18
19					1	2	21		3	4	5	7	10	44	19
20					1	2	22		3	4	5	7	10	46	20
21					1	2	23		3	4	6	8	11	48	21
22					1	2	24		3	4	6	8	11	50	22
23					1	2	25		3	4	6	8	12	52	23
24					1	2	26		3	4	6	9	12	54	24
25	—	—	—	—	1	2	27	—	3	4	6	9	12	56	25

	$N_1 = 3$							$N_1 = 4$							
N_2	0.001	0.005	0.010	0.025	0.05	0.10	$2\overline{W}$	0.001	0.005	0.010	0.025	0.05	0.10	$2\overline{W}$	N_2
3					6	7	21								
4				—	6	7	24			—	10	11	13	36	4
5				6	7	8	27		—	10	11	12	14	40	5
6			—	7	8	9	30		10	11	12	13	15	44	6
7			6	7	8	10	33		10	11	13	14	16	48	7
8		—	6	8	9	11	36		11	12	14	15	17	52	8
9		6	7	8	10	11	39	—	11	13	14	16	19	56	9
10		6	7	9	10	12	42	10	12	13	15	17	20	60	10
11		6	7	9	11	13	45	10	12	14	16	18	21	64	11
12		7	8	10	11	14	48	10	13	15	17	19	22	68	12
13		7	8	10	12	15	51	11	13	15	18	20	23	72	13
14		7	8	11	13	16	54	11	14	16	19	21	25	76	14
15		8	9	11	13	16	57	11	15	17	20	22	26	80	15
16	—	8	9	12	14	17	60	12	15	17	21	24	27	84	16
17	6	8	10	12	15	18	63	12	16	18	21	25	28	88	17
18	6	8	10	13	15	19	66	13	16	19	22	26	30	92	18
19	6	9	10	13	15	20	69	13	17	19	23	27	31	96	19
20	6	9	11	14	17	21	72	13	18	20	24	28	32	100	20
21	7	9	11	14	17	21	75	14	18	21	25	29	33	104	21
22	7	10	12	15	18	22	78	14	19	21	26	30	35	108	22
23	7	10	12	15	19	23	81	14	19	22	27	31	36	112	23
24	7	10	12	16	19	24	84	15	20	23	27	32	38	116	24
25	7	11	13	16	20	25	87	15	20	23	28	33	38	120	25

TABLE A.8 Critical Values for W (Wilcoxon Rank-Sum Test) (*continued*)

	$N_1 = 5$							$N_1 = 6$							
N_2	0.001	0.005	0.010	0.025	0.05	0.10	$2\overline{W}$	0.001	0.005	0.010	0.025	0.05	0.10	$2\overline{W}$	N_2
5		15	16	17	19	20	55								
6		16	17	18	20	22	60	—	23	24	26	28	30	78	6
7	—	16	18	20	21	23	65	21	24	25	27	29	32	84	7
8	15	17	19	21	23	25	70	22	25	27	29	31	34	90	8
9	16	18	20	22	24	27	75	23	26	23	31	33	36	96	9
10	16	19	21	23	26	28	80	24	27	29	32	35	38	102	10
11	17	20	22	24	27	30	85	25	28	30	34	37	40	108	11
12	17	21	23	26	28	32	90	25	30	32	35	38	42	114	12
13	18	22	24	27	30	33	95	26	31	33	37	40	44	120	13
14	18	22	25	28	31	35	100	27	32	34	38	42	46	126	14
15	19	23	26	29	33	37	105	28	33	36	40	44	48	132	15
16	20	24	27	30	34	38	110	29	34	37	42	46	50	138	16
17	20	25	28	32	35	40	115	30	36	39	43	47	52	144	17
18	21	26	29	33	37	42	120	31	37	40	45	49	55	150	18
19	22	27	30	34	38	43	125	32	38	41	46	51	57	156	19
20	22	28	31	35	40	45	130	33	39	43	48	53	59	162	20
21	23	29	32	37	41	47	135	33	40	44	50	55	61	168	21
22	23	29	33	38	43	48	140	34	42	45	51	57	63	174	22
23	24	30	34	39	44	50	145	35	43	47	53	58	65	180	23
24	25	31	35	40	45	51	150	36	44	48	54	60	67	186	24
25	25	32	36	42	47	53	155	37	45	50	56	62	69	192	25

	$N_1 = 7$							$N_1 = 8$							
N_2	0.001	0.005	0.010	0.025	0.05	0.10	$2\overline{W}$	0.001	0.005	0.010	0.025	0.05	0.10	$2\overline{W}$	N_2
7	29	32	34	36	39	41	105								
8	30	34	35	38	41	44	112	40	43	45	49	51	55	136	8
9	31	35	37	40	43	46	119	41	45	47	51	54	58	144	9
10	33	37	39	42	45	49	126	42	47	49	53	56	60	152	10
11	34	38	40	44	47	51	133	44	49	51	55	59	63	160	11
12	35	40	42	46	49	54	140	45	51	53	58	62	66	168	12
13	36	41	44	48	52	56	147	47	53	56	60	64	69	176	13
14	37	43	45	50	54	59	154	48	54	58	62	67	72	184	14
15	38	44	47	52	56	61	161	50	56	60	65	69	75	192	15
16	39	46	49	54	58	64	168	51	58	62	67	72	78	200	16
17	41	47	51	56	61	66	175	53	60	64	70	75	81	208	17
18	42	49	32	58	63	69	182	54	62	66	72	77	84	216	18
19	43	50	54	60	65	71	189	56	64	68	74	80	87	224	19
20	44	52	56	62	67	74	196	57	66	70	77	83	90	232	20
21	46	53	58	64	69	76	203	59	68	72	79	33	92	240	21
22	47	55	59	66	72	79	210	60	70	74	81	88	95	248	22
23	48	57	61	68	74	81	217	62	71	76	84	90	98	256	23
24	49	58	63	70	76	84	224	64	73	78	86	93	101	264	24
25	50	60	64	72	78	86	231	65	75	81	89	96	104	272	25

	$N_1 = 9$							$N_1 = 10$							
N_2	0.001	0.005	0.010	0.025	0.05	0.10	$2\overline{W}$	0.001	0.005	0.010	0.025	0.05	0.10	$2\overline{W}$	N_2
9	52	56	59	62	66	70	171								
10	53	58	61	65	69	73	180	65	71	74	78	82	87	210	10
11	55	61	63	68	72	76	189	67	73	77	81	86	91	220	11
12	57	63	66	71	75	80	198	69	76	79	84	89	94	230	12

(continued)

TABLE A.8 Critical Values for W (Wilcoxon Rank-Sum Test) (*continued*)

	$N_1 = 9$							$N_1 = 10$							
N_2	0.001	0.005	0.010	0.025	0.05	0.10	$2\overline{W}$	0.001	0.005	0.010	0.025	0.05	0.10	$2\overline{W}$	N_2
13	59	65	68	73	78	83	207	72	79	82	88	92	98	240	13
14	60	67	71	76	81	86	216	74	81	85	91	96	102	250	14
15	62	69	73	79	84	90	225	76	84	88	94	99	106	260	15
16	64	72	76	82	87	93	234	78	86	91	97	103	109	270	16
17	66	74	78	84	90	97	243	80	89	93	100	106	113	280	17
18	68	76	81	87	93	100	252	82	92	96	103	110	117	290	18
19	70	78	83	90	96	103	261	84	94	99	107	113	121	300	19
20	71	81	85	93	99	107	270	87	97	102	110	117	125	310	20
21	73	83	88	95	102	110	279	89	99	105	113	120	128	320	21
22	75	85	90	98	105	113	288	91	102	108	116	123	132	330	22
23	77	88	93	101	108	117	297	93	105	110	119	127	136	340	23
24	79	90	95	104	111	120	306	95	107	113	122	130	140	350	24
25	81	92	98	107	114	123	315	98	110	116	126	134	144	360	25

	$N_1 = 11$							$N_1 = 12$							
N_2	0.001	0.005	0.010	0.025	0.05	0.10	$2\overline{W}$	0.001	0.005	0.010	0.025	0.05	0.10	$2\overline{W}$	N_2
11	81	87	91	96	100	106	253								
12	83	90	94	99	104	110	264	98	105	109	115	120	127	300	12
13	86	93	97	103	108	114	275	101	109	113	119	125	131	312	13
14	88	96	100	106	112	118	286	103	112	116	123	129	136	324	14
15	90	99	103	110	116	123	297	106	115	120	127	133	141	336	15
16	93	102	107	113	120	127	308	109	119	124	131	138	145	348	16
17	95	105	110	117	123	131	319	112	122	127	135	142	150	360	17
18	98	108	113	121	127	135	330	115	125	131	139	146	155	372	18
19	100	111	116	124	131	139	341	118	129	134	143	150	159	384	19
20	103	114	119	128	135	144	352	120	132	138	147	155	164	396	20
21	106	117	123	131	139	148	363	123	136	142	151	159	169	408	21
22	108	120	126	135	143	152	374	126	139	145	155	163	173	420	22
23	111	123	129	139	147	156	385	129	142	149	159	168	178	432	23
24	113	126	132	142	151	161	396	132	146	153	163	172	183	444	24
25	116	129	136	146	155	165	407	135	149	156	167	176	187	456	25

	$N_1 = 13$							$N_1 = 14$							
N_2	0.001	0.005	0.010	0.025	0.05	0.10	$2\overline{W}$	0.001	0.005	0.010	0.025	0.05	0.10	$2\overline{W}$	N_2
13	117	125	130	136	142	149	351								
14	120	129	134	141	147	154	364	137	147	152	160	166	174	406	14
15	123	133	138	145	152	159	377	141	151	156	164	171	179	420	15
16	126	136	142	150	156	165	390	144	155	161	169	176	185	434	16
17	129	140	146	154	161	170	403	148	159	165	174	182	190	448	17
18	133	144	150	158	166	175	416	151	163	170	179	187	196	462	18
19	136	148	154	163	171	180	429	155	168	174	183	192	202	476	19
20	139	151	158	167	175	185	442	159	172	178	188	197	207	490	20
21	142	155	162	171	180	190	455	162	176	183	193	202	213	504	21
22	145	159	166	176	185	195	468	166	180	187	198	207	218	518	22
23	149	163	170	180	189	200	481	169	184	192	203	212	224	532	23
24	152	166	174	185	194	205	494	173	188	196	207	218	229	546	24
25	155	170	178	189	199	211	507	177	192	200	212	223	235	560	25

	$N_1 = 15$							$N_1 = 16$							
N_2	0.001	0.005	0.010	0.025	0.05	0.10	$2\overline{W}$	0.001	0.005	0.010	0.025	0.05	0.10	$2\overline{W}$	N_2
15	160	171	176	184	192	200	465								
16	163	175	181	190	197	206	480	184	196	202	211	219	229	528	16

TABLE A.8 Critical Values for W (Wilcoxon Rank-Sum Test) (*continued*)

$N_1 = 15$

N_2	0.001	0.005	0.010	0.025	0.05	0.10	$2\overline{W}$
17	167	180	186	195	203	212	495
18	171	184	190	200	208	218	510
19	175	189	195	205	214	224	525
20	179	193	200	210	220	230	540
21	183	198	205	216	225	236	555
22	187	202	210	221	231	242	370
23	191	207	214	226	236	248	585
24	195	211	219	231	242	254	600
25	199	216	224	237	248	260	615

$N_1 = 16$

0.001	0.005	0.010	0.025	0.05	0.10	$2\overline{W}$	N_2
188	201	207	217	225	235	544	17
192	206	212	222	231	242	560	18
196	210	213	228	237	248	576	19
201	215	223	234	243	255	592	20
205	220	228	239	249	261	608	21
209	225	233	245	255	267	624	22
214	230	238	251	261	274	640	23
218	235	244	256	267	280	656	24
222	240	249	262	273	287	672	25

$N_1 = 17$

N_2	0.001	0.005	0.010	0.025	0.05	0.10	$2\overline{W}$
17	210	223	230	240	249	259	595
18	214	228	235	246	255	266	612
19	219	234	241	252	262	273	629
20	223	239	246	258	268	280	646
21	228	244	252	264	274	287	663
22	233	249	258	270	281	294	680
23	238	255	263	276	287	300	697
24	242	260	269	282	294	307	714
25	247	265	275	288	300	314	731

$N_1 = 18$

0.001	0.005	0.010	0.025	0.05	0.10	$2\overline{W}$	N_2
237	252	259	270	280	291	666	18
242	258	265	277	287	299	684	19
247	263	271	283	294	306	702	20
252	269	277	290	301	313	720	21
257	275	283	296	307	321	738	22
262	280	289	303	314	328	756	23
267	286	295	309	321	335	774	24
273	292	301	316	323	343	792	25

$N_1 = 19$

N_2	0.001	0.005	0.010	0.025	0.05	0.10	$2\overline{W}$
19	267	283	291	303	313	325	741
20	272	239	297	309	320	333	760
21	277	295	303	316	328	341	779
22	283	301	310	323	335	349	798
23	288	307	316	330	342	357	817
24	294	313	323	337	350	364	836
25	299	319	329	344	357	372	855

$N_1 = 20$

0.001	0.005	0.010	0.025	0.05	0.10	$2\overline{W}$	N_2
298	315	324	337	348	361	820	20
304	322	331	344	356	370	840	21
309	328	337	351	364	378	860	22
315	335	344	359	371	386	880	23
321	341	351	366	379	394	900	24
327	348	358	373	387	403	920	25

$N_1 = 21$

N_2	0.001	0.005	0.010	0.025	0.05	0.10	$2\overline{W}$
21	331	349	359	373	385	399	903
22	337	356	366	381	393	408	924
23	343	363	373	388	401	417	945
24	349	370	381	396	410	425	966
25	356	377	388	404	418	434	987

$N_1 = 22$

0.001	0.005	0.010	0.025	0.05	0.10	$2\overline{W}$	N_2
365	386	396	411	424	439	990	22
372	393	403	419	432	448	1012	23
379	400	411	427	441	457	1034	24
385	408	419	435	450	467	1056	25

$N_1 = 23$

N_2	0.001	0.005	0.010	0.025	0.05	0.10	$2\overline{W}$
23	402	424	434	451	465	481	1081
24	409	431	443	459	474	491	1104
25	416	439	451	468	483	500	1127

$N_1 = 24$

0.001	0.005	0.010	0.025	0.05	0.10	$2\overline{W}$	N_2
440	464	475	492	507	525	1176	24
448	472	484	501	517	535	1200	25

$N_1 = 25$

N_2	0.001	0.005	0.010	0.025	0.05	0.10	$2\overline{W}$
25	480	505	517	536	552	570	1275

Source: Table 1 in L. R. Verdooren. Extended tables of critical values for Wilcoxon's test statistic *Biometrika*, 1963, Volume 50, pp. 177–186. Reprinted by permission of Oxford University Press.

TABLE A.9 Critical Values for the Wilcoxon Matched-Pairs Signed-Ranks *T* Test*

	α Levels for a One-Tailed Test					α Levels for a One-Tailed Test			
	.05	.025	.01	.005		.05	.025	.01	.005
No. of Pairs	α Levels for a Two-Tailed Test				No. of Pairs	α Levels for a Two-Tailed Test			
N	.10	.05	.02	.01	*N*	.10	.05	.02	.01
5	0	—	—	—	28	130	116	101	91
6	2	0	—	—	29	140	126	110	100
7	3	2	0	—	30	151	137	120	109
8	5	3	1	0	31	163	147	130	118
9	8	5	3	1	32	175	159	140	128
10	10	8	5	3	33	187	170	151	138
11	13	10	7	5	34	200	182	162	148
12	17	13	9	7	35	213	195	173	159
13	21	17	12	9	36	227	208	185	171
14	25	21	15	12	37	241	221	198	182
15	30	25	19	15	38	256	235	211	194
16	35	29	23	19	39	271	249	224	207
17	41	34	27	23	40	286	264	238	220
18	47	40	32	27	41	302	279	252	233
19	53	46	37	32	42	319	294	266	247
20	60	52	43	37	43	336	310	281	261
21	67	58	49	42	44	353	327	296	276
22	75	65	55	48	45	371	343	312	291
23	83	73	62	54	46	389	361	328	307
24	91	81	69	61	47	407	378	345	322
25	100	89	76	68	48	426	396	362	339
26	110	98	84	75	49	446	415	379	355
27	119	107	92	83	50	466	434	397	373

*To be significant, the *T* obtained from the data must be equal to or less than the value shown in the table.

SOURCE: Kirk, R. E. (1984). *Elementary Statistics* (2nd ed.). Pacific Grove, CA: Brooks/Cole Publishing.

APPENDIX B Computational Formulas for ANOVAs

ALTERNATIVE TABLE 11.5 ANOVA Summary Table Using Computational Formulas

SOURCE	*df*	*SS*	*MS*	*F*
Between groups	$k - 1$	$\Sigma\left[\frac{\left(\Sigma X_g\right)^2}{n_g}\right] - \frac{\left(\Sigma X\right)^2}{N}$	$\frac{SS_b}{df_b}$	$\frac{MS_b}{MS_w}$
Within groups	$N - k$	$\Sigma\left[\Sigma X_g^2 - \frac{\left(\Sigma X_g\right)^2}{n_g}\right]$	$\frac{SS_w}{df_w}$	
Total	$N - 1$	$\Sigma X^2 - \frac{\left(\Sigma X\right)^2}{N}$		

ALTERNATIVE TABLE 11.13 Repeated Measures ANOVA Summary Table Using Computational Formulas

SOURCE	*df*	*SS*	*MS*	*F*
Subject	$n - 1$	$\Sigma\left[\frac{(\Sigma X_S)^2}{k}\right] - \frac{(\Sigma X)^2}{N}$	$\frac{SS_S}{df_S}$	
Between	$k - 1$	$\Sigma\left[\frac{(\Sigma X_t)^2}{n_t}\right] - \frac{(\Sigma X)^2}{N}$	$\frac{SS_b}{df_b}$	$\frac{MS_b}{MS_e}$
Error	$(k - 1)(n - 1)$	$\Sigma X^2 - \Sigma\left[\frac{(\Sigma X_S)^2}{k}\right] - \Sigma\left[\frac{(\Sigma X_t)^2}{n_t}\right] + \frac{(\Sigma X)^2}{N}$	$\frac{SS_e}{df_e}$	
Total	$N - 1$	$\Sigma X^2 - \frac{(\Sigma X)^2}{N}$		

ALTERNATIVE TABLE 12.8 Two-Way Randomized ANOVA Summary Table Using Computational Formulas

SOURCE	*df*	*SS*	*MS*	*F*
Factor A	$A - 1$	$\Sigma\left[\frac{(\Sigma X_A)^2}{n_A}\right] - \frac{(\Sigma X)^2}{N}$	$\frac{SS_A}{df_A}$	$\frac{MS_A}{MS_{Error}}$
Factor B	$B - 1$	$\Sigma\left[\frac{(\Sigma X_B)^2}{n_B}\right] - \frac{(\Sigma X)^2}{N}$	$\frac{SS_B}{df_B}$	$\frac{MS_B}{MS_{Error}}$
A × B	$(A - 1)(B - 1)$	$\Sigma\left[\frac{(\Sigma X_C)^2}{n_C}\right] - \frac{(\Sigma X)^2}{N} - SS_A - SS_B$	$\frac{SS_{A\times B}}{df_{A\times B}}$	$\frac{MS_{A\times B}}{MS_{Error}}$
Error	$AB(n - 1)$	$\Sigma X^2 - \Sigma\left[\frac{(\Sigma X_C)^2}{n_C}\right]$	$\frac{SS_{Error}}{df_{Error}}$	
Total	$N - 1$	$\Sigma X^2 - \frac{(\Sigma X)^2}{N}$		

APPENDIX C

Answers to Odd-Numbered Chapter Exercises and All Review Exercises

Chapter 1

1. Answers will vary. Here are some examples.

   Superstition and Intuition
   Breaking a mirror leads to 7 years of bad luck.
   A black cat crossing your path signifies bad luck.
   I have a feeling that something bad is going to happen on my trip next week.

   Authority
   You read in the newspaper that more Americans are overweight now than 10 years ago.
   You recently saw a TV commercial for a new diet product that was endorsed by a very slim soap opera star.

   Tenacity
   You have heard the Slim-Fast slogan so many times that you believe it must be true.

   Rationalism
   SUVs use more gas and spew more emissions than many other vehicles. Because emissions contribute significantly to air pollution, those who drive SUVs must be less concerned about polluting the environment.

   Empiricism
   I have observed that using note cards can be an effective means of studying for an exam.
   I have observed that using note cards can be an ineffective means of studying for an exam.

   Science
   Studies have shown that smoking has been linked to lung disease.
   Studies have shown that elaborative rehearsal leads to better retention than rote rehearsal.

3. Many scientists view being called a skeptic as a compliment because it means that they do not blindly accept findings and information. Skeptics need data to support an idea, and they insist on proper testing procedures when the data are collected. Being a skeptic also means applying three criteria that help define science: systematic empiricism, public verification, and solvable problems.
5. Research methods are equally important to all areas of psychology because all that we know about a discipline is gained through research. For those planning to pursue careers in clinical/counseling psychology, knowledge of research methods is important to determine whether a particular counseling method or drug is an effective treatment.
7. a. The independent variable is the amount of caffeine.
   b. The dependent variable is the anxiety level.
   c. The control group receives no caffeine, whereas the experimental group receives caffeine.
   d. The independent variable is manipulated.

Answers to Chapter 1 Review Exercises

Fill-in Self-Test Answers

1. intuition
2. tenacity
3. hypothesis
4. skeptic
5. Empirically solvable problems
6. Pseudoscience
7. description, prediction, explanation
8. Applied
9. case study
10. population
11. correlational
12. subject (participant)
13. independent
14. control

Multiple-Choice Self-Test Answers

1. d
2. a
3. b
4. d
5. a
6. c
7. b
8. b
9. c
10. b
11. d
12. d

Chapter 2

1. There is no correct answer to this question. It requires library work.
3. When participants in a study are classified as "at risk," this means that there is the potential for them to be under some emotional or physical risk. Participants "at minimal risk" are at no more risk than would be encountered in daily life or during the performance of routine physical or psychological examinations or tests.
5. Researchers must consider how informed consent works with children. It should be obtained from the legal guardian for all participants under 18 years of age. However, if the child is old enough to understand language, the researcher should also try to inform the child about the study. The researcher also needs to be particularly sensitive to whether or not the child feels comfortable exercising the rights provided through informed consent.

Answers to Chapter 2 Review Exercises

Fill-in Self-Test Answers

1. PsycINFO
2. Social Science Citation Index (SSCI)
3. informed consent
4. deception
5. institutional review board (IRB)

Multiple-Choice Self-Test Answers

1. c
2. a
3. a
4. c

Chapter 3

1. Alternative c is the best operational definition of depression.
3. c. +.83. Although this is not the strongest correlation coefficient, it is the strongest positive correlation. It therefore is the best measure of reliability.
5. If the observers disagreed 32 times out of 75, then they agreed 43 times out of 75. Thus, the interrater reliability is $43/75 = .57$. Because the interrater reliability is moderate, the librarians should use these data with caution. In other words, there may be a problem with either the measuring instrument or the individuals using the instrument, and therefore the data are not terribly reliable.

Answers to Chapter 3 Review Exercises

Fill-in Self-Test Answers

1. operational definition
2. Magnitude
3. nominal
4. interval
5. self-report measures

6. Reactivity
7. test-retest reliability
8. Interrater reliability
9. Content validity
10. construct validity

Multiple-Choice Self-Test Answers

1. d
2. b
3. a
4. b
5. a
6. b
7. a
8. d
9. c
10. b
11. d
12. b

Chapter 4

1. This research might best be conducted using some form of naturalistic observation. It would probably be best to use a disguised type of observation, either nonparticipant or participant. Thus, the researcher could have data collectors stationed at all of the locations of interest. These individuals either could be hidden or could appear to be part of the natural environment. In either situation, drivers would not notice that data were being collected. If the data recorders were hidden, they could use a checklist. However, if the data recorders were disguised participants, then a narrative record might be best so that drivers would not notice they were being observed. Thus, the person collecting data could either use a hidden tape recorder or communicate with another individual by cell phone. The concerns would be those already indicated.
3. Narrative records are full narrative descriptions of a participant's behavior. They tend to be slightly more subjective in nature and require that the data be coded into a quantitative form after they have been collected. Checklists, on the other hand, are more objective. They require more work before the data are collected in order to develop the checklist. However, once the checklist is developed, they tend to be easier to use and quantify than a narrative record.
5. The archival method is a descriptive method that involves describing data that existed before the time of the study. There are many sources for archival data such as the U.S. Census Bureau, the National Opinion Research Center, the Educational Testing Service, and local, state, and federal public records.
7. Action research involves people in the "real world" conducting their own research to answer their own questions. This means that, for example, individuals who own and run a particular company may want to know something about their clientele and in order to answer this question, they conduct their own research. Thus, the research has immediate application.
9. a. This is a loaded question because of the phrases *capitalist bankers* and *such high interest rates.* A better question would be "Do you believe bankers charge appropriate interest rates on credit card balances?"
   b. The problem with this question is in the alternatives. Students who charged an amount between the alternatives (say, $450) would not know which alternative to choose.
   c. This is a leading question. The phrase *Most Americans believe* leads the respondent to agree with the question. A better question would be "Do you believe that a credit card is a necessity?"

Answers to Chapter 4 Review Exercises

Fill-in Self-Test Answers

1. nonparticipant
2. ecological validity
3. disguised
4. Narrative records
5. static
6. Sampling bias
7. socially desirable response
8. random selection
9. Stratified random sampling
10. closed-ended questions
11. rating scale
12. leading question

Multiple-Choice Self-Test Answers

1. c
2. a
3. a

4. c
5. b
6. a
7. b
8. d
9. c
10. a
11. b
12. a

Chapter 5

1.

Speed	*f*	*rf*
62	1	.05
64	3	.15
65	4	.20
67	3	.15
68	2	.10
70	2	.10
72	1	.05
73	1	.05
76	1	.05
79	1	.05
80	1	.05
	20	1.00

3. Either a histogram or a frequency polygon could be used to graph these data. Because of the continuous nature of the speed data, a frequency polygon might be more appropriate. Both a histogram and a frequency polygon of the data are shown here.

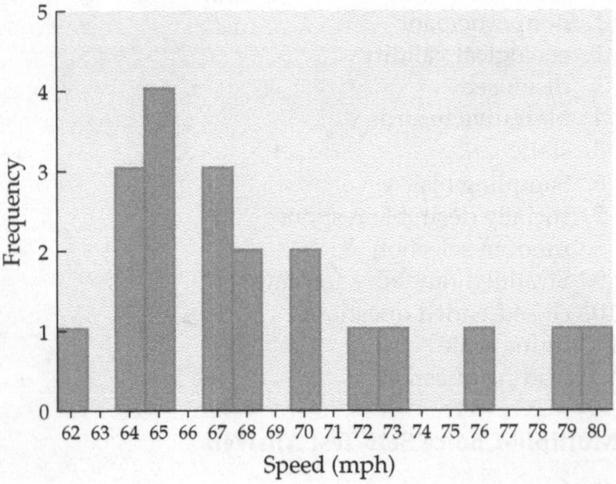

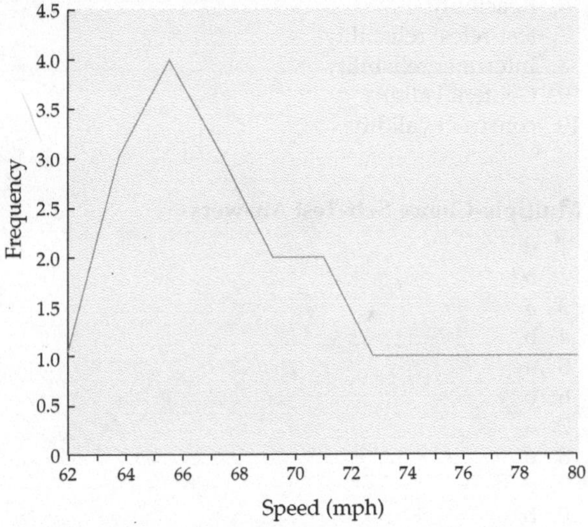

5. a. $\overline{X} = 7.3$
   Median = 8.5
   Mode = 11
   b. $\overline{X} = 4.83$
   Median = 5
   Mode = 5
   c. $\overline{X} = 6.17$
   Median = 6.5
   Mode = 3, 8
   d. $\overline{X} = 5.5$
   Median = 6
   Mode = 6
7. a. $z = +2.57$; proportion of cars that cost an equal amount or more = .0051
   b. $z = -2.0$; proportion of cars that cost an equal amount or more = .9773
   c. $z = +2.0$; percentile rank = 97.73
   d. $z = -3.14$; percentile rank = 0.08
   e. $z = -3.14$, $z = +2.0$; proportion between $= .4992 + .4772 = .9764$
   f. 16th percentile converts to a *z*-score of -0.99; $-0.99(3{,}500) + 23{,}000 = \$19{,}535$
9.

	X	*z-Score*	*Percentile Rank*
Ken	73.00	0.11	54.38
Drew	85.95	+1.55	93.94
Cecil	80.28	+0.92	82.00

Answers to Chapter 5 Review Exercises

Fill-in Self-Test Answers

1. frequency distribution
2. qualitative
3. histogram
4. central tendency
5. median
6. variation
7. average deviation
8. unbiased estimator
9. population; sample
10. positively
11. *z*-score
12. standard normal distribution

Multiple-Choice Self-Test Answers

1. c
2. d
3. d
4. c
5. b
6. b
7. c
8. a
9. a
10. a
11. b
12. b
13. b
14. a
15. c

Answers to Self-Test Problems

1. $\overline{X} = 6.25$, Md = 6.5, Mo = 11
2. range = 6, A.D. = 2, $\sigma = 2.26$
3. a. $z = -1.67$, proportion = .9526
   b. $z = +.80$, percentile rank = 78.81
   c. $87,400

Chapter 6

1. The first problem is with the correlation coefficient that was calculated. Correlation coefficients can vary between –1.0 and +1.0; they cannot be greater than ±1.0. Thus, the calculated correlation coefficient is incorrect. Second, correlation does not mean causation. Thus, observing a correlation between exercise and health does not mean we can conclude that exercise causes better health—they are simply related.
3. We would expect the correlation between GRE scores and graduate school GPAs to be much lower than that between SAT scores and undergraduate GPAs because both GRE scores and graduate school GPAs are restricted in range.
5. IQ with psychology exam scores: $r = .553, r^2 = 30.6\%$
   IQ with statistics exam scores: $r = .682, r^2 = 46.5\%$
   Psychology exam scores with statistics exam scores: $r = .626, r^2 = 39.2\%$
   All of the correlation coefficients are of moderate strength, with the correlation between IQ scores and statistics exam scores being the strongest and accounting for the most variability.

Answers to Chapter 6 Review Exercises

Fill-in Self-Test Answers

1. scatterplot
2. negative
3. causality; directionality
4. restricted range
5. Pearson product-moment
6. point-biserial
7. coefficient of determination
8. Regression analysis

Multiple-Choice Self-Test Answers

1. c
2. b
3. c
4. c
5. d
6. b
7. d
8. a
9. a
10. c
11. b
12. a

Chapter 7

1. a. $20/70 = .29$
   b. $50/70 = .71$
   c. $(20+50)/70 = 1.0$
   d. $(20/70) \times (50/70) = .21$
3. $(4/52)+(4/52) = .15$
5. $z = -0.80$, probability $= .21186$
7. $z = 0.40$, $z = -0.80$, probability $= .34458 \times .21186 = .073$
9. The counselors made a Type I error. They concluded that there was a difference between the freshmen class and the other classes when in reality there was no difference.
11. a. H_0: $\mu_{\text{Left-handed}} = \mu_{\text{Right-handed}}$
    H_a: $\mu_{\text{Left-handed}} \neq \mu_{\text{Right-handed}}$
    This is a two-tailed test.
    b. H_0: $\mu_{\text{8-hour}} \leq \mu_{\text{12-hour}}$
    H_a: $\mu_{\text{8-hour}} > \mu_{\text{12-hour}}$
    This is a one-tailed test.
    c. H_0: $\mu_{\text{Crate-training}} \leq \mu_{\text{No crate-training}}$
    H_a: $\mu_{\text{Crate-training}} > \mu_{\text{No crate-training}}$
    This is a one-tailed test.
13. Inferential statistics allow us to draw inferences about a population based on sample data. They do not simply describe a data set as do descriptive statistics. Inferential statistics allow us to test hypotheses and draw conclusions about those hypotheses based on sample data.

Answers to Chapter 7 Review Exercises

Fill-in Self-Test Answers

1. Probability
2. multiplication
3. addition
4. null hypothesis
5. directional or one-tailed hypothesis
6. Type I
7. statistical significance
8. Nonparametric

Multiple-Choice Self-Test Answers

1. c
2. a
3. d
4. a
5. d
6. a
7. d
8. b
9. b
10. c
11. c
12. a
13. d
14. b
15. d

Chapter 8

1. a. This is a one-tailed test.
   b. H_0: $\mu_{\text{private HS}} \leq \mu_{\text{HS in general}}$
   Ha: $\mu_{\text{private HS}} > \mu_{\text{HS in general}}$
   c. $z_{obt} = 2.37$
   d. $z_{cv} = \pm 1.645$ (one-tailed critical value)
   e. Reject H_0. High school students at private high schools score significantly higher on the SAT.
   f. The 95% CI is 1008.68−1091.32.
3. The t distributions are a family of symmetrical distributions that differ for each sample size. Therefore, t_{cv} changes for samples of different sizes. We must compute the degrees of freedom in order to determine t_{cv}.
5. a. This is a one-tailed test.
   b. H_0: $\mu_{\text{headphones}} \geq \mu_{\text{no headphones}}$
   Ha: $\mu_{\text{headphones}} < \mu_{\text{no headphones}}$
   c. $t_{obt} = -3.37$
   d. $t_{cv} = -1.796$
   e. Reject H_0. Those who listen to music via headphones score significantly lower on a hearing test.
   f. The 95% CI is 16.43–21.23.

Answers to Chapter 8 Review Exercises

Fill-in Self-Test Answers

1. sampling distribution
2. standard error of the mean
3. Student's t distribution
4. t test

Multiple-Choice Self-Test Answers

1. b
2. a
3. a
4. d

Answers to Self-Test Problems

1. a. one-tailed
   b. H_0: $\mu_{Chess} \le \mu_{General\ Population}$;
      H_a: $\mu_{Chess} > \mu_{General\ Population}$
   c. $z_{obt} = +3.03$
   d. $z_{cv} = \pm 1.645$
   e. Reject H_0. Students who play chess score significantly higher on the SAT.
   f. The 95% CI is 1024.74–1115.26.
2. a. one-tailed
   b. H_0: $\mu_{Classical\ Music} \le \mu_{General\ Population}$;
      H_a: $\mu_{Classical\ Music} > \mu_{General\ Population}$
   c. $t_{obt} = +3.05$
   d. $t_{cv} = \pm 1.796$
   e. Reject H_0. Those who listen to classical music score significantly higher on the concentration test.
   f. The 95% CI is 16.43–21.23.

Chapter 9

1. First, there was no control group of any sort in the study. Only one group was examined. Second, there was a fairly high attrition (mortality) rate. It is possible that those who dropped out of the program were not being helped by the treatment. Thus, had they remained, the improvement rate would not have been so high. There could also be history or maturation effects operating.
3. Internal validity has to do with the internal workings of a study, in other words, whether or not the study is well designed. A study with internal validity has no confounds. External validity has to do with the generalizability of a study. For example, was a random sample used so that the results can be generalized to the population?
5. a. An independent samples t-test should be used.
   b. H_0: $\mu_{Music} \ge \mu_{No\ music}$
      H_a: $\mu_{Music} < \mu_{No\ music}$
   c. $t(16) = -2.60, p < .01$.
   d. Reject H_0. Studying with no music leads to significantly higher test scores.
   e. d = 1.22—there is a large effect size.
   f.

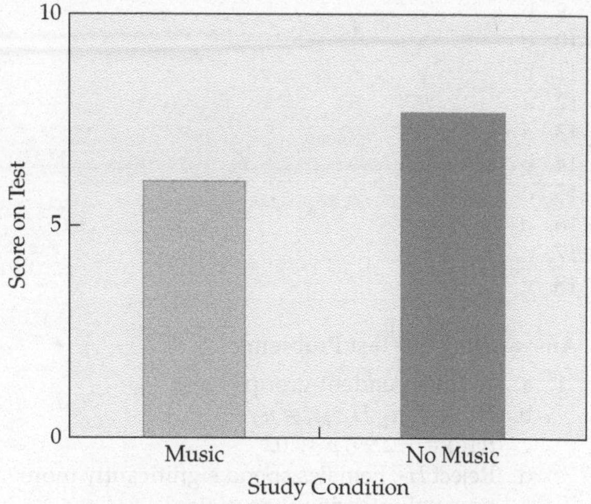

   g. The 95% confidence interval is ⁻2.83 – ⁻29.

Answers to Chapter 9 Review Exercises

Fill-in Self-Test Answers

1. between-subjects design
2. random assignment
3. pretest/posttest control group design
4. Internal validity
5. maturation effect
6. instrumentation
7. diffusion of treatment
8. double-blind
9. ceiling
10. external validity
11. conceptual
12. independent-groups *t* test
13. Cohen's *d*

Multiple-Choice Self-Test Answers

1. a
2. b
3. c
4. c
5. b
6. c

7. d
8. d
9. b
10. d
11. b
12. a
13. a
14. b
15. c
16. d
17. c
18. a

Answers to Self-Test Problems

1. a. An independent-groups t test.
   b. $H_0{:}\mu_1 = \mu_2,\ H_a{:}\ \mu_1 \neq \mu_2$
   c. $t(10) = -2.99, p < .02$
   d. Reject H_0. Females spend significantly more time volunteering than males.
   e. $d = 1.72$ or $r^2 = .47$. This is a large effect size.
   f.

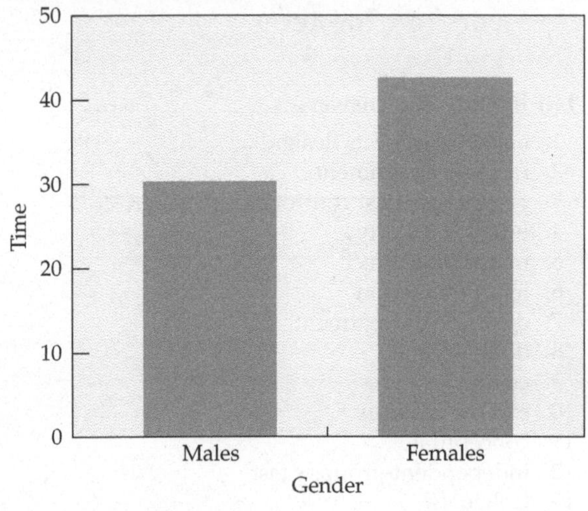

   g. The 95% CI is -21.51-3.15.

Chapter 10

1. This is a between-subjects design. If subjects are randomly assigned to one of the two conditions, then different subjects are used in each condition.
3. Within-subjects and matched-subjects designs are types of correlated-groups designs. This means that either the same individuals are used in all conditions (within-subjects) or that different subjects are used in each condition but that they are matched on one or more characteristics (matched-subjects). The phrase correlated-groups designs refers to the fact that there is a relationship of some sort between the subjects in each condition. In other words, the same people are used in each condition or the individuals were matched and are related on some characteristic.
5. a. A correlated groups t test should be used.
   b. $H_0{:}\mu_{\text{Music}} \geq \mu_{\text{No music}}$
   $H_a{:}\mu_{\text{Music}} < \mu_{\text{No music}}$
   c. $t(5) = 2.74, p < .025.$
   d. Reject H_0. Participants had significantly higher scores on the test when they studied without music.
   e. $d = 1.12$. This is a large effect size.
   f.

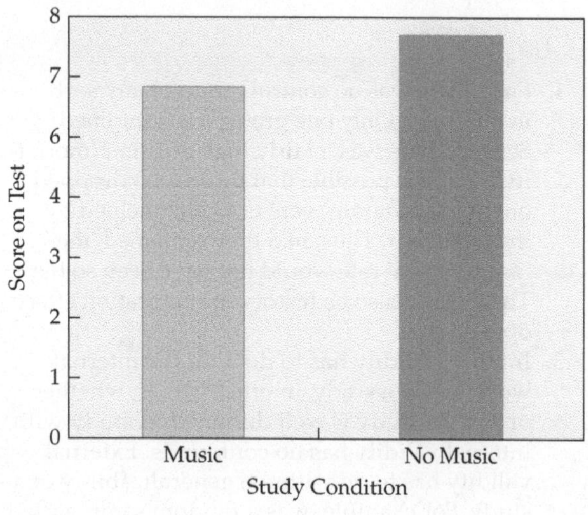

   g. The 95% confidence interval is $^-1.926 - ^-.074$

Answers to Chapter 10 Review Questions

Fill-in Self-Test Answers

1. order effects
2. counterbalancing
3. Latin square
4. correlated-groups t test
5. difference
6. standard error of the difference score

Multiple-Choice Self-Test Answers

1. b
2. a & c
3. d
4. c
5. a
6. a
7. a
8. b
9. d
10. c
11. a

Answers to Self-Test Problems

1. a. A correlated-groups *t* test.
   b. H_0: $\mu_1 = \mu_2$, or H_0: $\mu_1 - \mu_2 = 0$
   H_a: $\mu_1 \neq \mu_2$, or H_a: $\mu_1 - \mu_2 > 0$
   c. $t(5) = 2.78, p < .05$.
   d. Reject H_0. When participants studied with music, they scored significantly lower on the quiz.
   e. $d = 1.12$—this is a large effect size.
   f.

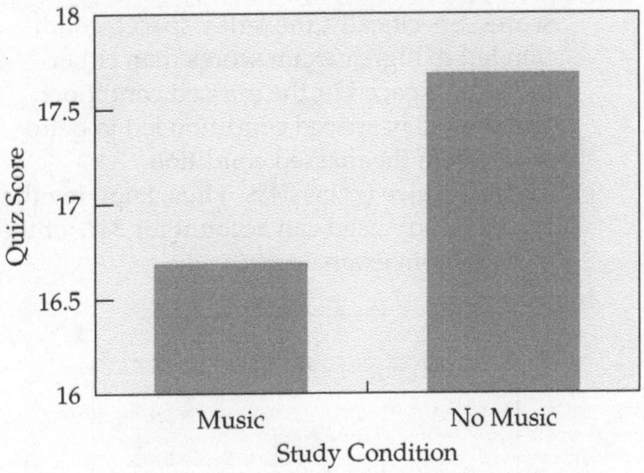

   g. The 95% CI is −1.93 −.07.

Chapter 11

1. Conducting a study with three or more levels of the independent variable allows a researcher to compare more than two kinds of treatment in one study, to compare two or more kinds of treatment with a control group, and to compare a placebo group with both the control and experimental groups.
3. Between-groups variance is the variance attributable to both systematic variance and error variance. Systematic variance may be due either to the effects of the independent variable or to confounds. Error variance may be due to chance, sampling error, or individual differences. Within-groups variance is always due to error variance (once again due to chance, sampling error, or individual differences).
5. If H_0 is true, then there is no effect of the independent variable and thus no systematic variance. The *F*-ratio is error variance divided by error variance and should be equal or close to 1. If H_a is supported, then there is systematic variance in addition to error variance in the numerator, and therefore the *F*-ratio will be greater than 1.
7. Eta-squared tells us how much of the variability in the dependent variable can be attributed to the independent variable.
9. a.

Source	*df*	*SS*	*MS*	*F*
Between groups	3	187.75	62.58	18.14
Within groups	16	55.20	3.45	
Total	19	242.95		

   b. Yes, $F(3, 16) = 18.14, p < .01$.
   c. $HSD_{.05} = 3.36$
   $HSD_{.01} = 4.31$
   d. The amount of sleep had a significant effect on creativity. Specifically, those who slept for 6 or 8 hours scored significantly higher on creativity than those who slept for either 2 or 4 hours.
   e. The effect size (η^2) is 77%. Thus, knowing the sleep condition to which participants were assigned can explain 77% of the variability in creativity scores.
   f.

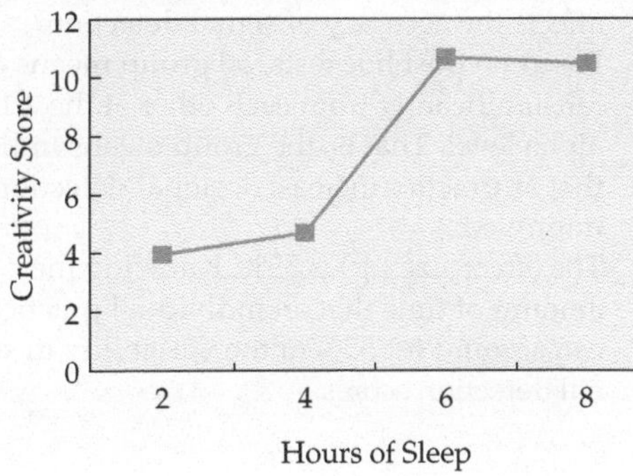

11. a.

Source	*df*	*SS*	*MS*	*F*
Between groups	2	4,689.27	2,344.64	0.77
Within groups	27	82,604.20	3,059.41	
Total	29	87,293.47		

b. No, $F(2, 27) = 0.77$, not significant.
c. Not necessary
d. The level of exercise did not affect stress level. There was, however, a very large amount of error variance.
e. The effect size (η^2) is 5%. Knowing the exercise condition to which a participant was assigned does not account for much of the variability in stress scores.
f.

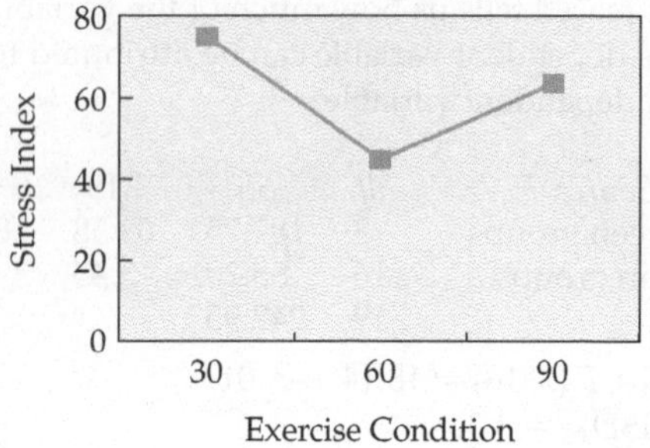

13. a.

Source	*df*	*SS*	*MS*	*F*
Participant	6	16.27	2.71	
Between	2	25.81	12.91	31.49
Error	12	4.87	0.41	
Total	20	46.95		

b. Yes, $F(2, 12) = 31.49, p < .01$.
c. $HSD_{.05} = 0.905$
$HSD_{.01} = 1.21$
d. The amount of time practiced significantly affects the accuracy of signal detection. Based on post hoc tests, all group means differ significantly from each other at the .01 alpha level. That is, the group means indicate that as practice increased, signal detection improved.
e. The effect size (η^2) is 55%. Knowing the amount of time that an individual practiced can account for 55% of the variability in signal detection scores.
f.

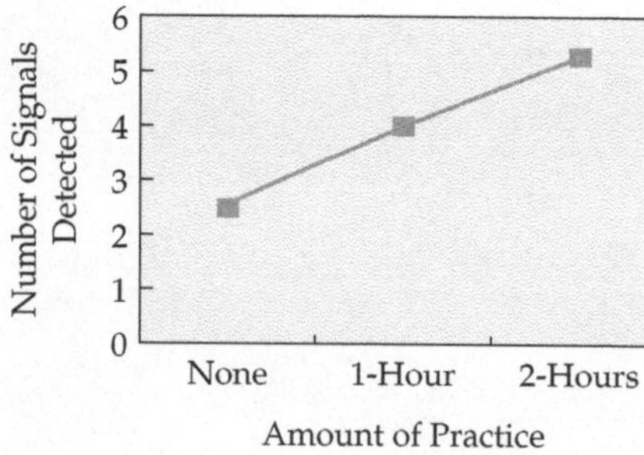

15.
a.

Source	*df*	*SS*	*MS*	*F*
Participant	14	136.96	9.78	
Between	2	3,350.96	1,675.48	94.02
Error	28	499.03	17.82	
Total	44	3,986.95		

b. Yes, $F(2, 28) = 94.02, p < .01$.
c. $HSD_{.05} = 3.85$
$HSD_{.01} = 4.96$
d. The type of study significantly affected exam scores. Specifically, the 6-day spaced condition led to higher exam scores than either the 3-day spaced or the massed condition; and the 3-day spaced condition led to better scores than the massed condition.
e. The effect size (η^2) is 84%. Thus, knowing the type of study used can account for 84% of the variability in exam scores.
f.

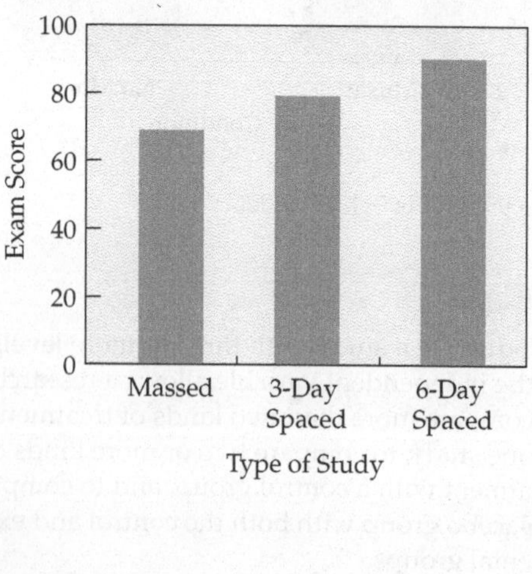

Answers to Chapter 11 Review Questions

Fill-in Self-Test Answers

1. Bonferroni adjustment
2. placebo
3. ANOVA
4. grand mean
5. between-groups
6. total sum of squares
7. mean square
8. Eta-squared
9. post hoc tests or Tukey's HSD
10. one-way repeated measures ANOVA

Multiple-Choice Self-Test Answers

1. b
2. d
3. b
4. b
5. a
6. c
7. a
8. d
9. c
10. a
11. a

Answers to Self-Test Problems

1. a.

Source	*df*	*SS*	*MS*	*F*
Participant	9	25		
Between	2	150		
Error	18	100		
Total	29			

$HSD_{.05} = 2.70$; $HSD_{.01} = 3.52$; eta squared = 55%.

2. a.

Source	*df*	*SS*	*MS*	*F*
Participant	5	9.12	1.82	
Between	2	10.19	5.10	3.67
Error	10	13.90	1.39	
Total	17	33.21		

Note: If calculated by hand, your SS scores may vary slightly due to rounding.

b. No, $F(2, 10) = 3.67$, not significant.

c. Post hoc tests are not necessary, but here are the answers if you want to practice: $HSD_{.05} = 1.86$; $HSD_{.01} = 2.53$.

d. Type of pain killer did not significantly affect effectiveness rating.

e. The effect size (η^2) is 31%. Thus, knowing the type of painkiller taken can account for only 31% of the variability in effectiveness scores.

f.

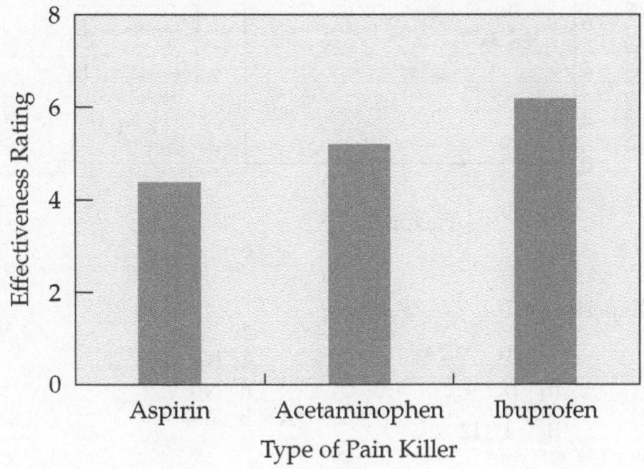

Chapter 12

1. One advantage is that manipulating more than one independent variable allows us to assess how the variables interact, which is called an interaction effect. In addition, because in the real world, behavior is usually contingent on more than one variable, designing experiments with more than one variable allows researchers to simulate a real-world setting more effectively.
3. This is a $3 \times 2 \times 2$ design (or a $2 \times 2 \times 3$). The independent variable Number of Hours has three levels, the independent variable Shallow/Deep Processing has two levels, and the independent variable Group/Individual study has two levels.
5. A 2×6 factorial design has two independent variables. Therefore, there is the possibility for two main effects—one for each variable—and one interaction between them.

7.

Experiment 1

	A_1	A_2
B_1	3	5
B_2	5	8

A: Yes
B: Yes
A × B: No

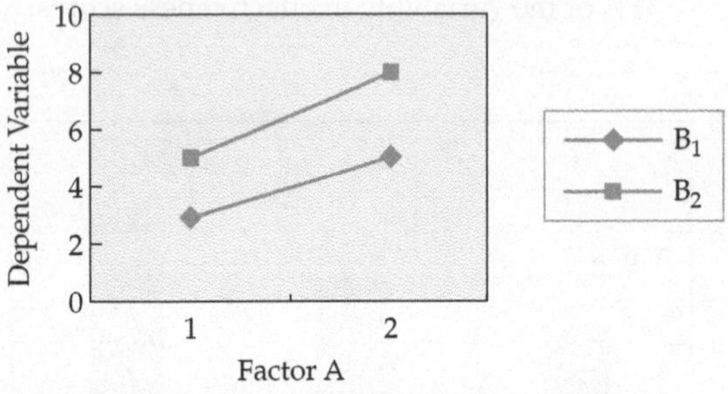

Experiment 2

	A_1	A_2
B_1	12	4
B_2	4	12

A: No
B: No
A × B: Yes

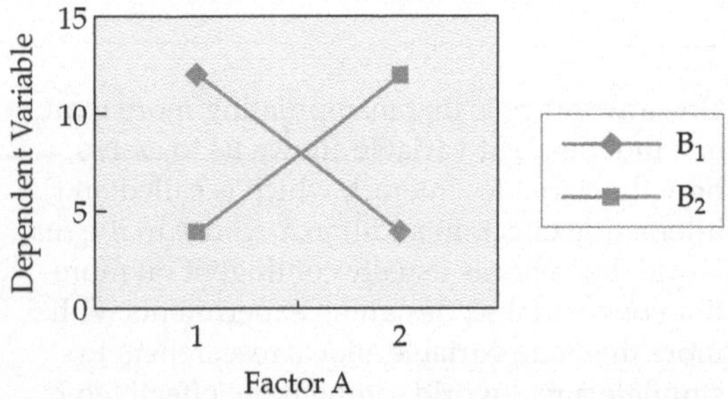

9. No, one of the variables has only two levels. If the *F*-ratio for that main effect is significant, it means that there were significant differences between those two groups, and Tukey's post hoc test is not necessary. However, it is necessary to compute Tukey's post hoc test for the main effect of the variable with six levels. In this case, the *F*-ratio tells us only that there is a significant difference between two of the groups, and we need to determine how many of the groups differ significantly from each other.

11. a.

Source	*df*	*SS*	*MS*	*F*
Gender	1	0.167	0.167	0.095
Pizza Brand	1	6.00	6.00	3.43
Gender × Pizza	1	130.67	130.67	74.67
Error	20	35.00	1.75	
Total	23	171.83		

Note: If calculated by hand, your *SS* scores may vary slightly due to rounding.

b. The only significant *F*-ratio is for the interaction, $F(1, 20) = 74.67, p < .01$.

c. There is no significant effect of gender on pizza preference. There is no significant effect of pizza brand on pizza preference. There is a significant interaction effect: The males prefer the low-fat pizza over the regular pizza, whereas the females prefer the regular over the low-fat.

d. The effect size (η^2) is only .09% for gender (gender accounts for less than .1% of the variability in preference scores) and 3.5% for pizza brand. However, the effect size is 76% for the interaction, meaning that the interaction of gender and pizza brand accounts for 76% of the variability in preference scores.

e. Because the variable Gender is not continuous, a bar graph is appropriate. However, because most students find it easier to interpret interactions with a line graph, this type of graph is also provided and may be used.

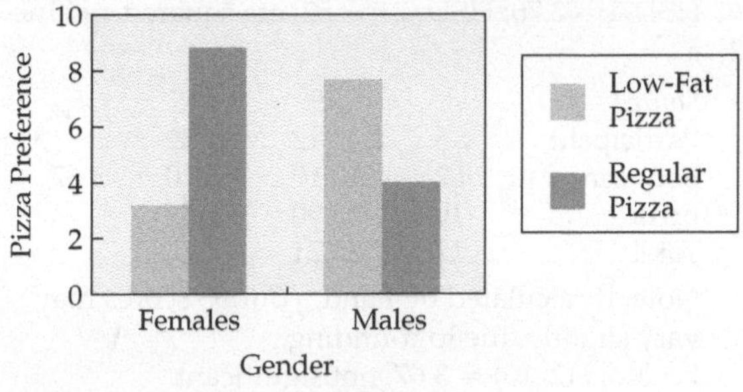

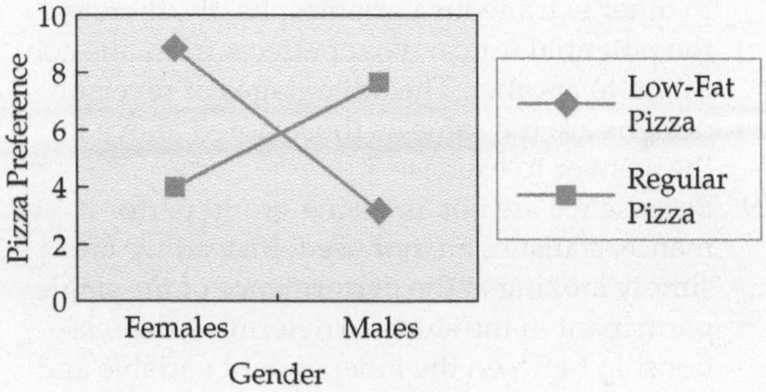

Answers to Chapter 12 Review Exercises

Fill-in Self-Test Answers

1. factorial notation
2. main effect
3. 2; 4; 6
4. 2; 1
5. SS_{Error}
6. eta-squared

Multiple-Choice Self-Test Answers

1. c
2. d
3. a
4. b
5. c
6. d
7. c
8. c
9. c
10. c
11. b
12. d

Answers to Self-Test Problems

1. a.

	Morning	*Afternoon*	*Evening*
Lecture only	9	7	6
Lecture/small-group	5	6	8

This is a 2 × 3 factorial design.

b. ANOVA SUMMARY TABLE

Source	*df*	*SS*	*MS*	*F*
A (Time)	2	1.67	0.835	.63
B (Teaching Method)	1	7.50	7.50	5.64
A × B	2	45.02	22.51	16.92
Within	24	32.00	1.33	
Total	29	86.19		

Note: If calculated by hand, your SS scores may vary slightly due to rounding

c. Factor A: $F(2, 24) = .63$, not significant.
Factor B: $F(1, 24) = 5.64, p < .05$.
Interaction: $F(2, 24) = 16.92, p < .01$.

d. There is no significant effect of time of day on attentiveness. There is a significant effect of teaching method on attentiveness such that those in the lecture-only groups were more attentive. There is a significant interaction effect such that as the time of day increased, attentiveness decreased for the lecture-only conditions; whereas as time of day increased, attentiveness increased for the lecture with small-group activities conditions.

e. The effect size (η^2) is 2% for time of day (time of day accounts for less than 2% of the variability in attentiveness scores), 9% for teaching method (teaching method accounts for 9% of the variability in attentiveness scores), and 52% for the interaction (the interaction of time of day and teaching method accounts for 52% of the variability in attentiveness scores).

f.

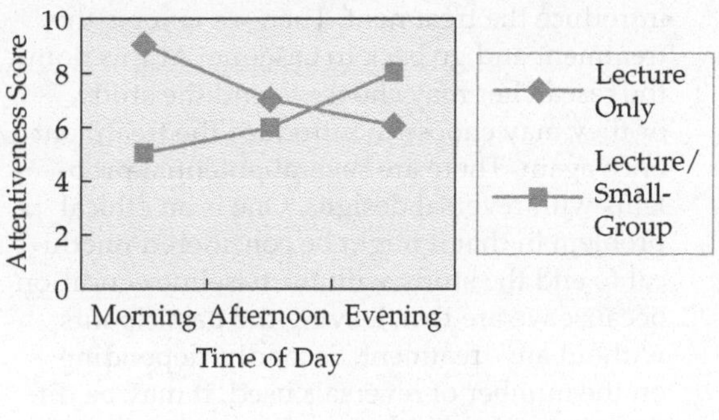

Chapter 13

1. A true experimental design uses a manipulated independent variable. A quasi-experimental design may have no independent variable (only one group was used and given the treatment) or a nonmanipulated independent variable (although two groups were used, they came to the study already differing, or they chose to participate or not participate in some treatment). Thus, although we can infer a causal relationship based on data from a true experimental design, we cannot do so based on data collected from a quasi-experimental design.
3. The researcher should use a single-group posttest-only design, in which each quiz given across the semester serves as a posttest measure. Because she has no comparison group, this type of study would have limitations.
5. These are all examples of developmental designs—designs in which age is the manipulated variable. With cross-sectional designs, individuals of different ages are studied at the same time, whereas with longitudinal designs, the same people are studied over many years or decades. A sequential design is a combined cross-sectional and longitudinal design. A researcher begins with participants of different ages (a cross-sectional design) and tests or measures them. Then, either months or years later, the research retests or measures the same individuals (a longitudinal design).
7. Reversal designs are basically within-participants designs with only one participant. The study begins with baseline measures. We then introduce the treatment. Then we reverse the treatment and go back to baseline. At this point, the researcher may choose to end the study, or they may choose to introduce the treatment once again. There are several potential problems with reversal designs. One is an ethical problem in that it might be considered unethical to end the study with the baseline condition because we are then leaving the participants without any treatment. Secondly, depending on the number of reversals used, it may be difficult to establish that any changes in behavior were actually due to the treatment. In other words, because there is only one participant and because there is no "control" participant, we do not know that the observed changes are actually due to the treatment—they may be due to other extraneous variables. Lastly, there is the potential for carryover effects from one condition to another. The advantages of reversal designs are the same as those noted above in the answer to exercise 5.
9. Because we are not assessing group performance, statistics are not used. Instead we are simply looking at the performance of the single participant in the study to determine the relationship between the independent variable and dependent variable. This is best accomplished by graphing the performance of the single participant and examining the resulting graph.

Answers to Chapter 13 Review Exercises

Fill-in Self-Test Answers

1. subject
2. single-group posttest only
3. time-series
4. nonequivalent control group pretest/posttest
5. cross-sectional
6. single-case
7. small-*n*
8. ABA reversal
9. multiple baseline across subjects

Multiple-Choice Self-Test Answers

1. d
2. d
3. d
4. a
5. d
6. b
7. d
8. a
9. b

Chapter 14

1. It is appropriate to use a chi-square test when the data are nominal and no parameters are known.
3. a. $\chi^2_{obt} = 8.94$
   b. $df = 1$
   c. $\chi^2_{cv} = 3.841$
   d. The number of students who go on to college from the teacher's high school is significantly greater than the number in the general population.

5. a. The Wilcoxon's rank-sum test should be used.
   b. H_0: $Md_{\text{No service}} \geq Md_{\text{Service}}$, H_a: $Md_{\text{No service}} < Md_{\text{Service}}$
   c. $Ws\ (n_1 = 6, n_2 = 6) = 23.5, p < .01$.
   d. Yes, reject H_0. Students who completed community service had significantly higher maturity scores.
7. a. The Wilcoxon matched-pairs signed-ranks *T* test should be used.
   b. H_0: $Md_{\text{Red}} \leqslant Md_{\text{Green}}$
      H_a: $Md_{\text{Red}} > Md_{\text{Green}}$
   c. $T(N{=}7){=}3, p < .05$.
   d. Reject H_0. Taste scores for the two sauces differed significantly. The red sauce is preferred.
9. The Friedman test would be used for a correlated-groups design, with ordinal data, and more than two conditions to compare. The Wilcoxon matched-pairs signed-ranks *T* test would be used for a correlated-groups design, with ordinal data and only two conditions to compare.

Answers to Chapter 14 Review Exercises

Fill-in Self-Test Answers

1. Observed; expected
2. chi-square test
3. phi coefficient
4. Wilcoxon rank-sum test
5. matched-pairs signed-ranks *T* test
6. between-subjects
7. nominal; ordinal
8. Kruskal-Wallis test

Multiple-Choice Self-Test Answers

1. d
2. d
3. c
4. c
5. b
6. a

Answers to Self-Test Problems

1. $\chi^2_{\text{obt}} = 1.45$
2. $df = 1$
3. $\chi^2_{\text{cv}} = 3.841$
4. Fail to reject H_0. The percentage of people who smoke in the South does not differ significantly from that in the general population.

2. a. $\chi^2_{\text{obt}}\ (N = 68) = 8.5, p < .01$.
   b. $df = 1$
   c. $\chi^2_{\text{cv}} = 3.841$
   d. Reject H_0. There is a significant difference in the frequency of workout preferences for males and females. Females prefer to work out together more than males.
3. a. The Wilcoxon rank-sum test.
   b. H_0: $Md_{\text{red}} \leqslant Md_{\text{green}}$, H_a: $Md_{\text{red}} > Md_{\text{green}}$
   c. $Ws\ (n_1 = 7, n_2 = 7) = 41$, not significant.
   d. No. Fail to reject H_0. There is no significant difference in tastiness scores.

Chapter 15

1. The title page contains the running head in the top margin, aligned on the left margin, along with the page number, aligned on the right margin. The title of the paper is centered in the top third of the page followed by the author's name(s) (centered) and then the author's affiliation(s) (centered). The Author Note is centered at the bottom of the page. The entire title page is double-spaced.
3. a. The number 50 should be written out because it begins a sentence. Alternatively, the sentence could be rewritten so that it does not begin with a number.
   b. The proper way to report an *F*-ratio is as follows: $F(1, 12) = 6.54, p = .05$.
   c. The word *data* is plural. Thus, the sentence should read "The data are presented in Table 1."
   d. The word *while* refers to time and should not be used in this sentence. The sentence should read "One group of participants took the medication, whereas the other group did not."

Answers to Chapter 15 Review Exercises

Fill-in Self-Test Answers

1. subjects, apparatus/materials, procedure
2. results
3. abstract

Multiple-Choice Self-Test Answers

1. c
2. c
3. d
4. b

APPENDIX

D Getting Started with Excel, SPSS, and the TI-84 Calculator

Using Excel 2007 or 2010

Installing the Analysis ToolPak. Before you begin to use Excel to analyze data, you may need to install the Data Analysis ToolPak. For Excel 2007, this can be accomplished by launching Excel and then clicking on the Microsoft Office icon at the top left of the page. At the bottom of the drop-down menu, there is a tab labeled **Excel Options**.

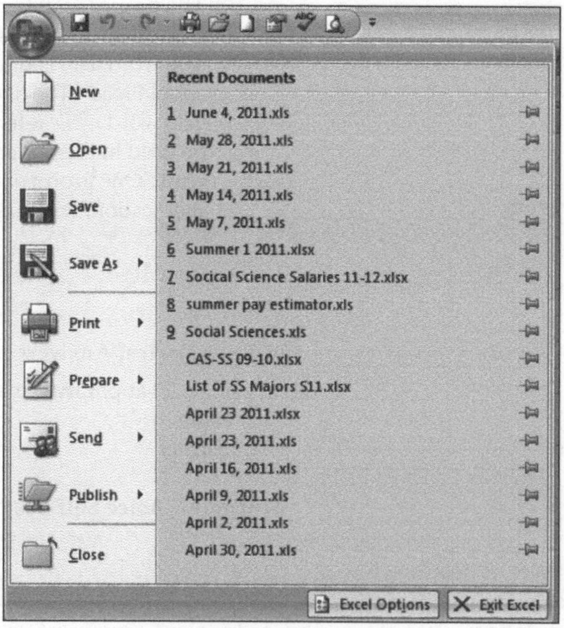

Click on **Excel Options**, and a dialog box of options will appear. On the left-hand side of the dialog box is a list of options; click on **Add-Ins** to open a pop-up window. The very top option in the pop-up window should be **Analysis ToolPak**. Click on this and then **GO**.

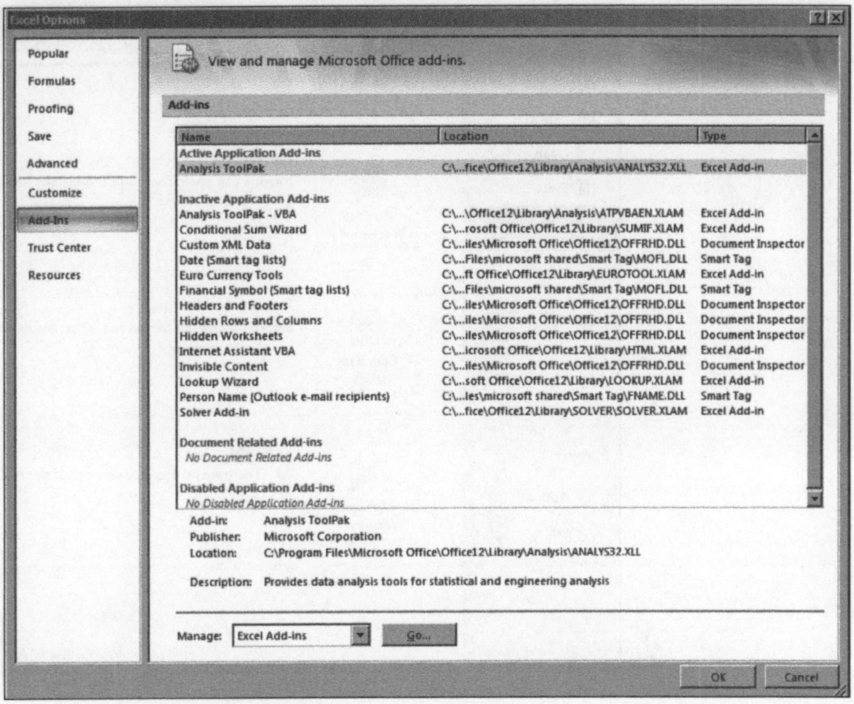

A dialog box in which **Analysis ToolPak** is the first option will appear. Check this and then click **OK**.

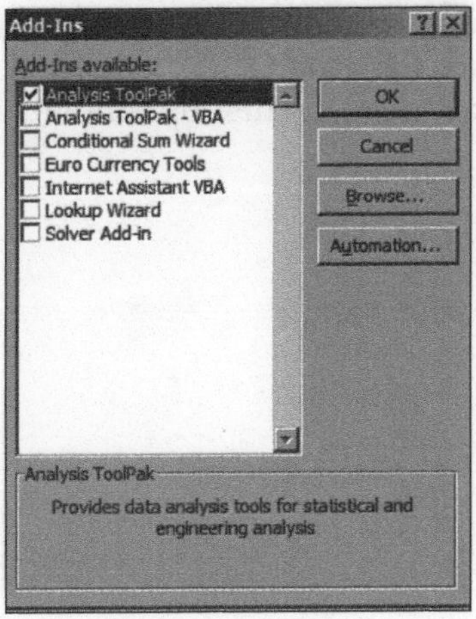

The ToolPak should now be installed on your computer.

For Excel 2010, the process is similar. Begin by clicking on the **File** tab at the top left of the screen (this tab replaces the Microsoft Office icon from 2007).

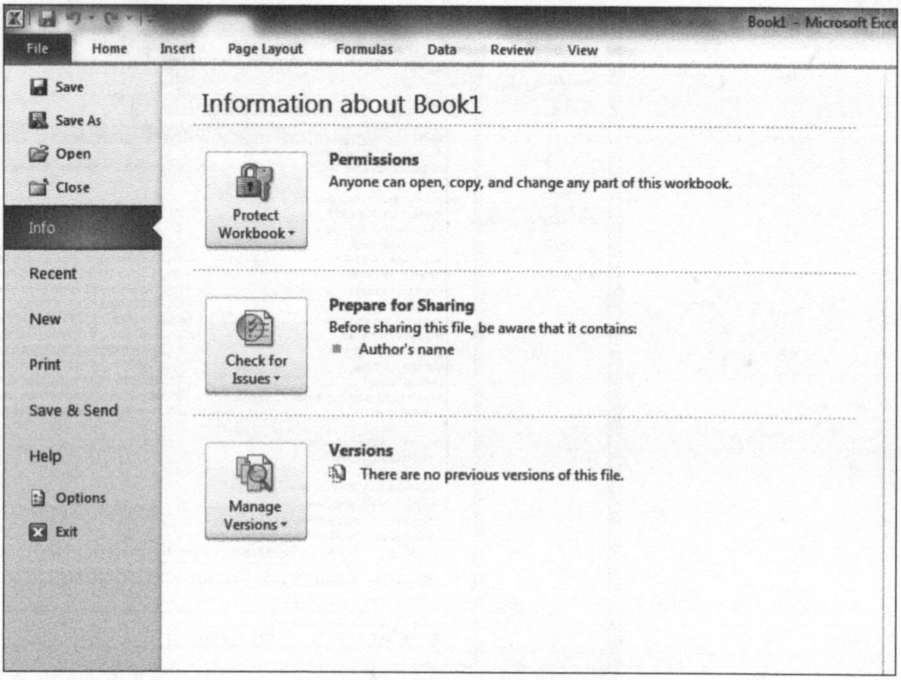

Next, click on **Options** toward the bottom of the drop-down menu. From here the process is similar to that for 2007. A dialog box of options will appear. On the left-hand side of the dialog box is a list of options; click on **Add-Ins** to open a pop-up window. The very top option in the pop-up window should be **Analysis ToolPak**. Click on this and then **GO**. A dialog box in which **Analysis ToolPak** is the first option will appear. Check this and then click **OK**.

Launching Excel. When you open Excel, you will be presented with a spreadsheet.

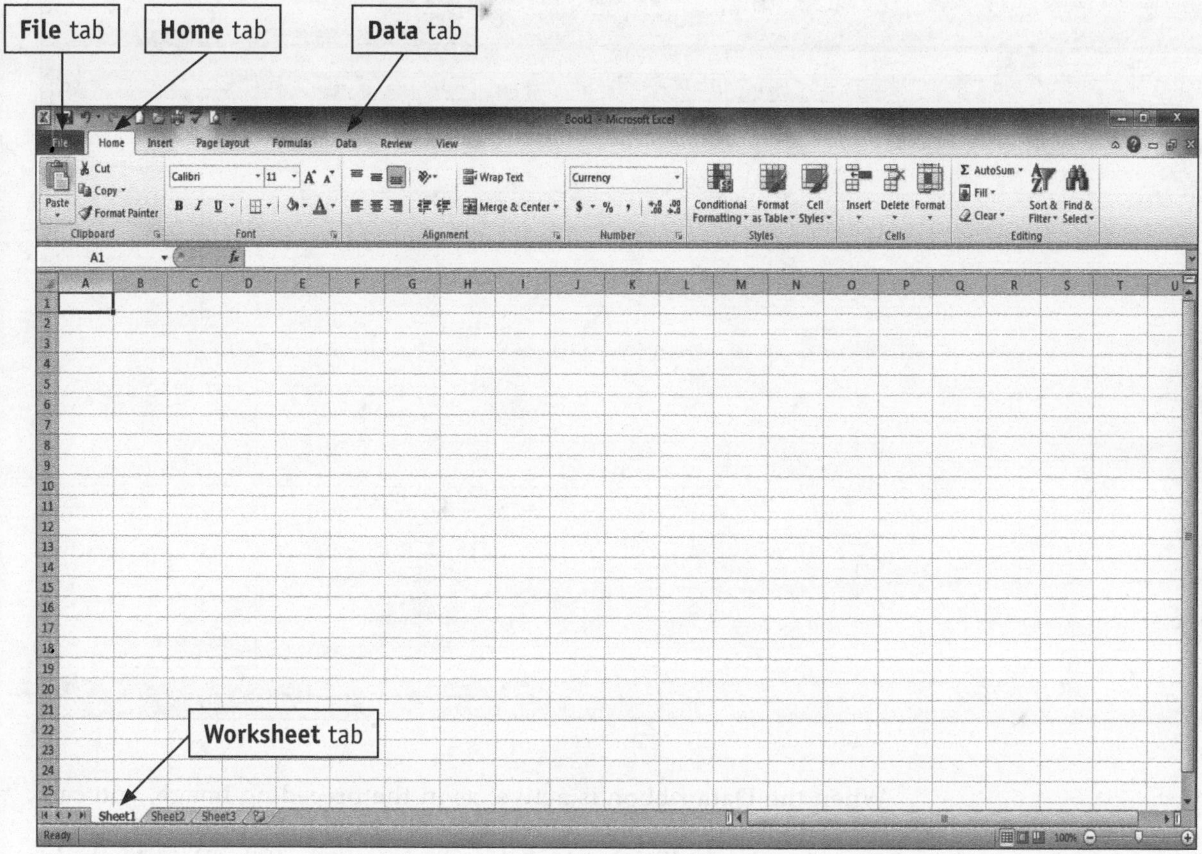

You can see in the preceding worksheet where the **File** tab is (in Excel 2007, the Office Button is here), along with the **Home**, **Data**, and **Worksheet** tabs. The spreadsheet has a series of columns and rows. The columns are labeled with letters, and the rows with numbers. A cell is the point at which a column and row intersect. Thus, cell A1 is highlighted in the preceding screen capture. We typically refer to cells with the column letter first and the row number second (e.g., D5). We will be entering data into the cells for the analyses we'll be conducting using Excel in subsequent modules. In addition, we'll be using the Data Analysis ToolPak for most of our analyses. The ToolPak can be accessed when the **Data** ribbon is active (see the following screen capture).

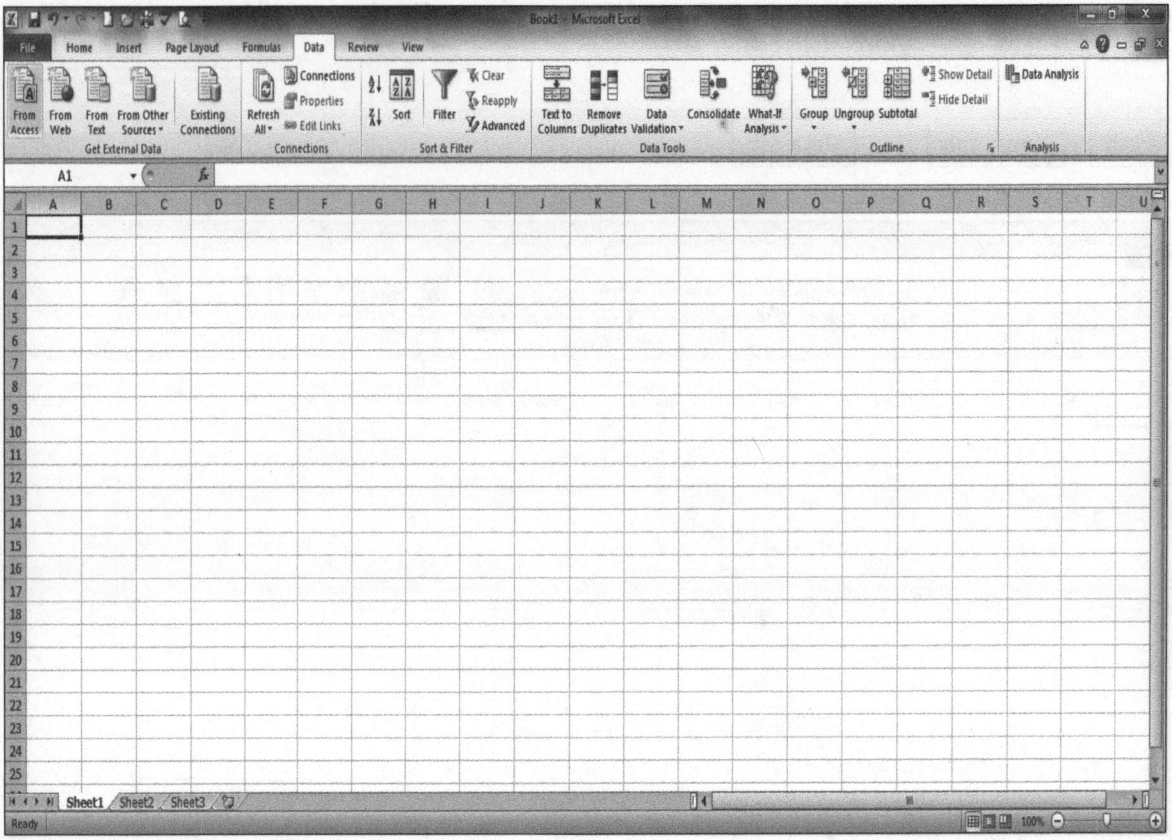

When the **Data** ribbon is active, as in the preceding image, you can see the **Data Analysis** option at the upper right of the screen. This option indicates that the ToolPak has been installed properly. If the **Data Analysis** option is not visible at the top right of the ribbon, then the ToolPak was not installed properly (see previous instructions on installing the ToolPak).

Entering Data. We can enter data into Excel by simply entering the numbers in the cells. For example, in the following image, I've entered some annual salary data for a small business. You can see that I labeled the data **Salary** in the first cell and then entered the numerical data in a column below the heading.

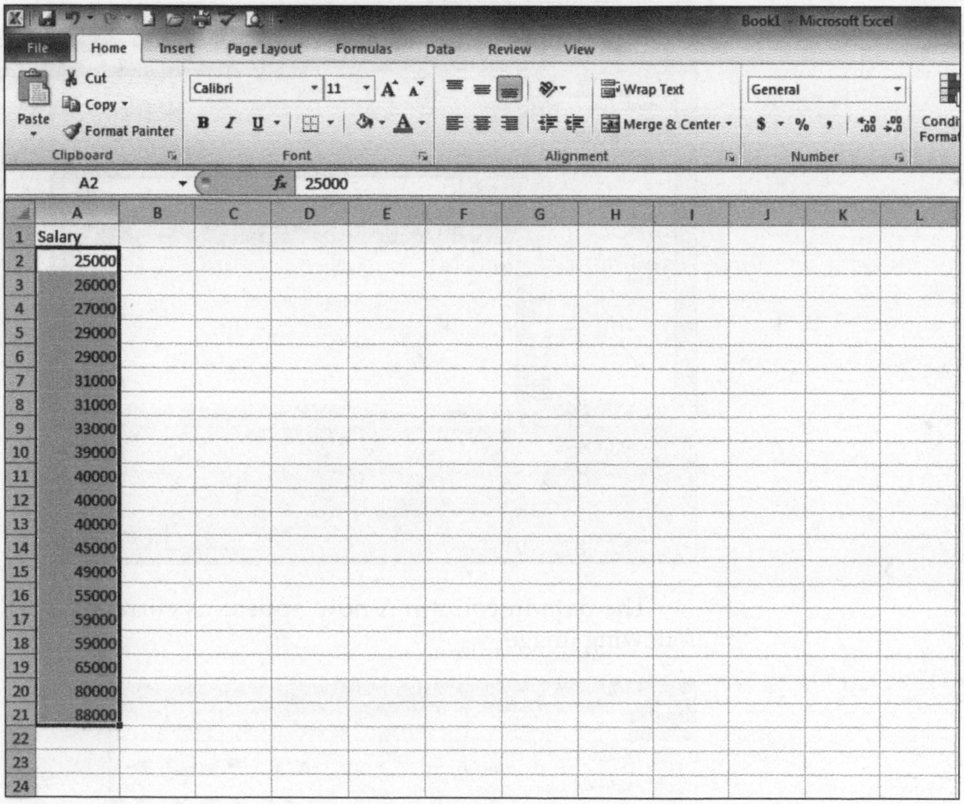

If I want the data to have a different appearance—for example, to indicate that it is currency—I can format the number type through the **Home** ribbon, **Number** window. To begin, highlight the data in column A (see the preceding image). Then activate the **Home** ribbon by double clicking on it (this has been done in the preceding image). You should see the **Number** window in the top right-hand side of the **Home** ribbon in the preceding image.

You can activate the **Number** window by clicking on the arrow in the bottom right of the window; you will receive a dialog box as in the following screen capture that will allow you to format the way you want the numerical data to appear in the cells. Because these data are salaries, let's choose **Currency** and then click **OK**.

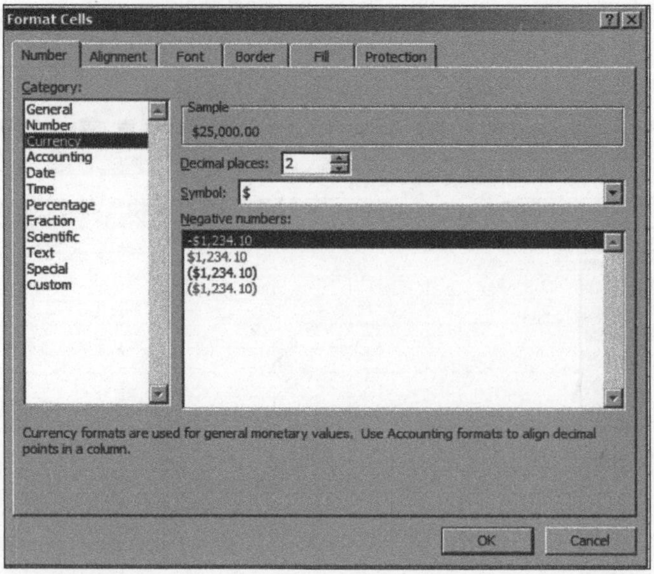

The data in column A now appear as currency as can be seen in the following image.

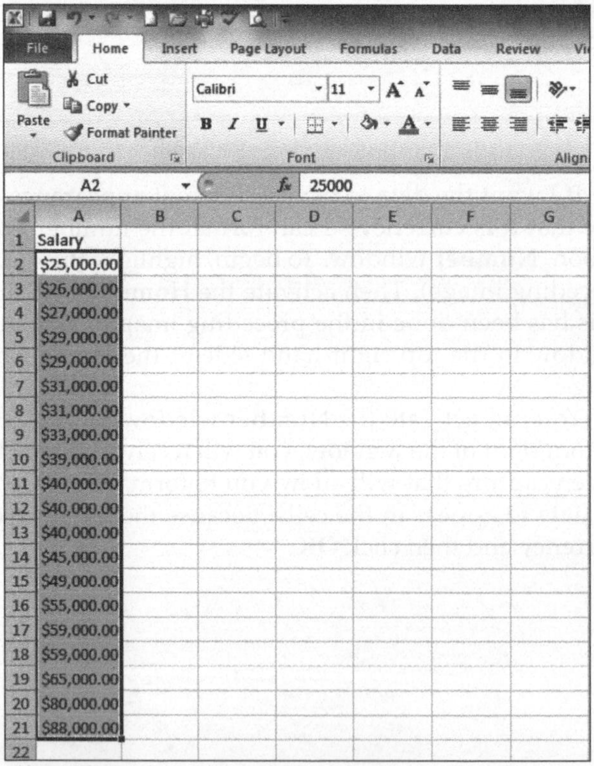

Using SPSS 18 or 19

To begin using SPSS, launch the SPSS program. When you initially start the program, you may receive a startup window such as the one below. Unless otherwise instructed by your professor, click **Cancel**. (Please note: SPSS 18 was marketed as PASW Statistics; it returned to being named SPSS in version 19)

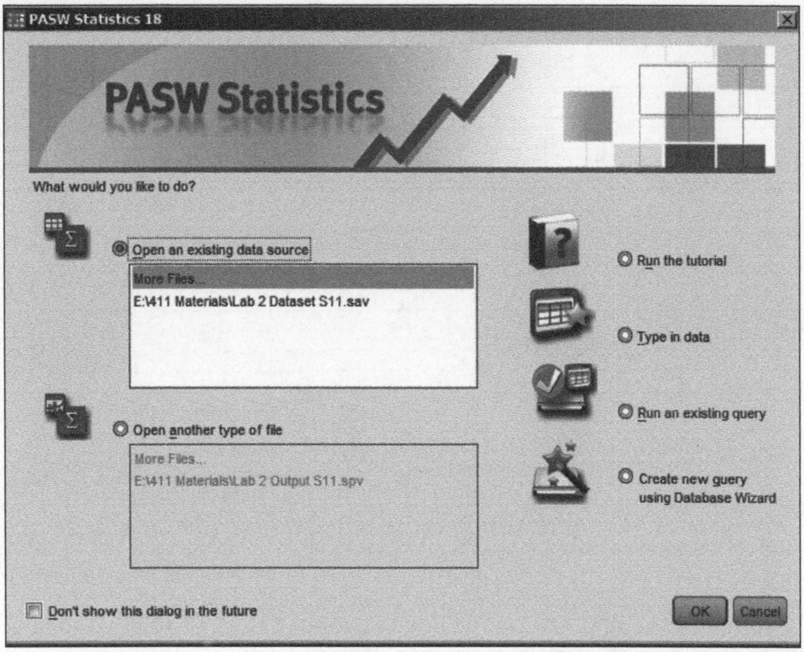

You should now have a view of the data spreadsheet, or the Data Editor, similar to the following image.

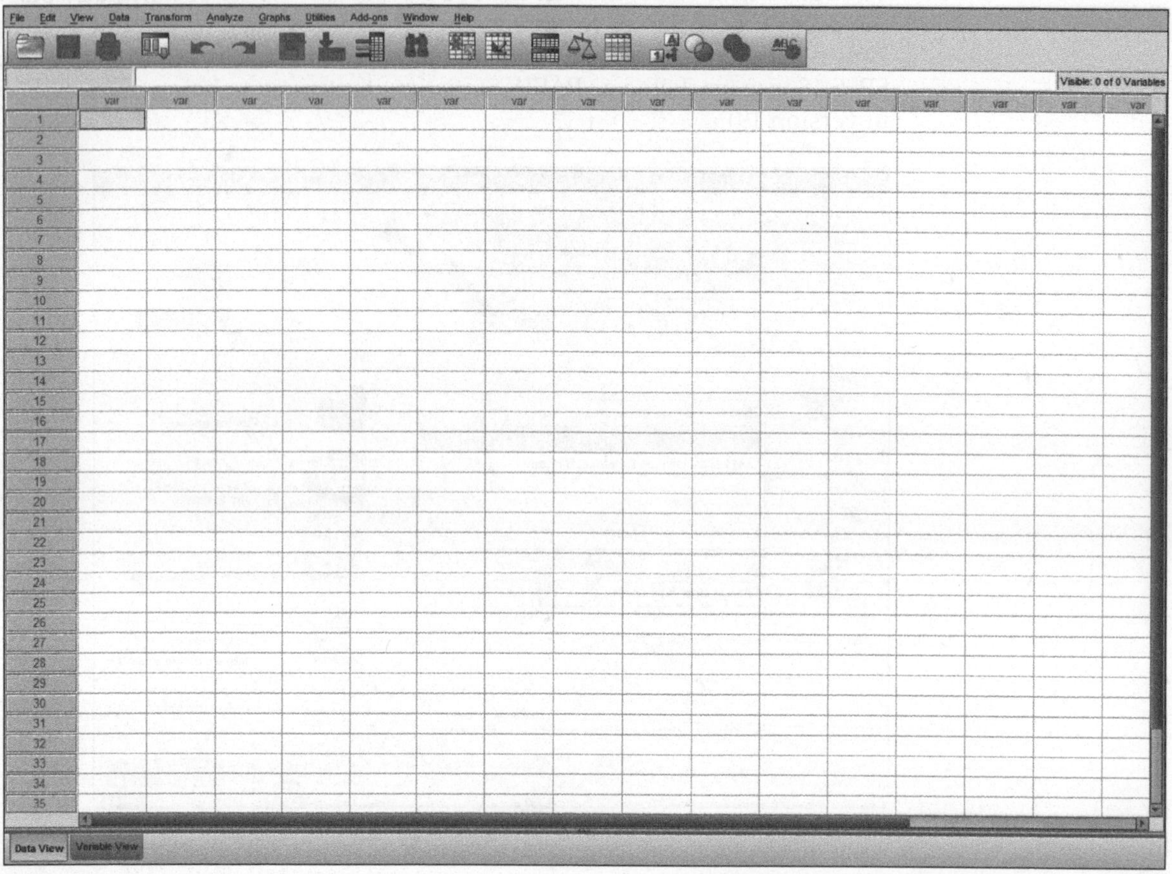

The main menu in SPSS runs across the top of the Data Editor and gives you the options from **File** on the far left to **Help** on the far right. We'll mainly be using the **Analyze** option to statistically analyze data. You can see the drop-down menu for the **Analyze** tab in the following image.

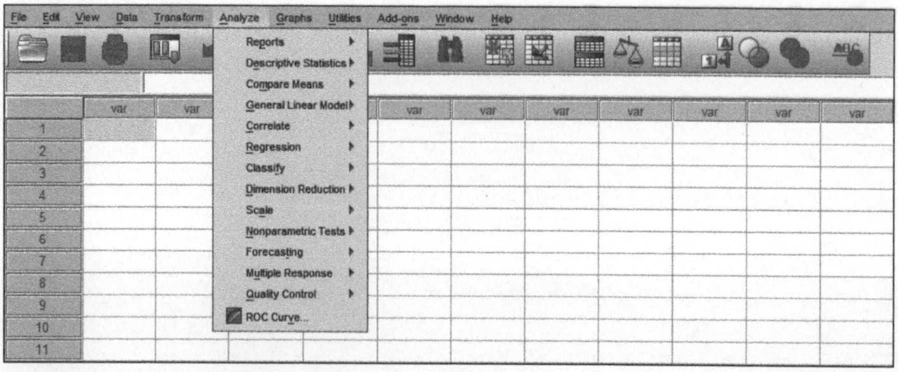

The icons that appear below the main menu provide some shortcut keys to allow you to do such things as Open Files, Save, Insert Cases, Insert Variable, and so on.

Entering Data. To enter the data into an SPSS spreadsheet, launch SPSS and enter the data into a column, as in the following spreadsheet in which I have entered the salary data from the previous Excel example. Given that I had already entered the data into Excel, I simply cut and pasted the data column into SPSS, minus the **Salary** heading.

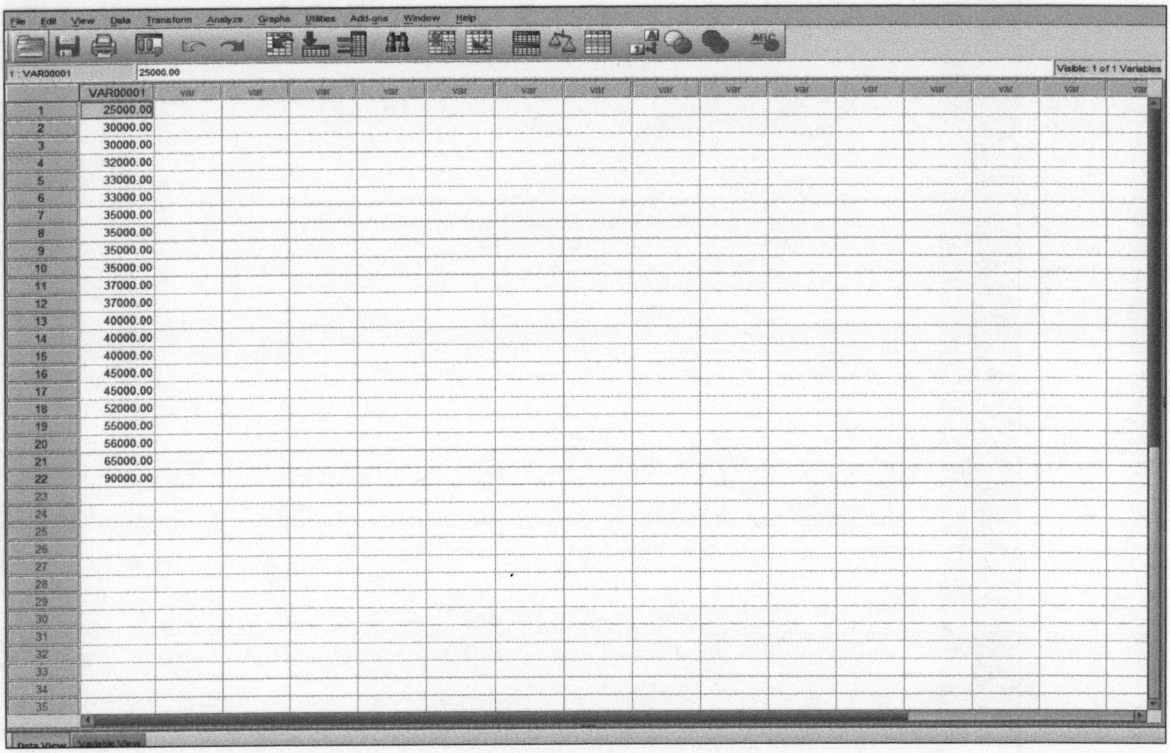

Notice that the variable is simply named VAR0001. To rename the variable to something appropriate for your data set, click on the **Variable View** tab at the bottom left of the screen. You will see the **Variable View** window active in the following image.

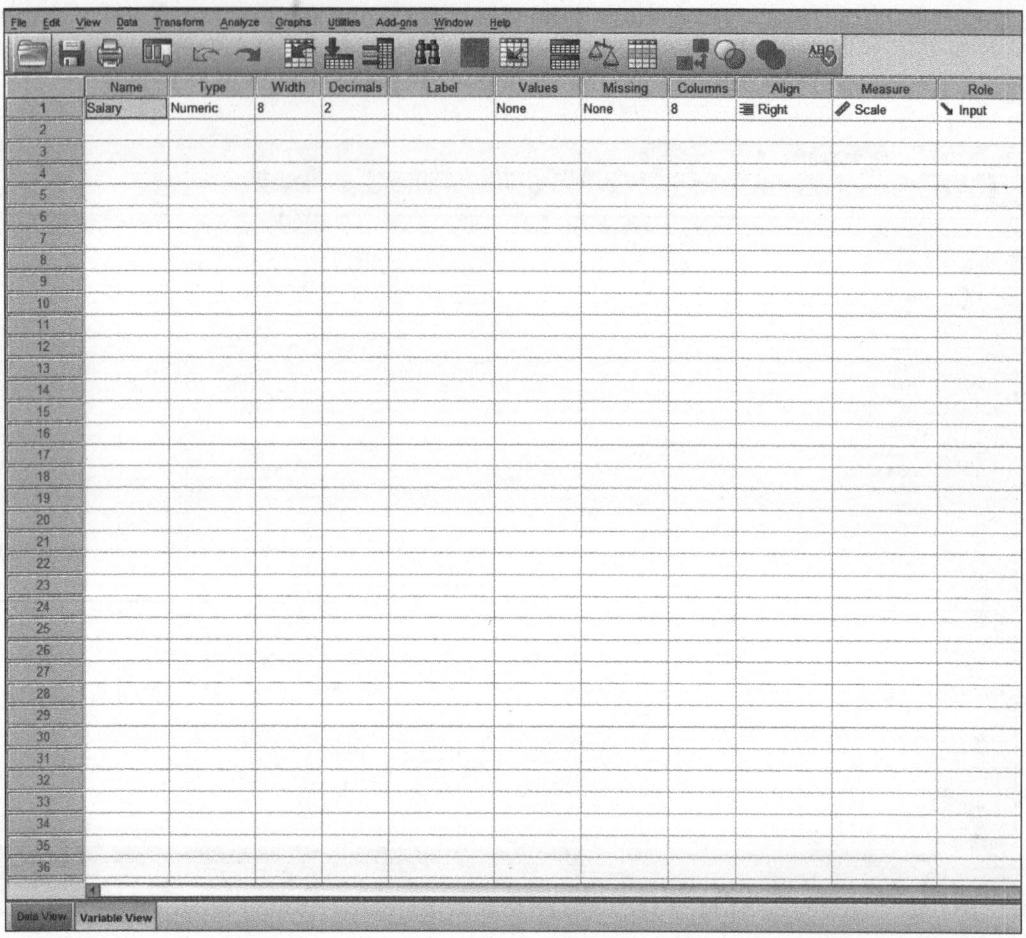

Type the name you wish to give the variable in the first column (labeled **Name**). The variable name cannot have any spaces in it. Because these data represent salary data, we'll type in **Salary**. You can also see that we can format this variable while the **Variable View** window is active by specifying the type of data, the width of the data, the number of decimals, and so on. To get back to the original spreadsheet, highlight the **Data View** tab at the bottom left of the screen. In the **Data View** window, we can now see that the **Salary** heading appears at the top of the column.

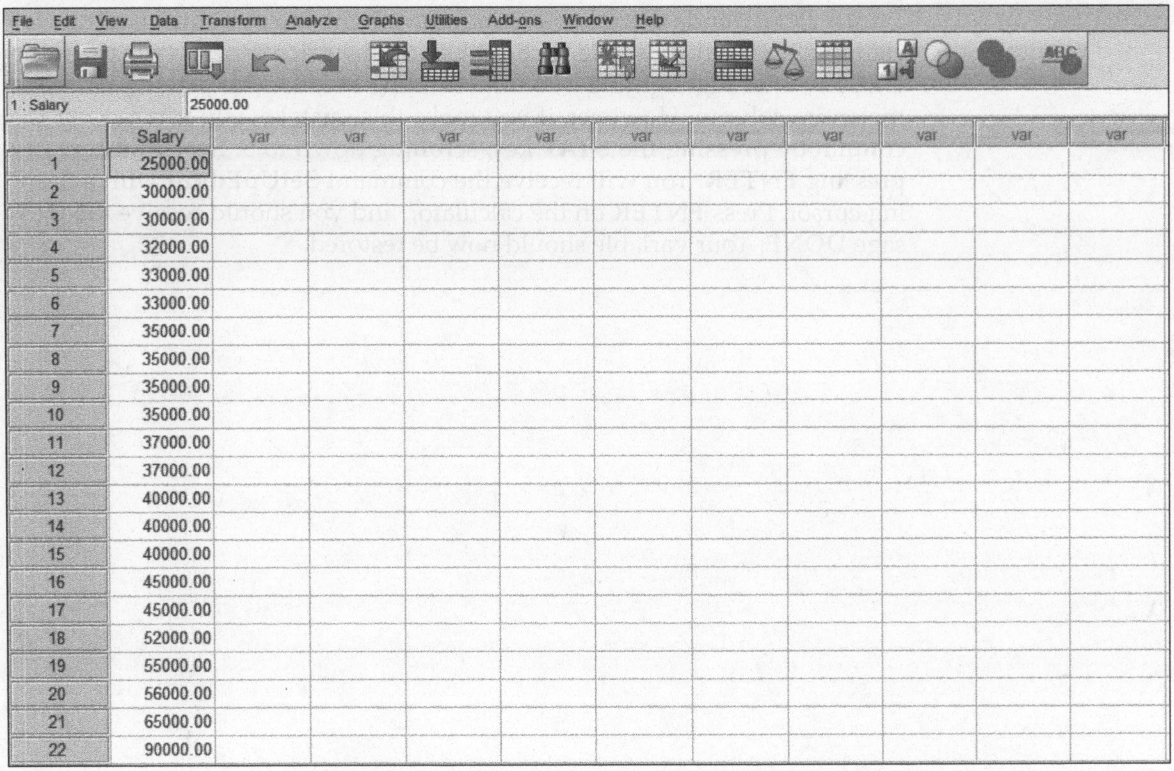

If I had not had data to paste into the Data Editor, I could have entered the data by highlighting each cell and typing in the data.

Using the TI-84 Calculator

Entering data into the TI-84 calculator is considerably easier than entering it into Excel or SPSS. With the calculator on, press the **STAT** key. **EDIT** should be highlighted at the top left of the screen along with **1: Edit** in the first row under the menu. Press the **ENTER** key at the bottom right of the calculator. You should now have a spreadsheet with six columns labeled **L1** through **L6** (you may only be able to see L1 through L3, but if you scroll to the right, columns L4 through L6 become available). To enter data into L1, move the cursor to the first position under L1 and type in the data. Press **ENTER** after you type each number. Your data should now be entered into L1 and be displayed in the column under L1.

To clear the data from a column, highlight the column heading (for example, L1) and press the **CLEAR** key on the calculator. Never press the **DEL** key after highlighting a column heading because this action will delete the entire column. However, if you make this mistake, you can recover the column by pressing the **STAT** key, scrolling down to **5: SetUpEditor**, and pressing **ENTER**. You will receive the command **SetUpEditor** with a flashing cursor. Press **ENTER** on the calculator, and you should receive the message **DONE**. Your variable should now be restored.

APPENDIX E

APA Sample Manuscript

This sample paper by Kim J. Driggers and Tasha Helms was originally published in the *Psi Chi Journal of Undergraduate Research* (2000, Vol. 5, pp. 76–80). This paper is reprinted with permission.

Running head: WILLINGNESS TO DATE 1

Running head is left justified and provides a short (50 characters or less) description of the topic of the paper. It is typed in all capital letters and preceded by the phrase "Running head:" on the title page only. The page number is right justified on the same line.

The Effects of Salary on Willingness to Date

Kim J. Driggers and Tasha Helms

Oklahoma State University

Title, author's name(s), and affiliation(s) are centered and double-spaced.

Author Note

Kim J. Driggers and Tasha Helms, Department of Psychology, Oklahoma State University.

Correspondence concerning this article should be addressed to Kim J. Driggers, Department of Psychology, Oklahoma State University, Stillwater, OK 74078.

The abstract is typed in block paragraph format and is between 150 and 250 words.

Abstract is centered at the top of page 2.

Abstract

The present experiment tested the role of salary in date selection by men and women. Male and female college students ($N = 150$) viewed pictures of the opposite sex and rated the target's attractiveness and their own willingness to date the target. The level of salary (i.e., \$20,000, \$60,000, and \$100,000) varied among three conditions. Statistical analyses yielded support for the hypothesis that as the target's salary increased, a participant's willingness to date the target would also increase. That is, as salary increased, both men's and women's willingness to date a target increased. We also found a significant main effect for the sex of participants; as salary increased, women's willingness to date a person increased significantly more than men's willingness.

The title of the paper appears at the top of page 3, centered. The introduction begins on the next line.

The Effects of Salary on Willingness to Date

To properly review current research in the area of date selection, it is first necessary to highlight theories that form the foundations upon which this research was built. Scientists have studied human mate selection for over a century. Darwin (1871) proposed that physical attractiveness and survival attributes were the essence of mate selection (a.k.a. *natural selection*). Many anthropologists and biologists have explained the factors of physical attractiveness and socioeconomic status (SES) on the basis of evolutionary principles. Often when selecting a mate, one's instinct is a driving factor. Men, according to sociobiologists, search for the most attractive woman to mate with in order to ensure reproductive success (Buss, 1987). Men thus must use physical appearance or related factors (e.g., age and health) to predict the fertility and genes of a woman. To men, mating with a highly attractive woman ensures that their offspring will have a "good" (i.e., viable) genetic makeup. Yet the suggested pattern for women is somewhat different. In terms of evolution, women are more selective than men in their mate selection. Women have more potential risks when choosing a mate (e.g., pregnancy, childbirth, child rearing) and thus concentrate more on a man's ability to provide for her and her offspring (Townsend & Levy, 1990b); hence commitment and the man's ability to offer resources are important factors when it comes to a woman's selection of a man.

In-text citation: Author's name is followed by publication date in parentheses.

End-of-sentence citation: Author's name and publication date are both in parentheses.

Use an ampersand (&) when authors' names are in parentheses.

Social psychologists explain these differences in mate selection as a social exchange between the sexes. Scientists have found the exchange of a man's security for an attractive woman is the basis of mate selection

(Rusbult, 1980). Elder (1969) found that men's personal prestige ratings increased when they were paired with an attractive woman. However, ratings of women in Elder's study were based on physical attractiveness only. Therefore, women are exchanging attractiveness for the resources men can provide.

These diverse theories highlight the importance of physical attractiveness and SES. Research (Buss, 1987; Darwin, 1871; Elder, 1969; Rusbult, 1980; Townsend & Levy, 1990b) suggests that physical attractiveness is a better predictor of mate selection in men, and SES is a better predictor of mate selection in women. Current studies have also found that both of these attributes play an integral part in female and male mate selection (e.g., Buss, 1987; Davis, 1985; Goode, 1996; Hill, Nocks, & Gardner, 1987; Hudson & Henze, 1969; Joshi & Rai, 1989; Sprecher, 1989; Townsend & Levy, 1990a, 1990b).

In parentheses, multiple citations are separated by semicolons.

When there are three to five authors, give all authors' names in the first citation, use the first author's name followed by 'et al.' for subsequent citations. If there are six or more authors, use the 'et al.' form for the first and subsequent citations.

Townsend and Levy (1990a) questioned participants regarding different types of relationships ranging from casual conversation to dating, sex, and other types of serious relationships. Participants rated their willingness to engage in these types of relationships based on a slide photograph of a person (face and torso were depicted in the picture). Results indicated that men and women were more likely to engage in all types of relationships when a person was physically attractive. Sprecher (1989), on the other hand, presented only a description of a person (e.g., occupation, salary, favorite color) as the stimulus. Sprecher also found that physical attractiveness played an important factor, even in the absence of visual stimuli.

Use "and" when authors' names are part of the text.

Other current studies have noted SES as an important predictor of interpersonal attraction. SES includes factors such as career, salary, and the attitudes and behaviors attributed to the concerned person (Joshi & Rai, 1989). Research indicates SES is an important element among both sexes in terms of date selection (Bell, 1976; Goode, 1996; Hill et al., 1987; Townsend & Levy, 1990b). For example, Hill et al. found that attractiveness ratings by both men and women of an unattractive target of the opposite sex increased as their SES increases. Although important to both sexes, SES is even more important to women than to men in terms of date selection (Bell, 1976; Buss, 1987; Goode, 1996; Hill et al., 1987; Nevid, 1984; Townsend & Levy, 1990a). Nevid (1984) asked participants to rate personal qualities (e.g., appearance, career, etc. in terms of their degree of importance in determining their choice of a romantic partner. No visual stimuli were used when the participant determined the order of importance of qualities. Results indicated that women rated SES higher (i.e., as more important) than men in their ranking of importance qualities. Townsend and Levy (1990a, 1990b) asked men and women how willing they were to enter into relationships after presenting them with a picture and description of a person. They found that SES was a better predictor for women than men when deciding whether or not to enter a serious relationship.

When there are three to five authors, use the first author's name followed by 'et al.' for subsequent citations.

The previously mentioned studies have evaluated the importance of SES in combination with other attributes. Moreover, SES typically has been studied as a global construct, it has never been broken down into its counterparts (i.e., career, salary, attitudes, and behaviors) for evaluation. What are the effects of salary alone on mate selection? How important is salary alone in the overall effect of SES? The present study examined the significance of salary on willingness to date. In order to eliminate the influence of physical attractiveness on ratings, the pictures used in the present study were considered low in physical attractiveness. The independent variable was the salary associated with the photo (three levels: $20,000, $60,000, and $100,000). The dependent variable was the participant's willingness to date a person. The primary hypothesis was that the participant's willingness to date a person would increase as the target's salary increases. Based on previous research, we hypothesized that this relation would be stronger for women.

The Method section begins right after the introduction ends, not on a new page. The word "Method" is centered in boldface.

Method

Subjects

Subsection headings are typed, in boldface, flush on the left margin. Subsection headings stand alone on a line.

The subjects in this study consisted of 150 college students (75 men, 75 women) attending a large Midwestern university. The average age of subjects was 21 years. The ethnic background of participants varied, with 71% of the sampling being Caucasian, 14% Asian American, 8% African American, and 7% Native American. Researchers accessed participants from the college library, dormitories, the student union, and laundry facilities. In these facilities, researchers accessed 55 subjects at student organizational meetings, 75 subjects at the university library, and the remaining 20 participants in the mezzanines of the dormitories. Only three participants approached refused to participate. Subjects were assigned to conditions ($N = 50$ each condition) based on the order in which they were approached by the experimenters.

Materials

The materials for the present study consisted of two pictures (one man, one woman) with a short description posted below each picture, and a questionnaire packet (i.e., informed consent sheet, short description of study, and questionnaire). A pre-testing group of 20 students selected the pictures used in this experiment. The pretest group selected the most unattractive male and female picture out of 30 different photographs. The male and female pictures the pretest group selected most often as unattractive were used in this study to control for attractiveness. The pictures focused on the faces and upper torso of a Caucasian man and a Caucasian woman separately, both dressed in casual clothes. Included in the short description paired with the picture was the person's age (i.e., 24), occupation (i.e., business field), pets (i.e., none), and marital status (i.e., single), with the only manipulated variable being salary. The salary values were $20,000, $60,000, and $100,000. The short descriptions were the same for both the female and male conditions.

The seven questions in the survey measured the participant's perception of the target's attractiveness and popularity and the participant's willingness to date the target individual. These questions were based on a 7-point Likert scale with the anchors being 1 (*not willing*) and 7 (*extremely willing*). The focus question in this study was "How willing would you be to go on a date with this person?" The other questions were fillers to distract the participant from determining the true purpose of the research.

Procedure

The three salary levels defined the three conditions for both the male and female groups. Each subject experienced only one of the three conditions, receiving a picture of the opposite sex. Each condition utilized the same female and male picture.

One of us was present for each individual participant and each of us tested 75 participants. We told the participants that the purpose of the study was to assess individuals' perceptions. Once the participant finished reading the brief description of the study and signed the informed consent, we presented the participant with a picture that included one of the short descriptions below it. Subjects were allotted 1 min to look at the picture, but they generally looked at it for 30s or less. After reading the description of the person and observing the picture, the participant responded to the questionnaire. Once completed, we gathered the questionnaire and picture and the participant was debriefed.

As with the Method section, the Results section does not begin on a new page. The heading is centered.

Results

We analyzed the scores of the focus question (willingness to date), in each condition, to determine any significant differences that might exist between conditions and sex. We found a significant increase in willingness to date across salary levels for both men and women (see Figure 1). We also analyzed effects of sex and salary level using a two-way analysis of variance (ANOVA) and found the main effect for sex was significant, $F(1, 150) = 4.58$, $p = .05$, with women ($M = 3.27$, $SD = 2.07$) receiving higher ratings than men ($M = 2.97$, $SD = 1.68$). Additional analyses indicated a significant main effect for salary level, $F(1, 150) = 294.96$, $p = .01$,

Tables and figures must be referred to in the text.

When statistical significance tests are presented, the name of the symbol for the test (e.g., *F, t, r*) is italicized. It is followed by the degrees of freedom, in parentheses, the test score, and the p-value (with 'p' italicized).

with scores increasing as salary increased. An interaction between sex and condition was also significant, $F(2, 150) = 5.40, p = .01$. Subsequent analyses indicated that men and women did not differ at the two lower salary levels; however, the willingness scores of the women were significantly higher than those of the men for the highest ($100,000) salary level $t\ (48) = 3.213, p = .04$.

Discussion

The Discussion section follows immediately after the Results section, not on a new page.

The purpose of this study was to examine the significance of salary on date selection preferences, while holding status and attractiveness constant. The first hypothesis was that subjects' willingness to date a person would increase as the target's salary increased. We also hypothesized that this relationship would be stronger for women. The data supported both hypotheses. Participants' willingness-to-date ratings increased as salary increased, and women were more willing than men to engage in a dating relationship, at least at the highest salary level.

Although evolutionary principles were not tested in this experiment, the results do overlap with findings based on these principles. Evolutionists have found that in terms of mate selection, women hold SES as a more important element than men. Thus, a woman may seek out a mate that has high SES in order to ensure support for her family (Townsend & Levy, 1990b). These results support these evolutionary principles in that women's willingness-to-date ratings did increase significantly more than men's ratings as salary increased. One contradictory result of the present study to these principles is that men's ratings also increased as salary increased, although not as much as women's. A possible explanation may be that this finding is due to an environmental influence because in today's society SES is an important attribute to both men and women (Bell, 1976; Goode, 1996; Hill et al., 1987; Townsend & Levy, 1990b). Thus evolutionary principles may explain the significant difference in men and women's willingness ratings, whereas environmental influences might account for the significant importance overall of SES to both men and women.

The findings presented in this study were not consistent with social psychology theories of mate selection. A common view is that mate selection is a social exchange between the man and the woman (i.e., man's security in exchange for an attractive woman; Rusbult, 1980). If this social exchange theory played a significant part in mate selection, men's ratings of the women would have been consistent across conditions because there was no change in attractiveness.

Although past studies (Goode, 1996; Hill et al., 1987; Joshi & Rai, 1989; Sprecher, 1989; Townsend & Levy, 1990b) have tested the role of physical attractiveness and other attributes combined, this study isolated the influence of salary. SES was found to be a significant factor in these past studies when combined with other attributes. After isolating salary as a single variable to be tested in date selection, the present findings were similar to past studies that combined salary with other attributes (Goode, 1996; Hill et al., 1987; Joshi & Rai, 1989; Sprecher, 1989; Townsend & Levy, 1990b).

This study was a partial replication of Townsend and Levy's study (1990b). The present study used the same format of questions (i.e., willingness to engage in specific relationships based on a Likert scale response), similar stimuli (i.e., pictures), and also similar methods of analysis. Their results indicated that SES in combination with other attributes (e.g., appearance, personality characteristics, etc.) was an important predictor of date selection in both men and women, but more so for women. This study supported past evidence when identifying the differences between men and women in the role of salary in date selection (Bell, 1976; Buss, 1987; Goode, 1996; Hill et al., 1987; Nevid, 1984; Townsend & Levy, 1990a).

Although the present findings support past research, the design involved a sample of college students whose responses were to hypothetical relationships with hypothetical partners, in only one region of the United States. A replication of this study with a sample encompassing a larger region or multiple regions would help to further support this hypothesis for the purpose of generalization to a more diverse population. Also, personal SES factors of the participants might influence ratings of the target. Controlling for this variable in future studies would broaden the knowledge of this attribute in date selection.

Other methods need to be developed to continue to test the role of SES in date selection. Showing a video of a person or having a person-to-person interaction are suggestions for future stimuli to further test this hypothesis. Future studies could also evaluate the impact of the participants' personal SES in their selections of romantic partners. If a participant has a high income, how important is that attribute to that person when selecting a date? Another future study might also investigate the importance of salary among lesbian and gay male relationships.

The word "References" is centered at the top of the page. It is not in boldface.

The Reference section begins on a new page and is typed in a hanging indent format. References are alphabetized according to the last name of the first author.

WILLINGNESS TO DATE 12

References

Bell, Q. (1976). *On human finery*. New York: Schocken Books.

Buss, D. M. (1987). Sex differences in human mate selection criteria: An evolutionary perspective. In C. B. Crawford, M. Smith, & D. Krebs (Eds.), *Sociobiology and psychology: Ideas, issues and applications* (pp. 335–352). Hillsdale, NJ: Erlbaum.

Buss, D. M. (1989). Sex differences in human mate preferences: Evolutionary hypotheses tested in 37 cultures. *The Behavioral and Brain Sciences, 12,* 1–49.

Darwin, C. (1871). *The descent of man, and selection in relation to sex.* London: John Murray.

Davis, K. (1985). The meaning and significance of marriage in contemporary society. In K. Davis (Ed.), *Contemporary marriage: Comparative perspectives on a changing institution* (pp. 1–21). New York: Russell Sage.

Elder, G. H., Jr. (1969). Appearance and education in marriage mobility. *American Sociological Review, 34,* 519–533. doi:10.2307/2091

Goode, E. (1996). Gender and courtship entitlement: Responses to personal ads. *Sex Roles, 34,* 141–169. doi:10.1007/BF01544

Hill, E. M., Nocks, E. S., & Gardner, L. (1987). Physical attractiveness: Manipulation by physique and status displays. *Ethology and Sociobiology, 8,* 143–154. doi:10.1016/0162-3095(87)90037-9

Hudson, J. W., & Henze, L. F. (1969). Campus values in mate selection: A replication. *Journal of Marriage and the Family, 31,* 772–775.

Format for a reference to a book.

Format for a reference from an edited book.

Format for a reference from a journal.

Joshi, K., & Rai, S. N. (1989). Effect of physical attractiveness and social status upon interpersonal attraction. *Psychological Studies, 34,* 193–197.

Nevid, J. S. (1984). Sex differences in factors of romantic attraction. *Sex Roles, 11,* 401–411. doi:10.1007/BF00287468

Rusbult, C. E. (1980). Commitment and satisfaction in romantic associations: A test of the investment model. *Journal of Experimental Social Psychology, 16,* 172–186. doi:10.1016/0022-1031(80)90007-4

Sprecher, S. (1989). The importance to males and females of physical attractiveness, earning potential, and expressiveness in initial attraction. *Sex Roles, 21,* 591–607. doi:10.1007/BF00289173

Townsend, J. M., & Levy, G. D. (1990a). Effects of potential partners' costume and physical attractiveness on sexuality and partner selection. *Journal of Psychology, 124,* 371–389.

Townsend, J. M., & Levy, G. D. (1990b). Effects of potential partners' physical attractiveness and socioeconomic status on sexuality and partner selection. *Archives of Sexual Behavior, 19,* 149–164. doi:10.1007/BF01542229

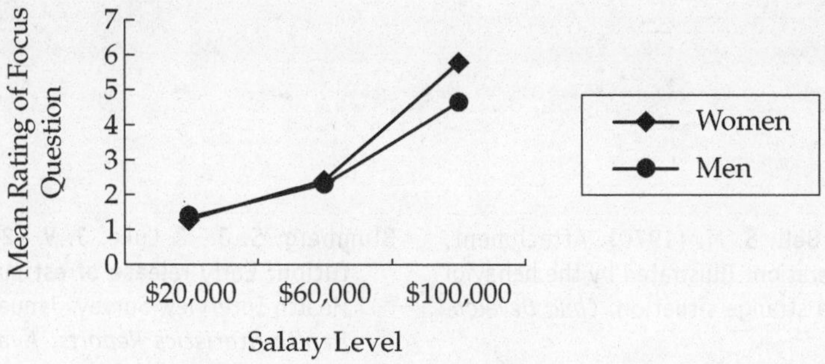

Figure Caption

Figure 1. Mean rating of male and female participants for each condition ($20,000, $60,000, $100,000) on focus question ("How willing would you be to go on a date with this person?").

References

Ainsworth, M. D. S., & Bell, S. M. (1970). Attachment, exploration, and separation: Illustrated by the behavior of one-year-olds in a strange situation. *Child Development, 41,* 49–67.

American Psychological Association. (1996). *Guidelines for ethical conduct in the care and use of animals.* Washington, DC: Author.

American Psychological Association. (2002). Ethical principles of psychologists and code of conduct. *American Psychologist, 57,* 1060–1073.

American Psychological Association. (2007). *Thesaurus of psychological index terms* (11th ed.). Washington, DC: Author.

American Psychological Association. (2009). *Publication manual of the American Psychological Association* (6th ed.). Washington, DC: Author.

Anastasi, A., & Urbina, S. (1997). *Psychological testing* (7th ed.). Upper Saddle River, NJ: Prentice Hall.

Arkes, H.R., & Hammond, K.R. (Eds.). (1986). *Judgment and decision making: An interdisciplinary reader.* Cambridge, England: Cambridge University Press.

Aronson, E., & Carlsmith, J. M. (1968). Experimentation in social psychology. In G. Lindzey & E. Aronson (Eds.), *Handbook of social psychology* (2nd ed., pp. 1–79). Reading, MA: Addison-Wesley.

Baumeister, R. F., Campbell, J. D., Drueger, J. I., & Vohs, K. D. (2003). Does high self-esteem cause better performance, interpersonal success, happiness, or healthier lifestyles? *Psychological Sciences in the Public Interest, 4,* 1–44.

Beede, K. E., & Kass, S. J. (2006). Engrossed in conversation: The impact of cell phones on simulated driving performance. *Accident Analysis and Prevention, 38,* 415–421

Berg, B. I. (2009). *Qualitative research methods for the social sciences.* Boston: Allyn & Bacon.

Blumberg, S. J., & Luke, J. V. (2011). Wireless substitution: Early release of estimates from the National Health Interview Survey, January-June 2011, *National Health Statistics Reports.* Avaliable from: www.cdc.gov/nchs/data/nhis/earlyrelease/wireless201112.htm

Bolt, M. (1998). *Instructor's resources* to accompany David G. Myers, *Psychology* (5th ed.). New York: Worth.

Bourque, L. B., & Fielder, E. P. (2003a). *How to conduct self-administered and mail surveys* (2nd ed.). Thousand Oaks, CA: Sage.

Bourque, L. B., & Fielder, E. P. (2003b). *How to conduct telephone surveys* (2nd ed.). Thousand Oaks, CA: Sage.

Bratton, R. L., Montero, D. P., Adams, K. S., Novas, M. A., McKay, R. C., Hall, L. J., Goust, J. G. et al. (2002). Effect of "ionized" wrist bracelets on musculoskeletal pain: A randomized, double-blind, placebo-controlled trial. *Mayo Clinic Proceedings, 77,* 1164–1168.

Bushman, B. J., & Anderson, C. A., (2007). Measuring the strength of the effect of violent media on aggression. *American Psychologist, 62,* 253–254.

Campbell, D. T. (1969). Reforms as experiments. *American Psychologist, 24,* 409–429.

Campbell, D. T., & Stanley, J. C. (1963). *Experimental and quasi-experimental designs for research.* Boston: Houghton Mifflin.

Cohen, J. (1988). *Statistical power analysis for the behavioral sciences.* Hillsdale, NJ: Erlbaum.

Cohen, J. (1992). A power primer. *Psychological Bulletin, 112,* 155–159.

Cowles, M. (1989). *Statistics in psychology: An historical perspective.* Hillsdale, NJ: Erlbaum.

Cozby, P. C. (2001). *Methods in behavioral research* (7th ed.). Mountain View, CA: Mayfield.

Dillman, D. A. (1978). *Mail and telephone surveys: The total design method.* New York: Wiley.

Dillman, D. A., Smyth, J. D., & Christian, I. M. (2009). *Internet, mail, and mixed-mode surveys: The tailored design method* (3rd ed.). Hoboken, NJ: Wiley.

Dula, C. S., Martin, B. A., Fox, R. T., & Leonard, R. L. (2011). Differing types of cellular phone conversations and dangerous driving. *Accident Analysis and Prevention, 43,* 187–193.

Erdos, P. L. (1983). *Professional mail surveys.* Malabar, FL: Robert E. Krieger.

Esterberg, K. G. (2002). *Qualitative methods in social research.* Boston: McGraw Hill.

Gilovich, T. (1991). *How we know what isn't so: The fallibility of human reason in everyday life.* New York: Free Press.

Goldstein, W. M., & Goldstein, I. (1978). *How we know: An exploration of the scientific process.* New York: Plenum.

Gordon, L. (1988). *Heroes of their own lives: The politics and history of family violence.* New York: Penguin Books.

Gould, S. J. (1985, June). The median isn't the message. *Discover, 6*(6), 40–42.

Greene, J., Speizer, H., & Wiitala, W. (2008). Telephone and web: Mixed-mode challenge. *Health Research and Educational Trust, 43,* 230–248.

Griggs, R. A., & Cox, J. R. (1982). The elusive thematic-materials effect in Wason's selection task. *British Journal of Psychology, 73,* 407–420.

Gunter, B. (2008). Media violence: Is there a case for causality? *American Behavioral Scientist, 51,* 1061–1122. DOI: 10.1177/0002764207312007

Hall, R. V., Axelrod, S., Foundopoulos, M., Shellman, J., Campbell, R. A., & Cranston, S. S. (1971). The effective use of punishment to modify behavior in the classroom. *Educational Technology, 11*(4), 24–26. Reprinted in K. D. O'Leary & S. O'Leary (Eds.). (1972). *Classroom management: The successful use of behavior modification.* New York: Pergamon.

Halpern, D. F. (1996). *Thought and knowledge: An introduction to critical thinking* (3rd ed.). Mahwah, NJ: Lawrence Erlbaum Associates, Inc.

Hinkle, D. E., Wiersma, W., & Jurs, S. G. (1988). *Applied statistics for the behavioral sciences* (2nd ed.). Boston: Houghton Mifflin.

Hite, S. (1987). *Women and love: A cultural revolution in progress.* New York: Knopf.

Jones, J. H. (1981). *Bad blood: The Tuskegee syphilis experiment.* New York: Free Press.

Keppel, G. (1991). *Design and analysis: A researcher's handbook* (3rd ed.). Engelwood Cliffs, NJ: Prentice Hall.

Kerlinger, F. N. (1986). *Foundations of behavioral research* (4th ed.). New York: Holt, Rinehart & Winston.

Kranzler, G., & Moursund, J. (1995). *Statistics for the terrified.* Englewood Cliffs, NJ: Prentice Hall.

Leary, M. R. (2001). *Introduction to behavioral research methods* (3rd ed.). Needham Heights, MA: Allyn & Bacon.

Li, C. (1975). *Path analysis: A primer.* Pacific Grove, CA: Boxwood Press.

Likert, R. (1932). A technique for the measurement of attitudes. *Archives of Psychology, 19,* 44–53.

Mercer, J. (2010). *Child development: Myths and misunderstandings.* New York: Sage.

Messer, W., Griggs, R. A., & Jackson, S. L. (1999). A national survey of undergraduate psychology degree options and major requirements. *Teaching of Psychology, 26,* 164–171.

Milgram, S. (1963). Behavioral study of obedience. *Journal of Abnormal and Social Psychology,* 67, 371–378.

Milgram, S. (1974). *Obedience to authority.* New York: Harper & Row.

Milgram, S. (1977). Ethical issues in the study of obedience. In S. Milgram (Ed.), *The individual in a social world* (pp. 188–199). Reading, MA: Addison-Wesley.

Mitchell, M., & Jolley, J. (2004). *Research design explained* (5th ed.). Belmont, CA: Wadsworth/Thomson.

Murray, J. P. (2008). Media violence: The effects are both real and strong. *American Behavioral Scientist, 51,* 1212–1230. DOI:10.1177/0002764207312018

Olson, R. K., & Forsberg, H. (1993). Disabled and normal readers' eye movements in reading and nonreading tasks. In D. M. Willows, R. Kruk, & E. Corcos (Eds.), *Visual processes in reading and reading disabilities* (pp. 377–391). Hillsdale, NJ: Erlbaum.

Paul, G. L. (1966). *Insight vs. desensitization in psychotherapy.* Stanford, CA: Stanford University Press.

Paul, G. L. (1967). Insight vs. desensitization in psychotherapy two years after termination. *Journal of Consulting Psychology, 31,* 333–348.

Peters, W. S. (1987). *Counting for something: Statistical principles and personalities.* New York: Springer-Verlag.

Pfungst, O. (1911). *Clever Hans (the horse of Mr. von Osten): A contribution to experimental, animal, and human psychology* (C. L. Rahn, Trans.). New York: Holt, Rinehart & Winston. (Republished, 1965.)

Rosenhan, D. C. (1973). On being sane in insane places. *Science, 179*, 250–258.

Salkind, N. J. (1997). *Exploring research* (3rd ed.). Upper Saddle River, NJ: Prentice Hall.

Schweigert, W. A. (1994). *Research methods & statistics for psychology*. Pacific Grove, CA: Brooks/Cole.

Sidman, M. (1960). *Tactics of scientific research*. New York: Basic Books.

Sommer, R., & Sommer, B. (2002). *A practical guide to behavioral research: Tools and techniques*. New York: Oxford University Press.

Spence, J. D., Jenkins, D. J. A., & Davignon, J. (2012). Egg yolk consumption and carotid plaque. *Atherosclerosis, 224*, 469–473.

Stanovich, K. E. (2007). *How to think straight about psychology* (8th ed.). Boston: Allyn & Bacon.

Stigler, S. M. (1986). *The history of statistics*. Cambridge, MA: Belknap Press.

Tankard, J., Jr. (1984). *The statistical pioneers*. Cambridge, MA: Schenkman.

U.S. Department of Health and Human Services. (1981, January 26). Final regulations amending basic HHS policy for the protection of human subjects. *Federal Register, 46*, 16.

Wallis, C. (1987, October 12). Back off, buddy. *Time*, 68–73.

Williams, T. M. (Ed.). (1986). *The impact of television: A natural experiment in three communities*. Orlando, FL: Academic Press.

Zimbardo, P. G. (1972). Pathology of imprisonment. *Transaction/Society, 9*, 4–8.

Glossary

ABA reversal design A single-case design in which baseline measures are taken, the independent variable is introduced and behavior is measured, and the independent variable is then removed and baseline measures taken again.

ABAB reversal design A design in which baseline and independent variable conditions are reversed twice.

absolute zero A property of measurement in which assigning a score of zero indicates an absence of the variable being measured.

action item A type of item used on a checklist to note the presence or absence of behaviors.

action research A method in which research is conducted by a group of people to identify a problem, attempt to resolve it, and then assess how successful their efforts were.

addition rule A probability rule stating that the probability of one outcome or another outcome occurring on a particular trial is the sum of their individual probabilities when the outcomes are mutually exclusive.

alternate-forms reliability A reliability coefficient determined by assessing the degree of relationship between scores on two equivalent tests.

alternative explanation The idea that it is possible that some other, uncontrolled, extraneous variable may be responsible for the observed relationship.

alternative hypothesis (H_a), or research hypothesis (H_1) The hypothesis that the researcher wants to support, predicting that a significant difference exists between the groups being compared.

ANOVA (analysis of variance) An inferential statistical test for comparing the means of three or more groups.

applied research The study of psychological issues that have practical significance and potential solutions.

archival method A descriptive research method that involves describing data that existed before the time of the study.

average deviation An alternative measure of variation that, like the standard deviation, indicates the average difference between the scores in a distribution and the mean of the distribution.

bar graph A graphical representation of a frequency distribution in which vertical bars are centered above each category along the *x*-axis and are separated from each other by a space, indicating the levels of the variable represent distinct, unrelated categories.

basic research The study of psychological issues to seek knowledge for its own sake.

behavioral measures Measures taken by carefully observing and recording behavior.

between-groups sum of squares The sum of the squared deviations of each group's mean from the grand mean, multiplied by the number of participants in each group.

between-groups variance An estimate of the effect of the independent variable and error variance.

between-subjects design An experiment in which different participants are assigned to each group.

Bonferroni adjustment Setting a more stringent alpha level for multiple tests to minimize Type I errors.

carryover effects A type of testing effect often present in within-subjects designs in which subjects "carry" something with them from one condition to another.

case study method An in-depth study of one or more individuals.

causality The assumption that a correlation indicates a causal relationship between the two variables.

ceiling effect A limitation of the measuring instrument that decreases its capability to differentiate between scores at the top of the scale.

central limit theorem A theorem which states that for any population with mean μ and standard deviation σ, the distribution of sample means for sample size N will have a mean of μ and a standard deviation of $\sigma/\sqrt{N}$ and will approach a normal distribution as N approaches infinity.

checklist A tally sheet on which the researcher records attributes of the participants and whether particular behaviors were observed.

chi-square (χ^2) goodness-of-fit test A nonparametric inferential procedure that determines how well an observed frequency distribution fits an expected distribution.

chi-square (χ^2) test of independence A nonparametric inferential test used when frequency data have been collected to determine how well an observed breakdown of people over various categories fits some expected breakdown.

class interval frequency distribution A table in which the scores are grouped into intervals and listed along with the frequency of scores in each interval.

closed-ended questions Questions for which participants choose from a limited number of alternatives.

cluster sampling A sampling technique in which clusters of participants that represent the population are used.

coefficient of determination (r^2) A measure of the proportion of the variance in one variable that is accounted for by another variable; calculated by squaring the correlation coefficient.

Cohen's *d* An inferential statistic for measuring effect size.

cohort A group of individuals born at about the same time.

cohort effect A generational effect in a study that occurs when the era in which individuals are born affects how they respond in the study.

college sophomore problem An external validity problem that results from using mainly college sophomores as participants in research studies.

conceptual replication A study based on another study that uses different methods, a different manipulation, or a different measure.

confidence interval An interval of a certain width that we feel confident will contain μ.

confound An uncontrolled extraneous variable or flaw in an experiment.

construct validity The degree to which a measuring instrument accurately measures a theoretical construct or trait that it is designed to measure.

content validity The extent to which a measuring instrument covers a representative sample of the domain of behaviors to be measured.

continuous variables Variables that usually fall along a continuum and allow for fractional amounts.

control Manipulating the independent variable in an experiment or any other extraneous variables that could affect the results of a study.

control group The group of participants that does not receive any level of the independent variable and serves as the baseline in a study.

convenience sampling A sampling technique in which participants are obtained wherever they can be found and typically wherever is convenient for the researcher.

correlated-groups design An experimental design in which the participants in the experimental and control groups are related in some way.

correlated-groups *t* test A parametric inferential test used to compare the means of two related (within- or matched-participants) samples.

correlation coefficient A measure of the degree of relationship between two sets of scores. It can vary between −1.00 and +1.00.

correlational method A method that assesses the degree of relationship between two variables.

counterbalancing A mechanism for controlling order effects either by including all orders of treatment presentation or by randomly determining the order for each participant.

criterion validity The extent to which a measuring instrument accurately predicts behavior or ability in a given area.

critical value The value of a test statistic that marks the edge of the region of rejection in a sampling distribution, where values equal to it or beyond it fall in the region of rejection.

cross-sectional design A type of developmental design in which participants of different ages are studied at the same time.

debriefing Providing information about the true purpose of a study as soon after the completion of data collection as possible.

deception Lying to the participants concerning the true nature of a study because knowing the true nature of the study might affect their performance.

degrees of freedom (*df*) The number of scores in a sample that are free to vary.

demand characteristics A type of subject effect in which subjects try to guess what characteristics the experimenter is in effect "demanding."

demographic questions Questions that ask for basic information, such as age, gender, ethnicity, or income.

dependent variable The variable in a study that is measured by the researcher.

description Carefully observing behavior in order to describe it.

descriptive statistics Numerical measures that describe a distribution by providing information on the central tendency of the distribution, the width of the distribution, and the shape of the distribution.

difference scores Scores representing the difference between participants' performance in one condition and their performance in a second condition.

diffusion of treatment A threat to internal validity in which observed changes in the behaviors or responses of participants may be due to information received from other participants in the study.

directionality The inference made with respect to the direction of a causal relationship between two variables.

discrete variables Variables that usually consist of whole number units or categories and are made up of chunks or units that are detached and distinct from one another.

disguised observation Studies in which the participants are unaware that the researcher is observing their behavior.

double-barreled question A question that asks more than one thing.

double-blind experiment An experimental procedure in which neither the experimenter nor the participant knows the condition to which each participant has been assigned—both parties are blind to the manipulation.

ecological validity The extent to which research can be generalized to real-life situations.

effect size The proportion of variance in the dependent variable that is accounted for by the manipulation of the independent variable.

empirically solvable problems Questions that are potentially answerable by means of currently available research techniques.

equal unit size A property of measurement in which a difference of 1 is the same amount throughout the entire scale.

error variance The amount of variability among the scores caused by chance or uncontrolled variables.

estimated standard error of the mean An estimate of the standard deviation of the sampling distribution.

eta-squared (η^2) An inferential statistic for measuring effect size with an ANOVA.

exact replication Repeating a study using the same means of manipulating and measuring the variables as in the original study.

expectancy effects The influence of the researcher's expectations on the outcome of the study.

expected frequency The frequency expected in a category if the sample data represent the population.

experimental group The group of participants that receives some level of the independent variable.

experimental method A research method that allows a researcher to establish a cause-and-effect relationship through manipulation of a variable and control of the situation.

experimenter effect A threat to internal validity in which the experimenter, consciously or unconsciously, affects the results of the study.

explanation Identifying the causes that determine when and why a behavior occurs.

external validity The extent to which the results of an experiment can be generalized.

face validity The extent to which a measuring instrument appears valid on its surface.

factorial design A design with more than one independent variable.

factorial notation The notation that indicates how many independent variables are used in a study and how many levels are used for each variable.

field studies A method that involves observing everyday activities as they happen in a natural setting.

floor effect A limitation of the measuring instrument that decreases its capability to differentiate between scores at the bottom of the scale.

focus group interview A method that involves interviewing 6 to 10 individuals at the same time.

***F*-ratio** The ratio of between-groups variance to within-groups variance.

frequency distribution A table in which all of the scores are listed along with the frequency with which each occurs.

frequency polygon A line graph of the frequencies of individual scores.

Friedman Test An inferential nonparametric test used to determine differences between three or more conditions on a ranked variable for a correlated-groups design.

grand mean The mean performance across all participants in a study.

Hawthorne effect A type of reactivity in which subjects improve or change an aspect of their behavior because they know that they are being studied rather than in response to the experimental manipulation.

histogram A graphical representation of a frequency distribution in which vertical bars centered above scores on the *x*-axis touch each other to indicate that the scores on the variable represent related, increasing values.

history effect A threat to internal validity in which an outside event that is not a part of the manipulation of the experiment could be responsible for the results.

hypothesis A prediction regarding the outcome of a study involving the potential relationship between at least two variables.

hypothesis testing The process of determining whether a hypothesis is supported by the results of a research study.

identity A property of measurement in which objects that are different receive different scores.

independent variable The variable in a study that is manipulated by the researcher.

independent-groups *t* test A parametric inferential test for comparing sample means of two independent groups of scores.

inferential statistics Procedures for drawing conclusions about a population based on data collected from a sample.

informed consent form A form given to individuals before they participate in a study to inform them of the general nature of the study and to obtain their consent to participate.

Institutional Review Board (IRB) A committee charged with evaluating research projects in which human participants are used.

instrumentation effect A threat to internal validity in which changes in the dependent variable may be due to changes in the measuring device.

interaction effect The effect of each independent variable across the levels of the other independent variable.

internal validity The extent to which the results of an experiment can be attributed to the manipulation of the independent variable rather than to some confounding variable.

interrater reliability A reliability coefficient that assesses the-agreement of observations made by two or more raters or judges.

interval scale A scale in which the units of measurement (intervals) between the numbers on the scale are all equal in size.

interview A method that typically involves asking questions in a face-to-face manner that may be conducted anywhere.

interviewer bias The tendency for the person asking the questions to bias the participants answers.

knowledge via authority Knowledge gained from those viewed as authority figures.

knowledge via empiricism Knowledge gained through objective observations of organisms and events in the real world.

knowledge via intuition Knowledge gained without being consciously aware of its source.

knowledge via rationalism Knowledge gained through logical reasoning.

knowledge via science Knowledge gained through a combination of empirical methods and logical reasoning.

knowledge via superstition Knowledge that is based on subjective feelings, interpreting random events as nonrandom events, or believing in magical events.

knowledge via tenacity Knowledge gained from repeated ideas that are stubbornly clung to despite evidence to the contrary.

Kruskal–Wallis Test An inferential nonparametric test used to determine differences between three or more groups on a ranked variable for a between-subjects design.

kurtosis How flat or peaked a normal distribution is.

laboratory observation Observing the behavior of humans or animals in a more contrived and controlled situation, usually in the laboratory.

Latin square A counterbalancing technique to control for order effects without using all possible orders.

leading question A question that sways the respondent to answer in a desired manner.

leptokurtic Normal curves that are tall and thin, with only a few scores in the middle of the distribution having a high frequency.

Likert rating scale A type of numerical rating scale developed by Renis Likert in 1932.

loaded question A question that includes nonneutral or emotionally laden terms.

longitudinal design A type of developmental design in which the same participants are studied repeatedly over time as they age.

magnitude (1) A property of measurement in which the ordering of numbers reflects the ordering of the variable; (2) an indication of the strength of the relationship between two variables.

mail survey A written survey that is self-administered.

main effect An effect of a single independent variable.

matched-subjects design A type of correlated-groups design in which participants are matched between conditions on variable(s) that the researcher believes is (are) relevant to the study.

maturation effect A threat to internal validity in which naturally occurring changes within the participants could be responsible for the observed results.

mean A measure of central tendency; the arithmetic average of a distribution.

mean square An estimate of either variance between groups or variance within groups.

measure of central tendency A number that characterizes the "middleness" of an entire distribution.

measure of variation A number that indicates the degree to which scores are either clustered or spread out in a distribution.

median A measure of central tendency; the middle score in a distribution after the scores have been arranged from highest to lowest or lowest to highest.

mesokurtic Normal curves that have peaks of medium height and distributions that are moderate in breadth.

mode A measure of central tendency; the score in a distribution that occurs with the greatest frequency.

mortality (attrition) A threat to internal validity in which differential dropout rates may be observed in the experimental and control groups, leading to inequality between the groups.

multiple-baseline design A single-case or small-*n* design in which the effect of introducing the independent variable is assessed over multiple participants, behaviors, or situations.

multiple-baseline design across behaviors A single-case design in which measures are taken at baseline and after the introduction of the independent variable at different times across multiple behaviors.

multiple-baseline design across subjects A small-*n* design in which measures are taken at baseline and after the introduction of the independent variable at different times across multiple participants.

multiple-baseline design across situations A single-case design in which measures are taken at baseline and after the introduction of the independent variable at different times across multiple situations.

multiple-group time-series design A design in which a series of measures are taken on two or more groups both before and after a treatment.

multiplication rule A probability rule stating that the probability of a series of outcomes occurring on successive trials is the product of their individual probabilities when the sequence of outcomes is independent.

narrative records Full narrative descriptions of a participant's behavior.

naturalistic observation Observing the behavior of humans or animals in their natural habitat.

negative correlation An inverse relationship between two variables in which an increase in one variable is related to a decrease in the other, and vice versa.

negative relationship A relationship between two variables in which an increase in one variable is accompanied by a decrease in the other variable.

negatively skewed distribution A distribution in which the peak is to the right of the center point and the tail extends toward the left or in the negative direction.

nominal scale A scale in which objects or individuals are assigned to categories that have no numerical properties.

nonequivalent control group posttest-only design A design in which at least two nonequivalent groups are given a treatment and then a posttest measure.

nonequivalent control group pretest/posttest design A design in which at least two nonequivalent groups are given a pretest, then a treatment, and then a posttest measure.

nonmanipulated independent variable The independent variable in a quasi-experimental design in which participants are not randomly assigned to conditions but rather come to the study as members of each condition.

nonparametric test A statistical test that does not involve the use of any population parameters; μ and σ are not needed,and the underlying distribution does not have to be normal.

nonparticipant observation Studies in which the researcher does not participate in the situation in which the research participants are involved.

nonprobability sampling A sampling technique in which the individual members of the population do not have an equal likelihood of being selected to be a member of the sample.

normal curve A symmetrical, bell-shaped frequency polygon representing a normal distribution.

normal distribution A theoretical frequency distribution that has certain special characteristics.

null hypothesis (H_0) The hypothesis predicting that no difference exists between the groups being compared.

observational method Making observations of human or animal behavior.

observed frequency The frequency with which participants fall into a category.

one-tailed hypothesis (directional hypothesis) An alternative hypothesis in which the researcher predicts the direction of the expected difference between the groups.

one-way randomized ANOVA An inferential statistical test for comparing the means of three or more groups using a between-participants design and one independent variable.

one-way repeated measures ANOVA An inferential statistical test for comparing the means of three or more groups using a correlated-groups design and one independent variable.

open-ended questions Questions for which participants formulate their own responses.

operational definition A definition of a variable in terms of the operations (activities) a researcher uses to measure or manipulate it.

order effects A problem for within-participants designs in which the order of the conditions has an effect on the dependent variable.

ordinal scale A scale in which objects or individuals are categorized, and the categories form a rank order along a continuum.

parametric test A statistical test that involves making assumptions about estimates of population characteristics, or parameters.

partial correlation A correlational technique that involves measuring three variables and then statistically removing the effect of the third variable from the correlation of the remaining two variables.

partially open-ended questions Closed-ended questions with an open-ended "Other" option.

participant observation Studies in which the researcher actively participates in the situation in which the research participants are involved.

participant (subject) variable A characteristic inherent in the participants that cannot be changed.

Pearson product-moment correlation coefficient (Pearson's *r*) The most commonly used correlation coefficient when both variables are measured on an interval or ratio scale.

percentile rank A score that indicates the percentage of people who scored at or below a given raw score.

personal interview A survey in which the questions are asked face-to-face.

person-who argument Arguing that a well-established statistical trend is invalid because we know a "person who" went against the trend.

phi coefficient (1) An inferential test used to determine effect size for a chi-square test; (2) the correlation coefficient used when both measured variables are dichotomous and nominal.

physical measures Measures of bodily activity (such as pulse or blood pressure) that may be taken with a piece of equipment.

placebo An inert substance that participants believe is a treatment.

placebo group A group or condition in which participants believe they are receiving treatment but are not.

platykurtic Normal curves that are short and more dispersed (broader).

point-biserial correlation coefficient The correlation coefficient used when one of the variables is measured on a dichotomous nominal scale and the other is measured on an interval or ratio scale.

population All of the people about whom a study is meant to generalize.

positive correlation A direct relationship between two variables in which an increase in one is related to an increase in the other, and a decrease in one is related to a decrease in the other.

positive relationship A relationship between two variables in which an increase in one variable is accompanied by an increase in the other variable.

positively skewed distribution A distribution in which the peak is to the left of the center point and the tail extends toward the right, or in the positive direction.

post hoc test When used with an ANOVA, a means of comparing all possible pairs of groups to determine which ones differ significantly from each other.

posttest-only control group design An experimental design in which the dependent variable is measured after the manipulation of the independent variable.

prediction Identifying the factors that indicate when an event or events will occur.

pretest/posttest control group design An experimental design in which the dependent variable is measured both before and after manipulation of the independent variable.

principle of falsifiability The idea that a scientific theory must be stated in such a way that it is possible to refute or disconfirm it.

probability The expected relative frequency of a particular outcome.

probability sampling A sampling technique in which each member of the population has an equal likelihood of being selected to be part of the sample.

pseudoscience Claims that appear to be scientific but that actually violate the criteria of science.

publicly verifiable knowledge Presenting research to the public so that it can be observed, replicated, criticized, and tested.

qualitative research A type of social research based on field observations that is analyzed without statistics.

qualitative variable A categorical variable for which each value represents a discrete category.

quantitative variable A variable for which the scores represent a change in quantity.

quasi-experimental method Research that compares naturally occurring groups of individuals; the variable of interest cannot be manipulated.

quota sampling A sampling technique that involves ensuring that the sample is like the population on certain characteristics but uses convenience sampling to obtain the participants.

random assignment Assigning participants to conditions in such a way that every participant has an equal probability of being placed in any condition.

random sample A sample achieved through random selection in which each member of the population is equally likely to be chosen.

random selection A method of generating a random sample in which each member of the population is equally likely to be chosen as part of the sample.

range A measure of variation; the difference between the lowest and the highest scores in a distribution.

rating scale A numerical scale on which survey respondents indicate the direction and strength of their response.

ratio scale A scale in which, in addition to order and equal units of measurement, an absolute zero indicates an absence of the variable being measured.

reactivity A possible reaction by participants in which they act unnaturally because they know they are being observed.

region of rejection The area of a sampling distribution that lies beyond the test statistic's critical value; when a score falls within this region, H_0 is rejected.

regression analysis A procedure that allows us to predict an individual's score on one variable based on knowing one or more other variables.

regression line The best-fitting straight line drawn through the center of a scatterplot that indicates the relationship between the variables.

regression to the mean A threat to internal validity in which extreme scores, upon retesting, tend to be less extreme, moving toward the mean.

reliability An indication of the consistency or stability of a measuring instrument.

representative sample A sample that is like the population.

response bias The tendency to consistently give the same answer to almost all of the items on a survey.

restrictive range A variable that is truncated and has limited variability.

reversal design A single-case design in which the independent variable is introduced and removed one or more times.

sample The group of people who participate in a study.

sampling bias A tendency for one group to be overrepresented in a sample.

sampling distribution A distribution of sample means based on random samples of a fixed size from a population.

scatterplot A figure that graphically represents the relationship between two variables.

self-report measures Usually questionnaires or interviews that measure how people report that they act, think, or feel.

sequential design A developmental design that is a combination of the cross-sectional and longitudinal designs.

single-blind experiment An experimental procedure in which either the participants or the experimenters are blind to the manipulation being made.

single-case design A design in which only one participant is used.

single-group design A research study in which there is only one group of participants.

single-group posttest-only design A design in which a single group of participants is given a treatment and then tested.

single-group pretest/posttest design A design in which a single group of participants takes a pretest, then receives some treatment, and then takes a posttest measure.

single-group time-series design A design in which a single group of participants is measured repeatedly before and after a treatment.

skeptic A person who questions the validity, authenticity, or truth of something purporting to be factual.

small-*n* design A design in which only a few participants are studied.

socially desirable response A response that is given because a respondent believes it is deemed appropriate by society.

Solomon four-group design A design with four groups that is a combination of the posttest-only control group design and the pretest/posttest control group design.

Spearman's rank-order correlation coefficient The correlation coefficient used when one (or more) of the variables is measured on an ordinal (ranking) scale.

split-half reliability A reliability coefficient determined by correlating scores on one half of a measure with scores on the other half of the measure.

standard deviation A measure of variation; the average difference between the scores in the distribution and the mean or central point of the distribution, or, more precisely, the square root of the average squared deviation from the mean.

standard error of the difference between means The standard deviation of the sampling distribution of differences between the means of independent samples in a two-sample experiment.

standard error of the difference scores The standard deviation of the sampling distribution of mean differences between dependent samples in a two-group experiment.

standard error of the mean The standard deviation of the sampling distribution.

standard normal distribution A normal distribution with a mean of 0 and a standard deviation of 1.

static item A type of item used on a checklist on which attributes that will not change are recorded.

statistical power The probability of correctly rejecting a false H_0.

statistical significance An observed difference between two descriptive statistics (such as means) that is unlikely to have occurred by chance.

stratified random sampling A sampling technique designed to ensure that subgroups or strata are fairly represented.

Student's *t* distribution A set of distributions that, although symmetrical and bell-shaped, are not normally distributed.

subject effect A threat to internal validity in which the subject, consciously or unconsciously, affects the results of the study.

sum of squares error The sum of the squared deviations of each score from its group (cell) mean; the within-groups sum of squares in a factorial design.

sum of squares factor A The sum of the squared deviation scores of each group mean for factor A minus the grand mean times the number of scores in each factor A condition.

sum of squares factor B The sum of the squared deviation scores of each group mean for factor B minus the grand mean times the number of scores in each factor B condition.

sum of squares interaction The sum of the squared difference of each condition mean minus the grand mean times the number of scores in each condition. SS_A and SS_B are then subtracted from this sum.

survey method Questioning individuals on a topic or topics and then describing their responses.

systematic empiricism Making observations in a systematic manner to test hypotheses and refute or develop a theory.

systematic replication A study that varies from an original study in one systematic way—for example, by using a different number or type of participants, a different setting, or more levels of the independent variable.

***t* test** A parametric inferential statistical test of the null hypothesis for a single sample where the population variance is not known.

telephone survey A survey in which the questions are read to participants over the telephone.

test A measurement instrument used to assess individual differences in various content areas.

testing effect A threat to internal validity in which repeated testing leads to better or worse scores.

test/retest reliability A reliability coefficient determined by assessing the degree of relationship between scores on the same test administered on two different occasions.

theory An organized system of assumptions and principles that attempts to explain certain phenomena and how they are related.

third-variable problem The problem of a correlation between two variables being dependent on another (third) variable.

total sum of squares The sum of the squared deviations of each score from the grand mean.

Tukey's honestly significant difference (HSD) A post hoc test used with ANOVAs for making all pairwise comparisons when conditions have equal *n*.

two-tailed hypothesis (nondirectional hypothesis) An alternative hypothesis in which the researcher predicts that the groups being compared differ but does not predict the direction of the difference.

Type I error An error in hypothesis testing in which the null hypothesis is rejected when it is true.

Type II error An error in hypothesis testing in which there is a failure to reject the null hypothesis when it is false.

undisguised observation Studies in which the participants are aware that the researcher is observing their behavior.

validity A measure of the truthfulness of a measuring instrument. It indicates whether the instrument measures what it claims to measure.

variable An event or behavior that has at least two values.

variance The standard deviation squared.

Wilcoxon matched-pairs signed-ranks *T* test A nonparametric inferential test for comparing sample medians of two dependent or related groups of scores.

Wilcoxon rank-sum test A nonparametric inferential test for comparing sample medians of two independent groups of scores.

within-groups sum of squares The sum of the squared deviations of each score from its group mean.

within-groups variance The variance within each condition; an estimate of the population error variance.

within-subjects design A type of correlated-groups design in which the same participants are used in each condition.

***z*-score (standard score)** A number that indicates how many standard deviation units a raw score is from the mean of a distribution.

***z* test** A parametric inferential statistical test of the null hypothesis for a single sample where the population variance is known.

Index